PHILOSOPHY OF SCIENCE

INTRODUCTION TO THE FOUNDATIONS
AND
CULTURAL ASPECTS OF THE SCIENCES

CHARLES SCRIBNER'S SONS *New York*

501
2463n

34 65
January, 1957

READINGS IN

Arranged and Edited by PHILIP P. WIENER

PROFESSOR OF PHILOSOPHY · CITY COLLEGE OF NEW YORK

READINGS

IN

PHILOSOPHY OF SCIENCE

Preface

The cultural problem of our scientific age which this volume is designed to meet was felicitously formulated by Dr. William S. Carlson, President of the State University of New York, in his talk before the National Conference on Higher Education (Chicago, March 7, 1953) when he said that American universities were suffering from "hardening of the arteries," a malignant malady that prevented communication or "conversation" among the various fields of knowledge. "So hardened are the categories that a man in one basic science cannot communicate with a man in another basic science." We need to loosen up the time-hardened categories of liberal versus vocational, pure versus applied science, humanities versus sciences: "What we need are teachers of the liberal arts who will take the world as it comes and illuminate it with the humanities, the sciences and history," Dr. Carlson went on. "We need also teachers in the specialized professions who can bring to the civilizing forces of the liberal arts the qualities of exactitude, precision, critical skepticism and emancipating doubt. With this creative interaction of intellectual disciplines, we can produce men and women who will think for themselves, who will seek the true meanings, who will criticize institutions and their calculated sophistries, who can explode the myth and label the lie for what it is. Indeed the future of civilization, as we know it, demands of us renewed faith in the ancient purpose of education, notably of higher education." In this way, he pointed out, future citizens "will not be prisoners of a society governed by single minded technicians and narrow minded experts. It will provide insurance that civilization will move forward." (*New York Times*, March 8, 1953, p. 68).

The relation of philosophy of science to the sciences is like the relation of philosophy of art to works of art, or of literary criticism to works of literature, or of philosophy of history to historical records. In all these "philosophies of X" the aim is not to furnish or prescribe particular solutions to technical problems in X but to clarify problems about X; e.g., how well it fulfills its professed aims or has progressed in its development, and how its results are related to other disciplines and problems of mankind. Thus when Einstein and the other scientist-philosophers in this book discuss the ideal goal and significance of their sciences they are not giving us rules for solving specific technical problems. These are best handled by specially trained scientists who can be

v

only provisionally classified according to the special problems engaging them. Scientists are philosophers when they look ahead to the future development of their sciences and consider also their role in furthering the life of reason for all mankind.

Thus philosophy of science consists of reflections on the basic assumptions, methods and logical structure within the various sciences, accompanied by a sense of the interrelations and values portended by the adventurous and free pursuit of scientific truth. Some of the readings penetrate far within special sciences so that the reader may become acquainted with what goes on inside, while other readings remain on the periphery looking out on the world's larger problems. Although the Readings are subdivided in four parts, the selections deal with overlapping topics and may be studied in any order, depending on the interests and background of the reader.

Selections requiring various kinds of scientific background on the part of the reader, from the elementary to the advanced level, have been included, since no two readers will have had equal familiarity with all the sciences on every level. It is hoped that these Readings are sufficiently representative to help meet the general educational needs of students of theoretical or applied sciences. Theory is broader than the practical needs from which the sciences arose historically, and furnishes practice with the prospects of undeveloped possibilities in return for the stimulation provided by society's growing needs. Philosophy of science has an educational responsibility in the preparation of future engineers, physicians, lawyers, teachers, journalists, ministers, and public administrators as well as research workers with regard to our cultural problem of keeping apace with rapidly advancing sciences. With no twentieth-century Aristotle in sight or even possible, we must learn in philosophy as in the sciences to work cooperatively on the problems of first principles.

Emphasis has been placed on the basic concepts and problems of the philosophy of science rather than on the defense of any one school of thought. Historical perspectives broaden the scope of logical analyses. A comparative study of the pervasive ways in which such basic notions as causality, continuity, emergence, field, probability, etc., function in diverse sciences takes one through all of the subject; the Analytical Index is designed to help in this approach. The References and Notes provide ample material for further study.

I am gratefully indebted to Professor Ernest Nagel for his suggestions to include certain topics, and to the invisible team of scientific and philosophic authors who have permitted me to assemble portions of their writings here. The original source and publisher are indicated on the first page of each selection.

P. P. W.

Contents

vii

C. Method and Problems of the Social Sciences

D. Philosophical Analyses and Syntheses

CONTENTS

PART A

*

Foundations of Mathematical and Physical Science

ALFRED NORTH WHITEHEAD

The Abstract Nature of Mathematics *

The study of mathematics is apt to commence in disappointment. The important applications of the science, the theoretical interest of its ideas, and the logical rigour of its methods, all generate the expectation of a speedy introduction to processes of interest. We are told that by its aid the stars are weighed and the billions of molecules in a drop of water are counted. Yet, like the ghost of Hamlet's father, this great science eludes the effort of our mental weapons to grasp it—" 'Tis here, 'tis there, 'tis gone"—and what we do see does not suggest the same excuse for illusiveness as sufficed for the ghost that it is too noble for our gross methods. "A show of violence," if ever excusable, may surely be "offered" to trivial results which occupy the pages of some elementary mathematical treatises.

The reason for this failure of the science to live up to its reputation is that its fundamental ideas are not explained to the student disentangled from the technical procedure which has been invented to facilitate their exact presentation in particular instances. Accordingly, the unfortunate learner finds himself struggling to acquire a knowledge of a mass of details which are not illuminated by any general conception. Without a doubt, technical facility is a first requisite for valuable mental activity: we shall fail to appreciate the rhythm of Milton, or the passion of Shelley, so long as we find it necessary to spell the words and are not quite certain of the forms of the individual letters. In this sense there is no royal road to learning. But it is equally an error to confine attention to technical processes, excluding consideration of general ideas. Here lies the road to pedantry.

The object of the following chapters is not to teach mathematics, but to enable students from the very beginning of their course to know what the science is about, and why it is necessarily the foundation of exact thought as applied to natural phenomena. All allusion in what follows to detailed deductions in any part of the science will be inserted merely for the purpose of example, and care will be taken to make the general argument comprehensible, even if here and there some technical process or

* From *An Introduction to Mathematics* by A. N. Whitehead. Oxford University Press, 1911. Chapter I, pp. 7–14. By permission of the publishers.

symbol which the reader does not understand is cited for the purpose of illustration.

The first acquaintance which most people have with mathematics is through arithmetic. That two and two make four is usually taken as the type of a simple mathematical proposition which everyone will have heard of. Arithmetic, therefore, will be a good subject to consider in order to discover, if possible, the most obvious characteristic of the science. Now, the first noticeable fact about arithmetic is that it applies to everything, to tastes and to sounds, to apples and to angels, to the ideas of the mind and to the bones of the body. The nature of the things is perfectly indifferent, of all things it is true that two and two make four. Thus we write down as the leading characteristic of mathematics that it deals with properties and ideas which are applicable to things just because they are things, and apart from any particular feelings, or emotions, or sensations, in any way connected with them. This is what is meant by calling mathematics an abstract science.

The result which we have reached deserves attention. It is natural to think that an abstract science cannot be of much importance in the affairs of human life, because it has omitted from its consideration everything of real interest. It will be remembered that Swift, in his description of Gulliver's voyage to Laputa, is of two minds on this point. He describes the mathematicians of that country as silly and useless dreamers, whose attention has to be awakened by flappers. Also, the mathematical tailor measures his height by a quadrant, and deduces his other dimensions by a rule and compasses, producing a suit of very ill-fitting clothes. On the other hand, the mathematicians of Laputa, by their marvellous invention of the magnetic island floating in the air, ruled the country and maintained their ascendency over their subjects. Swift, indeed, lived at a time peculiarly unsuited for gibes at contemporary mathematicians. Newton's *Principia* had just been written, one of the great forces which have transformed the modern world. Swift might just as well have laughed at an earthquake.

But a mere list of the achievements of mathematics is an unsatisfactory way of arriving at an idea of its importance. It is worth while to spend a little thought in getting at the root reason why mathematics, because of its very abstractness, must always remain one of the most important topics for thought. Let us try to make clear to ourselves why explanations of the order of events necessarily tend to become mathematical.

Consider how all events are interconnected. When we see the lightning, we listen for the thunder; when we hear the wind, we look for the waves on the sea; in the chill autumn, the leaves fall. Everywhere order reigns, so that when some circumstances have been noted we can foresee that others will also be present. The progress of science consists in observing these interconnections and in showing with a patient ingenuity that the events of this evershifting world are but examples of a few general connections or relations called laws. To see what is general in what is particular and what is permanent in what is transitory is the aim of scientific thought. In the eye of science, the fall of an apple, the motion of a planet round a sun, and the clinging of the atmosphere to the earth are all seen as examples of the law of gravity. This possibility of disentangling the most complex evanescent circumstances into various examples of permanent laws is the controlling idea of modern thought.

Now let us think of the sort of laws which we want in order completely to realize this scientific ideal. Our knowledge of the particular facts of the world around us is gained from our sensations. We see, and hear, and taste, and smell, and feel hot and cold, and push, and rub, and ache, and tingle. These are just our own personal sensations: my toothache cannot be your toothache, and my sight cannot be your sight. But we ascribe the origin of these sensations to relations between the things which form the external world. Thus the dentist extracts not the toothache but the tooth. And not only so, we also endeavour to imagine the world as one connected set of things which underlies all the perceptions of all people. There is not one world of things for my sensations and another for yours, but one world in which we both exist. It is the same tooth both for dentist and patient. Also we hear and we touch the same world as we see.

It is easy, therefore, to understand that we want to describe the connections between these external things in some way which does not depend on any particular sensations, nor even on all the sensations of any particular person. The laws satisfied by the course of events in the world of external things are to be described, if possible, in a neutral universal fashion, the same for blind men as for deaf men, and the same for beings with faculties beyond our ken as for normal human beings.

But when we have put aside our immediate sensations, the most serviceable part—from its clearness, definiteness, and universality—of what is left is composed of our general ideas of the abstract formal properties of things; in fact, the abstract mathematical ideas mentioned above. Thus it comes about that, step by step, and not realizing the full meaning of the process, mankind has been led to search for a mathematical description of the properties of the universe, because in this way only can a general idea of the course of events be formed, freed from reference to particular persons or to particular types of sensation. For example, it might be asked at dinner: "What was it which underlay my sensation of sight, yours of touch, and his of taste and smell?" the answer being "an apple." But in its final analysis, science seeks to describe an apple in terms of the positions and motions of molecules, a description which ignores me and you and him, and also ignores sight and touch and taste and smell. Thus mathematical ideas, because they are abstract, supply just what is wanted for a scientific description of the course of events.

This point has usually been misunderstood, from being thought of in too narrow a way. Pythagoras had a glimpse of it when he proclaimed that number was the source of all things. In modern times the belief that the ultimate explanation of all things was to be found in Newtonian mechanics was an adumbration of the truth that all science as it grows towards perfection becomes mathematical in its ideas.

[2]

CHARLES S. PEIRCE

How Mathematics Generalizes:*
*The Essence of Mathematics***

. . Modern mathematics is replete with ideas which may be applied to philosophy. I can only notice one or two. The manner in which mathematicians generalize is very instructive. Thus, painters are accustomed to

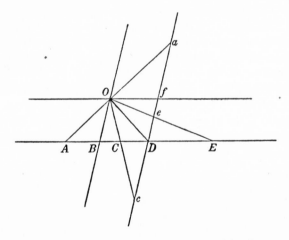

think of a picture as consisting geometrically of the intersections of its plane by rays of light from the natural objects to the eye. But geometers use a generalized perspective. For instance in the figure let O be the eye, let $A\ B\ C\ D\ E$ be the edgewise view of any plane, and let $a\ f\ e\ D\ c$ be the edgewise view of another plane. The geometers draw rays through O cutting both these planes, and treat the points of intersection of each ray

* From "The Architecture of Theories," *Monist* (Jan. 1891), 171 ff.
** Reprinted by permission of the publishers from *Collected Papers of Charles Sanders Peirce,* ed. by Charles Hartshorne and Paul Weiss, Volume IV, pp. 189–200, without paragraph numbers or editors' notes. Cambridge, Mass.: Harvard University Press, Copyright, 1933, by The President and Fellows of Harvard College.

with one plane as representing the point of intersection of the same ray with the other plane. Thus, *e* represents *E,* in the painter's way. *D* represents itself. *C* is represented by *c,* which is further from the eye; and *A* is represented by *a* which is on the other side of the eye. Such generalization is not bound down to sensuous images. Further, according to this mode of representation every point on one plane represents a point on the other, and every point on the latter is represented by a point on the former. But how about the point *f* which is in a direction from *O* parallel to the represented plane, and how about the point *B* which is in a direction parallel to the representing plane? Some will say that these are exceptions; but modern mathematics does not allow exceptions which can be annulled by generalization. As a point moves from *C* to *D* and thence to *E* and off toward infinity, the corresponding point on the other plane moves from *c* to *D* and thence to *e* and toward *f.* But this second point can pass through *f* to *a ;* and when it is there the first point has arrived at *A.* We therefore say that the first point has passed *through infinity,* and that every line joins in to itself somewhat like an oval. Geometers talk of the parts of lines at an infinite distance as points. This is a kind of generalization very efficient in mathematics.

Modern views of measurement have a philosophical aspect. There is an indefinite number of systems of measuring along a line; thus, a perspective representation of a scale on one line may be taken to measure another, although of course such measurements will not agree with what we call the distances of points on the latter line. To establish a system of measurement on a line we must assign a distinct number to each point of it, and for this purpose we shall plainly have to suppose the numbers carried out into an infinite number of places of decimals. These numbers must be ranged along the line in unbroken sequence. Further, in order that such a scale of numbers should be of any use, it must be capable of being shifted into new positions, each number continuing to be attached to a single distinct point. Now it is found that if this is true for "imaginary" as well as for real points (an expression which I cannot stop to elucidate), any such shifting will necessarily leave two numbers attached to the same points as before. So that when the scale is moved over the line by any continuous series of shiftings of one kind, there are two points which no numbers on the scale can ever reach, except the numbers fixed there. This pair of points, thus unattainable in measurement, is called the Absolute. These two points may be distinct and real, or they may coincide, or they may be both imaginary. As an example of a linear quantity with a double absolute we may take probability, which ranges from an unattainable absolute certainty *against* a proposition to an equally unattainable absolute certainty *for* it. A line, according to ordinary notions, we have seen is a linear quantity where the two points at infinity coincide. A velocity is another example. A train going with infinite velocity from Chicago to New York would be at all the points on the line at the very same instant, and if the time of transit were reduced to less than nothing it would be moving in the other direction. An angle is a familiar example of a mode of magnitude with no real immeasurable values. One of the questions philosophy has to consider is whether the development of the universe is like the increase of an angle, so that it proceeds forever without tending toward anything unattained, which I take to be the Epicurean view, or whether the universe sprang from a chaos in the infinitely distant past to tend toward something different in the infinitely distant future, or whether the universe sprang from nothing in the past to go on indefinitely toward a point in the infinitely distant future, which, were it attained, would be the mere nothing from which it set out.

The doctrine of the absolute applied to space comes to this, that either—

First, space is, as Euclid teaches, both *unlimited* and *immeasurable*, so that the infinitely distant parts of any plane seen in perspective appear as a straight line, in which case the sum of the three angles of a triangle amounts to 180°; or,

Second, space is *immeasurable* but *limited,* so that the infinitely distant parts of any plane seen in perspective appear as a circle, beyond which all is blackness, and in this case the sum of the three angles of a triangle is less than 180° by an amount proportional to the area of the triangle; or,

Third, space is *unlimited* but *finite* (like the surface of a sphere), so that it has no infinitely distant parts; but a finite journey along any straight line would bring one back to his original position, and looking off with an unobstructed view one would see the back of his own head enormously magnified, in which case the sum of the three angles of a triangle exceeds 180° by an amount proportional to the area.

Which of these three hypotheses is true we know not. . . . It is true that according to the axioms of geometry the sum of the three angles of a triangle are precisely 180°; but these axioms are now exploded, and geometers confess that they, as geometers, know not the slightest reason for supposing them to be precisely true. They are expressions of our inborn conception of space, and as such are entitled to credit, so far as their truth could have influenced the formation of the mind. But that affords not the slightest reason for supposing them exact.

Now, metaphysics has always been the ape of mathematics. Geometry suggested the idea of a demonstrative system of absolutely certain philosophical principles; and the ideas of the metaphysicians have at all times been in large part drawn from mathematics. The metaphysical axioms are imitations of the geometrical axioms; and now that the latter have been thrown overboard, without doubt the former will be sent after them. It is evident, for instance, that we can have no reason to think that every phenomenon in all its minutest details is precisely determined by law. That there is an arbitrary element in the universe we see,—namely, its variety. This variety must be attributed to spontaneity in some form.

Had I more space, I now ought to show how important for philosophy is the mathematical conception of continuity. . . .

. . . .

The Essence of Mathematics

It does not seem to me that mathematics depends in any way upon logic. It reasons, of course. But if the mathematician ever hesitates or errs in his reasoning, logic cannot come to his aid. He would be far more liable to commit similar as well as other errors there. On the contrary, I am persuaded that logic cannot possibly attain the solution of its problems without great use of mathematics. Indeed all formal logic is merely mathematics applied to logic.

It was Benjamin Peirce, whose son I boast myself, that in 1870 first defined mathematics as "the science which draws necessary conclusions." * This was a hard saying at the time; but today, students of philosophy of mathematics generally acknowledge its substantial correctness.

The common definition, among such people as ordinary schoolmasters, still is that mathematics is the science of quantity. As this is inevitably understood in English, it seems to be a misunderstanding of a definition which may be very old,[1] the original meaning being that mathematics is the science of *quantities,* that is, forms possessing quantity. We perceive that Euclid was aware that a large branch of geometry had nothing to do with measurement (unless as an aid in demonstrating); and, therefore a Greek geometer of his age (early in the third century B.C.) or later could not define mathematics as the science of that which the abstract noun quantity expresses. A line, however, was classed as a quantity, or *quantum,* by Aristotle (*Metaphysica, 102a, 14–20*) and his followers; so that even perspective (which deals wholly with intersections and projections, not at all with lengths) could be said to be a science of quantities, "quantity" being taken in the concrete sense. That this was what was originally meant by the definition "Mathematics is the science of quantity," is sufficiently shown by the circumstance that those writers who first enunciate it, about A.D. 500, that is, Ammonius Hermiae and Boethius, make astronomy and music branches of mathematics; and it is confirmed by the reasons they give for doing so.[2] Even Philo of Alexandria (100 B.C.), who defines mathematics as the science of ideas furnished by sensation and reflection in respect to their necessary consequences, since he includes under mathematics, besides its more essential parts, the theory of numbers and geometry, also the practical arithmetic of the Greeks, geodesy, mechanics, optics (or projective geometry), music, and astronomy, must be said to take the word 'mathematics' in a different sense from ours. That Aristotle did not regard mathematics as the science of quantity, in

* "Linear Associative Algebra" (1870), sec. 1; see *American Journal of Mathematics,* vol. 4 (1881).

the modern abstract sense, is evidenced in various ways. The subjects of mathematics are, according to him, the how much and the continuous. (See *Metaph.* K iii 1061 a 33). He referred the continuous to his category of *quantum;* and therefore he did make *quantum,* in a broad sense, the one object of mathematics.

Plato, in the Sixth book of the *Republic,*[3] holds that the essential characteristic of mathematics lies in the peculiar kind and degree of its abstraction, greater than that of physics but less than that of what we now call philosophy; and Aristotle follows his master in this definition. It has ever since been the habit of metaphysicians to extol their own reasonings and conclusions as vastly more abstract and scientific than those of mathematics. It certainly would seem that problems about God, Freedom, and Immortality are more exalted than, for example, the question how many hours, minutes, and seconds would elapse before two couriers travelling under assumed conditions will come together; although I do not know that this has been proved. But that the methods of thought of the metaphysicians are, as a matter of historical fact, in any aspect, not far inferior to those of mathematics is simply an infatuation. One singular consequence of the notion which prevailed during the greater part of the history of philosophy, that metaphysical reasoning ought to be similar to that of mathematics, only more so, has been that sundry mathematicians have thought themselves, as mathematicians, qualified to discuss philosophy; and no worse metaphysics than theirs is to be found.

Kant regarded mathematical propositions as synthetical judgments *a priori;* wherein there is this much truth, that they are not, for the most part, what he called analytical judgments; that is, the predicate is not, in the sense he intended, contained in the definition of the subject. But if the propositions of arithmetic, for example, are true cognitions, or even forms of cognition, this circumstance is quite aside from their mathematical truth. For all modern mathematicians agree with Plato and Aristotle that mathematics deals exclusively with hypothetical states of things, and asserts no matter of fact whatever; and further, that it is thus alone that the necessity of its conclusions is to be explained. This is the true essence of mathematics; and my father's definition is in so far correct that it is impossible to reason necessarily concerning anything else than a pure hypothesis. Of course, I do not mean that if such pure hypothesis happened to be true of an actual state of things, the reasoning would thereby cease to be necessary. Only, it never would be known apodictically to be true of an actual state of things. Suppose a state of things of a perfectly definite, general description. That is, there must be no room for doubt as to whether anything, itself determinate, would or would not come under that description. And suppose, further, that this description refers to nothing occult—nothing that cannot be summoned up fully into the imagination. Assume, then, a range of possibilities equally definite and equally subject to the imagination; so that, so far as the given description of the supposed state of things is general, the different ways in which it might be made determinate could never introduce doubtful or occult features. The assumption, for example, must not refer to any matter of fact. For questions of fact are not within the purview of the imagination. Nor must it be such that, for example, it could lead us to ask whether the vowel OO can be imagined to be sounded on as high a pitch as the vowel EE. Perhaps it would have to be restricted to pure spatial, temporal, and logical relations. Be that as it may, the question whether in such a state of things, a certain other similarly definite state of things, equally a matter of the imagination, could or could not, in the assumed range of possibility, ever occur, would be one in reference to which one of the two answers, *Yes* and *No,* would be true, but never both. But all pertinent facts would be within the beck and call of the imagination; and consequently nothing but the operation of thought would be necessary to render the true answer. Nor, supposing the answer to cover the whole range of possibility assumed, could this be rendered otherwise than by reasoning that would be apodictic, general, and exact. No knowledge of what actually is, no *positive* knowledge, as we say, could result. On the other hand, to assert that any source of information that is restricted to actual facts could afford us a necessary knowledge, that is, knowledge relating to a whole general range of possibility, would be a flat contradiction in terms.

Mathematics is the study of what is true of hypothetical states of things. That is its essence and definition. Everything in it, therefore, beyond the first precepts for the construction of the hypotheses, has to be of the nature of apodictic inference. No doubt, we may reason imperfectly and jump at a conclusion; still, the conclusion so guessed at is, after all, that in a certain supposed state of things something would necessarily be true. Conversely, too, every apodictic inference is, strictly speaking, mathematics. But mathematics, as a serious science, has, over and above its essential character of being hypothetical, an accidental characteristic peculiarity —a *proprium,* as the Aristotelians used to say—which is of the greatest logical interest. Namely, while all the "philosophers" follow Aristotle in holding no demonstration to be thoroughly satisfactory except what they call a "direct" demonstration, or a "demonstration why"—by which they mean a demonstration which employs only general concepts and concludes nothing but what would be an item of a definition if all its terms were themselves distinctly defined—the mathematicians, on the contrary, entertain a contempt for that style of reasoning, and glory in what the philosophers stigmatize as "mere" indirect demonstrations, of "demonstrations that." Those propositions which can be deduced from others by reasoning of the kind that the philosophers extol are set down by mathematicians as "corollaries." That is to say, they are like those geometrical truths which Euclid did not deem worthy of particular mention, and which his editors inserted with a garland, or corolla, against each in the margin, implying perhaps that it was to them that such honor as might attach to these insignificant remarks was due. In the theorems, or at least in all the major theorems, a different kind of reasoning is demanded. Here, it will not do to confine oneself to general terms. It is necessary to set down, or to imagine, some individual and definite schema, or diagram—in geometry, a figure composed of lines with letters attached; in algebra an array of letters of which some are repeated. This schema is constructed so as to conform to a hypothesis set forth in general terms in the thesis of the theorem. Pains are taken so to construct it that there would be something closely similar in every possible state of things to which the hypothetical description in the thesis would be applicable, and furthermore to construct it so that it shall have no other characters which could influence the reasoning. How it can be that, although the reasoning is based upon the study of an individual schema, it is nevertheless necessary, that is, applicable, to all possible cases, is one of the questions we shall have to consider. Just now, I wish to point out that after the schema has been constructed according to the precept virtually contained in the thesis, the assertion of the theorem is not evidently true, even for the individual schema; nor will any amount of hard thinking of the philosophers' corollarial kind ever render it evident. Thinking in general terms is not enough. It is necessary that something should be DONE. In geometry, subsidiary lines are drawn. In algebra permissible transformations are made. Thereupon, the faculty of observation is called into play. Some relation between the parts of the schema is remarked. But would this relation subsist in every possible case? Mere corollarial reasoning will sometimes assure us of this. But, generally speaking, it may be necessary to draw distinct schemata to represent alternative possibilities. Theorematic reasoning invariably depends upon experimentation with individual schemata. We shall find that, in the last analysis, the same thing is true of the corollarial reasoning, too; even the Aristotelian "demonstration why." Only in this case, the very words serve as schemata. Accordingly, we may say that corollarial, or "philosophical" reasoning is reasoning with words; while theorematic, or mathematical reasoning proper, is reasoning with specially constructed schemata.

Another characteristic of mathematical thought is the extraordinary use it makes of abstractions. Abstractions have been a favorite butt of ridicule in modern times. Now it is very easy to laugh at the old physician who is represented as answering the question, why opium puts people to sleep, by saying that it is because it has a dormitive virtue. It is an answer that no doubt carries vagueness to its last extreme. Yet, invented as the story was to show how little meaning there might be in an abstraction, nevertheless the physician's answer does contain a truth that modern philosophy has generally denied: it does assert that there really is in opium *something* which explains its always putting people to sleep. This has, I say, been denied by modern philosophers generally. Not, of course, explicitly; but when they say that the different events of people going to sleep after taking opium have really nothing in common, but only that the mind classes them together—and this is what they virtually do say in denying the reality of generals—they do implicitly deny that there is any true explanation of opium's generally putting people to sleep.

Look through the modern logical treatises, and you will find that they almost all fall into one or other of two errors, as I hold them to be; that of setting aside the doctrine of abstraction (in the sense in which an abstract noun marks an abstraction) as a grammatical topic with which the logician need not particularly concern himself; and that of confounding abstraction, in this sense, with that operation of the mind by which we pay attention to one feature of a percept to the disregard of others. The two things are entirely disconnected. The most ordinary fact of perception, such as "it is light," involves *precisive* abstraction, or *prescission*. But *hypostatic* abstraction, the abstraction which transforms "it is light" into "there is light here," which is the sense which I shall commonly attach to the word abstraction (since *prescission* will do for precisive abstraction) is a very special mode of thought. It consists in taking a feature of a percept or percepts (after it has already been prescinded from the other elements of the percept), so as to take propositional form in a judgment (indeed, it may operate upon any judgment whatsoever), and in conceiving this fact to consist in the relation between the subject of that judgment and another subject, which has a mode of being that merely consists in the truth of propositions of which the corresponding concrete term is the predicate. Thus, we transform the proposition, "honey is sweet," into "honey possesses sweetness." "Sweetness" might be called a fictitious thing, in one sense. But since the mode of being attributed to it *consists* in no more than the fact that some things are sweet, and it is not pretended, or imagined, that it has any other mode of being, there is, after all, no fiction. The only profession made is that we consider the fact of honey being sweet under the form of a relation; and so we really can. I have selected sweetness as an instance of one of the least useful of abstractions. Yet even this is convenient. It facilitates such thoughts as that the sweetness of honey is particularly cloying; that the sweetness of honey is something like the sweetness of a honeymoon; etc. Abstractions are particularly congenial to mathematics. Everyday life first, for example, found the need of that class of abstractions which we call *collections*. Instead of saying that some human beings are males and all the rest females, it was found convenient to say that *mankind* consists of the male *part* and the female *part*. The same thought makes classes of collections, such as pairs, leashes, quatrains, hands, weeks, dozens, baker's dozens, sonnets, scores, quires, hundreds, long hundreds, gross, reams, thousands, myriads, lacs, millions, milliards, milliasses, etc. These have suggested a great branch of mathematics.[4] Again, a point moves: it is by abstraction that the geometer says that it "describes a line." This line, though an abstraction, itself moves; and this is regarded as generating a surface; and so on. So likewise, when the analyst treats operations as themselves subjects of operations, a method whose utility will not be denied, this is another instance of abstraction. Maxwell's notion of a tension exercised upon lines of electrical force, transverse to them, is somewhat similar. These examples exhibit the great rolling billows of abstraction in the ocean of mathematical thought; but when we come to a minute examination of it, we shall find, in every department, incessant ripples of the same form of thought, of which the examples I have mentioned give no hint.

Another characteristic of mathematical thought is that it can have no success where it cannot generalize. One cannot, for example, deny that chess is mathematics, after a fashion; but, owing to the exceptions which everywhere confront the mathematician in this field—such as the limits of the board; the single steps of king, knight, and pawn; the finite number of squares; the peculiar mode of capture by pawns; the queening of pawns; castling—there results a mathematics whose wings are effectually clipped, and which can only run along the ground. Hence it is that a mathematician often finds what a chess-player might call a gambit to his advantage; exchanging a smaller problem that involves exceptions for a larger one free from them. Thus, rather than suppose that parallel lines, unlike all other pairs of straight lines in a plane, never meet, he supposes that they intersect at infinity. Rather than suppose that some equations have roots while others have not, he supplements real quantity by the infinitely greater realm of imaginary quantity. He tells us with ease how many inflexions a plane curve of any description has; but if we ask how many of these are real, and how many merely fictional, he is unable to say. He is perplexed by three-dimensional space, because not all pairs of straight lines intersect, and finds it to his advantage to use quaternions which represent a sort of four-fold continuum, in order to avoid the exception. It is because exceptions so hamper the mathematician that almost all the relations with which he chooses to deal are of the nature of correspondences; that is to say, such relations that for every relate there is the same number of correlates, and for every correlate the same number of relates.

Among the minor, yet striking characteristics of mathematics, may be mentioned the fleshless and skeletal build of its propositions; the peculiar difficulty, complication, and stress of its reasonings; the perfect exactitude of its results; their broad universality; their practical infallibility. It is easy to speak with precision upon a general theme. Only, one must commonly surrender all ambition to be certain. It is equally easy to be certain. One has only to be sufficiently vague. It is not so difficult to be pretty precise and fairly certain at once about a very narrow subject. But to reunite, like mathematics, perfect exactitude and practical infallibility with unrestricted universality, is remarkable. But it is not hard to see that all these characters of mathematics are inevitable consequences of its being the study of hypothetical truth.

It is difficult to decide between the two definitions of mathematics; the one by its method, that of drawing necessary conclusions; the other by its aim and subject matter, as the study of hypothetical states of things. The former makes or seems to make the deduction of the consequences of hypotheses the sole business of the mathematician as such. But it cannot be denied that immense genius has been exercised in the mere framing of such general hypotheses as the field of imaginary quantity and the allied idea of Riemann's surface, in imagining non-Euclidian measurement, ideal numbers, the perfect liquid. Even the framing of the particular hypotheses of special problems almost always calls for good judgment and knowledge, and sometimes for great intellectual power, as in the case of Boole's logical algebra. Shall we exclude this work from the domain of mathematics? Perhaps the answer should be that, in the first place, whatever exercise of intellect may be called for in applying mathematics to a question not propounded in mathematical form (it) is certainly not pure mathematical thought; and in the second place, that the mere creation of a hypothesis may be a grand work of poietic genius, but cannot be said to be scientific, inasmuch as that which it produces is neither true nor false, and therefore is not knowledge. This reply suggests the further remark that if mathematics is the study of purely imaginary states of things, poets must be great mathematicians, especially that class of poets who write novels of intricate and enigmatical plots. Even the reply which is obvious, that by *studying* imaginary states of things we mean *studying* what is true of them, perhaps does not fully meet the objection. The article *Mathematics* in the ninth edition of the *Encyclopaedia Britannica* makes mathematics consist in the study of a particular sort of hypotheses, namely, those that are exact, etc., as there set forth at some length. The article is well worthy of consideration.

The philosophical mathematician, Dr. Richard Dedekind, holds mathematics to be a branch of logic.[5] This would not result from my father's definition, which runs, not that mathematics is the science of *drawing* necessary conclusions—which would be deductive logic—but that it is the science which *draws* necessary conclusions. It is evident, and I know as a fact, that he had this distinction in view. At the time when he thought out this definition, he, a mathematician, and I, a logician, held daily discussions about a large subject which interested us both; and he was struck, as I was, with the contrary nature of his interest and mine in the same propositions. The logician does not care particularly about this or that hypothesis or its consequences, except so far as these things may throw a light upon the nature of reasoning. The mathematician is intensely interested in efficient methods of reasoning, with a view to their possible extension to new problems; but he does not, *quâ* mathematician, trouble himself minutely to dissect those parts of this method whose correctness is a matter of course. The different aspects which the algebra of logic will assume for the two men is instructive in this respect. The mathematician asks what value this algebra has as a calculus. Can it be applied to unravelling a complicated question? Will it, at one stroke, produce a remote consequence? The logician does not wish the algebra to have that character. On the contrary, the greater number of distinct logical steps, into which the algebra breaks up an inference, will for him constitute a superiority of it over another which moves more swiftly to its conclusions. He demands that the algebra shall analyze a reasoning into its last elementary steps. Thus, that which is a merit in a logical algebra for one of these students is a demerit in the eyes of the other. The one studies the science of drawing conclusions, the other the science which draws necessary conclusions.

But, indeed, the difference between the two sciences is far more than that between two points of view. Mathematics is purely hypothetical: it produces nothing but conditional propositions. Logic, on the contrary, is categorical in its assertions. True, it is not merely, or even mainly, a mere discovery of what really is, like metaphysics. It is a normative science. It thus has a strongly mathematical character, at least in its methodeutic division; for here it analyzes the problem of how, with given means, a required end is to be pursued. This is, at most, to say that it has to call in the aid of mathematics; that it has a mathematical branch. But so much may be said of every science. There is a mathematical logic, just as there is a mathematical optics and a mathematical economics. Mathematical logic is formal logic. Formal logic, however, is by no means the whole of logic, or even its principal part. It is hardly to be reckoned as a part of logic proper. . . .

[3]

BERTRAND RUSSELL

Geometry
in the Perceived World

PREFACE TO NICOD'S WORK *

The history of this problem [the relation between geometry and sense-perception] in modern times is well known. Kant asserted that geometry is based on an *a priori* intuition of space and that experience could never contradict it because space constitutes a part of our manner of perceiving the world. Non-Euclidean geometry has led most thinkers to abandon this opinion; although from the logical point of view, it might be easy to maintain that Lobachevsky's work did not go counter to the Kantian philosophy. Another stronger but less known argument was employed against Kant; it is the argument derived from the attempt to reduce pure mathematics, at first to arithmetic, and then to logic. The implication was that

* From *Foundations of Geometry and Induction,* containing translation by P. P. Wiener of Jean Nicod's *La Géométrie dans le Monde Sensible* with Preface by Bertrand Russell (London: Kegan Paul, Trench, Trubner & Co., 1930), pp. 5–9. Nicod's Introduction and Chapter I follow, pp. 11–21. By permission of the publisher.

an *a priori* intuition is no more necessary for abstract geometry than for the doctrine of the syllogism.

However, it was still possible to adopt a point of view which has certain affinities with that of Kant; for example, it was the view-point assumed by Henri Poincaré, who maintained that Euclidean geometry is neither true nor false, but that it is simply a convention. In a certain sense, this point of view may still be possible: in all experiment or physical observation, it is *the group* of applicable physical laws which constitutes the object of study, and if the results do not correspond to our expectation, we have a certain choice as to which of these laws should be modified. For example, Henri Poincaré would have maintained that if an astronomical observation seemed to prove that the sum of the angles of a triangle is not exactly equal to two right angles, this phenomenon would be more easily explained by assuming that light does not travel in a straight line than by giving up the system of Euclidean geometry. It is not surprising that Poincaré should have adopted this view; what is surprising, is that the progress of physics should have since shown in its own realm, that this point of view was ill taken. In fact, the eclipse observations undertaken to verify the Einsteinian theory of gravitation are explained usually by admitting both that space is non-Euclidean and that light is not propagated strictly in a straight line. Undoubtedly, it is still *possible* to hold to the view that space is Euclidean, as Dr. Whitehead does, but it is at least doubtful whether such a theory furnishes the most convenient explanation of the phenomenon.

In the following pages there will be found a different criticism, more fundamental than the theory of Henri Poincaré. When a logical or mathematical system is applied to the empirical world, we can distinguish, according to Jean Nicod's observation, two kinds of simplicity: simplicity intrinsic to the system and simplicity extrinsic to it. Intrinsic simplicity is the simplicity of the laws that establish the relations among the entities taken as primitive in the system. Extrinsic simplicity is the simplicity of the empirical interpretation of these entities. The points, lines, and planes of geometry give it the character of intrinsic simplicity, because they enable the axioms to be stated briefly; but they do not constitute what is empirically given in the sensible world. Consequently if our geometry is to be applied to the perceived world, we shall have to define points, straight lines, and planes by means of terms which are at least similar to our sense-data. In fact, this definition is extremely complicated, and thus removes any character of *extrinsic* simplicity from our conventional geometry. To regain this extrinsic simplicity, we must start from data which are not in conformity with ordinary geometry, Euclidean or non-Euclidean; and we must formulate gradually, if we can, suitable logical constructs that enjoy the required properties. We cannot say in advance whether we shall obtain greater extrinsic simplicity by taking recourse to straight lines and Euclidean or non-Euclidean planes, although we admit that the possibility of one of the systems implies the possibility of the other and reciprocally.

Dr. Whitehead has examined, from the point of view of mathematical

logic, how we can define in terms of empirical data the entities that traditional geometry considers as primitive. His method of "extensive abstraction" has great value and efficacy in this regard. But this method starts
from the knowledge of the completed mathematical system which is the
object to be attained, and goes back to entities more analogous to those of
sense perception. The method adopted by Nicod follows the inverse order:
starting from data of perception, it tries to attain the various geometries
that can be built on them. This is a difficult and novel problem. To treat
it logically, the author assumes as a starting point an entirely schematic
simplicity of sensations, although it is easy to imagine some animals among
whom it might exist. In his first example, he shows us an animal possessing
only the sense of hearing and a perception of temporal succession, who
produces notes of varying pitch as he proceeds up and down the keyboard
of a piano. Now, such an animal, if we suppose him endowed with sufficient
logical power, will be able to produce two geometries, both, naturally, in
one dimension. The animals presented next come nearer to man in their
perceptions; although they differ from most of us in that they are logicians
and metaphysicians as penetrating as Nicod himself.

The distinction between pure geometry and physical geometry, which
has gradually appeared of late, is presented as clearly as possible in Jean
Nicod's work, the first part of which deals with pure geometry. This distinction and its consequences are not yet comprehended by philosophers as
much as they deserve. In pure geometry we assume as a starting point the
existence of a group of entities whose relations have definite logical properties and we deduce from them the propositions of the geometry under consideration. The existence of groups of entities having relations of this
nature can in all usual cases be deduced from arithmetic. For example, all
the possible triads of real numbers arranged in their natural order form
the points of a tri-dimensional Euclidean space. The whole question belongs
to the realm of pure logic and no longer raises philosophical problems. But
in physical geometry, we are confronted with a much more interesting
problem because it is far from having been completely solved. We know
that experimental physics employs geometry; from this it follows that the
geometry which it employs is applicable to the empirical world to the
degree in which physics is exact. That is to say, it ought to be possible to
find groups of sense-data and relations among these data such that the
relations which are derived from these groups may approximately satisfy
the axioms of the geometry employed in physics. Or, if the sense-data alone
are not sufficient, they ought to be complemented in the same way as they
are in physics, by means of inferences and inductions whose use is authorized by ordinary scientific method; for example, the inference which allows
us to assume that the moon has another side which we do not see. This
point of view is supported and facilitated by the absorption of geometry by
physics as a result of the theory of relativity. However, the psychological
aspect of this problem has been studied very little, probably because few
psychologists possess a sufficient knowledge of modern physics or mathe-

matical logic. We must build a bridge by beginning on both ends at the same time: that is to say, on one side, by bringing together the assumptions of physics and the data of psychology and, on the other, by manipulating the psychological data in such a way that we may build logical constructions that approximately satisfy the axioms of physical geometry. Jean Nicod has, in the last of these tasks, made progress of the highest importance. He has created a method much superior to that of his predecessors. We cannot say yet that the two sides of the bridge meet in his work, but the gap that remains to be filled today is smaller than it was before the writing of the following pages. . . .

JEAN NICOD

Geometry
in the Perceived World

INTRODUCTION

Experience is the only test of the truth of particular propositions concerning objects around us. Let us call the group of such objects *physical,* taking the word in its widest sense. We are taking physics as an entirely empirical science: it attains certainty or probability only in the degree to which experience verifies its findings. Its sole claim upon our credence is the exactness with which it tells us what we shall see, hear, and touch in accordance with what we have seen, heard, and touched. If that is not its only task, such is anyway the end by which it wishes to be judged. No one would object to the feasibility of analyzing physics and its claims of verification in relation to what is given to the senses.

The analysis is still far from being achieved. Writers most occupied with the empirical meaning of propositions about the material world give us, in fact, only the most summary account of this meaning itself. They take any proposition from physics and say: "In experience it means something *like* this." But not exactly this. For on closer examination we would find that no physical fact is verified by sensations without ambiguity. Any perceived fact, we say, can spring from various physical causes, although not all these causes are equally probable; in other words, our senses can deceive us about objects. But, on the other hand, these same senses can also correct us by means of perceptions which are sometimes very different in kind from our first impressions. Thus the presentation of a physical fact in my experience goes beyond my present observation and extends into the group of my past and future observations. Because of this extension the sensory manifestations of various physical facts are not as distinct from one another as these facts themselves, but are, on the contrary, intimately fused. If one wishes to obtain the last word about the exact sensory meaning of any physical proposition whatsoever, he must seek it right in that realm of experience which is subject to the laws of physics. With respect to verification, as Duhem has well observed, all branches of physics form one whole. It is the form and structure of this whole that we wish to study in order to discern the concrete meaning of those simple and complicated, ordinary and sophisticated laws which make up our knowledge of nature.

Surely this content is already present in our mind. It furnishes us with special insights continually. But its wholeness escapes us. It stays in the shadow and yet guides us to the light; we know how to use it, but we do not know how to analyse it.

The reason for this strange fact is that the formation and growth of physics are pervasively dominated by the quest for simple laws, or rather, for the simple expression of laws. This expression can be obtained, indeed, only by cloaking the complexities of things with simple names. For nature is such that simple things do not enjoy simple laws, so that, in order to simplify laws, we must complicate the meaning of their terms. Energy, matter, object, space and time—all these physical terms and, generally, every word that physics employs outside of terms having simple designations, derive their meaning and utility from this tyrannical desire for simple and forceful embodiments of the laws of the sensible world.

The real complexity of these laws is hidden away in the very simplicity of the new terms, and emerges naturally again in the process of applying them, but then no longer overwhelms the mind. It even ceases then to be distinct from the mind which might be said to cling to these new terms because of their aesthetic appeal. Thus the objective world becomes eclipsed by its symbolic representation, and in Physics where we draw these symbolic pictures, we must learn over again how to look at the natural world.

Such an enterprise has not been undertaken until now. The result is that we believe in laws which are founded only on experience although we do not know exactly what they mean in terms of experience. It is true that the undertaking is difficult and, moreover, long. Besides, it would not fit those programs which philosophers have been accustomed to follow. For their sole interest in the sensory content of judgments about reality was determined exclusively by the desire to use it in arguments about the *general* nature of matter or of physics. These arguments proceeded from the existence of this sensory content, and not from its more determinate structures; and the existence of the sensible world being so indubitable that the most summary designation sufficed to render it obvious, philosophers went no further. The empirical analysis of nature, as soon as it was designated, no longer seemed to be actually worth while making.

We must think otherwise, however. The discernment of the sensory order around us, which forms the qualitative background of our life and of our science, and which is ever present, however indistinctly, should certainly be a source of curiosity to any philosopher, even if his metaphysics should not obtain any aid from it. Such is the end at which we aim. We hope to approach it by the study of the objective aspect of geometry. It is impossible, in fact, to possess a proper idea of the order of our sensations if we are hampered by a false or confused idea of space.

This study might be a preface to the analysis of physics in terms of experience. It is also a beginning in it. For we shall find that the universal order of space to which every physical proposition seems to refer is, in truth, nothing but the very group of the laws of physics. The properties of space are already the most general schemata of physics and are nothing else. Thus—we shall be convinced of it as we proceed—the study of the spatial structure of a sensory universe is the study of the form and totality of all its laws.

We propose in this work to ascertain in what way geometry is an aid to physics; how its propositions are applied to the order of the perceived world; how knowledge of them helps us in the formulation of experiments and laws. For every statement in physics teems with geometry: every prediction of a perceptual fact is dependent on a certain disposition of the objects and observers, which is expressible in geometrical terms.

We are asking *how* geometry is exemplified in nature and not *why* it is. We are investigating the structure of the facts, not the reasons which render them possible or necessary. Analysis, indeed, should precede explanation; analysis is always possible, whereas explanation is not always possible.

In this problem, geometry appears as a form to which the objective world serves as matter. The natural order of this analysis is to study first what this form is, then what this matter is, and finally the particular way in which we find one in the other. Let us, in the first place, become acquainted with geometry in so far as it is a formal and wholly abstract science of the implications of certain principles involving terms and relations whose meanings are indeterminate. Let us next examine what terms and what relations are actually perceived by us in nature. Finally, let us investigate what meanings derived from these terms and relations are in agreement with the terms and relations of geometry, and comprise the laws of experience.

·   ·   ·   ·   ·   ·   ·   ·

CHAPTER I

PURE GEOMETRY IS AN EXERCISE IN LOGIC

What then is geometry considered as purely formal? It is whatever we can know about its structure without knowing its object; whatever we can understand in a treatise on geometry without being acquainted with the nature of the entities which it discusses.

In Kant's time, this point of view had not yet been reached. For geometry, which since Euclid was tending to liberate its proofs from the matter furnished by figures, for the purpose of basing them only on pure reason, had not yet succeeded in doing so. Deprived of concrete diagrams, its proofs seemed without force; the very concatenation of the propositions seemed to belong to these figures and not to the purely logical relations involved. All geometrical knowledge was in this way conceived as inseparable from the apprehension of space—a primitive matter, which, by imparting next its order to the sensible world, played with regard to the latter, the contrary rôle of a form. Thus the imperfect character and peculiar nature of the proofs of mathematicians furnished philosophers with the impression of a special mystery, and committed them to involved theories designed to account for the alleged existence of proofs which did not draw their force from ordinary logic.

But the actual progress of geometrical science allows us to conceive the problem more simply. Indeed, while the philosophers were speculating over the extra-rational character of geometrical proof, the geometers succeeding in doing away with it altogether. They made it a principle that proof by figures is only the outline of a proof. They regarded the appeal to intuition as the index of a lacuna, the sign of the use of an assumed principle which they tried to make explicit; they would not accept any proof as correct unless it formed a completely formal chain.

To obtain a proof, in this state of formal perfection, it is no longer *necessary* to illustrate it by a figure, to relate it to a matter, to attribute a determinate meaning to the geometrical expressions which it involves, for these concrete values add nothing to its force. It is *possible* to be convinced that the theorems flow from the axioms and postulates without knowing the meaning of *a point, a straight line* or *distance*; there is not a geometer today who would deny this. By becoming rigorous, that is to say explicit, geometrical proof has detached itself from all objects.

We do not have here any paradoxical development. Quite on the contrary, it puts an end to the paradox which opposes geometrical reasoning to all other reasoning. For a good demonstration, stated without anything implicit, is valuable for its form alone, independently of the truth and even of the meaning of its system of propositions. We may be astonished at this important fact, but we cannot doubt it. By freeing itself from all figures, by detaching itself from the meaning of the material terms which figure in it, geometrical demonstration has simply returned to common reason.

It is then possible today, as it was not a century ago, to take a completely abstract and fundamental view of geometrical science as independent of any object. It then appears as a chain of formal reasoning, which is in a certain sense blind, and which draws consequences from a group of premises formulated in terms of entities whose meanings, indifferent to the argument, remain quite indeterminate. Such is the universality of geometry. It is under this form, devoid still of any reality, that it may be fixed in our minds now. For, by conceiving it, at first, disengaged from any object, we are prepared to discern without any preconceived idea the objects of the universe to which the science is in fact applied.

Suppose then that we have not been taught geometry in school, and that we are acquainted with none of the particular terms of that science. Undoubtedly, the very things with which it is commonly supposed to deal, cannot fail to be familiar to us. But let us suppose that nobody has ever taught us their scientific names, and that, like the child Pascal, we call a straight line a bar and a circle a ring. Let us imagine that someone puts in our hands one of those treatises on geometry which aim only at rigour and which disdain all figures. What shall we get from it? Let us try, however, to read it.

It is composed of a small number of initial statements entitled "axioms" or "postulates" and other propositions entitled "theorems," which appear to spring from the first by virtue of texts entitled "demonstrations." But if we understand the terms of current language only, and in particular the terms of ordinary logic, all the properly geometrical terms such as "point," "straight line," "distance," are entirely unknown to us; and these new terms seem to us at first very numerous. However, we soon notice that they are for the most part introduced as simple abbreviations of complex expressions, in which we find only a small number of unknown terms. The latter are always identical, and must be only those contained in the initial propositions. There will be, for example, the class of "points," the relation of three points "in a straight line," and the relation of two couples of points "separated by the same distance"; thus, the term "sphere" will be defined as the abbreviation of the complex expression "class of points separated from a certain point by a constant distance."

We have taken inventory of the unknown expressions and we have reduced them to three. However, we have not eliminated them; since we are not aware of any subsistent expressions, we must admit that we do not understand what the "axioms," "postulates," "theorems" mean. But, to our surprise, we understand perfectly the intermediary steps called "demonstrations." The terms which embarrass us are still to be found there, but it is enough for us to understand the ordinary words which accompany them, and which belong to the logical sheathing of language, in order to follow the argument step by step, to grasp its march, to enjoy its ingenuity, and to discern its precision.

There is something surprising in this fact that the rigour or force of a demonstration can be apprehended without any knowledge of its matter. We are astonished to be able to proceed thus with our eyes closed. But this very force of form is found again in the most simple reasoning, and is valid in any given case because it holds for all possible and impossible cases. That is the constitutive fact of logic, remarkable, certainly, but common.

Then what do we learn from our reading? We may answer by saying: "I do not know what the author of this treatise calls a point, nor *a fortiori* what he calls three points in a straight line and two couples of points separated by a constant distance. But I know that if these three things really have, as he asserts, the properties that the axioms and postulates state, they cannot fail to have at the same time all the properties that the theorems state."

Reflecting on the fact that we have been able to establish the connection which links the various propositions in which these three terms with unassigned meanings figure, we can rise even to a more general view-point. Instead of assigning to these terms determinate but unknown meanings, we can take them as variables—a symbolic means of expressing this universal truth: "if a class π, a relation R having as terms three members of π, and relation S having as terms two couples of members of π satisfy the axioms and postulates—in other words—if the assignment of three meanings π, R, S to the three expressions *point, in a straight line, separated by a constant distance*, transforms the axioms and postulates into true assertions— the meanings π, R, S also satisfy the theorems."

A geometrical proposition ceases then to be determinate and susceptible of being true or false by itself. It is no more than a formula with blanks to be filled by all kinds of different propositions, some false, others true, according to the meanings attributed to its variables: it is only a *propositional function;* and the systematic implication, *for all meanings*, of the propositional functions that are theorems as derived from the propositional functions that are axioms and postulates* forms all the instruction that we can obtain, in our ignorance, from the geometrical treatise which fell into our hands.

Let us close the treatise now and ask ourselves what motives could have impelled its author to write it. Perhaps it was the unique charm of the logical adventure, the singular pleasure of deducing the implications of a group of propositions chosen—like the rules of games of mental entertainment—for the sake of the diversity and harmony of their consequences. Perhaps, on the contrary, the author has tried to imitate nature by making axioms in accordance with natural objects. Has he not modelled his axioms on the demonstrated or conjectural properties of certain entities which are found in his universe, and perhaps also in ours? Let us try then to discover, or at least to conceive, one or more systems of meanings satisfying the axioms of our author: we shall say that such a system of meanings is a *solution of this group of axioms.*

The domain of numbers furnishes an answer first. Let us in fact attribute these meanings:

(1) to the variable class of *points, the class of ordered trios of real numbers taken with their signs;*

(2) to the variable relation *in a straight line, the relation of three trios of real numbers* (x_1, y_1, z_1), (x_2, y_2, z_2), (x_3, y_3, z_3) expressed by the equations

---

* The difference between a postulate and an axiom is only a matter of degree in regard to evidence, and does not exist for us because both, deprived of any fixed meaning, lack altogether any self-evidence. We shall then call *axioms* all the premises of a treatise on geometry in order to simplify language. Such is, besides, the usage of several modern mathematicians.

$$\frac{x_1 - x_2}{y_1 - y_2} = \frac{x_2 - x_3}{y_2 - y_3}, \frac{x_1 - x_2}{z_1 - z_2} = \frac{x_2 - x_3}{z_2 - z_3}.$$

(3) To the variable relation *separated by a constant distance, the relation of two couples of trios of real numbers* (x_1, y_1, z_1), (x_2, y_2, z_2); (x_3, y_3, z_3), (x_4, y_4, z_4) expressed by the equation

$$(x_1 - x_2)^2 + (y_1 - y_2)^2 + (z_1 - z_2)^2$$
$$= (x_3 - x_4)^2 + (y_3 - y_4)^2 + (z_3 - z_4)^2.$$

It is known that the system of meanings (1), (2), (3) satisfies the axioms of Euclidean geometry.

This geometry admits then of one interpretation or purely arithmetic "solution." However, abstract geometry being more often confounded with its application to a particular interpretation called "space," the arithmetic interpretation is commonly introduced under the indirect form of a measure of space. But this detour is superfluous. As soon as geometry is conceived by itself as a form devoid of all application, it is seen that this scheme is applicable directly to numbers without any necessity of regarding them as measures or representations of a determinate subject matter. It is by thus substituting the purely arithmetic meanings (1), (2), and (3) for *points, rectilinearity,* and *congruence,* that the axioms, and consequently, the theorems are resolved into arithmetical propositions. For example, the axiom which says that if the points a, b, c are in a straight line, and if the points b, c, d are also in a straight line, then the points a, b, d are in a straight line becomes in this interpretation: If the numbers x_a, y_a, z_a; x_b, y_b, z_b; x_c, y_c, z_c have the relation

$$\frac{x_a - x_b}{y_a - y_b} = \frac{x_b - x_c}{y_b - y_c}, \frac{x_a - x_b}{z_a - z_b} = \frac{x_b - x_c}{z_b - z_c},$$

and if the numbers x_b, y_b, z_b; x_c, y_c, z_c; x_d, y_d, z_d have the relation

$$\frac{x_b - x_c}{y_b - y_c} = \frac{x_c - x_d}{y_c - y_d}, \frac{x_b - x_c}{z_b - z_c} = \frac{x_c - x_d}{z_c - z_d},$$

then the numbers x_a, y_a, z_a; x_b, y_b, z_b; x_d, y_d, x_d will have the relation

$$\frac{x_a - x_b}{y_a - y_b} = \frac{x_b - x_d}{y_b - y_d}, \frac{x_a - x_b}{z_a - z_b} = \frac{x_b - x_d}{z_b - x_d},$$

which is in fact an arithmetical theorem.

It is true that these arithmetical meanings of the primitive expressions in our treatise on geometry are not *simple,* and that being complex, they seem all the more artificial. Is it not strange that a point can be a class of three numbers? Not at all, since "point" is, prior to such a class definition, an empty word.

The discovery of one system of meanings satisfying a group of axioms is always logically very important: it constitutes the proof that these axioms do not contradict one another; and this is the only known proof of consistency. So arithmetic is one guarantee of the compatibility of the axioms of geometry. But there are perhaps, outside the domain of numbers, other "solutions" for this same group of axioms: it is the search for these that constitutes the object of this work.

[4]

PIERRE DUHEM

Mathematical Deduction and Physical Theory *

§I.—*Physical Approximation and Mathematical Precision.*

When we set out to construct a physical theory, at first we have to choose among those properties given to observation the ones which we shall take as primary qualities, and represent them by algebraic or geometric symbols. [After] this operation, we must accomplish a second: Among the algebraic or geometric symbols representing the primary properties we must establish relations; these relations will serve as principles for the deductions through which the theory will be developed.

It would seem natural, therefore, to analyze now this second operation, *the statement of hypotheses.* But before drawing the plan of the foundations to support a house and before selecting the materials with which to build it, it is indispensable to know what the structure will be and what stresses it will exert on its base. Hence, only at the end of our study shall we be able to state precisely what conditions are imposed on the choice of hypotheses.

Consequently, we are going to take up immediately the third operation constitutive of any theory, the *mathematical development.*

Mathematical deduction is an intermediary process; its object is to teach us that on the strength of the fundamental hypotheses of the theory the coming together of such and such circumstances will entail such and such consequences; if such and such facts are produced, another fact will be produced. For example, it will tell us that on the strength of the hypotheses of Thermodynamics, when we submit a block of ice to a certain pressure, the block will melt when the thermometer reads a certain number.

Does mathematical deduction introduce directly into its calculations the facts we call *circumstances* in the concrete form in which we observe them? Does it draw from them the facts we call *consequences* in the concrete form in which we ascertain them? Certainly not. The apparatus used

* From Pierre Duhem, *The Aim and Structure of Physical Theory,* translated by Philip P. Wiener (Princeton University Press, 1953), Part II, Ch. III, sections I and II. By permission of the publisher.

for compression, a block of ice, and a thermometer are things the physicist manipulates in the laboratory; they are not elements belonging to the domain of algebraic calculation. Hence, in order to enable the mathematician to introduce in his formulas the concrete circumstances of an experiment, it is necessary to translate these circumstances into numbers by the intermediary of measurements. For example, the words *a certain pressure* must be replaced by a certain number of atmospheres which he will substitute for the letter P in his equation. Similarly, what the mathematician will obtain at the end of his calculation is a certain number; it will be necessary to refer back to the method of measurement in order to make this number correspond to a concrete and observable fact; for example, in order to make the numerical value taken by the letter T in the algebraic equation correspond to a certain thermometer reading.

Thus at both its starting and terminal points, the mathematical development of a physical theory cannot be welded to observable facts except by a translation. In order to introduce the circumstances of an experiment into the calculations, we must construct a version which replaces the language of concrete observation by the language of numbers; in order to verify the result that a theory predicts for that experiment, a translation exercise must transform a numerical value into a reading formulated in experimental language. As we have already indicated, the methods of measurement are the dictionary making possible these two translations in either direction.

But translation is treacherous; *traduttore, traditore* (to translate is to betray); there is never a complete equivalence between the two texts in which one is a translated version of the other. Between the concrete facts, as the physicist observes them, and the numerical symbols by which these facts are represented in the calculations of the theorist, there is an extremely great difference. We shall later have an opportunity to analyze and take note of the principal characteristics of this difference. Right now only one of these will occupy our attention.

First of all, let us consider what we shall call a *theoretical fact*, that is to say, that set of mathematical data through which a concrete fact is replaced in the reasoning and calculations of the theorist. For example, let us take this fact: The temperature is distributed in a certain manner over a certain body.

In such a *theoretical fact* there is nothing vague or indecisive; everything is determined in a precise manner; the body studied is geometrically defined; its sides are true lines without thickness; its points true points without dimensions; the different lengths and angles determining its shape are exactly known; to each point of this body there is a corresponding temperature, and this temperature is for each point a number not to be confused with any other number.

Opposite this *theoretical fact* let us place the *practical fact* translated by it. Here we no longer see anything of the precision we have just ascertained. The body is no longer a geometrical solid; it is a concrete block;

however sharp its edges, none is a geometrical intersection of two surfaces but is a more or less rounded and dented spine; its points are more or less worn down and blunt; the thermometer no longer gives us the temperature at each point but a sort of mean temperature relative to a certain volume whose very extent cannot be too exactly fixed; besides, we cannot assert that this temperature is a certain number to the exclusion of any other number; we cannot declare, for example, that this temperature is strictly equal to 10°; we can only assert that the difference between this temperature and 10° does not exceed a certain fraction of a degree depending on the precision of our thermometric methods.

Thus, whereas the contours of the drawing are fixed by a line of precise hardness, the contours of the object are misty, fringed, and shadowy. It is impossible to describe the practical fact without attenuating by the use of the words *approximately* or *nearly* whatever is too well determined by each proposition; on the other hand, all the elements constituting the theoretical fact are defined with rigorous exactness.

Whence we have this consequence: *An infinity of different theoretical facts may be taken for the translation of the same practical fact.*

For example, to say in a proposition of theoretical fact that such a certain line has a length of 1 centimeter, or 0.999 cm., or 0.993 cm., or 1.002 cm., or 1.003 cm., is to formulate propositions which are for the mathematician essentially different; but we change nothing of the practical fact translated by the theoretical fact if our means of measurement do not allow us to evaluate lengths less than .001 cm. To say that the temperature of a body is 10°, or 9.99° or 10.01° is to formulate three incompatible theoretical facts, but these three incompatible facts correspond to one and the same practical fact when our thermometer is accurate only to a fifth of a degree.

A practical fact is not translated therefore by a single theoretical fact but by a kind of bundle including an infinity of different theoretical facts; each of the mathematical elements brought together in order to constitute one of these facts may vary from one fact to another; but the variation to which they are susceptible cannot exceed a certain limit, namely, the limit of error within which the measurement of this element is blotted; the more perfect the methods of measurement are, the closer is the approximation and the narrower the limit, but it never comes so close that it vanishes.

§II—*Mathematical Deductions Physically Useful and Those Not.*

These remarks we have made are very simple, and are familiar commonplaces to the physicist; nevertheless, they imply serious consequences for the mathematical development of a theory.

When the numerical data of a calculation are fixed in a precise manner, this calculation, no matter how long and complicated it is, likewise yields knowledge of the exact numerical value of the result. If we change the value of the data, we generally change the value of the result. Consequently, when we have represented the conditions of an experiment by a clearly defined theoretical fact, the mathematical development will represent by another clearly defined theoretical fact the result that this experiment should provide; if we change the theoretical fact which translates the conditions of the experiment, the theoretical fact which translates the result will change likewise. If, for example, in the formula deduced from thermodynamic hypotheses connecting the melting point of ice with the pressure, we replace the letter P representing the pressure by a certain number, we shall know the number that must be substituted for the letter T, symbol of the temperature of the melting point; if we change the numerical value attributed to the pressure, we also change the numerical value of the melting point.

Now, according to what we have seen in section I above, if the conditions of an experiment are concretely given, we shall not be able to translate them by a definite theoretical fact without ambiguity; we have to correlate them with a whole bundle of theoretical facts, infinite in number. Consequently, the calculations of the theorist will not forecast the experimental result in the form of a unique theoretical fact but in the form of an infinity of different theoretical facts.

In order to translate, for example, the conditions of our experiment on the melting point of ice, we shall not be able to substitute a single and unique numerical value, say 10 atmospheres, for the symbol P of the pressure; if the limit of error of the manometer we use is a tenth of an atmosphere, we shall have to assume that P may take all the values included between 9.95 and 10.05 atmospheres. Naturally, to each of these values of the pressure our formula will correlate a different value of the melting point of ice.

Thus, experimental conditions given in a concrete manner are translated by a bundle of theoretical facts; the mathematical development of the theory correlates this first bundle of theoretical facts with a second, intended to stand for the result of the experiment.

These latter theoretical facts will not be able to serve us in the same form in which we obtain them; we shall have to translate them and put them in the form of practical facts; only then shall we know truly the result assigned to our experiment by our theory. We shall not, for instance, have to stop with the diverse numerical values of the letter T derived from our thermodynamic formula, but it will be necessary to find out to what really observable readings, visible on the graduated scale of our thermometer, the indicated values correspond.

Now, when we have made this new translation, the inverse of the one with which we first busied ourselves, viz., the translation exercise intended to transform theoretical into practical facts, what shall we have obtained?

It may turn out that the bundle of infinitely numerous theoretical facts by which mathematical deduction assigns to our experiment the result that should be produced, will not furnish us after the translation with several different practical facts but with only one single practical fact.

It may happen, for instance, that two of the numerical values found for the letter T do not ever differ by even a hundredth of a degree, and that the limit of sensitivity of our thermometer is a hundredth of a degree, so that all these different theoretical values of T correspond practically to one and the same reading on the scale of the thermometer.

In such a case mathematical deduction will have attained its end; it will have allowed us to assert that on the strength of the hypotheses on which our theory rests, a certain experiment done under certain practically given conditions, should yield a certain concrete and observable result; it will have made possible the comparison of the consequences of the theory with the facts.

But it will not always be thus. As a result of mathematical deduction an infinity of theoretical facts present themselves as possible consequences of our experiment; by translating these theoretical facts into concrete language it may happen that we obtain not a single practical fact but several practical facts which the sensitivity of our instruments will allow us to distinguish. It may happen, for instance, that the different numerical values given by our thermodynamic formula for the melting point of ice present deviations of a tenth of a degree, or even one degree, whereas our thermometer allows us to evaluate a hundredth of a degree. In that case the mathematical deduction will have lost its usefulness; the conditions of an experiment being practically given, we shall no longer be able to state in a practically definite way the result that should be observed.

A mathematical deduction, stemming from the hypotheses on which a theory rests, may therefore be useful or otiose, according to whether or not it permits us to derive a *practically definite* prediction of the result of an experiment whose conditions are *practically given*.

This evaluation of the utility of a mathematical deduction is not always absolute; it depends on the degree of sensitivity of the apparatus used in observing the result of the experiment. Let us suppose, for example, that a practically given pressure is correlated with a bundle of melting points of ice; that between two of these melting points there is sometimes a difference greater than a hundredth of a degree but never more than a tenth of a degree; the mathematical deduction that yielded this formula will be called useful by the physicist whose thermometer measures only tenths of a degree, and useless to the physicist whose instrument accurately detects a difference of a hundredth of a degree. In that way we see how much the judgment concerning the utility of a mathematical development will vary from time to time, from one laboratory to another, and from one physicist to another, according to the skill of the designers, the improvement of the apparatus, and the intended application of the experiment.

This evaluation may also depend on the sensitivity of the means of measurement used to translate into numbers the practically given conditions of experiment.

Let us take up again the thermodynamic formula which has served us constantly as an example. We are in possession of a thermometer which discriminates accurately a difference of a hundredth of a degree; in order that our formula may state without practical ambiguity the melting point of ice under a given pressure, it will be necessary and sufficient that the formula should yield us the numerical value of the letter T correct to the hundredth of a degree.

Now, if we employ a crude manometer, incapable of distinguishing two pressures when their difference is less than ten atmospheres, it may happen that a practically given pressure corresponds to melting points differing by more than a hundredth of a degree in the formula; whereas if we determined the pressure with a more sensitive manometer, accurately distinguishing two pressures which differ by one atmosphere, the formula would correlate with a given pressure a melting point known with an approximation higher than a hundredth of a degree. The formula which was useless when we employed the first manometer would become useful if we employed the second.

[5]

HENRI POINCARÉ

Hypotheses in Physics *

The Rôle of Experiment and Generalization. Experiment is the sole source of truth. It alone can teach us anything new; it alone can give us certainty. These are two points that can not be questioned.

But then, if experiment is everything, what place will remain for mathematical physics? What has experimental physics to do with such an aid, one which seems useless and perhaps even dangerous?

And yet mathematical physics exists, and has done unquestionable service. We have here a fact that must be explained.

The explanation is that merely to observe is not enough. We must use our observations, and to do that we must generalize. This is what men always have done; only as the memory of past errors has made them more and more careful, they have observed more and more, and generalized less and less.

Every age has ridiculed the one before it, and accused it of having generalized too quickly and too naïvely. Descartes pitied the Ionians; Descartes, in his turn, makes us smile. No doubt our children will some day laugh at us.

* H. Poincaré, *Science and Hypothesis,* translated by G. B. Halsted. New York: The Science Press. 1905. Ch. IX. By permission of the publisher.

But can we not then pass over immediately to the goal? Is not this the means of escaping the ridicule that we foresee? Can we not be content with just the bare experiment?

No, that is impossible; it would be to mistake utterly the true nature of science. The scientist must set in order. Science is built up with facts, as a house is with stones. But a collection of facts is no more a science than a heap of stones is a house.

And above all the scientist must foresee. Carlyle has somewhere said something like this: "Nothing but facts are of importance. John Lackland passed by here. Here is something that is admirable. Here is a reality for which I would give all the theories in the world." Carlyle was a fellow countryman of Bacon; but Bacon would not have said that. That is the language of the historian. The physicist would say rather: "John Lackland passed by here; that makes no difference to me, for he never will pass this way again."

We all know that there are good experiments and poor ones. The latter will accumulate in vain; though one may have made a hundred or a thousand, a single piece of work by a true master, by a Pasteur, for example, will suffice to tumble them into oblivion. Bacon would have well understood this; it is he who invented the phrase *Experimentum crucis*. But Carlyle would not have understood it. A fact is a fact. A pupil has read a certain number on his thermometer; he has taken no precaution; no matter, he has read it, and if it is only the fact that counts, here is a reality of the same rank as the peregrinations of King John Lackland. Why is the fact that this pupil has made this reading of no interest, while the fact that a skilled physicist had made another reading might be on the contrary very important? It is because from the first reading we could not infer anything. What then is a good experiment? It is that which informs us of something besides an isolated fact; it is that which enables us to foresee, that is, that which enables us to generalize.

For without generalization foreknowledge is impossible. The circumstances under which one has worked will never reproduce themselves all at once. The observed action then will never recur; the only thing that can be affirmed is that under analogous circumstances an analogous action will be produced. In order to foresee, then, it is necessary to invoke at least analogy, that is to say, already then to generalize.

No matter how timid one may be, still it is necessary to interpolate. Experiment gives us only a certain number of isolated points. We must unite these by a continuous line. This is a veritable generalization. But we do more; the curve that we shall trace will pass between the observed points and near these points; it will not pass through these points themselves. Thus one does not restrict himself to generalizing the experiments, but corrects them; and the physicist who should try to abstain from these corrections and really be content with the bare experiment would be forced to enunciate some very strange laws.

The bare facts, then, would not be enough for us; and that is why we must have science ordered, or rather organized.

It is often said experiments must be made without a preconceived idea. That is impossible. Not only would it make all experiment barren, but that would be attempted which could not be done. Every one carries in his mind his own conception of the world, of which he can not so easily rid himself. We must, for instance, use language; and our language is made up only of preconceived ideas and can not be otherwise. Only these are unconscious preconceived ideas, a thousand times more dangerous than the others.

Shall we say that if we introduce others, of which we are fully conscious, we shall only aggravate the evil? I think not. I believe rather that they will serve as counterbalances to each other—I was going to say as antidotes; they will in general accord ill with one another; they will come into conflict with one another, and thereby force us to regard things under different aspects. This is enough to emancipate us. He is no longer a slave who can choose his master.

Thus, thanks to generalization, each fact observed enables us to foresee a great many others; only we must not forget that the first alone is certain, that all others are merely probable. No matter how solidly founded a prediction may appear to us, we are never *absolutely* sure that experiment will not contradict it, if we undertake to verify it. The probability, however, is often so great that practically we may be content with it. It is far better to foresee even without certainty than not to foresee at all.

One must, then, never disdain to make a verification when opportunity offers. But all experiment is long and difficult; the workers are few; and the number of facts that we need to foresee is immense. Compared with this mass the number of direct verifications that we can make will never be anything but a negligible quantity.

Of this few that we can directly attain, we must make the best use; it is very necessary to get from every experiment the greatest possible number of predictions, and with the highest possible degree of probability. The problem is, so to speak, to increase the yield of the scientific machine.

Let us compare science to a library that ought to grow continually. The librarian has at his disposal for his purchases only insufficient funds. He ought to make an effort not to waste them.

It is experimental physics that is entrusted with the purchases. It alone, then, can enrich the library.

As for mathematical physics, its task will be to make out the catalogue. If the catalogue is well made, the library will not be any richer, but the reader will be helped to use its riches.

And even by showing the librarian the gaps in his collections, it will enable him to make a judicious use of his funds; which is all the more important because these funds are entirely inadequate.

Such, then, is the rôle of mathematical physics. It must direct generalization in such a manner as to increase what I just now called the yield of science. By what means it can arrive at this, and how it can do it without danger, is what remains for us to investigate.

The Unity of Nature. Let us notice first of all that every generalization implies in some measure the belief in the unity and simplicity of nature. As to the unity there can be no difficulty. If the different parts of the universe were not like the members of one body, they would not act on one another, they would know nothing of each other; and we in particular would know only one of these parts. We do not ask, then, if nature is one, but how it is one.

As for the second point, that is not such an easy matter. It is not certain that nature is simple. Can we without danger act as if it were?

There was a time when the simplicity of Mariotte's [Boyle's] law was an argument invoked in favor of its accuracy; when Fresnel himself, after having said in a conversation with Laplace that nature was not concerned about analytical difficulties, felt himself obliged to make explanations, in order not to strike too hard at prevailing opinion.

To-day ideas have greatly changed; and yet, those who do not believe that natural laws have to be simple, are still often obliged to act as if they did. They could not entirely avoid this necessity without making impossible all generalization, and consequently all science.

It is clear that any fact can be generalized in an infinity of ways, and it is a question of choice. The choice can be guided only by considerations of simplicity. Let us take the most commonplace case, that of interpolation. We pass a continuous line, as regular as possible, between the points given by observation. Why do we avoid points making angles, and too abrupt turns? Why do we not make our curve describe the most capricious zigzags? It is because we know beforehand, or believe we know, that the law to be expressed can not be so complicated as all that.

We may calculate the mass of Jupiter from either the movement of its satellites, or the perturbations of the major planets, or those of the minor planets. If we take the averages of the determinations obtained by these three methods, we find three numbers very close together, but different. We might interpret this result by supposing that the coefficient of gravitation is not the same in the three cases. The observations would certainly be much better represented. Why do we reject this interpretation? Not because it is absurd, but because it is needlessly complicated. We shall only accept it when we are forced to, and that is not yet.

To sum up, ordinarily every law is held to be simple till the contrary is proved.

This custom is imposed upon physicists by the causes that I have just explained. But how shall we justify it in the presence of discoveries that show us every day new details that are richer and more complex? How shall we even reconcile it with the belief in the unity of nature? For if everything depends on everything, relationships where so many diverse factors enter can no longer be simple.

If we study the history of science, we see happen two inverse phenomena, so to speak. Sometimes simplicity hides under complex appearances; sometimes it is the simplicity which is apparent, and which disguises extremely complicated realities.

What is more complicated than the confused movements of the planets? What simpler than Newton's law? Here nature, making sport, as Fresnel said, of analytical difficulties, employs only simple means, and by combining them produces I know not what inextricable tangle. Here it is the hidden simplicity which must be discovered.

Examples of the opposite abound. In the kinetic theory of gases, one deals with molecules moving with great velocities, whose paths, altered by incessant collisions, have the most capricious forms and traverse space in every direction. The observable result is Mariotte's [Boyle's] simple law. Every individual fact was complicated. The law of great numbers has reestablished simplicity in the average. Here the simplicity is merely apparent, and only the coarseness of our senses prevents our perceiving the complexity.

Many phenomena obey a law of proportionality. But why? Because in these phenomena there is something very small. The simple law observed, then, is only a result of the general analytical rule that the infinitely small increment of a function is proportional to the increment of the variable. As in reality our increments are not infinitely small, but very small, the law of proportionality is only approximate, and the simplicity is only apparent. What I have just said applies to the rule of the superposition of small motions, the use of which is so fruitful, and which is the basis of optics.

And Newton's law itself? Its simplicity, so long undetected, is perhaps only apparent. Who knows whether it is not due to some complicated mechanism, to the impact of some subtile matter animated by irregular movements, and whether it has not become simple only through the action of averages and of great numbers? In any case, it is difficult not to suppose that the true law contains complementary terms, which would become sensible at small distances. If in astronomy they are negligible as modifying Newton's law, and if the law thus regains its simplicity, it would be only because of the immensity of celestial distances.

No doubt, if our means of investigation should become more and more penetrating, we should discover the simple under the complex, then the complex under the simple, then again the simple under the complex, and so on, without our being able to foresee what will be the last term.

We must stop somewhere, and that science may be possible, we must stop when we have found simplicity. This is the only ground on which we can rear the edifice of our generalizations. But this simplicity being only apparent, will the ground be firm enough? This is what must be investigated.

For that purpose, let us see what part is played in our generalizations by the belief in simplicity. We have verified a simple law in a good many particular cases; we refuse to admit that this agreement, so often repeated, is simply the result of chance, and conclude that the law must be true in the general case.

Kepler notices that a planet's positions, as observed by Tycho, are all on one ellipse. Never for a moment does he have the thought that by a strange play of chance, Tycho never observed the heavens except at a moment when the real orbit of the planet happened to cut this ellipse.

What does it matter then whether the simplicity be real, or whether it covers a complex reality? Whether it is due to the influence of great numbers, which levels down individual differences, or to the greatness or smallness of certain quantities, which allows us to neglect certain terms, in no case is it due to chance. This simplicity, real or apparent, always has a cause. We can always follow, then, the same course of reasoning, and if a simple law has been observed in several particular cases, we can legitimately suppose that it will still be true in analogous cases. To refuse to do this would be to attribute to chance an inadmissible rôle.

There is, however, a difference. If the simplicity were real and essential, it would resist the increasing precision of our means of measure. If then we believe nature to be essentially simple, we must, from a simplicity that is approximate, infer a simplicity that is rigorous. This is what was done formerly; and this is what we no longer have a right to do.

The simplicity of Kepler's laws, for example, is only apparent. That does not prevent their being applicable, very nearly, to all systems analogous to the solar system; but it does prevent their being rigorously exact.

The Rôle of Hypothesis. All generalization is a hypothesis. Hypothesis, then, has a necessary rôle that no one has ever contested. Only, it ought always, as soon as possible and as often as possible, to be subjected to verification. And, of course, if it does not stand this test, it ought to be abandoned without reserve. This is what we generally do, but sometimes with rather an ill humor.

Well, even this ill humor is not justified. The physicist who has just renounced one of his hypotheses ought, on the contrary, to be full of joy; for he has found an unexpected opportunity for discovery. His hypothesis, I imagine, had not been adopted without consideration; it took account of all the known factors that it seemed could enter into the phenomenon. If the test does not support it, it is because there is something unexpected and extraordinary; and because there is going to be something found that is unknown and new.

Has the discarded hypothesis, then, been barren? Far from that, it may be said it has rendered more service than a true hypothesis. Not only has it been the occasion of the decisive experiment, but, without having made the hypothesis, the experiment would have been made by chance, so that nothing would have been derived from it. One would have seen nothing extraordinary; only one fact the more would have been catalogued without deducing from it the least consequence.

Now on what condition is the use of hypothesis without danger?

The firm determination to submit to experiment is not enough; there are still dangerous hypotheses; first, and above all, those which are tacit and unconscious. Since we make them without knowing it, we are powerless to abandon them. Here again, then, is a service that mathematical physics can render us. By the precision that is characteristic of it, it compels us to formulate all the hypotheses that we should make without it, but unconsciously.

Let us notice besides that it is important not to multiply hypotheses beyond measure,* and to make them only one after the other. If we construct a theory based on a number of hypotheses, and if experiment condemns it, which of our premises is it necessary to change? It will be impossible to know. And inversely, if the experiment succeeds, shall we believe that we have demonstrated all the hypotheses at once? Shall we believe that with one single equation we have determined several unknowns?

We must equally take care to distinguish between the different kinds of hypotheses. There are first those which are perfectly natural and from which one can scarcely escape. It is difficult not to suppose that the influence of bodies very remote is quite negligible, that small movements follow a linear law, that the effect is a continuous function of its cause. I will say as much of the conditions imposed by symmetry. All these hypotheses form, as it were, the common basis of all the theories of mathematical physics. They are the last that ought to be abandoned.

There is a second class of hypotheses, that I shall term neutral. In most questions the analyst assumes at the beginning of his calculations either that matter is continuous or, on the contrary, that it is formed of atoms. He might have made the opposite assumption without changing his results. He would only have had more trouble to obtain them; that is all. If, then, experiment confirms his conclusions, will he think that he has demonstrated, for instance, the real existence of atoms? . . .

These neutral hypotheses are never dangerous, if only their character is not misunderstood. They may be useful, either as devices for computation, or to aid our understanding by concrete images, to fix our ideas as the saying is. There is, then, no occasion to exclude them.

The hypotheses of the third class are the real generalizations. They are the ones that experiment must confirm or invalidate. Whether verified or condemned, they will always be fruitful. But for the reasons that I have set forth, they will only be fruitful if they are not too numerous.

Origin of Mathematical Physics. Let us penetrate further, and study more closely the conditions that have permitted the development of mathematical physics. We observe at once that the efforts of scientists have always aimed to resolve the complex phenomenon directly given by experiment into a very large number of elementary phenomena.

---

* This principle of parsimony is known in the history of logic as "Occam's razor" after the medieval philosopher Occam ("Do not multiply hypotheses more than is necessary").—Ed.

This is done in three different ways: first, in time. Instead of embracing in its entirety the progressive development of a phenomenon, the aim is simply to connect each instant with the instant immediately preceding it. It is admitted that the actual state of the world depends only on the immediate past, without being directly influenced, so to speak, by the memory of a distant past. Thanks to this postulate, instead of studying directly the whole succession of phenomena, it is possible to confine ourselves to writing its 'differential equation.' For Kepler's laws we substitute Newton's law.

Next we try to analyze the phenomenon in space. What experiment gives us is a confused mass of facts presented on a stage of considerable extent. We must try to discover the elementary phenomenon, which will be, on the contrary, localized in a very small region of space.

Some examples will perhaps make my thought better understood. If we wished to study in all its complexity the distribution of temperature in a cooling solid, we could never succeed. Everything becomes simple if we reflect that one point of the solid can not give up its heat directly to a distant point; it will give up its heat only to the points in the immediate neighborhood, and it is by degrees that the flow of heat can reach other parts of the solid. The elementary phenomenon is the exchange of heat between two contiguous points. It is strictly localized, and is relatively simple, if we admit, as is natural, that it is not influenced by the temperature of molecules whose distance is sensible.

I bend a rod. It is going to take a very complicated form, the direct study of which would be impossible. But I shall be able, however, to attack it, if I observe that its flexure is a result only of the deformation of the very small elements of the rod, and that the deformation of each of these elements depends only on the forces that are directly applied to it, and not at all on those which may act on the other elements.

In all these examples, which I might easily multiply, we admit that there is no action at a distance, or at least at a great distance. This is a hypothesis. It is not always true, as the law of gravitation shows us. It must, then, be submitted to verification. If it is confirmed, even approximately, it is precious, for it will enable us to make mathematical physics, at least by successive approximations.

If it does not stand the test, we must look for something else analogous; for there are still other means of arriving at the elementary phenomenon. If several bodies act simultaneously, it may happen that their actions are independent and are simply added to one another, either as vectors or as scalars. The elementary phenomenon is then the action of an isolated body. Or again, we have to deal with small movements, or more generally, with small variations, which obey the well-known law of superposition. The observed movement will then be decomposed into simple movements, for example, sound into its harmonics, white light into its monochromatic components.

When we have discovered in what direction it is advisable to look for the elementary phenomenon, by what means can we reach it?

First of all, it will often happen that in order to detect it, or rather to detect the part of it useful to us, it will not be necessary to penetrate the mechanism; the law of great numbers will suffice.

Let us take again the instance of the propagation of heat. Every molecule emits rays towards every neighboring molecule. According to what law, we do not need to know. If we should make any supposition in regard to this, it would be a neutral hypothesis and consequently useless and incapable of verification. And, in fact, by the action of averages and thanks to the symmetry of the medium, all the differences are leveled down, and whatever hypothesis may be made, the result is always the same.

The same circumstance is presented in the theory of electricity and in that of capillarity. The neighboring molecules attract and repel one another. We do not need to know according to what law; it is enough for us that this attraction is sensible only at small distances, that the molecules are very numerous, that the medium is symmetrical, and we shall only have to let the law of great numbers act.

Here again the simplicity of the elementary phenomenon was hidden under the complexity of the resultant observable phenomenon; but, in its turn, this simplicity was only apparent, and concealed a very complex mechanism.

The best means of arriving at the elementary phenomenon would evidently be experiment. We ought by experimental contrivance to dissociate the complex sheaf that nature offers to our researches, and to study with care the elements as much isolated as possible. For example, natural white light would be decomposed into monochromatic lights by the aid of the prism, and into polarized lights by the aid of the polarizer.

Unfortunately that is neither always possible nor always sufficient, and sometimes the mind must outstrip experiment. I shall cite only one example, which has always struck me forcibly.

If I decompose white light, I shall be able to isolate a small part of the spectrum, but however small it may be, it will retain a certain breadth. Likewise the natural lights, called *monochromatic*, give us a very narrow line, but not, however, infinitely narrow. It might be supposed that by studying experimentally the properties of these natural lights, by working with finer and finer lines of the spectrum, and by passing at last to the limit, so to speak, we should succeed in learning the properties of a light strictly monochromatic.

That would not be accurate. Suppose that two rays emanate from the same source, that we polarize them first in two perpendicular planes, then bring them back to the same plane of polarization, and try to make them interfere. If the light were *strictly* monochromatic, they would interfere. With our lights, which are nearly monochromatic, there will be no interference, and that no matter how narrow the line. In order to be otherwise it would have to be several million times as narrow as the finest known lines.

Here, then, the passage to the limit would have deceived us. The mind must outstrip the experiment, and if it has done so with success, it is because it has allowed itself to be guided by the instinct of simplicity.

The knowledge of the elementary fact enables us to put the problem in an equation. Nothing remains but to deduce from this by combination the complex fact that can be observed and verified. This is what is called *integration,* and is the business of the mathematician.

It may be asked why, in physical sciences, generalization so readily takes the mathematical form. The reason is now easy to see. It is not only because we have numerical laws to express; it is because the observable phenomenon is due to the superposition of a great number of elementary phenomena *all alike.* Thus quite naturally are introduced differential equations. . . .

It is then thanks to the approximate homogeneity of the matter studied by physicists, that mathematical physics could be born.

In the natural sciences, we no longer find these conditions: homogeneity, relative independence of remote parts, simplicity of the elementary fact; and this is why naturalists are obliged to resort to other methods of generalization.

[6]

CARL G. HEMPEL

Geometry and Empirical Science *

I. INTRODUCTION

The most distinctive characteristic which differentiates mathematics from the various branches of empirical science, and which accounts for its fame as the queen of the sciences, is no doubt the peculiar certainty and necessity of its results. No proposition in even the most advanced parts of empirical science can ever attain this status; a hypothesis concerning "matters of empirical fact" can at best acquire what is loosely called a high probability or a high degree of confirmation on the basis of the relevant evidence available; but however well it may have been confirmed by careful tests, the possibility can never be precluded that it will have to be discarded later in the light of new and disconfirming evidence. Thus, all the theories and hypotheses of empirical science share this provisional

* Reprinted by permission of the author and the editors from the *American Mathematical Monthly,* 52, 1945, pp. 7-17.

character of being established and accepted "until further notice," whereas a mathematical theorem, once proved, is established once and for all; it holds with that particular certainty which no subsequent empirical discoveries, however unexpected and extraordinary, can ever affect to the slightest extent. It is the purpose of this paper to examine the nature of that proverbial "mathematical certainty" with special reference to geometry, in an attempt to shed some light on the question as to the validity of geometrical theories, and their significance for our knowledge of the structure of physical space.

The nature of mathematical truth can be understood through an analysis of the method by means of which it is established. On this point I can be very brief: it is the method of mathematical demonstration, which consists in the logical deduction of the proposition to be proved from other propositions, previously established. Clearly, this procedure would involve an infinite regress unless some propositions were accepted without proof; such propositions are indeed found in every mathematical discipline which is rigorously developed; they are the *axioms* or *postulates* (we shall use these terms interchangeably) of the theory. Geometry provides the historically first example of the axiomatic presentation of a mathematical discipline. The classical set of postulates, however, on which Euclid based his system, has proved insufficient for the deduction of the well known theorems of so-called euclidean geometry; it has therefore been revised and supplemented in modern times, and at present various adequate systems of postulates for euclidean geometry are available; the one most closely related to Euclid's system is probably that of Hilbert.

2. THE INADEQUACY OF EUCLID'S POSTULATES

The inadequacy of Euclid's own set of postulates illustrates a point which is crucial for the axiomatic method in modern mathematics: Once the postulates for a theory have been laid down, every further proposition of the theory must be proved exclusively by logical deduction from the postulates; any appeal, explicit or implicit to a feeling of self-evidence, or to the characteristics of geometrical figures, or to our experience concerning the behavior of rigid bodies in physical space, or the like, is strictly prohibited; such devices may have a heuristic value in guiding our efforts to find a strict proof for a theorem, but the proof itself must contain absolutely no reference to such aids. This is particularly important in geometry, where our so-called intuition of geometrical relationships, supported by reference to figures or to previous physical experiences, may induce us tacitly to make use of assumptions which are neither formulated in our postulates nor provable by means of them. Consider, for example, the theorem that in a triangle the three medians bisecting the sides intersect in one point which divides each of them in the ratio of 1 : 2. To prove this theorem, one shows first that in any triangle *ABC* (see figure) the line

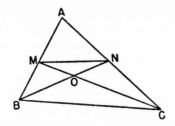

segment *MN* which connects the centers of *AB* and *AC* is parallel to *BC* and therefore half as long as the latter side. Then the lines *BN* and *CM* are drawn, and an examination of the triangles *MON* and *BOC* leads to the proof of the theorem. In this procedure, it is usually taken for granted that *BN* and *CM* intersect in a point *O* which lies between *B* and *N* as well as between *C* and *M*. This assumption is based on geometrical intuition, and indeed, it cannot be deduced from Euclid's postulates; to make it strictly demonstrable and independent of any reference to intuition, a special group of postulates has been added to those of Euclid; they are the postulates of order. One of these—to give an example—asserts that if *A, B, C* are points on a straight line *l*, and if *B* lies between *A* and *C*, then *B* also lies between *C* and *A*.—Not even as "trivial" an assumption as this may be taken for granted; the system of postulates has to be made so complete that all the required propositions can be deduced from it by purely logical means.

Another illustration of the point under consideration is provided by the proposition that triangles which agree in two sides and the enclosed angle, are congruent. In Euclid's Elements, this proposition is presented as a theorem; the alleged proof, however, makes use of the ideas of motion and superimposition of figures and thus involves tacit assumptions which are based on our geometric intuition and on experiences with rigid bodies, but which are definitely not warranted by—*i.e.* deducible from—Euclid's postulates. In Hilbert's system, therefore, this proposition (more precisely: part of it) is explicitly included among the postulates.

3. Mathematical Certainty

It is this purely deductive character of mathematical proof which forms the basis of mathematical certainty: What the rigorous proof of a theorem—say the proposition about the sum of the angles in a triangle—establishes is not the truth of the proposition in question but rather a conditional insight to the effect that that proposition is certainly true *provided that* the postulates are true; in other words, the proof of a mathematical proposition establishes the fact that the latter is logically implied by the postulates of the theory in question. Thus, each mathematical theorem can be cast into the form

$$(P_1 \cdot P_2 \cdot P_3 \cdot \cdot \cdot \cdot \cdot P_N) \rightarrow T$$

where the expression on the left is the conjunction (joint assertion) of all the postulates, the symbol on the right represents the theorem in its customary formulation, and the arrow expresses the relation of logical implication or entailment. Precisely this character of mathematical theorems is the reason for their peculiar certainty and necessity, as I shall now attempt to show.

It is typical of any purely logical deduction that the conclusion to which it leads simply re-asserts (a proper or improper) part of what has already been stated in the premises. Thus, to illustrate this point by a very elementary example, from the premise, "This figure is a right triangle," we can deduce the conclusion, "This figure is a triangle"; but this conclusion clearly reiterates part of the information already contained in the premise. Again, from the premises, "All primes different from 2 are odd" and "n is a prime different from 2," we can infer logically that n is odd; but this consequence merely repeats part (indeed a relatively small part) of the information contained in the premises. The same situation prevails in all other cases of logical deduction; and we may, therefore, say that logical deduction—which is the one and only method of mathematical proof—is a technique of conceptual analysis: it discloses what assertions are concealed in a given set of premises, and it makes us realize to what we committed ourselves in accepting those premises; but none of the results obtained by this technique ever goes by one iota beyond the information already contained in the initial assumptions.

Since all mathematical proofs rest exclusively on logical deductions from certain postulates, it follows that a mathematical theorem, such as the Pythagorean theorem in geometry, asserts nothing that is *objectively* or *theoretically* new as compared with the postulates from which it is derived, although its content may well be *psychologically new* in the sense that we were not aware of its being implicitly contained in the postulates.

The nature of the peculiar certainty of mathematics is now clear: A mathematical theorem is certain *relatively* to the set of postulates from which it is derived; i.e., it is necessarily true *if* those postulates are true; and this is so because the theorem, if rigorously proved, simply re-asserts part of what has been stipulated in the postulates. A truth of this conditional type obviously implies no assertions about matters of empirical fact and can, therefore, never get into conflict with any empirical findings, even of the most unexpected kind; consequently, unlike the hypotheses and theories of empirical science, it can never suffer the fate of being disconfirmed by new evidence: A mathematical truth is irrefutably certain just because it is devoid of factual, or empirical content. Any theorem of geometry, therefore, when cast into the conditional form described earlier, is analytic in the technical sense of logic, and thus true *a priori*; i.e., its truth can be established by means of the formal machinery of logic alone, without any reference to empirical data.

4. Postulates and Truth

Now it might be felt that our analysis of geometrical truth so far tells only half of the relevant story. For while a geometrical proof no doubt enables us to assert a proposition conditionally—namely on condition that the postulates are accepted—is it not correct to add that geometry also unconditionally asserts the truth of its postulates and thus, by virtue of the deductive relationship between postulates and theorems, enables us unconditionally to assert the truth of its theorems? Is it not an unconditional assertion of geometry that two points determine one and only one straight line that connects them, or that in any triangle, the sum of the angles equals two right angles? That this is definitely not the case is evidenced by two important aspects of the axiomatic treatment of geometry which will now be briefly considered.

The first of these features is the well-known fact that in the more recent development of mathematics, several systems of geometry have been constructed which are incompatible with euclidean geometry, and in which, for example, the two propositions just mentioned do not necessarily hold. Let us briefly recollect some of the basic facts concerning these *non-euclidean geometries*. The postulates on which euclidean geometry rests include the famous postulate of the parallels, which, in the case of plane geometry, asserts in effect that through every point P not on a given line l there exists exactly one parallel to l, i.e., one straight line which does not meet l. As this postulate is considerably less simple than the others, and as it was also felt to be intuitively less plausible than the latter, many efforts were made in the history of geometry to prove that this proposition need not be accepted as an axiom, but that it can be deduced as a theorem from the remaining body of postulates. All attempts in this direction failed, however; and finally it was conclusively demonstrated that a proof of the parallel principle on the basis of the other postulates of euclidean geometry (even in its modern, completed form) is impossible. This was shown by proving that a perfectly self-consistent geometrical theory is obtained if the postulate of the parallels is replaced by the assumption that through any point P not on a given straight line l there exist at least two parallels to l. This postulate obviously contradicts the euclidean postulate of the parallels, and if the latter were actually a consequence of the other postulates of euclidean geometry, then the new set of postulates would clearly involve a contradiction, which can be shown not to be the case. This first non-euclidean type of geometry, which is called hyperbolic geometry, was discovered in the early 20's of the last century almost simultaneously, but independently by the Russian N. I. Lobatschefskij, and by the Hungarian J. Bolyai. Later, Riemann developed an alternative geometry, known as elliptical geometry, in which the axiom of the parallels is replaced by the postulate that no line has any parallels. (The acceptance of this postulate, however, in contradistinction to that of hyperbolic geometry, requires the modification of some further axioms of euclidean geometry, if a consistent new theory is to result.) As is to be expected, many of the theorems of these non-euclidean geometries are at variance with those of euclidean theory; thus, e.g., in the hyperbolic geometry of two dimensions, there exist, for each straight line l, through any point P not on l, infinitely many straight lines which do not meet l; also, the sum of the angles in any triangle is less than two right angles. In elliptic geometry, this angle sum is always greater than two right angles; no two straight lines are parallel; and while two different points usually determine exactly one straight line connecting them (as they always do in euclidean geometry), there are certain pairs of points which are connected by infinitely many different straight lines. An illustration of this latter type of geometry is provided by the geometrical structure of that curved two-dimensional space which is represented by the surface of a sphere, when the concept of straight line is interpreted by that of great circle on the sphere. In this space, there are no parallel lines since any two great circles intersect; the endpoints of any diameter of the sphere are points connected by infinitely many different "straight lines," and the sum of the angles in a triangle is always in excess of two right angles. Also, in this space, the ratio between the circumference and the diameter of a circle (not necessarily a great circle) is always less than 2π.

Elliptic and hyperbolic geometry are not the only types of non-euclidean geometry; various other types have been developed; we shall later have occasion to refer to a much more general form of non-euclidean geometry which was likewise devised by Riemann.

The fact that these different types of geometry have been developed in modern mathematics shows clearly that mathematics cannot be said to assert the truth of any particular set of geometrical postulates; all that pure mathematics is interested in, and all that it can establish, is the deductive consequences of given sets of postulates and thus the necessary truth of the ensuing theorems relatively to the postulates under consideration.

A second observation which likewise shows that mathematics does not assert the truth of any particular set of postulates refers to *the status of the concepts in geometry*. There exists, in every axiomatized theory, a close parallelism between the treatment of the propositions and that of the concepts of the system. As we have seen, the propositions fall into two classes: the postulates, for which no proof is given, and the theorems, each of which has to be derived from the postulates. Analogously, the concepts fall into two classes: the primitive or basic concepts, for which no definition is given, and the others, each of which has to be precisely defined in terms of the primitives. (The admission of some undefined concepts is clearly necessary if an infinite regress in definition is to be avoided.) The analogy goes farther: Just as there exists an infinity of theoretically suitable axiom systems for one and the same theory—say, euclidean geometry—so there also exists an infinity of theoretically possible choices for the primitive terms of that theory; very often—but not always—different axiomatizations of the same theory involve not only different postulates, but also different sets of primitives. Hilbert's axiomatization of plane geometry contains six primitives: point, straight line, incidence (of a point on a line), betweenness (as a relation of three points on a straight line), congruence for line segments, and congruence for angles. (Solid geometry, in Hilbert's axiomatization, requires two further primitives, that of plane and that of incidence of a point on a plane.) All other concepts of geometry, such as those of angle, triangle, circle, etc., are defined in terms of these basic concepts.

But if the primitives are not defined within geometrical theory, what meaning are we to assign to them? The answer is that it is entirely unnecessary to connect any particular meaning with them. True, the words "point," "straight line," etc., carry definite connotations with them which relate to the familiar geometrical figures, but the validity of the propositions is completely independent of these connotations. Indeed, suppose that in axiomatized euclidean geometry, we replace the over-suggestive terms "point," "straight line," "incidence," "betweenness," etc., by the neutral terms "object of kind 1," "object of kind 2," "relation No. 1," "relation No. 2," etc., and suppose that we present this modified wording of geometry to a competent mathematician or logician who, however, knows nothing of the customary connotations of the primitive terms. For this logician, all proofs would clearly remain valid, for as we saw before, a rigorous proof in geometry rests on deduction from the axioms alone without any reference to the customary interpretation of the various geometrical concepts used. We see therefore that indeed no specific meaning has to be attached to the primitive terms of an axiomatized theory; and in a precise logical presentation of axiomatized geometry the primitive concepts are accordingly treated as so-called logical variables.

As a consequence, geometry cannot be said to assert the truth of its postulates, since the latter are formulated in terms of concepts without any specific meaning; indeed, for this very reason, the postulates themselves do not make any specific assertion which could possibly be called true or false! In the terminology of modern logic, the postulates are not sentences, but sentential functions with the primitive concepts as variable arguments. This point also shows that the postulates of geometry cannot be considered as "self-evident truths," because where no assertion is made, no self-evidence can be claimed.

5. PURE AND PHYSICAL GEOMETRY

Geometry thus construed is a purely formal discipline; we shall refer to it also as *pure geometry*. A pure geometry, then,—no matter whether it is of the euclidean or of a non-euclidean variety—deals with no specific subject-matter; in particular, it asserts nothing about physical space. All its theorems are analytic and thus true with certainty precisely because they are devoid of factual content. Thus, to characterize the import of pure geometry, we might use the standard form of a movie-disclaimer: No portrayal of the characteristics of geometrical figures or of the spatial properties or relationships of actual physical bodies is intended, and any similarities between the primitive concepts and their customary geometrical connotations are purely coincidental.

But just as in the case of some motion pictures, so in the case at least of euclidean geometry, the disclaimer does not sound quite convincing: Historically speaking, at least, euclidean geometry has its origin in the generalization and systematization of certain empirical discoveries which were made in connection with the measurement of areas and volumes, the practice of surveying, and the development of astronomy. Thus understood, geometry has factual import; it is an empirical science which might be called, in very general terms, the theory of the structure of physical space, or briefly, *physical geometry*. What is the relation between pure and physical geometry?

When the physicist uses the concepts of point, straight line, incidence, etc., in statements about physical objects, he obviously connects with each of them a more or less definite physical meaning. Thus, the term "point" serves to designate physical points, i.e., objects of the kind illustrated by pin-points, cross hairs, etc. Similarly, the term "straight line" refers to straight lines in the sense of physics, such as illustrated by taut strings or by the path of light rays in a homogeneous medium. Analogously, each of the other geometrical concepts has a concrete physical meaning in the statements of physical geometry. In view of this situation, we can say that physical geometry is obtained by what is called, in contemporary logic, a semantical interpretation of pure geometry. Generally speaking, a semantical interpretation of a pure mathematical theory, whose primitives are not assigned any specific meaning, consists in giving each primitive (and thus, indirectly, each defined term) a specific meaning or designatum. In the case of physical geometry, this meaning is physical in the sense just illustrated; it is possible, however, to assign a purely arithmetical meaning to each concept of geometry; the possibility of such an arithmetical interpretation of geometry is of great importance in the study of the consistency and other logical characteristics of geometry, but it falls outside the scope of the present discussion.

By virtue of the physical interpretation of the originally uninterpreted primitives of a geometrical theory, physical meaning is indirectly assigned also to every defined concept of the theory; and if every geometrical term is now taken in its physical interpretation, then every postulate and every theorem of the theory under consideration turns into a statement of physics, with respect to which the question as to truth or falsity may meaningfully be raised—a circumstance which clearly contradistinguishes the propositions of physical geometry from those of the corresponding uninterpreted pure theory. Consider, for example, the following postulate of pure euclidean geometry: For any two objects x, y of kind 1, there exists exactly one object l of kind 2 such that both x and y stand in relation No. 1 to l. As long as the three primitives occurring in this postulate are uninterpreted, it is obviously meaningless to ask whether the postulate is true. But by virtue of the above physical interpretation, the postulate turns into the following statement: For any two physical points x, y there exists exactly one physical straight line l such that both x and y lie on l. But this is a physical hypothesis, and we may now meaningfully ask whether it is true or false. Similarly, the theorem about the sum of the angles in a triangle turns into the assertion that the sum of the angles (in the physical sense) of a figure bounded by the paths of three light rays equals two right angles.

Thus, the physical interpretation transforms a given pure geometrical theory—euclidean or non-euclidean—into a system of physical hypotheses which, if true, might be said to constitute a theory of the structure of physical space. But the question whether a given geometrical theory in physical interpretation is factually correct represents a problem not of pure mathematics but of empirical science; it has to be settled on the basis of suitable experiments or systematic observations. The only assertion the mathematician can make in this context is this: If all the postulates of a given geometry, in their physical interpretation, are true, then all the theorems of that geometry, in their physical interpretation, are necessarily true, too, since they are logically deducible from the postulates. It might seem, therefore, that in order to decide whether physical space is euclidean or non-euclidean in structure, all that we have to do is to test the respective postulates in their physical interpretation. However, this is not directly feasible; here, as in the case of any other physical theory, the basic hypotheses are largely incapable of a direct experimental test; in geometry, this is particularly obvious for such postulates as the parallel axiom or Cantor's axiom of continuity in Hilbert's system of euclidean geometry, which makes an assertion about certain infinite sets of points on a straight line. Thus, the empirical test of a physical geometry no less than that of any other scientific theory has to proceed indirectly; namely, by deducing from the basic hypotheses of the theory certain consequences, or predictions, which are amenable to an experimental test. If a test bears out a prediction, then it constitutes confirming evidence (though, of course, no conclusive proof) for the theory; otherwise, it disconfirms the theory. If an adequate amount of confirming evidence for a theory has been established, and if no disconfirming evidence has been found, then the theory may be accepted by the scientist "until further notice."

It is in the context of this indirect procedure that pure mathematics and logic acquire their inestimable importance for empirical science: While formal logic and pure mathematics do not in themselves establish any assertions about matters of empirical fact, they provide an efficient and entirely indispensable machinery for deducing, from abstract theoretical assumptions, such as the laws of Newtonian mechanics or the postulates of euclidean geometry in physical interpretation, consequences concrete and specific enough to be accessible to direct experimental test. Thus, e.g., pure euclidean geometry shows that from its postulates there may be deduced the theorem about the sum of the angles in a triangle, and that this deduction is possible no matter how the basic concepts of geometry are interpreted; hence also in the case of the physical interpretation of euclidean geometry. This theorem, in its physical interpretation, is accessible to experimental test; and since the postulates of elliptic and of hyperbolic geometry imply values different from two right angles for the angle sum of a triangle, this particular proposition seems to afford a good opportunity for a crucial experiment. And no less a mathematician than Gauss did indeed perform this test; by means of optical methods—and thus using the interpretation of physical straight lines as paths of light rays—he ascertained the angle sum of a large triangle determined by three mountain tops. Within the limits of experimental error, he found it equal to two right angles.

6. On Poincaré's Conventionalism Concerning Geometry

But suppose that Gauss had found a noticeable deviation from this value; would that have meant a refutation of euclidean geometry in its physical interpretation, or, in other words, of the hypothesis that physical space is euclidean in structure? Not necessarily; for the deviation might have been accounted for by a hypothesis to the effects that the paths of the light rays involved in the sighting process were bent by some disturbing force and thus were not actually straight lines. The same kind of reference to deforming forces could also be used if, say, the euclidean theorems of congruence for plane figures were tested in their physical interpretation by means of experiments involving rigid bodies, and if any violations of the theorems were found. This point is by no means trivial; Henri Poincaré, the great French mathematician and theoretical physicist, based on considerations of this type his famous *conventionalism concerning geometry*. It was his opinion that no empirical test, whatever its outcome, can conclusively invalidate the euclidean conception of physical space; in other words, the validity of euclidean geometry in physical science can always be preserved—if necessary, by suitable changes in the theories of physics, such as the introduction of new hypotheses concerning deforming or deflecting forces. Thus, the question as to whether physical space has a euclidean or a non-euclidean structure would become a matter of convention, and the decision to preserve euclidean geometry at all costs would recommend itself, according to Poincaré, by the greater simplicity of euclidean as compared with non-euclidean geometrical theory.

It appears, however, that Poincaré's account is an oversimplification. It rightly calls attention to the fact that the test of a physical geometry G always presupposes a certain body P of non-geometrical physical hypotheses (including the physical theory of the instruments of measurement and observation used in the test), and that the so-called test of G actually bears on the combined theoretical system $G \cdot P$ rather than on G alone.

Now, if predictions derived from $G \cdot P$ are contradicted by experimental findings, then a change in the theoretical structure becomes necessary. In classical physics, G always was euclidean geometry in its physical interpretation, GE; and when experimental evidence required a modification of the theory, it was P rather than GE which was changed. But Poincaré's assertion that this procedure would always be distinguished by its greater simplicity is not entirely correct; for what has to be taken into consideration is the simplicity of the total system $G \cdot P$, and not just that of its geometrical part. And here it is clearly conceivable that a simpler total theory in accordance with all the relevant empirical evidence is obtainable by going over to a non-euclidean form of geometry rather than by preserving the euclidean structure of physical space and making adjustments only in part P.

And indeed, just this situation has arisen in physics in connection with the development of the general theory of relativity: If the primitive terms of geometry are given physical interpretations along the lines indicated before, then certain findings in astronomy represent good evidence in favor of a total physical theory with a non-euclidean geometry as part G. According to this theory, the physical universe at large is a three-dimensional curved space of a very complex geometrical structure; it is finite in volume and yet unbounded in all directions. However, in comparatively small areas, such as those involved in Gauss' experiment, euclidean geometry can serve as a good approximative account of the geometrical structure of space. The kind of structure ascribed to physical space in this theory may be illustrated by an analogue in two dimensions; namely, the surface of a sphere. The geometrical structure of the latter, as was pointed out before, can be described by means of elliptic geometry, if the primitive term "straight line" is interpreted as meaning "great circle," and if the other primitives are given analogous interpretations. In this sense, the surface of a sphere is a two-dimensional curved space of non-euclidean structure, whereas the plane is a two-dimensional space of euclidean structure. While the plane is unbounded in all directions, and infinite in size, the spherical surface is finite in size and yet unbounded in all directions: a two-dimensional physicist, travelling along "straight lines" of that space would never encounter any boundaries of his space; instead, he would finally return to his point of departure, provided that his life span and his technical facilities were sufficient for such a trip in consideration of the size of his "universe." It is interesting to note that the physicists of that world, even if they lacked any intuition of a three-dimensional space, could empirically ascertain the fact that their two-dimensional space was curved. This might be done by means of the method of travelling along straight lines; another, simpler test would consist in determining the angle sum in a triangle; again another in determining, by means of measuring tapes, the ratio of the circumference of a circle (not necessarily a great circle) to its diameter; this ratio would turn out to be less than π.

The geometrical structure which relativity physics ascribes to physical space is a three-dimensional analogue to that of the surface of a sphere, or, to be more exact, to that of the closed and finite surface of a potato, whose curvature varies from point to point. In our physical universe, the curvature of space at a given point is determined by the distribution of masses in its neighborhood; near large masses such as the sun, space is strongly curved, while in regions of low mass-density, the structure of the universe is approximately euclidean. The hypothesis stating the connection between the mass distribution and the curvature of space at a point has been approximately confirmed by astronomical observations concerning the paths of light rays in the gravitational field of the sun.

The geometrical theory which is used to describe the structure of the physical universe is of a type that may be characterized as a generalization of elliptic geometry. It was originally constructed by Riemann as a purely mathematical theory, without any concrete possibility of practical application at hand. When Einstein, in developing his general theory of relativity, looked for an appropriate mathematical theory to deal with the structure of physical space, he found in Riemann's abstract system the conceptual tool he needed. This fact throws an interesting sidelight on the importance for scientific progress of that type of investigation which the "practical-minded" man in the street tends to dismiss as useless, abstract mathematical speculation.

Of course, a geometrical theory in physical interpretation can never be validated with mathematical certainty, no matter how extensive the experimental tests to which it is subjected; like any other theory of empirical science, it can acquire only a more or less high degree of confirmation. Indeed, the considerations presented in this article show that the demand for mathematical certainty in empirical matters is misguided and unreasonable; for, as we saw, mathematical certainty of knowledge can be attained only at the price of analyticity and thus of complete lack of factual content. Let me summarize this insight in Einstein's words:

"As far as the laws of mathematics refer to reality, they are not certain; and as far as they are certain, they do not refer to reality."

[7]

W. K. CLIFFORD

On the Bending of Space *

The peculiar topic of this chapter has been position, position namely of a point P relative to a point A. This relative position led naturally to a consideration of the geometry of steps. I proceeded on the hypothesis that all position is relative, and therefore to be determined only by a stepping process. The relativity of position was a postulate deduced from the customary methods of determining position, such methods in fact always giving relative position. *Relativity of position is thus a postulate derived from experience.* The late Professor Clerk-Maxwell fully expressed the weight of this postulate in the following words:—

All our knowledge, both of time and place, is relative. When a man has acquired the habit of putting words together, without troubling himself to form the thoughts which ought to correspond to them, it is easy for him to frame an antithesis between this relative knowledge and a so-called absolute knowledge, and to point out our ignorance of the absolute position of a point as an instance of the limitation of our faculties. Any one, however, who will try to imagine the state of a mind conscious of knowing the absolute position of a point will ever after be content with our relative knowledge.[1]

*This chapter from *The Common Sense of the Exact Sciences* (1885) is an interesting exploration of the relations of space, time, and physical phenomena by two philosopher-scientists, William Kingdon Clifford and Karl Pearson. Pearson edited this posthumous work of Clifford and wrote the whole chapter IV on Position from which section 19 is reprinted here, saying of these pages "whatever is in them of value I owe to Clifford; whatever is feeble or obscure is my own" (Preface, p. vii). As an original geometer Clifford contributed to the theories of non-Euclidean geometry, projective geometry, bi-quaternions, Riemannian surfaces, universal algebra, and algebraic forms. In his philosophy Clifford was influenced by Spinoza, and conceived matter as co-extensive with what he called "mind-stuff." In ethics, Clifford attacked theological systems for obscuring the essential contribution of the moral self to the "tribal self" of human society. Clifford took the side of the Darwinians against their clerical opponents.

In these pages written at the time of the Michelson-Morley experiments, there are obvious anticipations of relativity theory and the assimilation of space, time and physical changes. Ernst Mach greatly admired Clifford's work, and both paved the way for some of Einstein's conceptions of space, time, and motion, and abolition of the ether.

Clifford's works were mostly posthumous publications: *Elements of Dynamic* (1879–1887); *Seeing and Thinking*, popular science lectures (1879); *Lectures and Essays*, edited with an Introduction by the Spinozistic legal philosopher Sir Frederick Pollock (1879); *Mathematical Papers*, edited by R. Tucker with an Introduction by Henry J. S. Smith (1882); *The Common Sense of the Exact Sciences*, edited and completed by Karl Pearson (1885).—Ed.

It is of such great value to ascertain how far we can be certain of the truth of our postulates in the exact sciences that I shall ask the reader to return to our conception of position albeit from a somewhat different standpoint. I shall even ask him to attempt an examination of that state of mind which Professor Clerk-Maxwell hinted at in his last sentence.

Suppose we had a tube of exceedingly small bore bent into a circular shape, and within this tube a worm of length A B. Then in the limiting case when we make the bore of the tube and the worm infinitely fine, we shall be considering space of one dimension. For so soon as we have fixed *one* point, C, on the tube, the length of arc C A suffices to determine the position of the worm. Assuming that the worm is incapable of recognising anything outside its own tube-space, it would still be able to draw certain inferences as to the nature of the space in which it existed were it capable of distinguishing some mark C on the side of its tube. Thus it would notice when it returned to the point C, and it would find that this return would continually recur as it went round in the bore; in other words, the worm would readily postulate the finiteness of space. Further, since the worm would always have the same *amount of bending,* since all parts of a circle are of the same shape, it might naturally assume the *sameness* of all space, or that space possessed the same properties at all points. This assumption

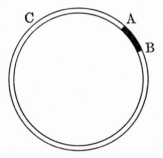

is precisely akin to the one we make when we assert that the postulates of Euclidean geometry, which, experience teaches us, are practically true for the space immediately about us, are also true for all space; we assume the sameness of our three-dimensioned space. The worm would, however, have better reason for its postulate than we have, because it would have visited every part of its own one-dimensioned space.

Besides the finiteness and sameness of its space the worm might assert the relativity of position, and determine its position by the length of the arc; between C and A. Let us now make a variation in our problem and suppose the worm incapable either of making or of recognising any mark on the tube. Then it would clearly be impossible for the worm to ascertain whether its space were limited or not; it would never know when it had made a complete revolution in its tube. In fact, since the worm would always possess the same amount of bending, it would naturally associate *that bending with its physical constitution, and not with the space which it was traversing.* It might thus very reasonably suppose its space was infinite, or that it was moving in an infinitely long tube. If the worm thus associated bending with its physical condition it would find no difference between motion in space of constant bend (a circle) and motion in what is termed *homaloidal* or flat space (a straight line); if suddenly transferred from one to the other it would attribute the feeling arising from difference of bending to some change which had taken place in its physical constitu-tion. Hence in one-dimensioned space of constant bend all position is neces-sarily relative, and the finite or infinite character of space will be postulated according as it is possible or not to fix a point in it.[2]

Let us now suppose our worm moving in a different sort of tube; for example, that shadow of a circle we have called an ellipse. In such a tube the degree of bending is not everywhere the same; the worm as it passes from the place of least bending C to the place of most bending D, will pass

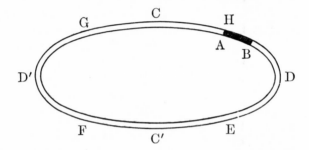

through a succession of bendings, and each point H between C and D will have its own degree of bending. Hence there is something quite apart from the position of H relative to C which characterizes the point H; namely, associated with H is a particular degree of bending, and the position of the point H in C D is at once fixed if we know the degree of bending there. Thus the worm might determine *absolute* position in its space by the degree of bending associated with its position. The worm is now able to appreciate differences of bend, and might even form a scale of bending rising by equal differences. The zero of such scale might be anywhere the worm pleased, and degrees of greater and less bend might be measured as positive and negative quantities from that zero. This zero might in fact be purely imaginary; that is, represent a degree of bending non-existent in the worm's space; for example, in the case of an ellipse, absolute straightness, a conception which the worm might form as a limit to its experience of degrees of bend.[3] Thus it would seem that in space of 'varying bend,' or space which is not the same, position is not necessarily relative. The rela-tivity has ceased to belong to position in space; it has been transferred to the scale of bending formed by the worm; it has become a relativity of *physical feeling*. In the case of an elliptic tube there are owing to its symmetry four points of equal bend, as H, E, F, and G, but there is the following distinction between H, F and E, G. If the worm be going round in the direction indicated by the letters C H D E, at H or F it will be passing from positions of less to positions of greater bending, but at E or G from positions of greater to positions of less bending. Thus the worm might easily draw a distinction between H, F and E, G. It would only be liable to suppose the points H and F identical because they possess the same degree of bending. We might remove even this possible doubt by supposing the worm to be moving in a pear-shaped tube, as in the accompanying figure; then there will be only two points of equal bend, like H and G, which are readily distinguished in the manner mentioned above.

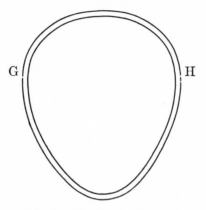

We might thus conclude that in one-dimensioned space of variable bend, position is not necessarily relative. There is, however, one point to be noted with regard to this statement. We have assumed that the worm will associate change of bending with change of position in space, but the worm would be sensible of it as a change of physical state or as a change of feeling. Hence the worm might very readily be led into the error of postulating the sameness of its space, and attributing all the changes in its bend, really due to its position in space, to some periodic (if it moves uniformly round its tube) or irregular (if it moves in any fashion backwards and forwards) changes to which its physical constitution was subject. Similar results might also arise if the worm were either moving in space of the same bend, which bend could be changed by some external agency as a whole, or again if its space were of varying bend, which was also capable of changing in any fashion with time. The reader can picture these cases by supposing the tube made of flexible material. The worm might either attribute change in its degree of bend to change in the character of its space or to change in its physical condition not arising from its position in space. We conclude that the relativity of position is not necessarily true for one-dimensioned space of varying bend.

When we proceed from one to two-dimensioned space, we obtain results of an exactly similar character. If we take perfectly even (so-called *homaloidal*) space of two dimensions, that is, a plane, then a perfectly flat figure can be moved about anywhere in it without altering its shape. If by analogy to an infinitely thin worm we take an infinitely thin flat-fish, this fish would be incapable of determining position could it leave no landmarks in its plane space. So soon as it had fixed two points in its plane it would be able to determine *relative* position.

Now, suppose that instead of taking this homaloidal space of two dimensions we were still to take a perfectly same space but one of finite bend, that is, the surface of a sphere. Then let us so stretch and bend our flat-fish that it would fit on to some part of the sphere. Since the surface of the sphere is everywhere space of the same shape, the fish would then be capable of moving about on the surface without in any way altering the amount of bending and stretching which we had found it necessary to apply to make the fish fit in any one position. Were the fish incapable of leaving landmarks on the surface of the sphere, it would be totally unable to determine position; if it could leave at least two landmarks it would be able to determine *relative* position. Just as the worm in the circular tube, the fish without landmarks might reasonably suppose its space infinite, or even look upon it as perfectly flat (homaloidal) and attribute the constant degree of bend and stretch to its physical nature.

Let us now pass to some space of two dimensions which is not same —to some space, for example, like the saddle-back surface—which has a varying bend. In this case the fish, if it fitted at one part of the surface, would not necessarily fit at another. If it moved about in its space, it would be needful that a continual process of bending and stretching should be carried on. Thus every part of this two-dimensioned space would be defined by the particular amount of bend and stretch necessary to make the fish fit it, or, as it is usually termed, by the *curvature*. In surfaces with some degree of symmetry there would necessarily be parts of equal curvature, and in some cases the fish might perhaps distinguish between these points in the same fashion as the worm distinguished between points of equal curvature in the case of an elliptic tube. In irregular surfaces, however, it is not necessary that such points of equal curvature should arise. We are thus led to conclusions like those we have formed for one-dimensioned space, namely: Position in space of two dimensions which is not same might be determined *absolutely* by means of the curvature. Our fish has only to carry about with it a scale of degrees of bending and stretching to correspond with various positions on the surface in order to determine absolutely its position in its space. On the other hand, the fish might very readily attribute all these changes of bend and stretch to variations of its physical nature in nowise dependent on its position in space. Thus it might believe itself to have a most varied physical life, a continual change of physical feeling quite independent of the geometrical character of the space in which it dwelt. It might suppose that space to be perfectly same, or even degrade it to the 'dreary infinity of a homaloid.'[4]

As a result, then, of our consideration of one and two-dimensioned space, we find that, if these spaces be not same (*a fortiori* not homaloidal), we should by reason of their curvature have a means of determining absolute position. But we see that a being existing in these dimensions would most probably attribute the effects of curvature to changes in its own physical condition in nowise connected with the geometrical character of its space.

What lesson may we learn by analogy for the three-dimensioned space in which we ourselves exist? To begin with, we assume that all our space is perfectly *same*, or that solid figures do not change their shape in passing from one position to another. We base this postulate of sameness upon the results of observation in that somewhat limited portion of space of which we are cognizant.[5] Supposing our observations to be correct, it by no means follows that because the portion of space of which we are cognisant is for practical purposes same, that therefore *all* space is same.[6] Such an assumption is a mere dogmatic extension to the unknown of a postulate, which may perhaps be true for the space upon which we can experiment. To make such dogmatic assertions with regard to the unknown is rather characteristic of the medieval theologian than of the modern scientist. On the like basis with this postulate as to the sameness of our space stands the further assumption that it is homaloidal. When we assert that our space is everywhere same, we suppose it of constant curvature (like the circle as one and the sphere as two-dimensioned space); when we suppose it homaloidal we assume that this curvature is zero (like the line as one and the plane as two-dimensioned space). This assumption appears in our geometry under the form that two parallel planes, or two parallel lines in the same plane—that is, planes, or lines in the same plane, which however far produced will never meet—have a *real* existence in our space. This real existence, of which it is clearly impossible for us to be cognisant, we postulate as a result built upon our experience of what happens in a limited portion of space. We may postulate that the portion of space of which we are cognisant is practically homaloidal, but we have clearly no right to dogmatically extend this postulate to *all* space. A constant curvature, imperceptible for that portion of space upon which we can experiment, or even a curvature which may vary in an almost imperceptible manner with the time, would seem to satisfy all that experience has taught us to be true of the space in which we dwell.

But we may press our analogy a step further, and ask, since our hypothetical worm and fish might very readily attribute the effects of changes in the bending of their spaces to changes in their own physical condition, whether we may not in like fashion be treating merely as physical variations effects which are really due to changes in the curvature of our space; whether, in fact, some or all of those causes which we term physical may not be due to the geometrical construction of our space. There are three kinds of variation in the curvature of our space which we ought to consider as within the range of possibility.

(I) Our space is perhaps really possessed of a curvature varying from point to point, which we fail to appreciate because we are acquainted with only a small portion of space, or because we disguise its small changes under changes in our physical condition which we do not connect with our change of position. The mind that could recognize this varying curvature might be assumed to know the absolute position of a point. For such a mind the postulate of the relativity of position would cease to have a meaning. It does not seem so hard to conceive such a state of mind as the late Professor Clerk-Maxwell would have had us believe. It would be one capable of distinguishing those so called physical changes which are really geometrical or due to the change of position in space.

(II) Our space may be really same (of equal curvature), but its degree of curvature may change as a whole with time. In this way our geometry based on the sameness of space would still hold good for all parts of space, but the change of curvature might produce in space a succession of apparent physical changes.

(III) We may conceive our space to have everywhere a nearly uniform curvature, but that slight variations of the curvature may occur from point to point, and themselves vary with the time. These variations of the curvature with the time may produce effects which we not unnaturally attribute to physical causes independent of the geometry of our space. We might even go so far as to assign to this variation of the curvature of space 'what really happens' in that phenomenon which we term the motion of matter.*

We have introduced these considerations as to the nature of our space to bring home to the reader the character of the postulates we make in the exact sciences. These postulates are *not*, as too often assumed, necessary and universal truths; they are merely axioms based on our experience of a certain limited region. Just as in any branch of physical inquiry we start by making experiments, and basing on our experiments a set of axioms which form the foundation of an exact science, so in geometry our axioms are really, though less obviously, the result of experience. On this ground geometry has been properly termed . . . a *physical* science. The danger of asserting dogmatically that an axiom based on the experience of a limited region holds universally will now be to some extent apparent to the reader. It may lead us to entirely overlook, or when suggested, at once reject a possible explanation of phenomena. The hypothesis that space is not homaloidal, and again, that its geometrical character may change with the time, may or may not be destined to play a great part in the physics of the

---

* This remarkable possibility seems first to have been suggested by Professor Clifford in a paper presented to the Cambridge Philosophical Society in 1870 (*Mathematical Papers*, p. 21). I may add the following remarks: The most notable physical quantities which vary with position and time are heat, light, and electro-magnetism. It is these which we ought peculiarly to consider when seeking for any physical changes which may be due to changes in the curvature of space. If we suppose the boundary of any arbitrary figure in space to be distorted by the variation of space-curvature, there would, by analogy from one and two dimensions, be no change in the volume of the figure arising from such distortion. Further, if we *assume* as an axiom that space resists curvature with a resistance proportional to the change, we find that waves of 'space-displacement' are precisely similar to those of the elastic medium which we suppose to propagate light and heat. We also find that 'space-twist' is a quantity exactly corresponding to magnetic induction, and satisfying relations similar to those which hold for the magnetic field. It is a question whether physicists might not find it simpler to assume that space is capable of a varying curvature, and of a resistance to that variation, than to suppose the existence of a subtle medium pervading an invariable homaloidal space.—Karl Pearson.

future; yet we cannot refuse to consider them as possible explanations of physical phenomena, because they may be opposed to the popular dogmatic belief in the universality of certain geometrical axioms—a belief which has arisen from centuries of indiscriminating worship of the genius of Euclid.

[8]

HANS REICHENBACH

The Philosophical Significance of the Theory of Relativity *

I

The philosophical significance of the theory of relativity has been the subject of contradictory opinions. Whereas many writers have emphasized the philosophical implications of the theory and have even tried to interpret it as a sort of philosophical system, others have denied the existence of such implications and have voiced the opinion that Einstein's theory is merely a physical matter, of interest only to the mathematical physicist. These critics believe that philosophical views are constructed by other means than the methods of the scientist and are independent of the results of physics.

Now it is true that what has been called the philosophy of relativity represents, to a great extent, the fruit of misunderstandings of the theory rather than of its physical content. Philosophers who regard it as an ultimate wisdom that everything is relative are mistaken when they believe that Einstein's theory supplies evidence for such a sweeping generalization; and their error is even deeper when they transfer such a relativity to the field of ethics, when they claim that Einstein's theory implies a relativism of men's duties and rights. The theory of relativity is restricted to the cognitive field. That moral conceptions vary with the social class and the structure of civilization is a fact which is not derivable from Einstein's theory; the parallelism between the relativity of ethics and that of space and time is nothing more than a superficial analogy, which blurs the essential logical differences between the fields of volition and cognition. It appears understandable that those who were trained in the precision of mathematico-physical methods wish to divorce physics from such blossoms of philosophizing.

* From *Albert Einstein: Philosopher-Scientist,* edited by Paul A. Schilpp, Library of Living Philosophers, 1949. Pp. 289–311; Einstein's Reply, pp. 676–679. Reprinted by permission of the authors, editor, and publishers.

Yet it would be another mistake to believe that Einstein's theory is not a philosophical theory. This discovery of a physicist has radical consequences for the theory of knowledge. It compels us to revise certain traditional conceptions that have played an important part in the history of philosophy, and it offers solutions for certain questions which are as old as the history of philosophy and which could not be answered earlier. Plato's attempt to solve the problems of geometry by a theory of ideas, Kant's attempt to account for the nature of space and time by a *"reine Anschauung"* and by a transcendental philosophy, these represent answers to the very questions to which Einstein's theory has given a different answer at a later time. If Plato's and Kant's doctrines are philosophical theories, then Einstein's theory of relativity is a philosophical and not a merely physical matter. And the questions referred to are not of a secondary nature but of primary import for philosophy; that much is evident from the central position they occupy in the systems of Plato and Kant. These systems are untenable if Einstein's answer is put in the place of the answers given to the same questions by their authors; their foundations are shaken when space and time are not the revelations of an insight into a world of ideas, or of a vision grown from pure reason, which a philosophical apriorism claimed to have established. The analysis of knowledge has always been the basic issue of philosophy; and if knowledge in so fundamental a domain as that of space and time is subject to revision, the implications of such criticism will involve the whole of philosophy.

To advocate the philosophical significance of Einstein's theory, however, does not mean to make Einstein a philosopher; or, at least, it does not mean that Einstein is a philosopher of primary intent. Einstein's primary objectives were all in the realm of physics. But he saw that certain physical problems could not be solved unless the solutions were preceded by a logical analysis of the fundamentals of space and time, and he saw that this analysis, in turn, presupposed a philosophic readjustment of certain familiar conceptions of knowledge. The physicist who wanted to understand the Michelson experiment had to commit himself to a philosophy for which the meaning of a statement is reducible to its verifiability, that is, he had to adopt the verifiability theory of meaning if he wanted to escape a maze of ambiguous questions and gratuitous complications. It is this positivist, or let me rather say, empiricist commitment which determines the philosophical position of Einstein. It was not necessary for him to elaborate on it to any great extent; he merely had to join a trend of development characterized, within the generation of physicists before him, by such names as Kirchhoff, Hertz, Mach, and to carry through to its ultimate consequences a philosophical evolution documented at earlier stages in such principles as Occam's razor and Leibniz' identity of indiscernibles.

Einstein has referred to this conception of meaning in various remarks, though he has never felt it necessary to enter into a discussion of its grounds or into an analysis of its philosophical position. The exposition and substantiation of a philosophical theory is nowhere to be found in his writings. In fact, Einstein's philosophy is not so much a philosophical system as a philosophical attitude; apart from occasional remarks, he left it to others to say what philosophy his equations entail and thus remained a philosopher by implication, so to speak. That is both his strength and his weakness; his strength, because it made his physics so conclusive; his weakness, because it left his theory open to misunderstandings and erroneous interpretations.

It seems to be a general law that the making of a new physics precedes a new philosophy of physics. Philosophic analysis is more easily achieved when it is applied to concrete purposes, when it is done within the pursuit of research aimed at an interpretation of observational data. The philosophic results of the procedure are often recognized at a later stage; they are the fruit of reflection about the methods employed in the solution of the concrete problem. But those who make the new physics usually do not have the leisure, or do not regard it as their objective, to expound and elaborate the philosophy implicit in their constructions. Occasionally, in popular presentations, a physicist attempts to explain the logical background of his theories; thus many a physicist has been misled into believing that philosophy of physics is the same as a popularization of physics. Einstein himself does not belong to this group of writers who do not realize that what they achieve is as much a popularization of philosophy as it is one of physics, and that the philosophy of physics is as technical and intricate as is physics itself. Nevertheless, Einstein is not a philosopher in the technical sense either. It appears to be practically impossible that the man who is looking for new physical laws should also concentrate on the analysis of his method; he will perform this second task only when such analysis is indispensable for the finding of physical results. The division of labor between the physicist and the philosopher seems to be an inescapable consequence of the organization of the human mind.

It is not only a limitation of human capacities which calls for a division of labor between the physicist and the philosopher. The discovery of general relations that lend themselves to empirical verification requires a mentality different from that of the philosopher, whose methods are analytic and critical rather than predictive. The physicist who is looking for new discoveries must not be too critical; in the initial stages he is dependent on guessing, and he will find his way only if he is carried along by a certain faith which serves as a directive for his guesses. When I, on a certain occasion, asked Professor Einstein how he found his theory of relativity, he answered that he found it because he was so strongly convinced of the harmony of the universe. No doubt his theory supplies a most successful demonstration of the usefulness of such a conviction. But a creed is not a philosophy; it carries this name only in the popular interpretation of the term. The philosopher of science is not much interested in the thought processes which lead to scientific discoveries; he looks for a logical analysis of the completed theory, including the relationships establishing its validity. That is, he is not interested in the context of discovery, but in the context of justification. But the critical attitude may make a man incapable of discovery; and, as long as he is successful, the creative physicist may very well prefer his creed to the logic of the analytic philosopher.

The philosopher has no objections to a physicist's beliefs, so long as they are not advanced in the form of a philosophy. He knows that a personal faith is justified as an instrument of finding a physical theory, that it is but a primitive form of guessing, which is eventually replaced by the elaborate theory, and that it is ultimately subject to the same empirical tests as the theory. The philosophy of physics, on the other hand, is not a product of creed but of analysis. It incorporates the physicist's beliefs into the psychology of discovery; it endeavors to clarify the meanings of physical theories, independently of the interpretation by their authors, and is concerned with logical relationships alone.

Seen from this viewpoint it appears amazing to what extent the logical analysis of relativity coincides with the original interpretation by its author, as far as it can be constructed from the scanty remarks in Einstein's publications. In contradistinction to some developments in quantum theory, the logical schema of the theory of relativity corresponds surprisingly with the program which controlled its discovery. His philosophic clarity distinguishes Einstein from many a physicist whose work became the source of a philosophy different from the interpretation given by the author. In the following pages I shall attempt to outline the philosophical results of Einstein's theory, hoping to find a friendly comment by the man who was the first to see all these relations, even though he did not always formulate them explicitly. And the gratitude of the philosopher goes to this great physicist whose work includes more implicit philosophy than is contained in many a philosophical system.

II

The logical basis of the theory of relativity is the discovery that many statements, which were regarded as capable of demonstrable truth or falsity, are mere definitions.

This formulation sounds like the statement of an insignificant technical discovery and does not reveal the far-reaching implications which make up the philosophical significance of the theory. Nonetheless it is a complete formulation of the *logical* part of the theory.

Consider, for instance, the problem of geometry. That the unit of measurement is a matter of definition is a familiar fact; everybody knows that it does not make any difference whether we measure distances in feet or meters or light-years. However, that the comparison of distances is also a matter of definition is known only to the expert of relativity. This result can also be formulated as the definitional character of congruence. That a certain distance is congruent to another distance situated at a different place can never be proved to be true; it can only be maintained in the sense of a definition. More precisely speaking, it can be maintained as true only after a definition of congruence is given; it therefore depends on an original comparison of distances which is a matter of definition. A comparison of distances by means of the transport of solid bodies is but one definition of congruence. Another definition would result if we regarded a rod, once it had been transported to another location, as twice as long, thrice transported as three times as long, and so on. A further illustration refers to time: that the simultaneity of events occurring at distant places is a matter of definition was not known before Einstein based his special theory of relativity on this logical discovery.

The definitions employed for the construction of space and time are of a particular kind: they are co-ordinative definitions. That is, they are given by the co-ordination of a physical object, or process, to some fundamental concept. For instance, the concept "equal length" is defined by reference to a physical object, a solid rod, whose transport lays down equal distances. The concept "simultaneous" is defined by the use of light-rays which move over equal distances. The definitions of the theory of relativity are all of this type; they are co-ordinative definitions.

In the expositions of the theory of relativity the use of different definitions is often illustrated by a reference to different observers. This kind of presentation has led to the erroneous conception that the relativity of space-time measurements is connected with the subjectivity of the observer, that the privacy of the world of sense perception is the origin of the relativity maintained by Einstein. Such Protagorean interpretation of Einstein's relativity is utterly mistaken. The definitional character of simultaneity, for instance, has nothing to do with the perspective variations resulting for observers located in different frames of reference. That we co-ordinate different definitions of simultaneity to different observers merely serves as a simplification of the presentation of logical relationships. We could as well interchange the co-ordination and let the observer located in the "moving" system employ the time definition of the observer located in the system "at rest," and vice versa; or we could even let both employ the same time definition, for instance that of the system "at rest." Such variations would lead to different transformations; for instance, the last mentioned definition would lead, not to the Lorentz transformation, but to the classical transformation from a system at rest to a moving system. It is convenient to identify one definitional system with one observer; to speak of different observers is merely a mode of speech expressing the plurality of definitional systems. In a logical exposition of the theory of relativity the observer can be completely eliminated.

Definitions are arbitrary; and it is a consequence of the definitional character of fundamental concepts that with the change of the definitions various descriptional systems arise. But these systems are equivalent to each other, and it is possible to go from each system to another one by a suitable transformation. Thus the definitional character of fundamental concepts leads to a plurality of equivalent descriptions. A familiar illustration is given by the various descriptions of motion resulting when the system regarded as being at rest is varied. Another illustration is presented by the various geometries resulting, for the same physical space, through changes in the definition of congruence. All these descriptions represent different languages saying the same thing; equivalent descriptions, therefore, express the same physical content. The theory of equivalent descriptions is also applicable to other fields of physics; but the domain of space and time has become the model case of this theory.

The word "relativity" should be interpreted as meaning "relative to a certain definitional system." That relativity implies plurality follows because the variation of definitions leads to the plurality of equivalent descriptions. But we see that the plurality implied is not a plurality of different views, or of systems of contradictory content; it is merely a plurality of equivalent languages and thus of forms of expression which do not contradict each other but have the same content. Relativity does not mean an abandonment of truth; it only means that truth can be formulated in various ways.

I should like to make this point quite clear. The two statements "the room is 21 feet long" and "the room is 7 yards long" are equivalent descriptions; they state the same fact. That the simple truth they express can be formulated in these two ways does not eliminate the concept of truth; it merely illustrates the fact that the number characterizing a length is relative to the unit of measurement. All relativities of Einstein's theory are of this type. For instance, the Lorentz transformation connects different descriptions of space-time relations which are equivalent in the same sense as the statements about a length of 21 feet and a length of 7 yards.

Some confusion has arisen from considerations referring to the property of simplicity. One descriptional system can be simpler than another; but that fact does not make it "truer" than the other. The decimal system is simpler than the yard-food-inch system; but an architect's plan drawn in feet and inches is as true a description of a house as a plan drawn in the decimal system. A simplicity of this kind, for which I have used the name of *descriptive simplicity,* is not a criterion of truth. Only within the frame of inductive considerations can simplicity be a criterion of truth; for instance, the simplest curve between observational data plotted in a diagram is regarded as "truer," i.e., more probable, than other connecting curves. This *inductive simplicity,* however, refers to non-equivalent descriptions and does not play a part in the theory of relativity, in which only equivalent descriptions are compared. The simplicity of descriptions used in Einstein's theory is therefore always a descriptive simplicity. For instance, the fact that non-Euclidean geometry often supplies a simpler description of physical space than does Euclidean geometry does not make the non-Euclidean description "truer."

Another confusion must be ascribed to the theory of conventionalism, which goes back to Poincaré. According to this theory, geometry is a matter of convention, and no empirical meaning can be assigned to a statement about the geometry of physical space. Now it is true that physical space can be described by both a Euclidean and a non-Euclidean geometry; but it is an erroneous interpretation of this relativity of geometry to call a statement about the geometrical structure of physical space meaningless. The choice of a geometry is arbitrary only so long as no definition of congruence is specified. Once this definition is set up, it becomes an empirical question *which* geometry holds for a physical space. For instance, it is an empirical fact that, when we use solid bodies for the definition of congruence, our physical space is practically Euclidean within terrestrial dimensions. If, in a different part of the universe, the same definition of congruence were to lead to a non-Euclidean geometry, that part of universal space would have a geometrical structure different from that of our world. It is true that a Euclidean geometry could also be introduced for that part of the universe; but then the definition of congruence would no longer be given by solid bodies.[1] The combination of a statement about a geometry with a statement of the co-ordinative definition of congruence employed is subject to empirical test and thus expresses a property of the physical world. The conventionalist overlooks the fact that only the incomplete statement of a geometry, in which a reference to the definition of congruence is omitted, is arbitrary; if the statement is made complete by the addition of a reference to the definition of congruence, it becomes empirically verifiable and thus has physical content.

Instead of speaking of conventionalism, therefore, we should speak of the relativity of geometry. Geometry is relative in precisely the same sense as other relative concepts. We might call it a convention to say that Chicago is to the left of New York; but we should not forget that this conventional statement can be made objectively true as soon as the point of reference is included in the statement. It is not a convention but a physical fact that Chicago is to the left of New York, seen, for instance, from Washington, D.C. The relativity of simple concepts, such as left and right, is well known. That the fundamental concepts of space and time are of the same type is the essence of the theory of relativity.

The relativity of geometry is a consequence of the fact that different geometries can be represented on one another by a one-to-one correspondence. For certain geometrical systems, however, the representation will not be continuous throughout, and there will result singularities in individual points or lines. For instance, a sphere cannot be projected on a plane without a singularity in at least one point; in the usual projections, the North Pole of the sphere corresponds to the infinity of the plane. This peculiarity involves certain limitations for the relativity of geometry. Assume that in one geometrical description, say, by a spherical space, we have a normal causality for all physical occurrences; then a transformation to certain other geometries, including the Euclidean geometry, leads to violations of the principle of causality, to *causal anomalies*. A light signal going from a point A by way of the North Pole to a point B in a finite time will be so represented within a Euclidean interpretation of this space, that it moves from A in one direction towards infinity and returns from the other side towards B, thus passing through an infinite distance in a finite time. Still more complicated causal anomalies result for other transformations.[2] If the principle of normal causality, i.e., a continuous spreading from cause to effect in a finite time, or *action by contact,* is set up as a necessary prerequisite of the description of nature, certain worlds cannot be interpreted by certain geometries. It may well happen that the geometry thus excluded is the Euclidean one; if Einstein's hypothesis of a closed universe is correct, a Euclidean description of the universe would be excluded for all adherents of a normal causality.

It is this fact which I regard as the strongest refutation of the Kantian conception of space. The relativity of geometry has been used by Neo-Kantians as a back door through which the apriorism of Euclidean geometry was introduced into Einstein's theory: if it is always possible to select a Euclidean geometry for the description of the universe, then the Kantian insists that it be this description which should be used, because Euclidean geometry, for a Kantian, is the only one that can be visualized. We see that this rule may lead to violations of the principle of causality; and since causality, for a Kantian, is as much an *a priori* principle as Euclidean geometry, his rule may compel the Kantian to jump from the frying pan into the fire. There is no defense of Kantianism, if the statement of the geometry of the physical world is worded in a complete form, including all its physical implications; because in this form the statement is empirically verifiable and depends for its truth on the nature of the physical world.[3]

It should be clear from this analysis that the plurality of equivalent descriptions does not rule out the possibility of true empirical statements. The empirical content of statements about space and time is only stated in a more complicated way.

III

Though we now possess, in Einstein's theory, a complete statement of the relativity of space and time, we should not forget that this is the result of a long historical development. I mentioned above Occam's razor and Leibniz' identity of indiscernibles in connection with the verifiability theory of meaning. It is a matter of fact that Leibniz applied his principle successfully to the problem of motion and that he arrived at a relativity of motion on logical grounds. The famous correspondence between Leibniz and Clarke,—the latter a contemporary defender of Newton's absolutism,—presents us with the same type of discussion which is familiar from the modern discussions of relativity and reads as though Leibniz had taken his arguments from expositions of Einstein's theory. Leibniz even went so far as to recognize the relationship between causal order and time order.[4] This conception of relativity was carried on at a later time by Ernst Mach, who contributed to the discussion the important idea that a relativity of rotational motion requires an extension of relativism to the concept of inertial force. Einstein has always acknowledged Mach as a forerunner of his theory.

Another line of development, which likewise found its completion through Einstein's theory, is presented by the history of geometry. The discovery of non-Euclidean geometries by Gauss, Bolyai, and Lobachewski was associated with the idea that physical geometry might be non-Euclidean; and it is known that Gauss tried to test the Euclidean character of terrestrial geometry by triangular measurements from mountain tops. But the man to whom we owe the philosophical clarification of the problem of geometry is Helmholtz. He saw that physical geometry is dependent on the definition of congruence by means of the solid body and thus arrived at a clear statement of the nature of physical geometry, superior in logical insight to Poincaré's conventionalism developed several decades later. It was Helmholtz, too, who clarified the problem of a visual presentation of non-Euclidean geometry by the discovery that visualization is a fruit of experiences with solid bodies and light-rays. We find in Helmholtz' writings the famous statement that imagining something visually means depicting the series of sense perceptions which one would have if one lived in such a world. That Helmholtz did not succeed in dissuading contemporary philosophers from a Kantian apriorism of space and time is not his fault. His philosophical views were known only among a small group of experts. When, with Einstein's theory, the public interest turned toward these problems, philosophers began to give in and to depart from Kant's apriorism. Let us hope that this development will continue and eventually include even those philosophers who in our day still defend an apriorist philosophy against the attacks of the mathematical physicist.

Although there exists a historical evolution of the concepts of space and motion, this line of development finds no analogue in the concept of time. The first to speak of a relativity of the measure of time, i.e., of what is called the uniform flow of time, was Mach. However, Einstein's idea of a relativity of simultaneity has no forerunners. It appears that this discovery could not be made before the perfection of experimental methods of physics. Einstein's relativity of simultaneity is closely associated with the assumption that light is the fastest signal, an idea which could not be conceived before the negative outcome of such experiments as that by Michelson.

It was the combination of the relativity of time and of motion which made Einstein's theory so successful and led to results far beyond the reach of earlier theories. The discovery of the special theory of relativity, which none of Einstein's forerunners had thought of, thus became the key to a general theory of space and time, which included all the ideas of Leibniz, Gauss, Riemann, Helmholtz, and Mach, and which added to them certain fundamental discoveries which could not have been anticipated at an earlier stage. In particular, I refer to Einstein's conception according to which the geometry of physical space is a function of the distribution of masses, an idea entirely new in the history of geometry.

This short account shows that the evolution of philosophical ideas is guided by the evolution of physical theories. The philosophy of space and time is not the work of the ivory tower philosopher. It was constructed by men who attempted to combine observational data with mathematical analysis. The great synthesis of the various lines of development, which we owe to Einstein, bears witness to the fact that philosophy of science has taken over a function which philosophical systems could not perform.

IV

The question of what is space and time has fascinated the authors of philosophical systems over and again. Plato answered it by inventing a world of "higher" reality, the world of ideas, which includes space and time among its ideal objects and reveals their relations to the mathematician who is able to perform the necessary act of vision. For Spinoza space was an attribute of God. Kant, on the other hand, denied the reality of space and time and regarded these two conceptual systems as forms of visualization, i.e., as constructions of the human mind, by means of which the human observer combines his perceptions so as to collect them into an orderly system.

The answer we can give to the question on the basis of Einstein's theory is very different from the answers of these philosophers. The theory of relativity shows that space and time are neither ideal objects nor forms of order necessary for the human mind. They constitute a relational system expressing certain general features of physical objects and thus are descriptive of the physical world. Let us make this fact quite clear.

It is true that, like all concepts, space and time are inventions of the human mind. But not all inventions of the human mind are fit to describe the physical world. By the latter phrase we mean that the concepts refer to certain physical objects and differentiate them from others. For instance, the concept "centaur" is empty, whereas the concept "bear" refers to certain physical objects and distinguishes them from others. The concept "thing," on the other hand, though not empty, is so general that it does not differentiate between objects. Our examples concern one-place predicates, but the same distinction applies to two-place predicates. The relation "telepathy" is empty, whereas the relation "father" is not. When we say that non-empty one-place predicates like "bear" describe real objects, we must also say that non-empty many-place predicates like "father" describe real relations.

It is in this sense that the theory of relativity maintains the reality of space and time. These conceptual systems describe relations holding between physical objects, namely, solid bodies, light-rays, and watches. In addition, these relations formulate physical laws of great generality, determining some fundamental features of the physical world. Space and time have as much reality as, say, the relation "father" or the Newtonian forces of attraction.

The following consideration may serve as a further explanation why geometry is descriptive of physical reality. As long as only one geometry, the Euclidean geometry, was known, the fact that this geometry could be used for a description of the physical world represented a problem for the philosopher; and Kant's philosophy must be understood as an attempt to explain why a structural system derived from the human mind can account for observational relations. With the discovery of a plurality of geometries the situation changed completely. The human mind was shown to be capable of inventing all kinds of geometrical systems, and the question, which of the systems is suitable for the description of physical reality, was turned into an empirical question, i.e., its answer was ultimately left to empirical data. Concerning the empirical nature of this answer we refer the reader to our considerations in Section II; it is the combined statement of geometry and co-ordinative definitions which is empirical. But, if the statement about the geometry of the physical world is empirical, geometry describes a property of the physical world in the same sense, say, as temperature or weight describe properties of physical objects. When we speak of the reality of physical space we mean this very fact.

As mentioned above, the objects whose general relationship is expressed in the spatio-temporal order are solid bodies, light-rays, and natural watches, i.e., closed periodic systems, like revolving atoms or revolving planets. The important part which light-rays play in the theory of relativity derives from the fact that light is the fastest signal, i.e., represents the fastest form of a causal chain. The concept of causal chain can be shown to be the basic concept in terms of which the structure of space and time is built up. The spatio-temporal order thus must be regarded as the expression of the causal order of the physical world. The close connection between space and time on the one hand and causality on the other hand is perhaps the most prominent feature of Einstein's theory, although this feature has not always been recognized in its significance. Time order, the order of *earlier* and *later,* is reducible to causal order; the cause is always earlier than the effect, a relation which cannot be reversed. That Einstein's theory admits of a reversal of time order for certain events, a result known from the relativity of simultaneity, is merely a consequence of this fundamental fact. Since the speed of causal transmission is limited, there exist events of such a kind that neither of them can be the cause or the effect of the other. For events of this kind a time order is not defined, and either of them can be called earlier or later than the other.

Ultimately even spatial order is reducible to causal order; a space point B is called closer to A than a space point C, if a direct light-signal, i.e., a fastest causal chain, from A to C passes by B. For a construction of geometry in terms of light-rays and mass-points, i.e., a light-geometry, I refer to another publication.[5]

The connection between time order and causal order leads to the question of the direction of time. I should like to add some remarks about this problem which has often been discussed, but which has not always been stated clearly enough. The relation between cause and effect is an asymmetrical relation; if P is the cause of Q, then Q is not the cause of P. This fundamental fact is essential for temporal order, because it makes time a serial relation. By a serial relation we understand a relation that orders its elements in a linear arrangement; such a relation is always asymmetrical and transitive, like the relation "smaller than." The time of Einstein's theory has these properties; that is necessary, because otherwise it could not be used for the construction of a serial order.

But what we call the direction of time must be distinguished from the asymmetrical character of the concepts "earlier" and "later." A relation can be asymmetrical and transitive without distinguishing one direction from the opposite one. For instance, the points of a straight line are ordered by a serial relation which we may express by the words "before" and "after." If A is before B, then B is not before A, and if A is before B and B is before C, then A is before C. But which direction of the line we should call "before" and which one "after" is not indicated by the nature of the line; this definition can only be set up by an arbitrary choice, for instance, by pointing into one direction and calling it the direction of "before." In other words, the relations "before" and "after" are structurally indistinguishable and therefore interchangeable; whether we say that point A is before point B or after point B is a matter of arbitrary definition. It is different with the relation "smaller than" among real numbers. This relation is also a serial relation and thus asymmetrical and transitive; but in addition, it is structurally different from its converse, the relation "larger than," a fact expressible through the difference of positive and negative numbers. The square of a positive number is a positive number, and the square of a negative number is also a positive number. This peculiarity enables us to define the relation "smaller than:" a number which cannot be the square of another number is smaller than a number which is the square of another number. The series of real numbers possesses therefore a direction: the direction "smaller than" is not interchangeable with the direction "larger than;" these relations are therefore not only asymmetrical but also *unidirectional*.

The problem of the time relation is whether it is unidirectional. The relation "earlier than" which we use in everyday life is structurally different from the relation "later than." For instance, we may make up our mind to go to the theatre tomorrow; but it would be nonsensical to make up our mind to go to the theatre yesterday. The physicist formulates this distinction as the *irreversibility of time*: time flows in one direction, and the flow of time cannot be reversed. We see that, in the language of the theory of relations, the question of the irreversibility of time is expressed, not by the question of whether time is an asymmetrical relation, but by the question of whether it is a unidirectional relation.

For the theory of relativity, time is certainly an asymmetrical relation, since otherwise the time relation would not establish a serial order; but it is not unidirectional. In other words, the irreversibility of time does not find an expression in the theory of relativity. We must not conclude that that is the ultimate word which the physicist has to say about time. All we can say is that, as far as the theory of relativity is concerned, we need not make a qualitative distinction between the two directions of time, between the "earlier" and "later." A physical theory may very well abstract from certain properties of the physical world; that does not mean that these properties do not exist. The irreversibility of time has so far been dealt with only in thermodynamics, where it is conceived as being merely of a statistical nature, not applicable to elementary processes. This answer is none too satisfactory; particularly in view of the fact that it has led to certain paradoxes. Quantum physics so far, however, has no better answer. I would like to say that I regard this problem as at present unsolved and do not agree with those who believe that there is no genuine problem of the direction of time.

It is an amazing fact that the mathematico-physical treatment of the concept of time formulated in Einstein's theory has led to a clarification which philosophical analysis could not achieve. For the philosopher such concepts as time order and simultaneity were primitive notions inaccessible to further analysis. But the claim that a concept is exempt from analysis often merely springs from an inability to understand its meaning. With his reduction of the time concept to that of causality and his generalization of time order toward a relativity of simultaneity, Einstein has not only changed our conceptions of time; he has also clarified the meaning of the classical time concept which preceded his discoveries. In other words, we know better today what absolute time means than anyone of the adherents of the classical time conceptions. Absolute simultaneity would hold in a world in which there exists no upper limit for the speed of signals, i.e., for causal transmission. A world of this type is as well imaginable as Einstein's world. It is an empirical question to which type our world belongs. Experiment has decided in favor of Einstein's conception. As in the case of geometry, the human mind is capable of constructing various forms of a temporal schema; the question which of these schemes fits the physical world, i.e., is true, can only be answered by reference to observational data. What the human mind contributes to the problem of time is not one definite time order, but a plurality of possible time orders, and the selection of one time order as the real one is left to empirical observation. Time is the order of causal chains; that is the outstanding result of Einstein's discoveries. The only philosopher who anticipated this result was Leibniz; though, of course, in his day it was impossible to conceive of a relativity of simultaneity. And Leibniz was a mathematician as well as a philosopher. It appears that the solution of the problem of time and space is reserved to philosophers who, like Leibniz, are mathematicians or to mathematicians who, like Einstein, are philosophers.

V

From the time of Kant, the history of philosophy shows a growing rift between philosophical systems and the philosophy of science. The system of Kant was constructed with the intention of proving that knowledge is the resultant of two components, a mental and an observational one; the mental component was assumed to be given by the laws of pure reason and conceived as a synthetic element different from the merely analytic operations of logic. The concept of a *synthetic a priori* formulates the Kantian position: there is a *synthetic a priori* part of knowledge, i.e., there are non-empty statements which are absolutely necessary. Among these principles of knowledge Kant includes the laws of Euclidean geometry, of absolute time, of causality and of the conservation of mass. His followers in the 19th century took over this conception, adding many variations.

The development of science, on the other hand, has led away from Kantian metaphysics. The principles which Kant regarded as *synthetic a priori* were recognized as being of a questionable truth; principles contradictory to them were developed and employed for the construction of knowledge. These new principles were not advanced with a claim to absolute truth but in the form of attempts to find a description of nature fitting the observational material. Among the plurality of possible systems, the one corresponding to physical reality could be singled out only by observation and experiment. In other words, the synthetic principles of knowledge which Kant had regarded as *a priori* were recognized as *a posteriori,* as verifiable through experience only and as valid in the restricted sense of empirical hypotheses.

It is this process of a dissolution of the *synthetic a priori* into which we must incorporate the theory of relativity, when we desire to judge it from the viewpoint of the history of philosophy. A line which began with the invention of non-Euclidean geometries 20 years after Kant's death runs uninterruptedly right up and into Einstein's theory of space and time. The laws of geometry, for 2000 years regarded as laws of reason, were recognized as empirical laws, which fit the world of our environment to a high degree of precision; but they must be abandoned for astronomic dimensions. The apparent self-evidence of these laws, which made them seem to be inescapable presuppositions of all knowledge, turned out to be the product of habit; through their suitability to all experiences of everyday life these laws had acquired a degree of reliability which erroneously was taken for absolute certainty. Helmholtz was the first to advocate the idea that human beings, living in a non-Euclidean world, would develop an ability of visualization which would make them regard the laws of non-Euclidean geometry as necessary and self-evident, in the same fashion as the laws of Euclidean geometry appear self-evident to us. Transferring this idea to Einstein's conception of time, we would say that human beings, in whose daily experiences the effects of the speed of light would be noticeably different from those of an infinite velocity, would become accustomed to the relativity of simultaneity and regard the rules of the Lorentz-transformation as necessary and self-evident, just as we regard the classical rules of motion and simultaneity self-evident. For instance, if a telephone connection with the planet Mars were established, and we would have to wait a quarter of an hour for the answer to our questions, the relativity of simultaneity would become as trivial a matter as the time difference between the standard times of different time zones is today. What philosophers had regarded as laws of reason turned out to be a conditioning through the physical laws of our environment; we have ground to assume that in a different environment a corresponding conditioning would lead to another adaptation of the mind.

The process of the dissolution of the *synthetic a priori* is one of the significant features of the philosophy of our time. We should not commit the mistake of considering it a breakdown of human abilities, if conceptions which we regarded as absolutely true are shown to be of limited validity and have to be abandoned in certain fields of knowledge. On the contrary, the fact that we are able to overcome these conceptions and to replace them by better ones reveals unexpected abilities of the human mind, a versatility vastly superior to the dogmatism of a pure reason which dictates its laws to the scientist.

Kant believed himself to possess a proof for his assertion that his *synthetic a priori* principles were necessary truths: According to him these principles were necessary conditions of knowledge. He overlooked the fact that such a proof can demonstrate the truth of the principles only if it is taken for granted that knowledge within the frame of these principles will always be possible. What has happened, then, in Einstein's theory is a proof that knowledge within the framework of Kantian principles is not possible. For a Kantian, such a result could only signify a breakdown of science. It is a fortunate fact that the scientist was not a Kantian and, instead of abandoning his attempts of constructing knowledge, looked for ways of changing the so-called *a priori* principles. Through his ability of dealing with space-time relations essentially different from the traditional frame of knowledge, Einstein has shown the way to a philosophy superior to the philosophy of the *synthetic a priori*.

It is the philosophy of empiricism, therefore, into which Einstein's relativity belongs. It is true, Einstein's empiricism is not the one of Bacon and Mill, who believed that all laws of nature can be found by simple inductive generalizations. Einstein's empiricism is that of modern theoretical physics, the empiricism of mathematical construction, which is so devised that it connects observational data by deductive operations and enables us to predict new observational data. Mathematical physics will always remain empiricist as long as it leaves the ultimate criterion of truth to sense perception. The enormous amount of deductive method in such a physics can be accounted for in terms of analytic operations alone.

In addition to deductive operations there is, of course, an inductive element included in the physics of mathematical hypotheses; but even the principle of induction, by far the most difficult obstacle to a radical empiricism, can be shown today to be justifiable without a belief in a *synthetic a priori*. The method of modern science can be completely accounted for in terms of an empiricism which recognizes only sense perception and the analytic principles of logic as sources of knowledge. In spite of the enormous mathematical apparatus, Einstein's theory of space and time is the triumph of such a radical empiricism in a field which had always been regarded as a reservation for the discoveries of pure reason.

The process of the dissolution of the *synthetic a priori* is going on. To the abandonment of absolute space and time quantum physics has added that of causality; furthermore, it has abandoned the classical concept of material substance and has shown that the constituents of matter, the atomic particles, do not possess the unambiguous nature of the solid bodies of the macroscopic world. If we understand by metaphysics the belief in principles that are non-analytic, yet derive their validity from reason alone, modern science is anti-metaphysical. It has refused to recognize the authority of the philosopher who claims to know the truth from intuition, from insight into a world of ideas or into the nature of reason or the principles of being, or from whatever super-empirical source. There is no separate entrance to truth for philosophers. The path of the philosopher is indicated by that of the scientist: all the philosopher can do is to analyze the results of science, to construe their meanings and stake out their validity. Theory of knowledge is analysis of science.

I said above that Einstein is a philosopher by implication. That means that making the philosophic implications of Einstein's theory explicit is the task of the philosopher. Let us not forget that it is implications of an enormous reach which are derivable from the theory of relativity, and let us realize that it must be an eminently philosophical physics that lends itself to such implications. It does not happen very often that physical systems of such philosophical significance are presented to us; Einstein's predecessor was Newton. It is the privilege of our generation that we have among us a physicist whose work occupies the same rank as that of the man who determined the philosophy of space and time for two centuries. If physicists present us with implicational philosophies of such excellence, it is a pleasure to be a philosopher. The lasting fame of the philosophy of modern physics will justly go to the man who made the physics rather than to those who have been at work deriving the implications of his work and who are pointing out its position in the history of philosophy. There are many who have contributed to the philosophy of Einstein's theory, but there is only one Einstein.

ALBERT EINSTEIN

Reply to Reichenbach by a "Non-Positivist"

Now I come to the theme of the relation of the theory of relativity to philosophy. Here it is Reichenbach's piece of work which, by the precision of deductions and by the sharpness of his assertions, irresistibly invites a brief commentary. . . . To the question: Do you consider true what Reichenbach has here asserted, I can answer only with Pilate's famous question: "What is truth?"

Let us first take a good look at the question: Is a geometry—looked at from the physical point of view—verifiable (viz., falsifiable) or not? Reichenbach, together with Helmholtz, says: Yes, provided that the empirically given solid body realizes the concept of "distance." Poincaré says no and consequently is condemned by Reichenbach. Now the following short conversation takes place:

Poincaré: The empirically given bodies are not rigid, and consequently can not be used for the embodiment of geometric intervals. Therefore, the theorems of geometry are not verifiable.

Reichenbach: I admit that there are no bodies which can be *immediately* adduced for the "real definition" of the interval. Nevertheless, this real definition can be achieved by taking the thermal volume-dependence, elasticity, electro- and magneto-striction, etc., into consideration. That this is really (and) without contradiction possible, classical physics has surely demonstrated.

Poincaré: In gaining the real definition improved by yourself you have made use of physical laws, the formulation of which presupposes (in this case) Euclidean geometry. The verification, and which you have spoken, refers, therefore, not merely to geometry but to the entire system of physical laws which constitute its foundation. An examination of geometry by itself is consequently not thinkable.—Why should it consequently not be entirely up to me to choose geometry according to my own convenience (i.e., Euclidean) and to fit the remaining (in the usual sense "physical") laws to this choice in such manner that there can arise no contradiction of the whole with experience?

(The conversation cannot be continued in this fashion because the respect of the [present] writer for Poincaré's superiority as thinker and author does not permit it; in what follows therefore, an anonymous non-positivist is substituted for Poincaré.—)

Reichenbach: There is something quite attractive in this conception. But, on the other hand, it is noteworthy that the adherence to the objective meaning of length and to the interpretation of the differences of coordinates as distances (in pre-relativistic physics) has not led to complications. Should we not, on the basis of this astounding fact, be justified in operating further at least tentatively with the concept of the measurable length, as if there were such things as rigid measuring-rods? In any case it would have been impossible for Einstein *de facto* (even if not theoretically) to set up the theory of general relativity, if he had not adhered to the objective meaning of length.

Against Poincaré's suggestion it is to be pointed out that what really matters is not merely the greatest possible simplicity of the geometry alone, but rather the greatest possible simplicity of all of physics (inclusive of geometry). This is what is, in the first instance, involved in the fact that today we must decline as unsuitable the suggestion to adhere to Euclidean geometry.

Non-Positivist: If, under the stated circumstances, you hold distance to be a legitimate concept, how then is it with your basic principle (meaning = verifiability)? Do you not have to reach the point where you must deny the meaning of geometrical concepts and theorems and to acknowledge meaning only within the completely developed theory of relativity (which, however, does not yet exist at all as a finished product)? Do you not have to admit that, in your sense of the word, no "meaning" can be attributed to the individual concepts and assertions of a physical theory at all, and to the entire system only insofar as it makes what is given in experience "intelligible?" Why do the individual concepts which occur in a theory require any specific justification anyway, if they are only indispensable within the framework of the logical structure of the theory, and the theory only in its entirety validates itself?

It seems to me, moreover, that you have not at all done justice to the really significant philosophical achievement of Kant. From Hume Kant had learned that there are concepts (as, for example, that of causal connection), which play a dominating rôle in our thinking, and which, nevertheless, can not be deduced by means of a logical process from the empirically given (a fact which several empiricists recognize, it is true, but seem always again to forget). What justifies the use of such concepts? Suppose he had replied in this sense: Thinking is necessary in order to understand the empirically given, *and concepts and "categories" are necessary as indispensable elements of thinking.* If he had remained satisfied with this type of an answer, he would have avoided scepticism and you would not have been able to find fault with him. He, however, was misled by the erroneous opinion—difficult to avoid in his time—that Euclidean geometry is necessary to thinking and offers *assured* (i.e., not dependent upon sensory experience) knowledge concerning the objects of "external" perception. From this easily understandable error he concluded the existence of synthetic judgments *a priori,* which are produced by the reason alone, and which, consequently, can lay claim to absolute validity. I think your censure is directed less against Kant himself than against those who today still adhere to the errors of "synthetic judgements *a priori.*"

MAX PLANCK

The Concept of Causality in Physics *

In the fight currently raging about the meaning and validity of the Law of Causality in modern physics, every attempt to clarify the conflicting opinions must begin with the statement that in this connection everything depends on a clear understanding of the sense in which the word "causality" is used in the science of physics. To be sure, it is agreed *a priori* that whenever a reference is made to a "causal relationship" between two successive events or occurrences, this term is understood to designate a certain regular connection between them, calling the earlier one the *cause,* and the latter one the *effect.* But the question is: What constitutes this specific type of connection? Is there any infallible sign to indicate that a happening in nature is causally determined by another?

It follows from the numerous inquiries heretofore undertaken into this question that the best and safest way to approach a clear answer is to relate the question to the possibility of making accurate predictions. In fact, there can be no more incontestable way to prove the causal relationship between any two events than to demonstrate that from the occurrence of one it is always possible to infer in advance the occurrence of the other. This point was quite familiar to the farmer who gave a visual demonstration to some sceptical peasants of the causal relationship between artificial fertilizers and the fertility of the soil, by intensively fertilizing his clover fields in certain narrow strips having the form of letters, so as to make the following sentence appear: "This strip was fertilized with calcium sulfate."

Therefore, I want to base all our subsequent considerations on the following simple proposition, equally applicable outside of the realm of physics: *"An occurrence is causally determined if it can be predicted with certainty."* Of course, this sentence is meant to express only that the possibility of making an accurate prediction for the future constitutes an infallible criterion of the presence of a causal relationship, but not that it is synonymous with the latter. I need to mention merely the well known

* Translated by Frank Gaynor from the German "Der Kausalbegriff in der Physik" in *Scientific Autobiography and Other Papers* by Max Planck; copyright by Philosophical Library, New York, 1949. Pp. 121–150, reprinted by permission of the publisher.

example that we can predict with a certainty while it is still day the coming of night, and yet this does not make day the cause of night.

But conversely, it also often happens that we assume the presence of a causal relationship even in cases where there is no question at all of the possibility of making accurate predictions. Just think of weather forecasts. The unreliability of weather prophets has become proverbial, and yet there is hardly any trained meteorologist who does not consider the atmospheric processes to be causally determined. All these considerations indicate that in order to find the right clues to the concept of causality, we must go still a little deeper.

In the case of weather forecasts, the thought suggests itself that their unreliability is due merely to the size and complicated nature of the object of the analysis, i.e. the atmosphere. If we single out a small portion of it—for instance, a cubic foot of air—we will be far more likely to make accurate predictions about its reaction to external influences, such as compression, heat, moisture, etc. We are familiar with certain laws of physics which enable us to predict, with more or less certainty, the readings of the corresponding measurements, such as the increase in pressure, rise in temperature, condensation, etc.

However, if we observe things still a little more closely, we shall soon reach a very remarkable conclusion. Simple as we may make the conditions, and precise as our measuring instruments may be, we shall never succeed in calculating in advance the results of the actual measurements with an absolute accuracy, in other words in making the predicted value of a magnitude agree to the last decimal place with the figure actually registered by the instruments; there always remains a certain margin of uncertainty—in contrast to the calculations in pure mathematics, as in the case of the square root of 2 or of π, which can be given accurately to any number of decimal places. And whatever applies to mechanical and thermal processes, holds true for all fields of physics, including electricity and optics.

Thus, all the above cited experiences force us to recognize the following principle as a firmly established fact: *It is never possible to predict a physical occurrence with unlimited precision.* If we now compare this principle with the proposition accepted above as our starting point, namely that an occurrence is causally determined if it can be predicted with certainty, we find ourselves facing an unavoidable dilemma: We may elect *either* to adhere literally to the exact wording of our basic proposition, in which case there cannot exist even one single instance in nature where a causal relationship would have to be assumed to prevail—*or* to subject that basic proposition to a certain modification, so designed as to provide room for the presupposition of strict causality.

A number of contemporary physicists and philosophers have chosen the first alternative. I shall refer to them here as *indeterminists*. They claim that genuine causality, strict regularity, actually does not exist in nature but is merely an illusion created by the operation of certain rules which are never of an exact universal validity, even though they often came very near to it. Upon closer consideration, the indeterminist discovers a statistical root in every law of physics, including the law of gravity and of electrical attraction; he regards them, one and all, as laws of probability, relating only to mean values of many similar observations, possessing only an approximate validity for individual instances.

A good example of such a statistical law is the dependence of the magnitude of gas pressure on the density and temperature. The pressure of a gas is produced by the continual impact against the walls of the vessel of a vast number of gas molecules moving at random in all directions with great velocity. A summary computation of the aggregate dynamic effect of their impact reveals that the pressure against the walls of the vessel is almost proportional to the density of the gas as well as to the mean square of the molecular velocity, a result which is in satisfactory agreement with measurement if we regard the temperature as a measure of molecular velocity.

A direct confirmation of this theory of gas pressure is furnished by investigations on the temporal variations of the pressure against a very small portion of the wall of the vessel. Such variations, produced by random molecular impacts, can be observed wherever molecules in rapid flight come in contact with easily movable bodies; they manifest themselves also in the Brownian molecular movement, as well as in the fact that very sensitive scales never come to a complete rest, but constantly execute minute irregular vibrations about their position of equilibrium.

Analogously with the gas laws, the indeterminists attribute every other kind of physical regularity, ultimately to the operation of chance. They see nature ruled exclusively by statistics, and their aim is to base all physics on the calculus of probabilities.

Actually, physical science has developed up to now on the very opposite foundation. It chose the *second* one of the two alternatives mentioned above: In order to be able to maintain the full and absolute validity of the law of causality, it modified slightly the basic proposition, that an occurrence is causally determined if it can be predicted with a certainty. This was done by using the word "occurrence" in a somewhat modified sense. Thus, theoretical physics considers as an occurrence not an actual individual process of measurement—which always includes accidental and unessential elements, too—but a certain, merely theoretical process; and in this manner it replaces the sense world, as given to us directly by our sense organs (or alternatively, by the measuring instruments which serve us as sharpened sense organs), by another world, the world picture of physics, which is a conceptual structure, arbitrary to a certain degree, created for the purpose of getting away from the uncertainty involved in every individual measurement and for making possible a precise interrelation of concepts.

Consequently, every measurable physical magnitude, every length, every time interval, every mass, every charge, has a double meaning, according as we regard it as directly given by some measurement, or conceive of it as translated into the world picture of physics. In the first interpretation, it is never capable of a sharp definition, and can therefore never be represented by a quite definite number; but in the world picture of physics it stands for a certain mathematical symbol, which lends itself to manipulation according to quite definite, precise rules. This goes for the height of a tower just as for the duration of the swing of a pendulum or for the brightness of an incandescent lamp. A clear and consistent distinction between the magnitudes of the sense world and the corresponding magnitudes of the world picture is absolutely essential for the clarification of concepts; without such a distinction it is impossible to discuss these questions intelligently and objectively.

It is absolutely untrue, although it is often asserted, that the world picture of physics contains, or may contain, directly observable magnitudes only. On the contrary, directly observable magnitudes are not found at all in the world picture. It contains symbols only. In fact, the world picture even contains constituents which have only a very indirect significance for the sense world, or no significance at all, such as ether waves, partial vibrations, frames of reference, etc. Primarily, such constituents play the part of dead weight or ballast, but they are incorporated because of the decisive advantage assured by the introduction of the world picture—that it permits us to carry through a strict determinism.

Of course, the world picture always remains a mere auxiliary concept. It is self-evident that in the last analysis, the things that really matter, are the occurrences in the sense world and the greatest possible accuracy in predicting them. In classical physics this is achieved as follows: First, an object found in the sense world—for instance, a system of material points—is symbolically represented in some measured condition, i.e. is translated into the world picture. One thus obtains a certain physical structure in a certain initial state. Similarly, suitable symbols are substituted in the framework of the world picture for external influences which operate subsequently on the object. One thus obtains the external forces acting on the structure, and the corresponding boundary conditions. The behavior of the structure is then unambiguously determined for all times by these data, and it can be computed with absolute accuracy from the differential equations of the theory. The coordinates and momenta of all material points of the structure are thus exhibited as quite definite functions of time. If then at any later time the symbols used in the world picture are retranslated into the sense world, one thus obtains a connection between a later occurrence in the sense world and a previous occurrence in the sense world, and this connection can be utilized for an approximate prediction of the later occurrence.

In summary, we may say: While in the sense world the prediction of an occurrence is always associated with a certain element of uncertainty, in the world picture of physics all occurrences follow one another in accordance with precisely definable laws—they are strictly determined causally. Therefore, the introduction of the world picture of physics—and herein lies its significance—reduces the uncertainty of predicting an occurrence in the sense world to the uncertainty in translating that occurrence from the sense world into the world picture and in retranslating it from the world picture into the sense world.

Classical physics was but little concerned with this uncertainty; its main concern was to follow through the causal point of view in the consideration of the occurrences in the world picture, and this was where it achieved its great results. Specifically, it succeeded also in finding a satisfactory interpretation, on the basis of a strict causality, for the above mentioned irregular vibratory phenomena corresponding to the Brownian molecular movement. The indeterminists see no real problem here. For since they look for irregularity behind every rule, statistical regularity is that which gives them direct satisfaction. Therefore, they are satisfied also with the assumption that the collision of two individual molecules, as well as the impact of the molecules against the wall of the vessel, occurs solely according to statistical laws. Nevertheless, this assumption is as little justified as would be the conclusion that the charge of an individual electron is located on its surface just because in a charged conductor the electrons are all located on its surface. On the other hand, the determinists who, on the contrary, look for a rule behind every irregularity, were led to the problem of basing a theory of the gas laws on the premise that the collision of two individual molecules is determined in a strict causal manner. The solution of this problem was the life work of Ludwig Boltzmann, and it represents one of the most beautiful triumphs of theoretic research. For it not only yields the principle, confirmed by actual measurements, that the mean energy of the oscillations about the state of equilibrium is proportional to the absolute temperature, but it permits also a remarkably accurate computation of the absolute number and mass of the molecules, based on a measurement of these oscillations, as in the case of a highly sensitive torsion balance.

Such outstanding achievements seemed to justify the hope that the world picture of classical physics would in principle accomplish its task, and that a steady improvement and refinement of the technique and methods of measurement would progressively reduce the significance of the uncertainties accompanying the translation into and from the sense world. But the introduction of the elementary quantum of action destroyed this hope at one blow and for good.

The so-called Uncertainty Principle, discovered and formulated by Heisenberg, constitutes a characteristic feature of quantum mechanics; it asserts that for any two canonically conjugate magnitudes, such as position and momentum or time and energy, only one can be measured to any desired degree of accuracy, so that an increase in the precision of the measurement of one magnitude is accompanied by a proportional decrease in the precision of measurement of the other. Consequently, when one magnitude is ascertained with absolute accuracy, the other one remains absolutely indefinite.

It is evident that this principle fundamentally precludes the possibility of translating into the sense world, with an arbitrary degree of accuracy, the simultaneous values of the coordinates and momenta of material points, as these are conceived in the world picture of classical physics; this circumstance constitutes a difficulty with respect to the recognition of a universal validity of the principle of strict causality, and it has even caused some indeterminists to regard the law of causality in physics as decisively refuted. However, upon closer scrutiny, this conclusion—founded on a confusion of the world picture with the sense world—proves a rash one, to say the very least. For there is another, more logical way out of the difficulty, a way which has often rendered excellent services on previous occasions—namely, the assumption that the attempt to determine simultaneously both the coordinates and the momentum of a material point is physically completely meaningless. However, the impossibility of giving an answer to a meaningless question must, of course, not be charged up against the law of causality, but solely against the premises which produced that particular question; in other words, in this particular instance, against the assumed structure of the world picture of physics. And since the classical world picture has failed, another must take its place.

This is what actually has happened. The new world picture of quantum mechanics is a product of the need to find a way of reconciling the quantum of action with the principle of strict determinism. For this purpose, the traditional primary constituent of the world picture, the material point, had to be deprived of its basic, elementary character; it was resolved into a system of material waves. These material waves constitute the primary elements of the new world picture. The material point in its old meaning now appears merely as a special borderline case, as an infinitesimally small parcel of waves, the momentum of which is totally indefinite, since its position is definite, according to Heisenberg's uncertainty principle. If we assign a certain range to the position of the material point, the value of the momentum also becomes approximately definite and the laws of classical mechanics then are approximately valid for positions and momenta.

In general, the laws of material waves are basically different from those of the classical mechanics of material points. However, the point of central importance is that the function characterizing material waves, i.e. the wave function or probability function (the term itself is of no importance here), is fully determined for all places and times by the initial and boundary conditions, according to quite definite principles of computation, whether we use Schroedinger's operators, Heisenberg's matrices, or Dirac's q-numbers.

We thus see that the principle of determinism is as strictly valid in the world picture of quantum mechanics as in that of classical physics.

The difference consists only in the symbols used and in the mathematics applied. Accordingly, in the realm of quantum mechanics, just as formerly in classical physics, the uncertainty in the prediction of the occurrences of the sense world is reduced to an uncertainty in the correlation of world picture and sense world, in other words, to an uncertainty in the translation of the symbols of the world picture into the sense world, and *vice versa*. The fact that this double uncertainty is involved is the most impressive proof of the importance of retaining the principle of determinism within the world picture.

Nevertheless, even a cursory glance shows how far the world picture of quantum mechanics has shifted from the sense world, and how much more difficult it is to translate an occurrence from the world picture of quantum mechanics into the sense world or *vice versa*, than was the case in classical physics. In the latter, the meaning of every symbol was immediately and directly intelligible; the position, the velocity, the momentum, the energy of a material point could be determined more or less accurately by measurements, and there appeared no obvious reason to doubt that a steady improvement of the technique and methods of measurement could not eventually reduce the remaining factor of uncertainty below any desired margin. On the other hand, the wave function of quantum mechanics supplies no direct clue whatever for any obvious interpretation of the sense world, simply because it does not refer to ordinary space at all but rather to the configurational space which has as many dimensions as there are coordinates present in the physical structure under consideration. Moreover—and this is where the real trouble lies—the wave function does not give us the values of the coordinates as functions of the time, but merely the probability that the coordinates may possess certain specific values at some specified time.

The indeterminists again seized on this circumstance as the occasion for a new attack against the law of causality. And this time their attack actually seems to promise them success; for on the basis of measurements it is possible to assign merely a statistical significance to the wave function. Nonetheless, once more the defenders of strict causality have the same way out as before: The assumption that the question concerning the meaning of a certain symbol of the world picture of quantum mechanics, such as a material wave, has no definite sense unless one also specifies the condition of the particular measuring apparatus used for translating the symbol into the sense world. For this reason, one is led to talk about the causal effect of the measuring instrument that is employed; and one is thereby expressing the fact that the particular uncertainty in question is determined at least in part by the circumstance that the magnitude of the value to be measured is dependent in a certain regular manner on the method used for measuring it.

However, this auxiliary hypothesis shunts the entire question to a track, the further course of which is still hidden in darkness. For now the indeterminists are justified in raising the question whether the concept of a causal influence of the measuring instrument on the measuring process has any intelligible meaning, since every attempt to examine such a causal effect directly requires some kind of measurement, and since with every new measurement a new causal influence and therefore a new uncertainty would be introduced into the problem.

And yet, this objection still does not dispose of the matter. For as every experimental physicist knows, besides the direct methods of investigation there exist also indirect ones, and the latter accomplish good results in many a case where the former have failed. However, I must take exception to the view (a very popular one these days, and certainly a very plausible one on the face of it) that a problem in physics merits examination only if it is established in advance that a definite answer to it can be obtained. If physicists had always been guided by this principle, the famous experiment of Michelson and Morley undertaken to measure the so-called absolute velocity of the earth, would never have taken place, and the theory of relativity might still be nonexistent. Accordingly, if the study of a question now regarded fairly universally as meaningless, such as that of the absolute velocity of the earth, has turned out to produce such extraordinary benefits to science, how much more worth while must it be to follow up a problem, the deeper meaning of which is still under debate and which is capable more than any other of enriching research.

But how are we to come to a decision? Obviously, there is no other alternative than to consider the two opposing views, to side with the one that appeals to us more, and then to investigate whether it leads to valuable or to worthless conclusions. At any rate, one must welcome the fact that physicists who are closely interested in this subject are split into two factions; one leans toward the theory of determinism, the other toward indeterminism. So far as I can see, the latter represent the majority nowadays, although it is difficult to establish the facts which may easily change in the course of time. Between these two viewpoints there is also room for a third position which in a certain sense is a mediating one, in that it assigns to certain concepts, such as the force of electrical attraction, a direct significance and a strict uniformity with respect to the sense world; whereas to other concepts, such as material waves, it assigns merely a statistical significance. However, because it lacks systematic unity this view does not appear to be very satisfactory. For this reason, I propose to disregard it now and to confine myself to a somewhat closer analysis of the two fully consistent viewpoints.

The indeterminist is satisfied in his quest for knowledge by the discovery that the wave function of quantum mechanics is merely a probability value. He has no further problem in connection with it. On the other hand, he sees unsolved problems in certain determinate laws of nature, such as Coulomb's law of electrical attraction; for he cannot be satisfied with Coulomb's formula for the force or the potential, but continues to search for exceptions, and is not content until he succeeds in determining the magnitude of the probability that the electrical force differs from Coulomb's value by some arbitrary pre-assigned value.

The determinist thinks along the very opposite lines in all these points. He assigns to Coulomb's law the satisfactory character of absolute validity. On the other hand, he recognizes the wave function as a mere probability magnitude only so long as the measuring instrument used in the study of the wave is disregarded, and he looks for inflexible laws connecting the properties of the wave function and the occurrences in the measuring apparatus. For this purpose, he must obviously include in the subject matter of his investigation both the wave function and the measuring instruments. In other words, he must translate into his physical world picture not only the entire experimental setup used for the production of the material waves—such as the high voltage battery, the incandescent filament, the radioactive compound—but also the measuring apparatus, such as the photographic plate, the ionization chamber, the point counter, together with all the processes occurring therein, and he must deal with all these objects as one single structure, as an isolated system. But this does not yet take care of the problem. On the contrary—it makes it even more complicated. For in this case, if the total structure is to retain its unique character it must neither be split up nor exposed to external influences, so that a direct examination is completely impossible. Nevertheless it now becomes possible to formulate certain new hypotheses concerning the internal processes of the system, and subsequently to test their consignments. Whether this procedure leads to any actual advance, is a question which only the future can answer. For the time being, it is still impossible to determine clearly what direction will lead to progress. At any rate, all the circumstances mentioned prove that the elementary quantum of action erects an objective barrier which limits the efficiency of the measuring apparatus available to physical science, and that, therefore, the desired progress will only give this barrier even sharper outlines than it had before.

Properly speaking, we have thus reached the end of our considerations which have demonstrated that an adherence to a strictly causal outlook—always taking the word "causal" in the modified sense explained previously—is by no means excluded from the viewpoint of even modern physics, though its necessity can never be proved either *a priori* or *a posteriori*. Nevertheless, not even a convinced determinist—indeed, especially not a convinced determinist—can escape at this point some doubts which prevent him from accepting as fully satisfactory, the interpretation of causality indicated above. For even if it should prove to be feasible to develop further the concept of causality along the lines described, the concept as here proposed involved a serious flaw. For it could be maintained that a relation possessing such profound significance as the causal connection between two successive events represents ought to be independent by its very nature from the human intellect which is considering it. Instead, we have not only linked at the very outset the concept of causality to the human intellect, specifically to the ability of man to predict an occurrence; but we have been able to carry through the deterministic viewpoint only with the expedient of replacing the directly given sense world by the world picture of physics, that is, by a provisional and alterable creation of the human power of imagination. These are anthropomorphic traits which ill-befit fundamental concepts of physics; and the question therefore arises whether it is not possible to give the concept of causality a deeper meaning by divesting it as far as it can be of its anthropomorphic character, and to make it independent of human artifacts such as the world picture of physics. Of course, we shall have to adhere to our basic premise, that an occurrence is causally determined if it can be predicted with a certainty, for otherwise we would lose the only solid foundation for our discussion. And we must feel bound to no less a degree to our second principle, that it is never possible, to predict an occurrence with absolute precision. It accordingly follows that if we are to speak at all of causality in nature, we must introduce some modification into our first basic proposition. To this extent the situation remains as it was before. But the type of modification which we introduced previously into the first basic proposition can be replaced by a totally different one.

In the preceding discussion what was modified was the object of the prediction—the occurrence. For we related the occurrences not to the directly given sense world, but to an artificially created world picture, and we thus found it possible to determine occurrences accurately. But instead of modifying the object of predictions we can alter our notion of the subject of the prediction, that is, of the predicting intellect. For every prediction presupposes somebody who does the predicting. Therefore, in the following discussion we shall direct our attention solely to the predicting subject, and shall consider as the objects of prediction the directly given occurrences of the sense world, without introducing an artificial world picture.

First of all, it is easy to see that the reliability of a prediction depends, to a high degree, on the individual personality of the one who is making it. If we consider again weather forecasts, it makes a great difference whether tomorrow's weather is forecast by an amateur who knows nothing about today's atmospheric pressure, wind direction, atmospheric temperature and humidity, or by a capable farmer who considers all these data and also has a great deal of experience, or finally, by a scientifically trained meteorologist who in addition to the local data also has access to the accurate information supplied by a great many weather-maps from near and far. The forecast of the experienced farmer is more reliable than that of the amateur, and the forecast of the trained meteorologist more reliable than that of either of those two. In view of this circumstance, it seems natural to suppose that an ideal intellect, intimately familiar with the most minute details of physical processes occurring concurrently everywhere, would be able to predict tomorrow's weather in all its details with an absolute accuracy. The same idea applies to every other prediction of physical occurrences.

Such an assumption signifies an extrapolation which cannot be demonstrated logically, though it cannot be refused in an *a priori* fashion either; it must therefore be judged not on the score of its truth, but only on the basis of its value. In consequence the actual impossibility of predicting even a single occurrence accurately in classical as well as in quantum physics, appears to be a natural consequence of the circumstance that man with his sense organs and measuring instruments is himself a part of nature, subject to its laws and confined within its limits, whereas the ideal intellect is free of all such limitations.

However, in order to be able to follow through such a view logically, we must comply with an important requirement: We must be on our guard against the temptation to make the ideal intellect the object of a scientific analysis, to regard it as something analogous to ourselves, and to ask of it how it obtains the knowledge which enables it to make precise predictions. The inquisitive human being who would do so, is quite likely to hear this answer to his question: "You resemble the intellect which you comprehend, not *me*!" And if after this reprimand he persists in his obstinacy and declares the concept of an ideal intellect to be meaningless and unnecessary, if not illogical, let him be reminded that not all statements which lack a logical foundation are scientifically worthless, and that his short-sighted formalism stops up the very fountain at which a Galileo, a Kepler, a Newton, and many other great physicists have quenched their thirst for scientific knowledge and insight. For all these men devotion to science was, consciously or unconsciously, a matter of faith—a matter of a serene faith in a rational world order.

Of course, this faith can no more be forced upon anybody than could one be commanded to see the truth or forbidden to commit an error. But the plain fact that we are able, at least to a certain degree, to subject future natural occurrences to our thought processes and to bend them to our will, would be a totally incomprehensible mystery, did it not permit us to surmise at least a certain harmony between the external world and the human intellect. The depth to which one conceives this harmony to extend is a matter of merely secondary importance.

In conclusion we may therefore say: The law of causality is neither true nor false. It is rather a heuristic principle, a signpost—and in my opinion, our most valuable signpost—to help us find our bearings in a bewildering maze of occurrences, and to show us the direction in which scientific research must advance in order to achieve fertile results. The law of causality, which immediately impresses the awakening soul of the child and plants the untiring question "*Why?*" into his mouth, remains a lifelong companion of the scientist and confronts him incessantly with new problems. For science is not a contemplative repose amidst knowledge already gained, but is indefatigable work and an ever progressive development.

WERNER HEISENBERG

Fundamental Problems of Present-day Atomic Physics *

Practically all public discussion of atomic physics is in fact concerned with atomic technology, i.e., the application of the enormous energy of atoms to weapons of war or to machines. The real science, however, of which this technology is but a branch development, is much less known to the general public. Occasionally there may be reports of the success of a British scientist in discovering a new elementary particle, or of new knowledge of the inner atomic forces gained in experiments with a new giant cyclotron in California, or again of Stalin Prizes awarded to two Russian scientists for their work in high altitude laboratories in the Caucasus. But the real aim, the common bond linking all the efforts of men of different nations and making them part of a pattern, this aim is hardly ever discussed. And yet this is precisely the object of atomic physics for the physicist. For him there is ever present in his work the centuries-old desire for a unified understanding of the world, and he judges every discovery, at least unconsciously, on its ability to bring him nearer to the goal of his ambition. That is why I should like to speak to you to-day about those fundamental ideas which combine various experiments and theories into atomic physics. I should like to explain what we are hoping for in our work and what will have happened when our hopes and wishes have been fulfilled.

To get an understanding of the basis of atomic physics we shall have to follow, step by step, the ideas which, two and a half thousand years ago, had led Greek natural philosophy to atomic theory, and we shall then have to make an attempt at finding a connection with these fundamental ideas even in the advances of the most modern atomic physics. It will therefore be no digression if I first outline briefly the pre-history and the history of atomic theory.

* Lecture delivered at the Eidgenössische Technische Hochschule, Zürich, on July 9th, 1948. [This is the latest of the lectures in Dr. Heisenberg's *Wandlungen in den Grundlagen der Naturwissenschaft*, translated into English by F. C. Hayes as *Philosophic Problems of Nuclear Science* (Pantheon, New York, 1952). Reprinted here by permission of Pantheon Books, Inc.]

At the beginning of Ionic natural philosophy we find the famous statement of Thales of Miletus that water is the origin of all things. This statement which appears so strange to us to-day, contains as Friedrich Nietzsche had already pointed out, three fundamental ideas of philosophy. First, the idea that there is an origin of all things, then that this question has to be answered rationally, and thirdly, that it must in the final resort be possible to 'understand' the world through a unified principle. These three implications are the more remarkable since it was, at that time, not at all an obvious step to look for the origin of things in something material rather than in life itself. Thales's statement is the first to contain the idea of a homogeneous fundamental substance of which the world is to consist, although the word 'substance' had certainly not the purely material sense which we, to-day, attribute so easily to it.

If there were only one such substance, then it would have to fill up all space uniformly and indiscriminately and the existing large variety of phenomena could never be explained. For this reason the philosophy of Anaximander, a pupil of Thales who also lived in Miletus, was based on a fundamental polarity, the contrast between Being and Becoming. A homogeneous existence ('*Sein*') gave rise to change, to Becoming. This, in turn, represented in a sense a corruption of the pure Being. It did so by shaping the play of the world by means of hatred and love. In Heraclitus's philosophy, Becoming assumed prime importance; fire became the basic element, that which moved, but it also represented Good and Light; war was the father of all things. Later, especially as a result of Anaxagoras's influence, the idea gained ground that the world consisted of several elementary substances which were believed to be homogeneous and indestructible; only their mixing and separation produced the variety of life. Empedocles adopted the famous elements earth, water, air and fire as the four 'basic roots' ('*Stammwurzeln*').

It was from this position that Leucippus and Democritus of Abdera effected the transition to materialism. The polarity of being and non-being was made worldly and became a contrast of Full and Empty. Pure Being contracted to a point, but it could repeat itself any number of times; it became indivisible and indestructible and hence it was called 'atom'. The world was reduced to atoms with empty space between them. A mixture of elements was thought to be like a mixture of two kinds of sand. The relative position and movement of atoms determined the qualities of substances and were thus responsible for variety in the world. Up to that time space had been conceived as something impossible *without* matter, but as something suspended *by* matter. Now, materialist philosophy endowed it with a certain independence, it became, as empty space between atoms, the carrier of geometry—that is, responsible for the whole wealth of shapes and all the varied phenomena of the world. The atoms themselves had no properties, neither colour, nor smell or taste. Properties of substances were produced indirectly by the relative position and movement of atoms. In Democritus we find these statements.

'Just as tragedy and comedy can be written using the same letters, so, many varied events in this world can be realized by the same atoms as long as they take up different positions and describe different movements.'[1]

'Sweet exists by convention, bitter by convention, colour by convention; atoms and Void (alone) exist in reality'[2] . . .

Thus, atomic theory realized Thales's fundamental demand that nature must be capable of interpretation in terms of a unified principle by recognizing only one basic substance, one fundamental form of Being, namely the atoms. This pure existence was contrasted with form and movement which personified the process of Becoming and caused the totality of events in nature. Plato, who in *Timaeus* accepted the ideas of atomic theory, distinguished five kinds of atoms, which differed in shape, and which were supposed to correspond to five basic substances. This assumption of five types of atoms could at first sight appear as a retrograde step, but basically Plato thought only of a single entity which happened to appear in different shapes. Nature's variety was the result of the diversity of mathematical structures. The whole wealth of life was reflected in the wealth of geometrical shapes which, themselves, were formed by that which really existed, the atoms.

I have briefly outlined this historical development because it makes quite plain the fundamental aim of atomic theory. It is to explain that the world consists, in the last resort, of a homogeneous substance, and that it is based on one unified principle. The multiplicity of phenomena has, somehow, to be related to the multiplicity of mathematical structures. Later developments add to these ideas the important conception of unalterable natural laws governing all events. Thus mathematical structures have been made to reach into the future, and allow us to predict future events. But these later developments adopt, almost unchanged, the basic ideas of atomic theory, and even at the present day they retain their creative power.

Before dealing with our modern problems from the point of view of those basic ideas, I should like to pursue their historical development a little further, because only such a background will enable us to understand the sense of the endeavours of our own time. At the beginning of the modern era (*Neuzeit*) the conception of basic substances developed from chemical experiences. Thus, since the seventeenth century, substances which could not be chemically further sub-divided, ranked as basic elements and all matter was to consist of them. We now know about ninety-five chemical elements which make up about half a million chemical compounds found in nature. To every such element was attributed a type of atom such as the carbon or oxygen atom, which themselves were thought to be indivisible and indestructible. The compound was formed by the arrangement of atoms of different elements in atomic groups, the so-called molecules, such an atomic group then representing the smallest unit of the chemical compound concerned.

This atomic physical interpretation of chemistry was finally successful at the end of the eighteenth century and henceforth it formed the basis for the great advances of chemistry, yet we can say that this victory of atomic theory did not do full justice to its basic conception. The world was supposed to have consisted, in the last resort, of a unified substance. But this basic demand had been lost sight of, for the assumption of nearly 100 different elements of whose mixtures all matter was to have consisted, implied a degree of complication totally opposed to the basic aim of atomic physics. In spite of this, such great successes were achieved that an atomic interpretation of chemistry was generally accepted. After all, it was an indisputable fact that chemical elements could not be further subdivided or transformed by chemical means.

However, as early as 1815, the Englishman Prout attempted to break through such views when he defended the hypothesis that all elements consisted ultimately of hydrogen. He formed this thesis as a result of observing atomic weights, which could for the first time be determined with reasonable accuracy. The atomic weights of many of the lighter elements were, fairly accurately, integral multiples of the lightest one, i.e. hydrogen. For instance, a helium atom is almost exactly four times as heavy as a hydrogen atom, so it was tempting to believe that an atom of helium consisted of four atoms of hydrogen. But it was another hundred years before we could be certain that the atoms of chemistry were not the final indivisible units of matter or, in other words, they were not really what the Greeks meant when they used the word atom.

Faraday's investigations, his discovery of the electron (i.e. the atom of electricity and radio-active radiation) led us finally to Rutherford and Bohr's famous atomic model and thus introduced the latest epoch of atomic physics. For almost forty years we have known that, with certain reservations, an atom of a chemical element has to be imagined as a planetary system on a minute scale. The largest part of its mass is concentrated in the atomic nucleus which is positively charged and whose diameter amounts to about 10^{-5} of the diameter of the atom. Round this nucleus circle the much lighter electrons whose number is just sufficient to neutralize the charge of the nucleus. The diameter of the outermost planetary orbit amounts in most atoms to about 10^{-7} millimetres. The reservations which I mentioned earlier are concerned with the basic difficulty of describing processes in an atom in the imagery of every-day language. It is true we know the natural laws which govern the movement of electrons round the nucleus so well that we can formulate them mathematically with complete accuracy, but we can only very roughly translate these laws into an imagery that can be visualized. This is because Planck's quantum hypothesis, on which these laws are based, contains an aspect which is not apprehensible in principle by visual images.

The shells of all atoms consist then of the same 'substance', namely of electrons, the lightest, negatively charged elementary particles. The diversity of types of atoms is a result of the diversity of atomic nuclei, which cannot be affected by chemical means. But we can bombard them with other elementary particles of high velocity and we find, as has been expected for some time, that the nucleus itself is composite, and also that one atomic nucleus can be transformed into another atomic nucleus. For some fifteen years we have known that all nuclei consist of two kinds of elementary units which we call protons and neutrons, protons being identical with the lightest nuclei, i.e. those of hydrogen, while neutrons are electrically neutral elementary particles of about the same mass as protons. We can tell how many protons and how many neutrons every atomic nucleus contains: thus, the nucleus of a hydrogen atom consists of one proton, the helium nucleus of two protons and two neutrons, the heavy nucleus of the uranium atom of 92 protons and 146 neutrons. The number of protons present determines the charge of the nucleus and hence the chemical properties of the atom.

The discovery that all atomic nuclei consisted of the same units led immediately to a problem soluble at least in theory, i.e. the artificial composition and decomposition of nuclei. Since Hahn's famous discovery that neutrons can cause the disintegration of uranium nuclei, the artificial disintegration and building up of nuclei has become an important branch of modern technology; we are now really able to transform one chemical element into another.

If we compare the present state of atomic physics with that of 150 years ago, we can immediately say that our modern views are much closer to the fundamental aim of atomic theory, which was an explanation of nature based on one homogeneous substance. In place of the hundred odd independent basic chemical substances we now have only three, which should more accurately be called three fundamental forms of matter, whose atoms we name electrons, protons and neutrons. All matter, dead or living, consists of these three kinds of elementary particles and of nothing else. Qualitative differences are caused by different arrangements and relative positions of these three basic units. The multiplicity of possible phenomena finds its reflection in the multiplicity of mathematical structures which can be realized with these three basic forms of Being.

This last point is characteristic not only of atomic physics but of the whole of exact science and I should like to treat it in greater detail, using chemistry as an example. We know accurately the laws which govern the movement of electrons round the nucleus. Hence every possible state of atoms, say in a complex molecule, must correspond to a solution of the equations representing those natural laws. Thus our mathematical formulations are richer in content than those of the Greeks; we are no longer restricted to geometrical structures but we use complicated systems of differential equations which can, especially in the case of atomic physics, be defined in multidimensional space. The totality of solutions of such equations corresponds to the totality of all possible states of atoms, the wide variety of possible chemical compounds being depicted by the totality of possible solutions of Schrödinger's differential equations.

However, in considering three basic substances, i.e. three kinds of elementary particles—electrons, protons and neutrons—as the component parts of all matter, we have not altogether covered the programme of atomic physics. We are reaching here the real aim of modern atomic physics. If only these three elementary particles existed, we could rest satisfied in the belief that there are three fundamentally different sorts of matter which can no longer be transformed into one another or related to one another. But in reality there are yet other forms of manifestation of matter, the most important being radiation. Since the famous formula of relativity theory has linked energy and mass, we know that every form of energy also possesses mass and that it can therefore be called a form of matter. According to Planck and Einstein, energy in radiation is concentrated in so-called light-quanta which can also be regarded as some kind of elementary particle. But beyond that, still other elementary particles have been found. In the early thirties Anderson discovered the positive electron which can be created in the transformation of radiation into matter when, occasionally, a high energy light quantum, for instance in X-radiation, passes close to a nucleus and produces a negative and a positive electron. A little later, Anderson found a further elementary particle which was a result of cosmic radiation in the atmosphere. It is about 200 times heavier than an electron and now goes by the name 'Meson'. Mesons have, however, a very short life, disappearing after something like a millionth of a second and changing into one electron and one other neutral elementary particle. Finally there have recently been discovered still other elementary particles which also have very short lives.

In the face of this development of atomic physics in the last few years it may easily appear as though atomic theory is again losing sight of its fundamental aim, as though the assumption of three basic substances was again being replaced by more complicated assumptions. This question raises immediately the problematical nature of modern nuclear physics. Our present concepts still seem to be too simple: there are many indications that further elementary particles exist which have not yet been observed because they have an extremely short life. Also, another important fact has been found experimentally: elementary particles can change into one another, and the characteristic of indestructibility no longer applies in the old sense, e.g. a collision between a neutron and a proton can produce a meson. This is a process characteristic in general for the collision of two elementary particles of high energy. In such an impact some new elementary particles are frequently formed and this happens the more, the higher the total energy available is. The process is best described if we say that the total available energy of the impact is used in a statistical manner to form elementary particles, and that it is distributed among these particles. The particles thus created have a definite mass and other definite properties, some of them being well-known elementary particles. Particles of the same kind are always identical in their properties and to that extent they are uniform; but they can be transformed into one another.

This step which has only been accepted in the last few years does, however, take us close to the real aim of atomic theory. Just as the Greeks had hoped, so we have now found there is only one fundamental substance of which all reality consists. If we have to give this substance a name, we can only call it 'energy'. But this fundamental 'energy' is capable of existence in different forms. It always appears in definite quanta which we consider the smallest indivisible units of all matter and which, for purely historical reasons, we do not call atoms but elementary particles. Among the basic forms of energy there are three specially stable kinds: electrons, protons and neutrons. Matter, in the real sense, consists of these with the addition of energy of motion. Then there are particles which always travel with the velocity of light and which embody radiation, and finally other forms with a short life of which only a few have been discovered so far. The variety of natural phenomena is thus created by the diversity of the manifestations of energy, just as the Greek natural philosophers had anticipated. If we wish to understand all these manifestations we should be able to represent them in mathematical form, in the last resort, simply by the totality of solutions of a system of equations, and it is here that we come up against the decisive problem of modern atomic theory. It is that the mathematical formulations which describe the properties of elementary particles are not yet entirely known, but only knowledge of them will enable us to predict the results of experiments, that is, to master events in the same manner as physics has done up to now. We can also see that little has been gained by the definition of one fundamental substance since all the wealth of phenomena is harboured by its manifestations. What understanding of matter we have achieved has finally been written down in mathematical equations, for no other language can dispose of such a wealth of expressions. Thus we can say that the real task of atomic physics in the next few years or decades will remain the experimental discovery and mathematical formulation of those natural laws which determine all the properties of elementary particles and their combinations. The discovery of a new particle in cosmic radiation will, for instance, provide us with new information about those laws. If extensive mathematical investigations are carried out to study the properties of bi-linear forms (used to represent observable quantities in modern nuclear theory) then we may discover something of the mathematical formulations which, in future theory, will describe also the properties of elementary particles.

Perhaps I may say a few words here about the peculiar difficulties with which we have to contend. In any mathematical description of nature we have to introduce certain mathematical symbols which are used for formulating equations which, in their turn, represent natural laws, e.g. we use symbols for the position and velocity of particles in Newtonian mechanics. If, however, we make use of any of the common symbols, such as the co-ordinates of a particle, we are already tacitly implying the existence of a given particle. Yet it is the decisive point of this last stage of atomic physics that particles can no longer be taken for granted, since we want to understand their existence and their properties; thus we cannot sensibly assume co-ordinates and mass of definite particles. The question arises as to what we can use. We have not yet really developed the mathematical tools which would grasp the complex events on a nuclear scale. It could, of course, be said that though particles cannot be definitely *given* but have to be *determined* they will nevertheless possess position and mass so that these variables can in any case be introduced into the equation. But is it really true that particles have position? They certainly have position with a considerable degree of accuracy, but are there not likely to occur similar and perhaps even more stringent limitations of accuracy such as have appeared in quantum mechanics? We can see what great difficulties atomic theory has to master here. Yet it is quite conceivable that in the not too distant future we shall be able to write down a single equation from which will follow the properties of matter in general.

If we really succeed in this, atomic theory will have reached its ultimate goal, and it may be worth finding out just what we shall have achieved. First, we shall have understood the unity of all matter in the sense in which the Greeks used that phrase. All matter consists of the same substance, energy which manifests itself in different forms, and the totality of these forms is governed by the totality of solutions of a system of equations. That would mean that the results of experiments in atomic physics could be predicted, at least in principle. We can also assume that these mathematical forms would not only apply to the branch of atomic physics, since even present-day atomic physics contains, at least in principle, chemistry, mechanics, optics, heat and electricity, and this will certainly apply to the atomic theory of the future. When we use so frequently the expression 'in principle' as a limitation, we mean that in most cases the complete mathematical mastery of a problem is technically impossible, for our mathematics just cannot cope with such complications. It is therefore not at all certain that the solution of the fundamental problem will yield much that is of use in practical application. But the expression 'in principle' means also that a solution of the fundamental questions can be of use in all cases where we have to deal with a solution of a specific problem.

There are, however, two counts on which we should question how far modern atomic theory would have satisfied Greek philosophers. The mathematical forms in the minds of the Greeks were geometrical shapes which could be visualized and which were, so to speak, traced in empty space by the atoms. Can the mathematical forms of our atomic theory be similarly visualized? Secondly, Greek atomic theory set out to describe the properties of all reality, mental processes and living organisms as well as purely material processes. Democritus said: 'there are only atoms and empty space.' Does modern atomic theory relate only to a narrower field and are we to assume that there exists, apart from atoms, something else—for instance, a soul? Or does our theory also maintain that 'there are only atoms and empty space'?

The first question has often been dealt with. In fact our modern atomic physics is much less visualizable than earlier scientists had hoped. But we have been reconciled to this because nature has taught us that it is closely and consistently linked with the existence of atoms. We could put it like this, though it would be a little inaccurate : anything that can be imagined and visualized cannot be indivisible. The indivisibility and homogeneity, in principle, of elementary particles makes it quite understandable that the mathematical forms of atomic theory can hardly be visualized. It would even seem unnatural if atoms lacked all the general qualities of matter like colour, smell, taste, tensile strength, and had yet retained geometrical properties. It is much more plausible to think that all these properties can be attributed to an atom only with the same reservations, and such reservations may also later enable us to relate space and matter more closely. The two concepts, atom and empty space, would then no longer stand side by side yet be completely independent of one another ; in this our atomic theory is even more consistent than that of the Greeks.

The second question will have to be discussed somewhat more fully. The statement that 'there are only atoms' meant to the Greeks, that all events, material and spiritual, must somehow be seen as movements of atoms. This would also apply to modern physics in-so-far as all processes are linked with changes in energy, and because of the atomic structure of energy, therefore linked with the movement of atoms. But the concepts 'soul' or 'life' certainly do not occur in atomic physics and they could not, even indirectly, be derived as complicated consequences of some natural law. Their existence certainly does not indicate the presence of any fundamental substance other than energy but it shows only the action of other kinds of forms which we cannot match with the mathematical forms of modern atomic physics. It follows that the mathematical structures of atomic physics are limited in their applicability to certain fields of experience and that, if we want to describe living or mental processes, we shall have to broaden these structures. It may be that we shall have to introduce yet other concepts which can be linked, without contradiction, with our existing systems of concepts. It may also become necessary to limit the range of previous concepts of atomic theory by attaching specific new conditions to them. In both cases we could regard such an extension as a broadened form of atomic theory and not as a theory describing only fundamentally different events.

If we accept such a wide definition of atomic theory we can immediately see how far removed we are from its completion. It would in fact amount to equating 'atomic theory' with a description of all reality, and this task will of course be infinite and will never be completed. We can only imagine a conclusion of atomic theory if we accept it in the limited sense I have sketched above. It would only have to deal with the special mathematical forms which serve for a description of the properties of elementary particles and the laws governing their transmutations at high energies. These mathematical forms may be very far-reaching but we cannot predict the magnitude of their range.

Even if we accept the second interpretation of the idea 'atomic theory', i.e. that 'there are only atoms and empty space' the materialism implied would in no way denote the anti-spiritual tendency which we commonly attach to this word. I hope that my previous explanations will have made that clear.

It may even be asked if we can still speak of materialism in this context. Let us seriously contemplate 'Just as tragedy and comedy can be written using the same letters so many varied events in this world can be realized by the same atoms as long as they take up different positions and describe different movements.'

It is important that we should understand the 'handwriting' of atoms for it is something which has not been thought out by man; it has far deeper meaning. Even when we shall have mastered and understood it, let us not forget that it is the content not the words which is important in a tragedy or comedy and that this also holds good for our world.

[11]

GEORGE GAMOW

The Creation of the Universe *

"Give me matter and I will construct a world out of it."—Immanuel Kant, *Allgemeine Naturgeschichte und Theorie des Himmels.*

The problems of cosmogony—that is, the theory of the origin of the world—have perplexed the human mind ever since the dawn of history. Among the ancients, the origin of the world was necessarily associated with a creative act by some deity, who separated light from darkness, raised and fixed the heavens high above the surface of the earth, and fashioned all the other features that characterized the highly limited world picture of early man.

As the centuries rolled by and men gradually accumulated knowledge about the various phenomena taking place in the world that formed their environment, the theories of cosmogony took a more scientific shape. The names of Buffon, Kant, and Laplace characterize the scientific era when the first attempts were made to understand the origin of the world exclusively as the result of natural causes. The theories of that time, which were limited essentially to the origin of our solar system, later underwent a process of multiple evolution; culminating in a reasonably complete and

* Published by The Viking Press, New York, 1952; Introduction (pp. 3–5) and Conclusion (pp. 137–139) reprinted by permission of the author and the publisher.

consistent theory of planetary formation recently developed by Carl von Weizsäcker and Gerard P. Kuiper.

In the meantime the progress of observational astronomy opened entirely new horizons of knowledge of the universe and reduced the old riddle of the birth of planets to a minor incident within a much broader picture of the evolution of the universe. The main problem of cosmogony today is to explain the origin and evolution of the giant stellar families, known as galaxies, which are scattered through the vast expanses of the universe as far as can be seen with the strongest telescopes. The key factor for the understanding of this large-scale cosmic evolution was provided about a quarter-century ago by a discovery of the American astronomer Edwin P. Hubble. Hubble found that the galaxies populating the space of the universe are in a state of rapid dispersion ("expanding universe"). This implies that once upon a time all the matter of the universe must have been uniformly squeezed into a continuous mass of hot gas. The close correlation between the observed phenomenon of expansion and certain mathematical consequences of Einstein's general theory of relativity was first recognized by an imaginative Belgian scientist, Abbé Georges Edouard Lemaître, who formulated an ambitious program for explaining the highly complex structure of the universe known to us today as the result of successive stages of differentiation which must have taken place as a concomitant of the expansion of the originally homogenous primordial material. If and when such a program is carried through in all details, we shall have a complete system of cosmogony that will satisfy the principal aim of science by reducing the observed complexity of natural phenomena to the smallest possible number of initial assumptions. Although such a program is far from completion as of today, considerable progress has been made on various parts of it, and the end seems to be already in sight.

It must be remarked here that at present there still exist rather fundamental differences between the points of view accepted by various scientists working in this field. Many of them (including the author of the present book) believe that the present state of the universe resulted from a continuous evolutionary process, which started in a highly compressed homogeneous material a few billion years ago—the hypothesis of "beginning." Others prefer to consider the universe as existing in about the same state throughout eternity—the hypothesis of a "steady-state universe." One of the proponents of the latter view in the field of stellar evolution is the noted Russian astronomer Vorontzoff-Velyaminov,[1] who was apparently forced by the philosophy of dialectic materialism to accept this hypothesis. In a rather different form, and certainly for an entirely different reason, similar views are held by the British astronomer Fred Hoyle,[2] who attempts to explain the alleged steady state of the universe by introducing a hypothesis of continuous creation of matter in intergalactic space. . . .

CONCLUSION

We now come to the end of our discourse, and picture of the creative process begins to emerge—somewhat hazy and fragmentary but in its general outlines quite definite. In the dim pregalactic past we perceive a glimpse of a metaphysical "St. Augustine's Era" when the universe, whatever it was made of, was involved in a gigantic collapse. Of course, we have no information about that era, which could have lasted from the minus infinity of time to about three billion years ago, since all "archaeological records" pertaining to that distant past must have been completely obliterated when the cosmic masses were squeezed into a pulp. The masses of the universe must have emerged from the Big Squeeze in a completely broken-up state, forming the primordial Ylem * of neutrons, protons, and electrons. As the Ylem cooled rapidly through expansion, these elementary particles began to stick to one another, forming aggregates of different complexities which were the prototypes of the atomic nuclei of today. During this early period of "nuclear cooking," which lasted not more than an hour of time, conditions throughout the universe closely approximated those existing in the center of an exploding atomic bomb. Cosmic space was full of high-energy gamma radiation, the mass-density of which greatly exceeded the density of ordinary atomic matter. The temperature throughout the universe was in the neighborhood of a billion degrees, but the density of matter was comparable to the density of atmospheric air at high altitudes.

Following that highly productive first hour of the history of our universe, nothing in particular happened for the next 30 million years. The gas, consisting of the newly formed atoms, continued to expand, and its temperature became lower and lower. Radiant energy, which at the beginning played a predominant role in the evolutionary process, gradually lost its importance and by the end of the thirty-millionth year yielded its priority in favor of ordinary atomic matter. As soon as matter took over, the force of Newtonian gravity, which represents one of the most important characteristics of "ponderable" matter, came into play, breaking up the hitherto homogeneous gas into gigantic clouds, the proto-galaxies. In that era the temperature dropped to approximately that which we call "room temperature," so that space was still rather warm, although completely dark.

While the original proto-galaxies were being driven farther and farther apart by continued expansion, material in their interiors began to condense into a multitude of much smaller aggregations, called proto-stars. Because of the comparatively small size of these proto-stars their contraction progressed quite rapidly. Very soon the temperature in their interiors

---

* From the Greek ὕλη, "the first substance from which the elements were supposed to be formed" (Webster's Dictionary).—Editor.

reached the value at which nuclear reactions between hydrogen and various light elements would take place, and space became bright again, being illuminated by myriads of stars. When the stars were formed by the condensation of the gaseous material of the proto-galaxies, some of that material was left over in their vicinity and from it sprang planetary systems. The planets were too small to create their own sources of nuclear energy; they cooled off fast and developed solid rocky crusts. With the help of the radiations from their respective suns, certain chemical compounds which were present on the surfaces of these planets went through an evolutionary process, as yet not well understood, by which organic materials of higher and higher complexity were developed. Thus the naked rocky surfaces of the planets were presently covered by the green carpets of woods and meadows. Animals appeared, first primitive and then more and more complicated, finally evolving into the human being who is intelligent enough to ask and to answer questions concerning the events which took place billions of years before he came into existence.

Probably one of the most striking conclusions from our inquiry into the history of the universe is the fact that the main evolutionary events of physical development occupied only such a tiny fraction of the total period. This, of course, only means that organic evolution takes place at a much slower rate than the large-scale physical processes in the universe.

Indeed, it took less than an hour to make the atoms, a few hundred million years to make the stars and planets, but three billion years to make man!

[12]

NORBERT WIENER

What Is Cybernetics? *

I have been occupied for many years with problems of communication engineering. These have led to the design and investigation of various sorts of communication machines, some of which have shown an uncanny ability to simulate human behavior, and thereby to throw light on the possible nature of human behavior. They have even shown the existence of a tremendous possibility of replacing human behavior, in many cases in which the human being is relatively slow and ineffective. We are thus in an immediate need of discussing the powers of these machines as they

* From *The Human Use of Human Beings: Cybernetics and Society* by Norbert Wiener. Houghton Mifflin Co., Boston. Copyright, 1950, by Norbert Wiener. Ch. I. By permission of the author and publisher.

impinge on the human being, and the consequences of this new and fundamental revolution in technique.

To those of us who are engaged in constructive research and in invention, there is a serious moral risk of aggrandizing what we have accomplished. To the public, there is an equally serious moral risk of supposing that in stating new potentials of fact, we scientists and engineers are thereby justifying and even urging their exploitation at any costs. It will therefore be taken for granted by many that the attitude of an investigator who is aware of the great new possibilities of the machine age, when employed for the purpose of communication and control, will be to urge the prompt exploitation of this new "know-how" for the sake of the machine and for the minimization of the human element in life. This is most emphatically not the purpose of the present book.

The purpose of this book is both to explain the potentialities of the machine in fields which up to now have been taken to be purely human, and to warn against the dangers of a purely selfish exploitation of these possibilities in a world in which to human beings, human things are all-important.

That we shall have to change many details of our mode of life in the face of the new machines is certain; but these machines are secondary in all matters of value that concern us to the proper evaluation of human beings for their own sake and to their employment as human beings, and not as second-rate surrogates for possible machines of the future. The message of this book as well as its title is *the human use of human beings*.

The problem of the definition of man is an odd one. To say that man is a featherless biped is merely to put him in the same class as a plucked chicken, a kangaroo, or a jerboa. This is a rather heterogeneous group, and it can be extended to our heart's content without throwing any further light on the true nature of man. It will not do to say that man is an animal with a soul. Unfortunately, the existence of the soul, whatever it may mean, is not available to the scientific methods of behaviorism; and although the Church assures us that men have souls and dogs do not, an equally authoritative institution known as Buddhism holds a different view.

What does differentiate man from other animals in a way which leaves us not the slightest degree of doubt, is that he is a talking animal. The impulse to communicate with his fellow beings is so strong that not even the double deprivation of blindness and deafness can completely obliterate it. It is not only that with adequate training the blind deaf-mute may become a Laura Bridgman or a Helen Keller, but even more, that without any training whatever, a Helen Keller will make a desperate attempt to break the almost impregnable barrier which separates her from the rest of the world. There are animals besides man which are social, and live in a continuous relation to their fellow creatures, but there is none in whom this desire for communication, or rather this necessity for communication, is the guiding motive of their whole life. What then is this communication, which is so human and so essential? I shall devote this chapter and indeed the greater part of this book to the introduction of concepts and theories contributing to the answer to this question.

One of the most interesting aspects of the world is that it can be considered to be made up of *patterns*. A pattern is essentially an arrangement. It is characterized by the order of the elements of which it is made, rather than by the intrinsic nature of these elements. Two patterns are identical if their relational structure can be put into a one-to-one correspondence, so that to each term of the one there corresponds a term of the other; and that to each relation of order between several terms of one, there corresponds a similar relation of order between the corresponding terms of the other. The simplest case of one-to-one correspondence is given by the ordinary process of counting. If I have five pennies in my pocket, and five apples in a basket, I can put my apples in a row, and lay one penny beside each. Each penny will correspond to one apple and one apple only, and each apple will correspond to one penny and one penny only.

However, the notion of one-to-one correspondence is not confined to finite sets, which can be given a number in the sense of elementary arithmetic. For example, the pattern of the sequence of whole numbers from 1 on is identical with that of the sequence of even numbers, since we can assign as a counterpart to each number its double, and since the before-and-after relations of the doubles will be the same as those of the original numbers. Again, a copy of a painting, if it is accurately made, will have the same pattern as the original, while a less perfect copy will have a pattern which is in some sense similar to that of the original.

The pattern of a thing may be spread out in space, as for example, the pattern of a wallpaper; or it may be distributed in time, as the pattern of a musical composition. The pattern of a musical composition again suggests the pattern of a telephone conversation, or the pattern of dots and dashes of a telegram. These two types of pattern are given the special designation of messages, not because their pattern itself differs in any way from the pattern of a musical composition, but because it is used in a somewhat different manner: namely, to convey information from one point to another, and even from one remote point to another.

A pattern which is conceived to convey information, or something transmissible from individual to individual, is not taken as an isolated phenomenon. To telegraph is to convey a message by the proper use of dots and dashes; and here it is necessary that these dots and dashes be a selection from among a set which contains other possibilities as well. If I am sending the letter *e*, it gains its meaning in part because I have not sent the letter *o*. If my only choice is to send the letter *e*, then the message is merely something that is either there or not there; and it conveys much less information.

In the early days of telephone engineering, the mere sending of a message was so much of a miracle that nobody asked how it should best be sent. The lines were able to take care of all the information forced on them, and the real difficulties were in the design of the terminal apparatus at the sending and receiving ends. Under these conditions, the problems concerning the maximum carrying capacity of telephone lines were not yet of any importance. However, as the art developed, and ways were found to compress several messages into a single line by the use of carriers and other similar means, economy in sending speech over the telephone lines began to develop an economic importance. Let me explain what we mean by "carriers" and by "carrier-telephony."

A mathematical theorem due to Fourier states that every motion within very broad limits can be represented as a sum of the very simplest sort of vibrations which give rise to pure musical notes. A way has been found to take an oscillation on an electric line, and to shift each one of the notes that make it up, by a certain constant pitch. In this manner, we may take a pattern in which several subsidiary patterns would otherwise be placed on top of each other, and separate them so that they are placed side by side in positions, and do not produce a mere confusion. Thus we may run three lines together in the typewriter in such a way that they are superimposed and blurred, or we may write them in their proper sequence, and keep them separate. This process of moving different messages into separate positions of pitch is known as *modulation*.

After modulation, the message may be sent over a line which is already carrying a message, if the displacement in pitch is sufficient. Under proper conditions, the message already transmitted and the new message will not affect one another; and it is possible to recover from the line both the original undisplaced message and the modulated message, in such a way that they go to separate terminal equipment. The modulated message may then be subjected to a process which is the inverse of modulation, and may be reduced to the form which it originally had before it was entrusted to the apparatus. Thus two messages may be sent along the same telephone line. By an extension of this process, many more than two messages may be sent over the same line. This process is known as carrier-telephony, and has vastly extended the usefulness of our telephone lines without any correspondingly great increase in investment.

Since the introduction of carrier methods, telephone lines have been used at a high efficiency of message transmission. Thus the question of how much information can be sent over a line has become significant, and with this, the measurement of information in general. This has been made more acute by the discovery that the very existence of electric currents in a line is the cause of what is called *line noise,* which blurs the messages, and offers an upper limit to their ability to carry information.

The earlier work on the theory of information was vitiated by the fact that it ignored noise-levels and other quantities of a somewhat random nature. It was only when the idea of randomness was fully understood, together with the applications of the related notions of probability, that the question of the carrying capacity of a telegraph or telephone line could even be asked intelligently. When this question was asked, it became clear that the problem of measuring the amount of information was of a piece with the related problem of the measurement of the regularity and irregularity of a pattern. It is quite clear that a haphazard sequence of symbols or a pattern which is purely haphazard can convey no information. Information thus must be in some way the measure of the regularity of a pattern, and in particular of the sort of pattern known as *time series*. By time series, I mean a pattern in which the parts are spread in time. This regularity is to a certain extent an abnormal thing. The irregular is always commoner than the regular. Therefore, whatever definition of information and its measure we shall introduce must be something which grows when the *a priori* probability of a pattern or a time series diminishes. We shall later find the proper numerical measure for the amount of information. This range of ideas was already familiar in the branch of physics known as statistical mechanics, and was associated with the famous second law of thermodynamics, which asserts that a system may lose order and regularity spontaneously, but that it practically never gains it.

A little later in this chapter, I shall give this law its proper statement in terms of the scientific notion of *entropy* which I shall then define. For the present this qualitative formulation of the law will suffice. The notion of information has proved to be subject to a similar law—that is, a message can lose order spontaneously in the act of transmission, but cannot gain it. For example, if one talks into a telephone with a great deal of line noise, and a great deal of loss of energy of the main message, the person at the other end may miss words that have been spoken, and may have to reconstruct them on the basis of the significant information of the context. Again, if a book is translated from one language into another, there does not exist that precise equivalence between the two languages which will permit the translation to have exactly the same meaning as the original. Under these conditions, the translator has only two alternatives: namely, to use phrases which are a little broader and vaguer than those of the original, and which certainly fail to contain its entire emotional context, or to falsify the original by introducing a message which is not precisely there, and which conveys his own meaning rather than that of the author. In either case, some of the author's meaning is lost.

An interesting application of the concept of amount of information is to the elaborate telegraph messages which are offered at Christmas or birthdays or other special occasions. The message may cover a whole page of text, but what is sent is just a code symbol such as *B7*, meaning the seventh coded message to be sent on birthdays. Such special messages are only possible because the sentiments expressed are merely conventional and repetitive. The moment the sender shows any originality in the sentiments he desires to convey, the reduced rates are no longer available. The meaning of the cheap-rate message is disproportionately small compared with the length of the message. We again see that the message is a transmitted pattern, which acquires its meaning by being a selection from a large number of possible patterns. The amount of meaning can be measured. It turns out that the less probable a message is, the more meaning it carries, which is entirely reasonable from the standpoint of our common sense.[1]

We ordinarily think of a message as sent from human being to human being. This need not be the case at all. If, being lazy, instead of getting out of bed in the morning, I press a button which turns on the heat, closes the window, and starts an electric heating unit under the coffeepot, I am sending messages to all these pieces of apparatus. If on the other hand, the electric egg boiler starts a whistle going after a certain number of minutes, it is sending me a message. If the thermostat records that the room is too warm, and turns off the oil burner, the message may be said to be a method of control of the oil burner. Control, in other words, is nothing but the sending of messages which effectively change the behavior of the recipient.

It is this study of messages, and in particular of the effective messages of control, which constitutes the science of *Cybernetics*,[2] which I christened in an earlier book. Its name signifies the art of pilot or steersman. Let it be noted that the word "governor" in a machine is simply the latinized Greek word for steersman.

It is the thesis of this book that society can only be understood through a study of the messages and the communication facilities which belong to it; and that in the future development of these messages and communication facilities, messages between man and machines, between machine and man, and between machine and machine, are destined to play an ever-increasing part.

To indicate the rôle of the message in man, let us compare human activity with activity of a very different sort; namely, the activity of the little figures which dance on the top of a music box. These figures dance in accordance with a pattern, but it is a pattern which is set in advance, and in which the past activity of the figures has practically nothing to do with the pattern of their future activity. There is a message, indeed; but it goes from the machinery of the music box to the figures, and stops there. The figures themselves have not a trace of any communication with the outer world, except this one-way stage of communication with the music box. They are blind, deaf, and dumb, and cannot vary their activity in the least from the conventionalized pattern.

Contrast with them the behavior of man, or indeed of any moderately intelligent animal such as a kitten. I call to the kitten and it looks up. I have sent it a message which it has received by its sensory organs, and which it registers in action. The kitten is hungry and lets out a pitiful wail. This time it is the sender of a message. The kitten bats at a swinging spool. The spool swings to the left, and the kitten catches it with its left paw. This time messages of a very complicated nature are both sent and received. The kitten is informed of the motion of its own paw by organs called proprioceptors or kinaesthetic organs. These organs are certain nerve end-bodies to be found in its joints, in its muscles, and in its tendons;

and by means of nervous messages sent by these organs, the animal is aware of the actual position and tensions of its tissues. It is only through these organs that anything like a skill is possible, not to mention the extreme dexterity of the kitten.

I have contrasted the behavior of the little figures on the music box on the one hand, and the human and animal behavior on the other. It might be supposed that the music box was an example typical of all machine behavior, in contrast to the behavior of living organisms. This is not so. The older machines, and in particular the older attempts to produce automata, did in fact work on a closed clockwork basis. On the other hand, the machines of the present day possess sense organs; that is, receptors for messages coming from the outside. These may be as simple as photoelectric cells which change electrically when a light falls on them, and which can tell light from dark. They may be as complicated as a television set. They may measure a tension by the change it produces in the conductivity of a wire exposed to it. They may measure temperature by means of a thermocouple, which is an instrument consisting of two distinct metals in contact with one another through which a current flows when one of the points of contact is heated. Every instrument in the repertory of the scientific-instrument maker is a possible sense organ, and may be made to record its reading remotely through the intervention of appropriate electrical apparatus. Thus the machine which is conditioned by its relation to the external world, and by the things happening in the external world, is with us and has been with us for some time.

The machine which acts on the external world by means of messages is also familiar. The automatic photo-electric door opener is known to every person who has passed through the Pennsylvania Station in New York, and is used in many other buildings as well. When the message constituted by the interception of a beam of light is sent to the apparatus, this message actuates the door, and opens it so that the passenger may go through.

The steps between the actuation of a machine of this type by sense organs and its performance of a task may be as simple as in the case of the electric door; or it may be in fact of any desired degree of complexity. A complex action is one in which the combination of the data introduced, which we call the *input*, to obtain an effect on the outer world, which we call the *output*, may involve a large number of combinations. These are combinations, both of the data put in at the moment and of the records taken from the past stored data which we call the *memory*. These are recorded in the machine. The most complicated machines yet made which transform input data into output data are the high-speed electrical computing machines, of which I shall speak later in more detail. The determination of the mode of conduct of these machines is given through a special sort of input, which frequently consists of punched cards or tapes or of magnetized wires, and which determines the way in which the machine is going to act in one operation, as distinct from the way in which it might have acted in another. Because of the frequent use of punched or magnetic tape in the control, the data which are fed in, and which indicate the mode of operation of one of these machines for combining information, are called the *taping*. I illustrate the situation by means of the following conventionalized diagram.

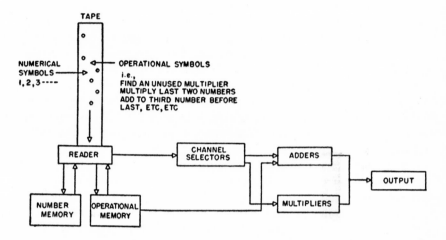

A TYPICAL TAPING SYSTEM

I have said that man and the animal have a kinaesthetic sense, by which they keep a record of the position and tensions of their muscles. For any machine subject to a varied external environment, in order to act effectively it is necessary that information concerning the results of its own action be furnished to it as part of the information on which it must continue to act. For example, if we are running an elevator, it is not enough to open the outside door because the orders we have given should make the elevator be at that door at the time we open it. It is important that the release for opening the door be dependent on the fact that the elevator is actually at the door, otherwise something might have detained it, and the passenger might step into the empty shaft. This control of a machine on the basis of its *actual* performance rather than its *expected* performance is known as *feedback,* and involves sensory members which are actuated by motor members and perform the function of *tell-tales* or *monitors*—that is, of elements which indicate a performance.

I have just mentioned the elevator as an example of feed-back. There are other cases where feedback is even more essential. For example, a gun-pointer takes information from his instruments of observation, and conveys it to the gun, so that the latter will point in such a direction that the missile will pass through the moving target at some time. Now, the gun itself must be used under all conditions of weather. In some of these the grease is warm, and the gun swings easily and rapidly. Under other conditions the grease is frozen or mixed with sand, and the gun is slow to answer the orders given to it. If these orders are reinforced by an extra

push given when the gun fails to respond easily to the orders and lags
behind them, then the error of the gun-pointer will be decreased. In order
to obtain a performance as uniform as possible, it is customary to put into
the gun a control feedback element which reads the lag of the gun behind
the position it should have according to the orders given it, and which
uses this difference to give the gun an extra push.

It is true that precautions must be taken so that the push is not
too hard, for if it is, the gun will swing past its proper position, and will
have to be pulled back in a series of oscillations, which may well become
wider and wider, and lead to a disastrous instability. If the feedback is
controlled and kept within limits sufficiently stringent, this will not occur,
and the existence of the feedback will increase the stability of performance
of the gun. In other words, the performance will become less dependent
on the frictional load; or what is the same thing, on the drag created by
the stiffness of the grease.

Something very similar to this occurs in human action. If I pick up
my cigar, I do not will to move any specific muscles. Indeed in many cases,
I do not know what those muscles are. What I do is to turn into action a
certain feedback mechanism; namely, a reflex in which the amount by
which I have yet failed to pick up the cigar is turned into a new and increased order to the lagging muscles, whichever they may be. In this way,
a fairly uniform voluntary command will enable the same task to be performed from widely varying initial positions, and irrespective of the
decrease of contraction due to fatigue of the muscles. Similarly, when I
drive a car, I do not follow out a series of commands dependent simply
on a mental image of the road and the task I am doing. If I find the car
swerving too much to the left, that causes me to turn it to the right; and
if I find it swerving too much to the right, that causes me to pull it to the
left. This depends on the actual performance of the car, and not simply
on the road; and it allows me to drive with nearly equal efficiency a light
Austin or a heavy truck, without having formed separate habits for the
driving of the two. I shall have more to say about this in the chapter in
this book on special machines, where we shall discuss the service that can
be done to neuropathology by the study of machines with defects in performance similar to those occurring in the human mechanism.

It is my thesis that the operation of the living individual and the
operation of some of the newer communication machines are precisely
parallel. Both of them have sensory receptors as one stage in their cycle
of operation: that is, in both of them there exists a special apparatus for
collecting information from the outer world at low energy levels, and for
making it available in the operation of the individual or of the machine.
In both cases these external messages are not taken *neat*, but through the
internal transforming powers of the apparatus, whether it be alive or dead.
The information is then turned into a new form available for the further
stages of performance. In both the animal and the machine this performance is made to be effective on the outer world. In both of them, their

performed action on the outer world, and not merely their *intended* action, is reported back to the central regulatory apparatus. This complex of behavior is ignored by the average man, and in particular does not play the rôle that it should in our habitual analysis of society.

This is true whether we consider human beings alone, or in conjunction with types of automata which participate in a two-way relation with the world about them. In this, our view of society differs from the ideal of society which is held by many Fascists, Strong Men in Business, and Government. Similar men of ambition for power are not entirely unknown in scientific and educational institutions. Such people prefer an organization in which all orders come from above, and none return. The human beings under them have been reduced to the level of effectors for a supposedly higher nervous organism. I wish to devote this book to a protest against this inhuman use of human beings; for in my mind, any use of a human being in which less is demanded of him and less is attributed to him than his full status is a degradation and a waste. It is a degradation to a human being to chain him to an oar and use him as source of power; but it is an almost equal degradation to assign him a purely repetitive task in a factory, which demands less than a millionth of his brain capacity. It is simpler to organize a factory or galley which uses individual human beings for a trivial fraction of their worth than it is to provide a world in which they can grow to their full stature. Those who suffer from a power complex find the mechanization of man a simple way to realize their ambitions. I say, that this easy path to power is in fact not only a rejection of everything that I consider to be of moral worth in the human race, but also a rejection of our now very tenuous opportunities for a considerable period of human survival.

The rest of this book is devoted to the development of this theme. In every chapter, we are studying either those respects in which the machine duplicates man, or those aspects of man which appear clearer in view of our study of the machine, or both. We begin with the two notions of *entropy* and of *progress*: notions which are completely necessary for the understanding of the orientation of man in the world, and notions which have been sadly misunderstood. We discuss the communicative behavior of man, as contrasted with that of the ant; and thereby are given a clearer idea of the function of learning in human society. Three more chapters are devoted to the problem of language, both in man and in the machine; and to those aspects of man in which human individuality resembles something essentially linguistic. We have a few words to say about law, and many to say about those widely misunderstood notions, secrecy and intellectual property. In the ninth chapter, we define and criticize the rôles of those two priests of communication in the modern world: the literary intellectual and the scientist. The tenth and eleventh chapters are devoted to the machine, and to the great changes it has made and may be expected to make in the life of the human being of the present generation. Finally, we devote one chapter to the study of certain specific influences, in appearance very different from one another, and in nature very similar, which furnish the chief stumbling blocks to a proper understanding of what communication should mean to us, and to a proper development of communication itself.

APPENDIX

An adequate measure of the amount of meaning should add the amount of meaning of completely independent messages. Now, there is another way of combining quantities related to information, in which we do not add these quantities. If we have two events, each of which occurs with a certain probability, and if there is no connection whatever between them, the joint event of their both occurring will have a probability which is the product of the probabilities of the separate events. For example, if we throw two dice, and there is a probability of one-sixth that each of them independently will show an ace, then the probability of throwing two aces is one-thirty-sixth. If we have two packs of cards, the probability of drawing a king in each pack will be one-thirteenth, and the probability of drawing a king separately from the other pack will be one-thirteenth, so that the probability of drawing a king separately from each pack will be a one-hundred-and-sixty-ninth, which is one-thirteenth of one-thirteenth. The probability of drawing two kings from one pack, if it is fairly shuffled, will be the probability of drawing one king the first time, which is one-thirteenth, multiplied by the probability of drawing a king the second time, in which case we have three favorable possibilities out of fifty-one; so that the probability of the second drawing independently is three-fifty-firsts, or one-seventeenth.

Since probabilities taken independently combine multiplicatively, while information combines additively, the relation between the amount of information given by a message and the probability of that message will be that between a set of numbers that multiply and a set that add. To the mathematicians, if one set of numbers adds, while the corresponding numbers of the second set multiply, the first set is said to consist of the *logarithms* of the second set, taken to an appropriate base.

The logarithm is, however, not completely determined when the original number is given, because its scale is not yet assigned. This scale determines a factor by which the logarithm can be multiplied, and this factor may be positive or negative. Probabilities are always less than 1 or equal to it, for 1 is the probability of absolute certainty, and there is no probability greater than certainty. This shows that the amount of information will be so determined that it is greater than zero when the probability of the corresponding event is less than one. It follows that the amount of information conveyed by an event which occurs with a certain probability will then be the *negative* logarithm of the probability on some appropriate scale, since the ordinary logarithm of a quantity less than 1 will be negative, and information is naturally taken to be positive.

A measure of information is a measure of order. Its negative will be a measure of disorder, and will be a negative number. It can be made artificially positive by adding a constant quantity, or starting from some value other than zero. This measure of disorder is known to the statistical mechanicist as *entropy,* and almost never spontaneously decreases in an isolated system. This again is the second law of thermodynamics.

[13]

RALPH H. MUNCH *

Instrumentation, Science, and Technology **

Instrumentation is one of the foundation stones of modern science and technology. It is important that we realize this. Likewise, it is important that we understand its interrelationships with science and technology. Some thought should also be given to the social implications of instrumentation.

Almost invariably the history of an instrument begins with the observation that a change in some variable produces a change in another more easily measured property of the system under observation. For instance, temperature measurements began when early workers observed that the volume of the gas enclosed in a thermoscope bulb was a function of temperature. It took over a century of study by many workers before this observation resulted in the use of mercury in glass thermometers, with a scale based on easily reproduced fixed points. During this period, temperature measurement was studied for its own sake; it was not a tool to be used to obtain more exact information about the effect of temperature on other phenomena. Even now we have research on temperature measurement in progress. It is directed toward more precise definition of the temperature scale, toward extending the scale to higher and lower ranges, and toward the development of more desirable measuring instruments. But now, most areas of the science of temperature measurement are so well known that they serve as tools for other branches of science and for industry.

Today, progress in the science of instrumentation is usually much more rapid. We have the advantage of the work done by our predecessors, and we have a steadily increasing number of workers in the field. We also have an avid demand from industry and the armed forces for improved

* Organic Chemicals Divisions, Monsanto Chemical Co., St. Louis, Mo.
** From the editorial in *Science*, Vol. 116, no. 3014 (Oct. 3, 1952), p. 3. Published by the American Association for the Advancement of Science. By permission of the author and publisher.

instruments of many types. We might take as an example a recently developed ultra-sonic viscometer. This instrument makes use of a magnetostriction oscillator to supply pulses of ultrasonic energy to a probe. The damping of the vibration of the probe is a function of the viscosity of the medium in which it is immersed. This instrument gives a continuous indication of the viscosity of the sample, and it has the advantage that, with one probe, it can cover a wide range of viscosities. Measurements can be made over a temperature range from $-109°$ F to $+650°$ F and at pressures ranging from the lowest attainable to thousands of pounds per square inch. There are no moving parts or orifices to be blocked. Here we have an instrument based on a completely different principle from those previously employed for measuring viscosity. The result is a device with unique advantages for many applications. Products as diverse as plastics, soil conditioners, treating agents for oil-well-drilling muds, paints, inks, synthetic fibers, starch, and gelatin will benefit from this improved tool for measuring viscosity.

It is important to realize that the basic ideas for instrumentation come from research in pure science. Our technology depends on instrumentation. The demands of our technology cause instruments to become available which, although they were designed for industrial use, often make research in pure science much easier. Thus, there is a fundamental relationship among pure science, instrumentation, and technology, with each benefiting from the others. This situation results in an increasingly rapid rate of progress in all three fields.

Instrumentation makes possible better products at lower cost in human labor. It does not, however, as some fear, put people out of work. It requires better trained workers to care for plants where instuments take over many of the operations formerly carried out manually, and it requires an instrument industry to supply the necessary instruments.

PART B

*

Basic Biological and Psychological

Concepts

THE OATH OF HIPPOCRATES

¶*I swear by Apollo the physician, and Æsculapius, and Health, and Panacea, and all the gods and goddesses, that according to my ability and judgment, I will keep this Oath and this stipulation—to regard him who taught me this Art equally dear to me as my parents, to share my substance with him, and relieve his necessities if required, to look upon his offspring in the same footing as my own brothers, and to teach them this art, if they shall wish to learn it, without fee or stipulation; and that by precept, lecture, and every other mode of instruction, I will impart a knowledge of the Art to my own sons, and those of my teachers, and to disciples bound by a stipulation and oath according to the law of medicine, but to none others. ¶I will follow that system of regimen which, according to my ability and judgment, I consider for the benefit of my patients, and abstain from whatever is deleterious and mischievous. I will give no deadly medicine to any one if asked, nor suggest any such counsel; and in like manner I will not give to a woman a pessary to produce abortion. With purity and with holiness I will pass my life and practice my Art. I will not cut persons laboring under the stone, but will leave this to be done by men who are practitioners of this work. ¶Into whatever houses I enter, I will go into them for the benefit of the sick, and will abstain from every voluntary act of mischief and corruption; and, further, from the seduction of females or males, of freemen and slaves. Whatever, in connection with my professional practice or not in connection with it, I see or hear, in the life of men, which ought not to be spoken of abroad, I will not divulge, as reckoning that all such should be kept secret. While I continue to keep this Oath unviolated, may it be granted to me to enjoy life and the practice of the art, respected by all men, in all times! But should I trespass and violate this Oath, may the reverse be my lot!*

CHARLES DARWIN

The Origin of Species

CHAPTER XV

RECAPITULATION AND CONCLUSION

Recapitulation of the objections to the theory of Natural Selection—Recapitulation of the general and special circumstances in its favour—Causes of the general belief in the immutability of species—How far the theory of Natural Selection may be extended—Effects of its adoption on the study of Natural History—Concluding remarks.

As this whole volume is one long argument, it may be convenient to the reader to have the leading facts and inferences briefly recapitulated.

That many and serious objections may be advanced against the theory of descent with modification through variation and natural selection, I do not deny. I have endeavoured to give to them their full force. Nothing at first can appear more difficult to believe than that the more complex organs and instincts have been perfected, not by means superior to, though analogous with, human reason, but by the accumulation of innumerable slight variations, each good for the individual possessor. Nevertheless, this difficulty, though appearing to our imagination insuperably great, cannot be considered real if we admit the following propositions, namely, that all parts of the organisation and instincts offer, at least, individual differences—that there is a struggle for existence leading to the preservation of profitable deviations of structure or instinct—and, lastly, that gradations in the state of perfection of each organ may have existed, each good of its kind. The truth of these propositions cannot, I think, be disputed.

It is, no doubt, extremely difficult even to conjecture by what gradations many structures have been perfected, more especially amongst broken and failing groups of organic beings, which have suffered much extinction, but we see so many strange gradations in nature, that we ought to be extremely cautious in saying that any organ or instinct, or any whole structure, could not have arrived at its present state by many graduated steps. There are, it must be admitted, cases of special difficulty opposed to the theory of natural selection; and one of the most curious of these is the existence in the same community of two or three defined castes of workers or sterile female ants; but I have attempted to show how these difficulties can be mastered.

With respect to the almost universal sterility of species when first crossed, which forms so remarkable a contrast with the almost universal fertility of varieties when crossed, I must refer the reader to the recapitulation of the facts given at the end of the ninth chapter, which seem to me conclusively to show that this sterility is no more a special endowment than is the capacity of two distinct kinds of trees to be grafted together; but that it is incidental on differences confined to the reproductive systems of the intercrossed species. We see the truth of this conclusion in the vast difference in the results of crossing the same two species reciprocally,— that is, when one species is first used as the father and then as the mother. Analogy from the consideration of dimorphic and trimorphic plants clearly leads to the same conclusion, for when the forms are illegitimately united, they yield few or no seed, and their offspring are more or less sterile; and these forms belong to the same undoubted species, and differ from each other in no respect except in their reproductive organs and functions.

Although the fertility of varieties when intercrossed and of their mongrel offspring has been asserted by so many authors to be universal, this cannot be considered as quite correct after the facts given on the high authority of Gärtner and Kölreuter. Most of the varieties which have been experimented on have been produced under domestication; and as domestication (I do not mean mere confinement) almost certainly tends to eliminate that sterility which, judging from analogy, would have affected the parent-species if intercrossed, we ought not to expect that domestication would likewise induce sterility in their modified descendants when crossed. This elimination of sterility apparently follows from the same cause which allows our domestic animals to breed freely under diversified circumstances; and this again apparently follows from their having been gradually accustomed to frequent changes in their conditions of life.

A double and parallel series of facts seems to throw much light on the sterility of species, when first crossed, and of their hybrid offspring. On the one side, there is good reason to believe that slight changes in the conditions of life give vigour and fertility to all organic beings. We know also that a cross between the distinct individuals of the same variety, and between distinct varieties, increases the number of their offspring, and certainly gives to them increased size and vigour. This is chiefly owing to the forms which are crossed having been exposed to somewhat different conditions of life; for I have ascertained by a laborious series of experiments that if all the individuals of the same variety be subjected during several generations to the same conditions, the good derived from crossing is often much diminished or wholly disappears. This is one side of the case. On the other side, we know that species which have long been exposed to nearly uniform conditions, when they are subjected under confinement to new and greatly changed conditions, either perish, or if they survive, are rendered sterile, though retaining perfect health. This does not occur, or only in a very slight degree, with our domesticated productions, which have long been exposed to fluctuating conditions. Hence when we find that hybrids produced by a cross between two distinct species are few in number, owing to their perishing soon after conception or at a very early age, or if surviving that they are rendered more or less sterile, it seems highly probable that this result is due to their having been in fact subjected to a great change in their conditions of life, from being compounded of two distinct organisations. He who will explain in a definite manner why, for instance, an elephant or a fox will not breed under confinement in its native country, whilst the domestic pig or dog will breed freely under the most diversified conditions, will at the same time be able to give a definite answer to the question why two distinct species, when crossed, as well as their hybrid offspring, are generally rendered more or less sterile, whilst two domesticated varieties when crossed and their mongrel offspring are perfectly fertile.

Turning to geographical distribution, the difficulties encountered on the theory of descent with modification are serious enough. All the individuals of the same species, and all the species of the same genus, or even higher group, are descended from common parents; and therefore, in however distant and isolated parts of the world they may now be found, they must in the course of successive generations have travelled from some one point to all the others. We are often wholly unable even to conjecture how this could have been effected. Yet, as we have reason to believe that some species have retained the same specific form for very long periods of time, immensely long as measured by years, too much stress ought not to be laid on the occasional wide diffusion of the same species; for during very long periods there will always have been a good chance for wide migration by many means. A broken or interrupted range may often be accounted for by the extinction of the species in the intermediate regions. It cannot be denied that we are as yet very ignorant as to the full extent of the various climatal and geographical changes which have affected the earth during modern periods; and such changes will often have facilitated migration. As an example, I have attempted to show how potent has been the influence of the Glacial period on the distribution of the same and of allied species throughout the world. We are as yet profoundly ignorant of the many occasional means of transport. With respect to distinct species of the same genus inhabiting distant and isolated regions, as the process of modification has necessarily been slow, all the means of migration will have been possible during a very long period; and consequently the difficulty of the wide diffusion of the species of the same genus is in some degree lessened.

As according to the theory of natural selection an interminable number of intermediate forms must have existed, linking together all the species in each group by gradations as fine as are our existing varieties, it may be asked: Why do we not see these linking forms all around us?

Why are not all organic beings blended together in an inextricable chaos?
With respect to existing forms, we should remember that we have no right
to expect (excepting in rare cases) to discover *directly* connecting links
between them, but only between each and some extinct and supplanted
form. Even on a wide area, which has during a long period remained continuous, and of which the climatic and other conditions of life change
insensibly in proceeding from a district occupied by one species into
another district occupied by a closely allied species, we have no just right
to expect often to find intermediate varieties in the intermediate zones.
For we have reason to believe that only a few species of a genus ever
undergo change; the other species becoming utterly extinct and leaving
no modified progeny. Of the species which do change, only a few within
the same country change at the same time; and all modifications are
slowly effected. I have also shown that the intermediate varieties which
probably at first existed in the intermediate zones, would be liable to be
supplanted by the allied forms on either hand; for the latter, from existing
in greater numbers, would generally be modified and improved at a
quicker rate than the intermediate varieties, which existed in lesser numbers; so that the intermediate varieties would, in the long run, he supplanted and exterminated.

On this doctrine of the extermination of an infinitude of connecting
links, between the living and extinct inhabitants of the world, and at each
successive period between the extinct and still older species, why is not
every geological formation charged with such links? Why does not every
collection of fossil remains afford plain evidence of the gradation and
mutation of the forms of life? Although geological research has undoubtedly revealed the former existence of many links, bringing numerous forms
of life much closer together, it does not yield the infinitely many fine
gradations between past and present species required on the theory; and
this is the most obvious of the many objections which may be urged
against it. Why, again, do whole groups of allied species appear, though
this appearance is often false, to have come in suddenly on the successive
geological stages? Although we now know that organic beings appeared on
this globe, at a period incalculably remote, long before the lowest bed of
the Cambrian system was deposited, why do we not find beneath this
system great piles of strata stored with the remains of the progenitors
of the Cambrian fossils? For on the theory, such strata must somewhere
have been deposited at these ancient and utterly unknown epochs of the
world's history.

I can answer these questions and objections only on the supposition
that the geological record is far more imperfect than most geologists believe. The number of specimens in all our museums is absolutely as nothing
compared with the countless generations of countless species which have
certainly existed. The parent-form of any two or more species would not
be in all its characters directly intermediate between its modified offspring, any more than the rock-pigeon is directly intermediate in crop

and tail between its descendants, the pouter and fantail pigeons. We should not be able to recognise a species as the parent of another and modified species, if we were to examine the two ever so closely, unless we possessed most of the intermediate links; and owing to the imperfection of the geological record, we have no just right to expect to find so many links. If two or three, or even more linking forms were discovered, they would simply be ranked by many naturalists as so many new species, more especially if found in different geological sub-stages, let their differences be ever so slight. Numerous existing doubtful forms could be named which are probably varieties; but who will pretend that in future ages so many fossil links will be discovered, that naturalists will be able to decide whether or not these doubtful forms ought to be called varieties? Only a small portion of the world has been geologically explored. Only organic beings of certain classes can be preserved in a fossil condition, at least in any great number. Many species when once formed never undergo any further change but become extinct without leaving modified descendants; and the periods, during which species have undergone modification, though long as measured by years, have probably been short in comparison with the periods during which they retain the same form. It is the dominant and widely ranging species which vary most frequently and vary most, and varieties are often at first local—both causes rendering the discovery of intermediate links in any one formation less likely. Local varieties will not spread into other and distant regions until they are considerably modified and improved; and when they have spread, and are discovered in a geological formation, they appear as if suddenly created there, and will be simply classed as new species. Most formations have been intermittent in their accumulation; and their duration has probably been shorter than the average duration of specific forms. Successive formations are in most cases separated from each other by blank intervals of time of great length; for fossiliferous formations thick enough to resist future degradations can as a general rule be accumulated only where much sediment is deposited on the subsiding bed of the sea. During the alternate periods of elevation and of stationary level the record will generally be blank. During these latter periods there will probably be more variability in the forms of life; during periods of subsidence, more extinction.

With respect to the absence of strata rich in fossils beneath the Cambrian formation, I can recur only to the hypothesis given in the tenth chapter; namely, that though our continents and oceans have endured for an enormous period in nearly their present relative positions, we have no reason to assume that this has always been the case; consequently formations much older than any now known may lie buried beneath the great oceans. With respect to the lapse of time not having been sufficient since our planet was consolidated for the assumed amount of organic change, and this objection, as urged by Sir William Thomson, is probably one of the gravest as yet advanced, I can only say, firstly, that we do not know at what rate species change as measured by years, and secondly, that many philosophers are not as yet willing to admit that we know enough of the constitution of the universe and of the interior of our globe to speculate with safety on its past duration.

That the geological record is imperfect all will admit; but that it is imperfect to the degree required by our theory, few will be inclined to admit. If we look to long enough intervals of time, geology plainly declares that species have all changed; and they have changed in the manner required by the theory, for they have changed slowly and in a graduated manner. We clearly see this in the fossil remains from consecutive formations invariably being much more closely related to each other, than are the fossils from widely separated formations.

Such is the sum of the several chief objections and difficulties which may be justly urged against the theory; and I have now briefly recapitulated the answers and explanations which, as far as I can see, may be given. I have felt these difficulties far too heavily during many years to doubt their weight. But it deserves especial notice that the more important objections relate to questions on which we are confessedly ignorant; nor do we know how ignorant we are. We do not know all the possible transitional gradations between the simplest and the most perfect organs; it cannot be pretended that we know all the varied means of Distribution during the long lapse of years, or that we know how imperfect is the Geological Record. Serious as these several objections are, in my judgment they are by no means sufficient to overthrow the theory of descent with subsequent modification.

.   .   .   .

I have now recapitulated the facts and considerations which have thoroughly convinced me that species have been modified, during a long course of descent. This has been effected chiefly through the natural selection of numerous successive, slight, favourable variations; aided in an important manner by the inherited effects of the use and disuse of parts; and in an unimportant manner, that is in relation to adaptive structures, whether past or present, by the direct action of external conditions, and by variations which seem to us in our ignorance to arise spontaneously. It appears that I formerly underrated the frequency and value of these latter forms of variations, as leading to permanent modifications of structure independently of natural selection. But as my conclusions have lately been much misrepresented, and it has been stated that I attribute the modification of species exclusively to natural selection, I may be permitted to remark that in the first edition of this work, and subsequently, I placed in a most conspicuous position—namely, at the close of the Introduction— the following words: "I am convinced that natural selection has been the main but not the exclusive means of modification." This has been of no avail. Great is the power of steady misrepresentation; but the history of science shows that fortunately this power does not long endure.

It can hardly be supposed that a false theory would explain, in so satisfactory a manner as does the theory of natural selection, the several large classes of facts above specified. It has recently been objected that this is an unsafe method of arguing; but it is a method used in judging of the common events of life, and has often been used by the greatest natural philosophers. The undulatory theory of light has thus been arrived at; and the belief in the revolution of the earth on its own axis was until lately supported by hardly any direct evidence. It is no valid objection that science as yet throws no light on the far higher problem of the essence or origin of life. Who can explain what is the essence of the attraction of gravity? No one now objects to following out the results consequent on this unknown element of attraction; notwithstanding that Leibniz formerly accused Newton of introducing "occult qualities and miracles into philosophy."

I see no good reason why the views given in this volume should shock the religious feelings of any one. It is satisfactory, as showing how transient such impressions are, to remember that the greatest discovery ever made by man, namely, the law of the attraction of gravity, was also attacked by Leibniz, "as subversive of natural, and inferentially of revealed, religion." A celebrated author and divine his written to me that "he has gradually learnt to see that it is just as noble a conception of the Deity to believe that He created a few original forms capable of self-development into other and needful forms, as to believe that He required a fresh act of creation to supply the voids caused by the action of His laws."

Why, it may be asked, until recently did nearly all the most eminent living naturalists and geologists disbelieve in the mutability of species? It cannot be asserted that organic beings in a state of nature are subject to no variation; it cannot be proved that the amount of variation in the course of long ages is a limited quality; no clear distinction has been, or can be, drawn between species and well-marked varieties. It cannot be maintained that species when intercrossed are invariably sterile, and varieties invariably fertile; or that sterility is a special endowment and sign of creation. The belief that species were immutable productions was almost unavoidable as long as the history of the world was thought to be of short duration; and now that we have acquired some idea of the lapse of time, we are too apt to assume, without proof, that the geological record is so perfect that it would have afforded us plain evidence of the mutation of species, if they had undergone mutation.

But the chief cause of our natural unwillingness to admit that one species has given birth to clear and distinct species, is that we are always slow in admitting great changes of which we do not see the steps. The difficulty is the same as that felt by so many geologists, when Lyell first insisted that long lines of inland cliffs had been formed, and great valleys excavated, by the agencies which we see still at work. The mind cannot possibly grasp the full meaning of the term of even a million years; it cannot add up and perceive the full effects of many slight variations, accumulated during an almost infinite number of generations.

Although I am fully convinced of the truth of the views given in this volume under the form of an abstract, I by no means expect to convince experienced naturalists whose minds are stocked with a multitude of facts all viewed, during a long course of years, from a point of view directly opposite to mine. It is so easy to hide our ignorance under such expressions as the "plan of creation," "unity of design," &c., and to think that we give an explanation when we only re-state a fact. Any one whose disposition leads him to attach more weight to unexplained difficulties than to the explanation of a certain number of facts will certainly reject the theory. A few naturalists, endowed with much flexibility of mind, and who have already begun to doubt the immutability of species, may be influenced by this volume; but I look with confidence to the future,—to young and rising naturalists, who will be able to view both sides of the question with impartiality. Whoever is led to believe that species are mutable will do good service by conscientiously expressing his conviction; for thus only can the load of prejudice by which this subject is overwhelmed be removed.

Several eminent naturalists have of late published their belief that a multitude of reputed species in each genus are not real species; but that other species are real, that is, have been independently created. This seems to me a strange conclusion to arrive at. They admit that a multitude of forms, which till lately they themselves thought were special creations, and which are still thus looked at by the majority of naturalists, and which consequently have all the external characteristic features of true species,—they admit that these have been produced by variation, but they refuse to extend the same view to other and slightly different forms. Nevertheless they do not pretend that they can define, or even conjecture, which are the created forms of life, and which are those produced by secondary laws. They admit variation as a *vera causa* in one case, they arbitrarily reject it in another, without assigning any distinction in the two cases. The day will come when this will be given as a curious illustration of the blindness of preconceived opinion. These authors seem no more startled at a miraculous act of creation than at an ordinary birth. But do they really believe that at innumerable periods in the earth's history certain elemental atoms have been commanded suddenly to flash into living tissues? Do they believe that at each supposed act of creation one individual or many were produced? Were all the infinitely numerous kinds of animals and plants created as eggs or seed, or as full grown? and in the case of mammals, were they created bearing the false marks of nourishment from the mother's womb? Undoubtedly some of these same questions cannot be answered by those who believe in the appearance or creation of only a few forms of life, or of some one form alone. It has been maintained by several authors that it is as easy to believe in the creation of a million beings as of one; but Maupertuis' philosophical axiom "of least action" leads the mind more willingly to admit the smaller number; and certainly we ought not to believe that innumerable beings within each great class have been created with plain, but deceptive, marks of descent from a single parent.

As a record of a former state of things, I have retained in the foregoing paragraphs, and elsewhere, several sentences which imply that naturalists believe in the separate creation of each species; and I have been much censured for having thus expressed myself. But undoubtedly this was the general belief when the first edition of the present work appeared. I formerly spoke to very many naturalists on the subject of evolution, and never once met with any sympathetic agreement. It is probable that some did then believe in evolution, but they were either silent, or expressed themselves so ambiguously that it was not easy to understand their meaning. Now things are wholly changed, and almost every naturalist admits the great principle of evolution. There are, however, some who still think that species have suddenly given birth, through quite unexplained means, to new and totally different forms; but, as I have attempted to show, weighty evidence can be opposed to the admission of great and abrupt modifications. Under a scientific point of view, and as leading to further investigation, but little advantage is gained by believing that new forms are suddenly developed in an inexplicable manner from old and widely different forms, over the old belief in the creation of species from the dust of the earth.

It may be asked how far I extend the doctrine of the modification of species. The question is difficult to answer, because the more distinct the forms are which we consider, by so much the arguments in favour of community of descent become fewer in number and less in force. But some arguments of the greatest weight extend very far. All the members of whole classes are connected together by a chain of affinities, and all can be classed on the same principle, in groups subordinate to groups. Fossil remains sometimes tend to fill up very wide intervals between existing orders.

Organs in a rudimentary condition plainly show that an early progenitor had the organ in a fully developed condition; and this in some cases implies an enormous amount of modification in the descendants. Throughout whole classes various structures are formed on the same pattern, and at a very early age the embryos closely resemble each other. Therefore I cannot doubt that the theory of descent with modification embraces all the members of the same great class or kingdom. I believe that animals are descended from at most only four or five progenitors, and plants from an equal or lesser number.

Analogy would lead me one step farther, namely, to the belief that all animals and plants are descended from some one prototype. But analogy may be a deceitful guide. Nevertheless all living things have much in common, in their chemical composition, their cellular structure, their laws of growth, and their liability to injurious influences. We see this even in so trifling a fact as that the same poison often similarly affects plants and animals; or that the poison secreted by the gall-fly produces monstrous growths on the wild rose or oak-tree. With all organic beings excepting perhaps some of the very lowest, sexual production seems to be essentially similar. With all, as far as is at present known the germinal vesicle is the same; so that all organisms start from a common origin. If we look even to the two main divisions—namely, to the animal and vegetable kingdoms —certain low forms are so far intermediate in character that naturalists have disputed to which kingdom they should be referred. As Professor Asa Gray has remarked, "the spores and other reproductive bodies of many of the lower algae may claim to have first a characteristically animal, and then an unequivocally vegetable existence." Therefore, on the principle of natural selection with divergence of character, it does not seem incredible that, from such low and intermediate form, both animals and plants may have been developed; and, if we admit this, we must likewise admit that all the organic beings which have ever lived on this earth may be descended from some one primordial form. But this inference is chiefly grounded on analogy and it is immaterial whether or not it be accepted. No doubt it is possible, as Mr. G. H. Lewes has urged, that at the first commencement of life many different forms were evolved; but if so we may conclude that only a very few have left modified descendants. For, as I have recently remarked in regard to the members of each great kingdom, such as the Vertebrata, Articulata, &c., we have distinct evidence in their embryological, homologous, and rudimentary structures, that within each kingdom all the members are descended from a single progenitor.

When the views advanced by me in this volume, and by Mr. Wallace, or when analogous views on the origin of species are generally admitted, we can dimly foresee that there will be a considerable revolution in natural history. Systematists will be able to pursue their labours as at present; but they will not be incessantly haunted by the shadowy doubt whether this or that form be a true species. This, I feel sure and I speak after experience, will be no slight relief. The endless disputes whether or not some fifty species of British brambles are good species will cease. Systematists will have only to decide (not that this will be easy) whether any form be sufficiently constant and distinct from other forms, to be capable of definition; and if definable, whether the differences be sufficiently important to deserve a specific name. This latter point will become a far more essential consideration than it is at present; for differences, however slight, between any two forms if not blended by intermediate gradations, are looked at by most naturalists as sufficient to raise both forms to the rank of species.

Hereafter we shall be compelled to acknowledge that the only distinction between species and well-marked varieties is, that the latter are known, or believed, to be connected at the present day by intermediate gradations, whereas species were formerly thus connected. Hence, without rejecting the consideration of the present existence of intermediate gradations between any two forms we shall be led to weigh more carefully and to value higher the actual amount of difference between them. It is quite possible that forms now generally acknowledged to be merely varieties may hereafter be thought worthy of specific names; and in this case scientific and common language will come into accordance. In short, we shall have to treat species in the same manner as those naturalists treat genera, who admit that genera are merely artificial combinations made for convenience.

This may not be a cheering prospect; but we shall at least be free from the vain search for the undiscovered and undiscoverable essence of the term species.

The other and more general departments of natural history will rise greatly in interest. The terms used by naturalists, of affinity, relationship, community of type, paternity, morphology, adaptive characters, rudimentary and aborted organs, &c., will cease to be metaphorical, and will have a plain signification. When we no longer look at an organic being as a savage looks at a ship, as something wholly beyond his comprehension; when we regard every production of nature as one which has had a long history; when we contemplate every complex structure and instinct as the summing up of many contrivances, each useful to the possessor, in the same way as any great mechanical invention is the summing up of the labour, the experience, the reason, and even the blunders of numerous workmen; when we thus view each organic being, how far more interesting—I speak from experience—does the study of natural history become!

A grand and almost untrodden field of inquiry will be opened, on the causes and laws of variation, on correlation, on the effects of use and disuse, on the direct action of external conditions, and so forth. The study of domestic productions will rise immensely in value. A new variety raised by man will be a more important and interesting subject for study than one more species added to the infinitude of already recorded species. Our classifications will come to be, as far as they can be so made, genealogies; and will then truly give what may be called the plan of creation. The rules for classifying will no doubt become simpler when we have a definite object in view. We possess no pedigrees or armorial bearings; and we have to discover and trace the many diverging lines of descent in our natural genealogies, by characters of any kind which have long been inherited. Rudimentary organs will speak infallibly with respect to the nature of long-lost structures. Species and groups of species which are called aberrant, and which may fancifully be called living fossils, will aid us in forming a picture of the ancient forms of life. Embryology will often reveal to us the structure, in some degree obscured, of the prototype of each great class.

When we feel assured that all the individuals of the same species, and all the closely allied species of most genera, have within a not very remote period descended from one parent, and have migrated from some one birthplace; and when we better know the many means of migration, then, by the light which geology now throws, and will continue to throw, on former changes of climate and of the level of the land, we shall surely be enabled to trace in an admirable manner the former migrations of the inhabitants of the whole world. Even at present, by comparing the differences between the inhabitants of the sea on the opposite sides of a continent, and the nature of the various inhabitants on that continent, in relation to their apparent means of immigration, some light can be thrown on ancient geography.

The noble science of Geology loses glory from the extreme imperfection of the record. The crust of the earth with its imbedded remains must not be looked at as a well-filled museum, but as a poor collection made at hazard and at rare intervals. The accumulation of each great fossiliferous formation will be recognised as having depended on an unusual concurrence of favourable circumstances, and the blank intervals between the successive stages as having been of vast duration. But we shall be able to gauge with some security the duration of these intervals by a comparison of the preceding and succeeding organic forms. We must be cautious in attempting to correlate as strictly contemporaneous two formations, which do not include many identical species, by the general succession of the forms of life. As species are produced and exterminated by slowly acting and still existing causes, and not by miraculous acts of creation ; and as the most important of all causes of organic change is one which is almost independent of altered and perhaps suddenly altered physical conditions, namely, the mutual relation of organism to organism,—the improvement of one organism entailing the improvement or the extermination of others ; it follows, that the amount of organic change in the fossils of consecutive formations probably serves as a fair measure of the relative though not actual lapse of time. A number of species, however, keeping in a body might remain for a long period unchanged, whilst within the same period several of these species by migrating into new countries and coming into competition with foreign associates, might become modified ; so that we must not overrate the accuracy of organic change as a measure of time.

In the future I see open fields for far more important researches. Psychology will be securely based on the foundation already well laid by Mr. Herbert Spencer, that of the necessary acquirement of each mental power and capacity by gradation. Much light will be thrown on the origin of man and his history.

Authors of the highest eminence seem to be fully satisfied with the view that each species has been independently created. To my mind it accords better with what we know of the laws impressed on matter by the Creator, that the production and extinction of the past and present inhabitants of the world should have been due to secondary causes, like those determining the birth and death of the individual. When I view all beings not as special creations, but as the lineal descendants of some few beings which lived long before the first bed of the Cambrian system was deposited, they seem to me to become ennobled. Judging from the past, we may safely infer that not one living species will transmit its unaltered likeness to a distant futurity. And of the species now living very few will transmit progeny of any kind to a far distant futurity ; for the manner in which all organic beings are grouped, shows that the greater number of species in each genus, and all the species in many genera, have left no descendants, but have become utterly extinct. We can so far take a prophetic glance into futurity as to foretell that it will be the common and widely-spread species, belonging to the larger and dominant groups within each class which will ultimately prevail and procreate new and dominant species. As all the living forms of life are the lineal descendants of those which lived long before the Cambrian epoch, we may feel certain that the ordinary succession by generation has never once been broken, and that no cataclysm has desolated the whole world. Hence we may look with some confidence to a secure future of great length. And as natural selection works solely by and for the good of each being, all corporeal and mental endowments will tend to progress towards perfection.

It is interesting to contemplate a tangled bank, clothed with many plants of many kinds, with birds singing on the bushes, with various insects flitting about, and with worms crawling through the damp earth, and to reflect that these elaborately constructed forms, so different from each other, and dependent upon each other in so complex a manner, have all been produced by laws acting around us. These laws, taken in the largest sense, being Growth with Reproduction; Inheritance which is almost implied by reproduction; Variability from the indirect and direct action of the conditions of life, and from use and disuse: a Ratio of Increase so high as to lead to a Struggle for Life, and as a consequence to Natural Selection, entailing Divergence of Character and the Extinction of less-improved forms. Thus, from the war of nature, from famine and death, the most exalted object which we are capable of conceiving, namely, the production of the higher animals, directly follows. There is grandeur in this view of life, with its several powers, having been originally breathed by the Creator into a few forms or into one; and that, whilst this planet has gone cycling on according to the fixed law of gravity, from so simple a beginning endless forms most beautiful and most wonderful have been, and are being evolved.

[15]

THOMAS H. HUXLEY

On the Educational Value of the
Natural History Sciences

The subject to which I have to beg your attention during the ensuing hour is "The Relation of Physiological Science to other branches of Knowledge." . . .

Regarding Physiological Science, then, in its widest sense—as the equivalent of *Biology*—the Science of Individual Life—we have to consider in succession:

1. Its position and scope as a branch of knowledge.

2. Its value as a means of mental discipline.

3. Its worth as practical information.

And lastly,

4. At what period it may best be made a branch of Education.

Our conclusions on the first of these heads must depend, of course, upon the nature of the subject-matter of Biology; and I think a few preliminary considerations will place before you in a clear light the vast difference which exists between the living bodies with which Physiological science is concerned, and the remainder of the universe;—between the phænomena of Number and Space, of Physical and of Chemical force, on the one hand, and those of Life on the other.

The mathematician, the physicist, and the chemist contemplate things in a condition of rest; they look upon a state of equilibrium as that to which all bodies normally tend.

The mathematician does not suppose that a quantity will alter, or that a given point in space will change its direction with regard to another point spontaneously. It is the same with the physicist. When Newton saw the apple fall he concluded at once that the act of falling was not the result of any power inherent in the apple, but that it was the result of the action of something else on the apple. In a similar manner, all physical force is regarded as the disturbance of an equilibrium to which things tended before its exertion,—to which they will tend again after its cessation.

The chemist equally regards chemical change in a body as the effect of the action of something external to the body changed. A chemical compound once formed would persist for ever, if no alteration took place in surrounding conditions.

But to the student of Life the aspect of Nature is reversed. Here, incessant, and, so far as we know, spontaneous change is the rule, rest the exception—the anomaly to be accounted for. Living things have no inertia, and tend to no equilibrium.

Permit me, however, to give more force and clearness to these somewhat abstract considerations by an illustration or two.

Imagine a vessel full of water, at the ordinary temperature, in an atmosphere saturated with vapour. The *quantity* and the *figure* of that water will not change, so far as we know, for ever.

Suppose a lump of gold be thrown into the vessel—motion and disturbance of figure exactly proportional to the momentum of the gold will take place. But after a time the effects of this disturbance will subside—equilibrium will be restored, and the water will return to its passive state.

Expose the water to cold—it will solidify—and in so doing its particles will arrange themselves in definite crystalline shapes. But once formed, these crystals change no further.

Again, substitute for the lump of gold some substance capable of entering into chemical relations with the water:—say, a mass of that substance which is called "protein"—the substance of flesh:—a very considerable disturbance of equilibrium will take place—all sorts of chemical compositions and decompositions will occur; but in the end, as before, the result will be the resumption of a condition of rest.

Instead of such a mass of *dead* protein, however, take a particle of *living* protein—one of those minute microscopic living things which throng our pools, and are known as Infusoria—such a creature, for instance, as an Euglena, and place it in our vessel of water. It is a round mass provided with a long filament, and except in this peculiarity of shape, presents no appreciable physical or chemical difference whereby it might be distinguished from the particle of dead protein.

But the difference in the phænomena to which it will give rise is immense: in the first place it will develop a vast quantity of physical force—cleaving the water in all directions with considerable rapidity by means of the vibrations of the long filament of cilium.

Nor is the amount of chemical energy which the little creature possesses less striking. It is a perfect laboratory in itself, and it will act and react upon the water and the matters contained therein; converting them into new compounds resembling its own substance, and at the same time giving up portions of its own substance which have become effete.

Furthermore, the Euglena will increase in size; but this increase is by no means unlimited, as the increase of a crystal might be. After it has grown to a certain extent it divides, and each portion assumes the form of the original, and proceeds to repeat the process of growth and division.

Nor is this all. For after a series of such divisions and subdivisions, these minute points assume a totally new form, lose their long tails—round themselves, and secrete a sort of envelope or box, in which they remain shut up for a time, eventually to resume, directly or indirectly, their primitive mode of existence.

Now, so far as we know, there is no natural limit to the existence of the Euglena, or of any other living germ. A living species once launched into existence tends to live for ever.

Consider how widely different this living particle is from the dead atoms with which the physicist and chemist have to do!

The particle of gold falls to the bottom and rests—the particle of dead protein decomposes and disappears—it also rests: but the *living* protein mass neither tends to exhaustion of its forces nor to any permanency of form, but is essentially distinguished as a disturber of equilibrium so far as force is concerned,—as undergoing continual metamorphosis and change, in point of form.

Tendency to equilibrium of force and to permanency of form, then, are the characters of that portion of the universe which does not live—the domain of the chemist and physicist.

Tendency to disturb existing equilibrium—to take on forms which succeed one another in definite cycles—is the character of the living world.

What is the cause of this wonderful difference between the dead particle and the living particle of matter appearing in other respects identical? that difference to which we give the name of Life?

I, for one, cannot tell you. It may be that, by and by, philosophers will discover some higher laws of which the facts of life are particular cases—very possibly they will find out some bond between physico-chemical phænomena on the one hand, and vital phænomena on the other. At present, however, we assuredly know of none; and I think we shall exercise a wise humility in confessing that, for us at least, this successive assumption of different states—(external conditions remaining the same) —this *spontaneity of action*—If I may use the term which implies more than I would be answerable for—which constitutes so vast and plain a practical distinction between living bodies and those which do not live, is an ultimate fact; indicating as such, the existence of a broad line of demarcation between the subject-matter of Biological and that of all other sciences.

For I would have it understood that this simple Euglena is the type of *all* living things, so far as the distinction between these and inert matter is concerned. That cycle of changes, which is constituted by perhaps not more than two or three steps in the Euglena, is as clearly manifested in the multitudinous stages through which the germ of an oak or of a man passes. Whatever forms the Living Being may take on, whether simple or complex, *production, growth, reproduction,* are the phænomena which distinguish it from that which does not live.

If this be true, it is clear that the student, in passing from the physico-chemical to the physiological sciences, enters upon a totally new order of facts; and it will next be for us to consider how far these new facts involve *new* methods, or require a modification of those with which he is already acquainted. Now a great deal is said about the peculiarity of the scientific method in general, and of the different methods which are pursued in the different sciences. The Mathematics are said to have one special method; Physics another, Biology a third, and so forth. For my own part, I must confess that I do not understand this phraseology.

So far as I can arrive at any clear comprehension of the matter, Science is not, as many would seem to suppose, a modification of the black art, suited to the tastes of the nineteenth century, and flourishing mainly in consequence of the decay of the Inquisition.

Science is, I believe, nothing but *trained and organized common sense,* differing from the latter only as a veteran may differ from a raw recruit: and its methods differ from those of common sense only so far as the guardsman's cut and thrust differ from the manner in which a savage wields his club. The primary power is the same in each case, and perhaps the untutored savage has the more brawny arm of the two. The *real* advantage lies in the point and polish of the swordsman's weapon; in the trained eye quick to spy out the weakness of the adversary; in the ready hand prompt to follow it on the instant. But, after all, the sword exercise is only the hewing and poking of the clubman developed and perfected.

So, the vast results obtained by Science are won by no mystical faculties, by no mental processes, other than those which are practised by every one of us, in the humblest and meanest affairs of life. A detective policeman discovers a burglar from the marks made by his shoe, by a mental process identical with that by which Cuvier restored the extinct animals of Montmartre from fragments of their bones. Nor does that process of induction and deduction by which a lady, finding a stain of a peculiar kind upon her dress, concludes that somebody has upset the ink-stand thereon, differ in any way, in kind, from that by which Adams and Leverrier discovered a new planet.

The man of science, in fact, simply uses with scrupulous exactness the methods which we all, habitually and at every moment, use carelessly; and the man of business must as much avail himself of the scientific method—must be as truly a man of science—as the veriest bookworm of us all; though I have no doubt that the man of business will find himself out to be a philosopher with as much surprise as M. Jourdain exhibited when he discovered that he had been all his life talking prose. If, however, there be no real difference between the methods of science and those of common life, it would seem, on the face of the matter, highly improbable that there should be any difference between the methods of the different sciences; nevertheless, it is constantly taken for granted that there is a very wide difference between the Physiological and other sciences in point of method.

In the first place it is said—and I take this point first, because the imputation is too frequently admitted by Physiologists themselves—that Biology differs from the Physico-chemical and Mathematical sciences in being "inexact."

Now, this phrase "inexact" must refer either to the *methods* or to the *results* of Physiological science.

It cannot be correct to apply it to the methods; for, as I hope to show you by and by, these are identical in all sciences, and whatever is true of Physiological method is true of Physical and Mathematical method.

Is it then the *results* of Biological science which are "inexact"? I think not. If I say that respiration is performed by the lungs; that digestion is effected in the stomach; that the eye is the organ of sight; that the jaws of a vertebrated animal never open sideways, but always up and down; while those of an annulose animal always open sideways, and never up and down —I am enumerating propositions which are as exact as anything in Euclid. How then has this notion of the inexactness of Biological science come about? I believe from two causes: first, because in consequence of the great complexity of the science and the multitude of interfering conditions, we are very often only enabled to predict approximately what will occur under given circumstances; and secondly, because, on account of the comparative youth of the Physiological sciences, a great many of their laws are still imperfectly worked out. But, in an educational point of view, it is most important to distinguish between the essence of a science and the accidents which surround it; and essentially, the methods and results of Physiology are as exact as those of Physics or Mathematics.

It is said that the Physiological method is especially *comparative*; [1] and this dictum also finds favour in the eyes of many. I should be sorry to suggest that the speculators on scientific classification have been misled by the accident of the name of one leading branch of Biology—*Comparative Anatomy*; but I would ask whether *comparison,* and that classification which is the result of comparison, are not the essence of every science whatsoever? How is it possible to discover a relation of cause and effect of *any* kind without comparing a series of cases together in which the supposed cause and effect occur singly, or combined? So far from comparison being in any way peculiar to Biological science, it is, I think, the essence of every science.

A speculative philosopher again tells us that the Biological sciences are distinguished by being sciences of observation and not of experiment! [2]

Of all the strange assertions into which speculation without practical acquaintance with a subject may lead even an able man, I think this is the very strangest. Physiology not an experimental science? Why, there is not a function of a single organ in the body which has not been determined wholly and solely by experiment? How did Harvey determine the nature of the circulation, except by experiment? How did Sir Charles Bell determine the functions of the roots of the spinal nerve, save by experiment? How do we know the use of a nerve at all, except by experiment? Nay, how do we know even that your eye is your seeing apparatus, unless you make the experiment of shutting it or that your ear is your hearing apparatus, unless you close it up and thereby discover that you become deaf?

It would really be much more true to say that Physiology is *the* experimental science *par excellence* of all sciences; that in which there is least to be learnt by mere observation, and that which affords the greatest field for the exercise of those faculties which characterise the experimental philosopher. I confess, if any one were to ask me for a model application of the logic of experiment, I should know no better work to put into his hands than Bernard's late Researches on the Functions of the Liver.[3]

Not to give this lecture a too controversial tone, however, I must only advert to one more doctrine, held by a thinker of our own age and country, whose opinions are worthy of all respect. It is, that the Biological sciences differ from all others, inasmuch as in *them* classification takes place by type and not by definition.[4]

It is said, in short, that a natural-history class is not capable of being defined—that the class Rosaceæ, for instance, or the class of Fishes, is not accurately and absolutely definable, inasmuch as its members will present exceptions to every possible definition and that the members of the class are united together only by the circumstance that they are all more like some imaginary average rose or average fish, than they resemble anything else.

But here, as before, I think the distinction has arisen entirely from confusing a transitory imperfection with an essential character. So long as our information concerning them is imperfect, we class all objects together according to resemblances which we *feel*, but cannot define; we group them round *types*, in short. Thus if you ask an ordinary person what kinds of animals there are, he will probably say, beasts, birds, reptiles, fishes, insects, &c. Ask him to define a beast from a reptile, and he cannot do it; but he says, things like a cow or a horse are beasts, and things like a frog or a lizard are reptiles. You see *he does* class by type, and not by definition. But how does this classification differ from that of a scientific Zoologist? How does the meaning of the scientific class-name of "Mammalia" differ from the unscientific of "Beasts"?

Why, exactly because the former depends on a definition, the latter on a type. The class Mammalia is scientifically defined as "all animals which have a vertebrated skeleton and suckle their young." Here is no reference to type, but a definition rigorous enough for a geometrician. And such is the character which every scientific naturalist recognizes as that to which his classes must aspire—knowing, as he does, that classification by type is simply an acknowledgment of ignorance and a temporary device.

So much in the way of negative argument as against the reputed differences between Biological and other methods. No such differences, I believe, really exist. The subject-matter of Biological science is different from that of other sciences, but the methods of all are identical; and these methods are—

1. *Observation* of facts—including under this head that *artificial observation* which is called *experiment*.

2. That process of tying up similar facts into bundles ticketed and ready for use, which is called *Comparison* and *Classification*,—the results of the process, the ticketed bundles, being named *General propositions*.

3. *Deduction*, which takes us from the general proposition to facts again—teaches us, if I may so say, to anticipate from the ticket what is inside the bundle. And finally—

4. *Verification*, which is the process of ascertaining whether, in point of fact, our anticipation is a correct one.

Such are the methods of all science whatsoever; but perhaps you will permit me to give you an illustration of their employment in the science of Life; and I will take as a special case the establishment of the doctrine of the *Circulation of the Blood*.

In this case, *simple observation* yields us a knowledge of the existence of the blood from some accidental hæmorrhage, we will say; we may even grant that it informs us of the localisation of this blood in particular vessels, the heart, &c., from some accidental cut or the like. It teaches also the existence of a pulse in various parts of the body, and acquaints us with the structure of the heart and vessels.

Here, however, *simple observation* stops, and we must have recourse to *experiment*.

You tie a vein, and you find that the blood accumulates on the side of the ligature opposite the heart. You tie an artery, and you find that the blood accumulates on the side near the heart. Open the chest, and you see the heart contracting with great force. Make openings into its principal cavities, and you will find that all the blood flows out, and no more pressure is exerted on either side of the arterial or venous ligature.

Now all these facts, taken together, constitute the evidence that the blood is propelled by the heart through the arteries, and returns by the veins—that, in short, the blood circulates.

Suppose our experiments and observations have been made on horses, then we group and ticket them into a general proposition thus:—*all horses have a circulation of their blood*.

Henceforward a horse is a sort of indication or label, telling us where we shall find a peculiar series of phænomena called the circulation of the blood.

Here is our *general proposition*, then.

How, and when, are we justified in making our next step—a *deduction* from it?

Suppose our physiologist, whose experience is limited to horses, meets with a zebra for the first time,—will he suppose that this generalization holds good for zebras also?

That depends very much on his turn of mind. But we will suppose him to be a bold man. He will say, "The zebra is certainly not a horse, but it is very like one,—so like, that it must be the 'ticket' or mark of a blood-circulation also; and I conclude that the zebra has a circulation."

That is a deduction, a very fair deduction, but by no means to be consided scientifically secure. This last quality in fact can only be given by *verification*—that is, by making a zebra the subject of all the experiments performed on the horse. Of course, in the present case, the *deduction* would be *confirmed* by this process of verification, and the result would be, not merely a positive widening of knowledge, but a fair increase of confidence in the truth of one's generalizations in other cases.

Thus, having settled the point in the zebra and horse, our philosopher would have great confidence in the existence of a circulation in the ass. Nay, I fancy most persons would excuse him, if in this case he did not take the trouble to go through the process of verification at all; and it would not be without a parallel in the history of the human mind, if our imaginary physiologist now maintained that he was acquainted with asinine circulation *à priori*.

However, if I might impress any caution upon your minds, it is the utterly conditional nature of all our knowledge,—the danger of neglecting the process of verification under any circumstances; and the film upon which we rest, the moment our deductions carry us beyond the reach of this great process of verification. There is no better instance of this than is afforded by the history of our knowledge of the circulation of the blood in the animal kingdom until the year 1824. In every animal possessing a circulation at all, which had been observed up to that time, the current of the blood was known to take one definite and invariable direction. Now, there is a class of animals called *Ascidians*, which possess a heart and a circulation, and up to the period of which I speak, no one would have dreamt of questioning the propriety of the deduction, that these creatures have a circulation in one direction; nor would any one have thought it worth while to verify the point. But, in that year, M. von Hasselt, happening to examine a transparent animal of this class, found, to his infinite surprise, that after the heart had beat a certain number of times, it stopped, and then began beating the opposite way—so as to reverse the course of the current, which returned by and by to its original direction.

I have myself timed the heart of these little animals. I found it as regular as possible in its periods of reversal: and I know no spectacle in the animal kingdom more wonderful than that which it presents—all the more wonderful that to this day it remains an unique fact, peculiar to this class among the whole animated world. At the same time I know of no more striking case of the necessity of the *verification* of even those deductions which seem founded on the widest and safest inductions.

Such are the methods of Biology—methods which are obviously identical with those of all other sciences, and therefore wholly incompetent to form the ground of any distinction between it and them.[5]

But I shall be asked at once, Do you mean to say that there is no difference between the habit of mind of a mathematician and that of a naturalist? Do you imagine that Laplace might have been put into the Jardin des Plantes, and Cuvier into the Observatory, with equal advantage to the progress of the sciences they professed?

To which I would reply, that nothing could be further from my thoughts. But different habits and various special tendencies of two sciences do not imply different methods. The mountaineer and the man of the plains have very different habits of progression, and each would be at a loss in the other's place; but the method of progression, by putting one leg before the other, is the same in each case. Every step of each is a combination of a lift and a push; but the mountaineer lifts more and the lowlander pushes more. And I think the case of two sciences resembles this.

I do not question for a moment, that while the Mathematician is busy with deductions *from* general propositions, the Biologist is more especially occupied with observation, comparison, and those processes which lead *to* general propositions. All I wish to insist upon is, that this difference depends not on any fundamental distinction in the sciences themselves, but on the accidents of their subject-matter, of their relative complexity, and consequent relative perfection.

The Mathematician deals with two properties of objects only, number and extension, and all the inductions he wants have been formed and finished ages ago. He is occupied now with nothing but deduction and verification.

The Biologist deals with a vast number of properties of objects, and his inductions will not be completed, I fear, for ages to come; but when they are, his science will be as deductive and as exact as the Mathematics themselves.

Such is the relation of Biology to those sciences which deal with objects having fewer properties than itself. But as the student, in reaching Biology, looks back upon sciences of a less complex and therefore more perfect nature; so, on the other hand, does he look forward to other more complex and less perfect branches of knowledge. Biology deals only with living beings as isolated things—treats only of the life of the individual; but there is a higher division of science still, which considers living beings as aggregates—which deals with the relation of living beings one to another —the science which *observes* men—whose *experiments* are made by nations one upon another, in battle-fields—whose *general propositions* are embodied in history, morality, and religion—whose *deductions* lead to our happiness or our misery—and whose *verifications* so often come too late, and serve only

"To point a moral, or adorn a tale"—

I mean the science of Society or *Sociology*.

I think it is one of the grandest features of Biology, that it occupies this central position in human knowledge. There is no side of the human mind which physiological study leaves uncultivated. Connected by innumerable ties with abstract science, Physiology is yet in the most intimate relation with humanity; and by teaching us that law and order, and a definite scheme of development, regulate even the strangest and wildest manifestations of individual life, she prepares the student to look for a goal even amidst the erratic wanderings of mankind, and to believe that history offers something more than an entertaining chaos—a journal of a toilsome, tragi-comic march nowhither.

The preceding considerations have, I hope, served to indicate the replies which befit the first two of the questions which I set before you at starting, viz. What is the range and position of Physiological Science as a branch of knowledge, and what is its value as a means of mental discipline?

Its *subject-matter* is a large moiety of the universe—its *position* is midway between the physico-chemical and the social sciences. Its *value* as a branch of discipline is partly that which it has in common with all sciences—the training and strengthening of common sense; partly that which is more peculiar to itself—the great exercise which it affords to the faculties of observation and comparison; and, I may add, the *exactness* of knowledge which it requires on the part of those among its votaries who desire to extend its boundaries.

If what has been said as to the position and scope of Biology be correct, our third question—What is the practical value of physiological instruction?—might, one would think, be left to answer itself.

On other grounds even, were mankind deserving of the title "rational," which they arrogate to themselves, there can be no question that they would consider, as the most necessary of all branches of instruction for themselves and for their children, that which professes to acquaint them with the conditions of the existence they prize so highly—which teaches them how to avoid disease and to cherish health, in themselves and those who are dear to them.

I am addressing, I imagine, an audience of educated persons; and yet I dare venture to assert that, with the exception of those of my hearers who may chance to have received a medical education, there is not one who could tell me what is the meaning and use of an act which he performs a score of times every minute, and whose suspension would involve his immediate death;—I mean the act of breathing—or who could state in precise terms why it is that a confined atmosphere is injurious to health.

The *practical value* of Physiological knowledge! Why is it that educated men can be found to maintain that a slaughter-house in the midst of a great city is rather a good thing than otherwise?—that mothers persist in exposing the largest possible amount of surface of their children to the cold, by the absurd style of dress they adopt, and then marvel at the peculiar dispensation of Providence, which removes their infants by bronchitis and gastric fever? Why is it that quackery rides rampant over the land; and that not long ago, one of the largest public rooms in this great city could be filled by an audience gravely listening to the reverend expositor of the doctrine—that the simple physiological phænomena known as spirit-rapping, table-turning, phreno-magnetism, and I know not what other absurd and inappropriate names, are due to the direct and personal agency of Satan?

Why is all this, except from the utter ignorance as to the simplest laws of their own animal life, which prevails among even the most highly educated persons in this country?

But there are other branches of Biological Science, besides Physiology proper, whose practical influence, though less obvious, is not, as I believe, less certain. I have heard educated men speak with an ill-disguised contempt of the studies of the naturalist, and ask, not without a shrug, "What is the use of knowing all about these miserable animals—what bearing has it on human life?"

I will endeavour to answer that question. I take it that all will admit there is definite Government of this universe—that its pleasures and pains are not scattered at random, but are distributed in accordance with orderly and fixed laws, and that it is only in accordance with all we know of the rest of the world, that there should be an agreement between one portion of the sensitive creation and another in these matters.

Surely then it interests us to know the lot of other animal creatures—however far below us, they are still the sole created things which share with us the capability of pleasure and the susceptibility to pain.

I cannot but think that he who finds a certain proportion of pain and evil inseparably woven up in the life of the very worms, will bear his own share with more courage and submission; and will, at any rate, view with suspicion those weakly amiable theories of the Divine government, which would have us believe pain to be an oversight and a mistake,—to be corrected by and by. On the other hand, the predominance of happiness among living things—their lavish beauty—the secret and wonderful harmony which pervades them all, from the highest of the lowest, are equally striking refutations of that modern Manichean doctrine, which exhibits the world as a slave-mill, worked with many tears, for mere utilitarian ends.

There is yet another way in which natural history may, I am convinced, take a profound hold upon practical life,—and that is, by its influence over our finer feelings, as the greatest of all sources of that pleasure which is derivable from beauty. I do not pretend that natural-history knowledge, as such, can increase our sense of the beautiful in natural objects. I do not suppose that the dead soul of Peter Bell, of whom the great poet of nature says,—

> A primrose by the river's brim,
> A yellow primrose was to him,—
> And it was nothing more,—

would have been a whit roused from its apathy by the information that the primrose is a Dicotyledonous Exogen, with a monopetalous corolla and central placentation. But I advocate natural-history knowledge from this point of view, because it would lead us to *seek* the beauties of natural objects, instead of trusting to chance to force them on our attention. To a person uninstructed in natural history, his country or sea-side stroll is a walk through a gallery filled with wonderful works of art, nine-tenths of which have their faces turned to the wall. Teach him something of natural history, and you place in his hands a catalogue of those which are worth turning around. Surely our innocent pleasures are not so abundant in this life, that we can afford to despise this or any other source of them. We should fear being banished for our neglect to that limbo, where the great Florentine tells us are those who, during this life, "wept when they might be joyful."

But I shall be trespassing unwarrantably on your kindness, if I do not proceed at once to my last point—the time at which Physiological Science should first form a part of the Curriculum of Education.

The distinction between the teaching of the facts of a science as instruction, and the teaching it systematically as knowledge, has already been placed before you in a previous lecture: and it appears to me that, as with other sciences, the *common facts* of Biology—the uses of parts of the body—the names and habits of the living creatures which surround us—may be taught with advantage to the youngest child. Indeed, the avidity of children for this kind of knowledge, and the comparative ease with which they retain it, is something quite marvellous. I doubt whether any toy would be so acceptable to young children as a vivarium of the same kind as, but of course on a smaller scale than, those admirable devices in the Zoological Gardens.

On the other hand, systematic teaching in Biology cannot be attempted with success until the student has attained to a certain knowledge of physics and chemistry: for though the phænomena of life are dependent neither on physical nor on chemical, but on vital forces, yet they result in all sorts of physical and chemical changes, which can only be judged by their own laws.

And now to sum up in a few words the conclusions to which I hope you see reason to follow me.

Biology needs no apologist when she demands a place—and a prominent place—in any scheme of education worthy of the name. Leave out the Physiological sciences from your curriculum, and you launch the student into the world, undisciplined in that science whose subject-matter would best develop his powers of observation; ignorant of facts of the deepest importance for his own and others' welfare; blind to the richest sources of beauty in God's creation; and unprovided with that belief in a living law, and an order manifesting itself in and through endless change and variety, which might serve to check and moderate that phase of despair through which, if he take an earnest interest in social problems, he will assuredly sooner or later pass.

Finally, one word for myself. I have not hesitated to speak strongly where I have felt strongly; and I am but too conscious that the indicative and imperative moods have too often taken the place of the more becoming subjunctive and conditional. I feel, therefore, how necessary it is to beg you to forget the personality of him who has thus ventured to address you, and to consider only the truth or error in what has been said.

[16]

WALTER B. CANNON

Self-Regulation of the Human Body*

Our bodies are made of extraordinarily unstable material. Pulses of energy, so minute that very delicate methods are required to measure them, course along our nerves. On reaching muscles they find there a substance so delicately sensitive to slight disturbance that, like an explosive touched off by a fuse, it may discharge in a powerful movement. Our sense organs are responsive to almost incredibly minute stimulations. Only recently have men been able to make apparatus which could even approach the sensitiveness of our organs of hearing. The sensory surface in the nose is affected by vanillin, 1 part by weight in 10,000,000 parts of air, and by mercaptan 1/23,000,000 of a milligram in a liter (approximately a quart) of air. And as for sight, there is evidence that the eye is sensitive to

* Reprinted from *The Wisdom of the Body* by Walter B. Cannon. Revised and enlarged edition, Copyright, 1939, by Walter B. Cannon. Pp. 19–25. By permission of W. W. Norton and Co., Inc., publishers.

5/1,000,000,000,000 erg, an amount of energy, according to Bayliss which is 1/3,000 that required to affect the most rapid photograph plate.

The instability of bodily structure is shown also by its quick change when conditions are altered. For example, we are all aware of the sudden stoppage of action in parts of the brain, accompanied by fainting and loss of consciousness, that occurs when there is a momentary check in the blood flow through its vessels. We know that if the blood supply to the brain wholly ceases for so short a time as seven or eight minutes certain cells which are necessary for intelligent action are so seriously damaged that they do not recover. Indeed, the high degree of instability of the matter of which we are composed explains why drowning, gas poisoning, or electric shock promptly brings on death. Examination of the body after such an accident may reveal no perceptible injury that would adequately explain the total disappearance of all the usual activities. Pathetic hope may rise that this apparently normal and natural form could be stirred to life gain. But there are subtle changes in the readily mutable stuff of the human organism which prevent, in these conditions, any return of vital processes.

When we consider the extreme instability of our bodily structure, its readiness for disturbance by the slightest application of external forces and the rapid onset of its decomposition as soon as favoring circumstances are withdrawn, its persistence through many decades seems almost miraculous. The wonder increases when we realize that the system is open, engaging in free exchange with the outer world, and that the structure itself is not permanent but is being continuously broken down by the wear and tear of action, and is continuously built up again by processes of repair.

II

The ability of living beings to maintain their own constancy has long impressed biologists. The idea that disease is cured by natural powers, by a *vis medicatrix naturae,* an idea which was held by Hippocrates (460–377 B.C.), implies the existence of agencies which are ready to operate correctively when the normal state of the organism is upset. More precise references to self-regulatory arrangements are found in the writings of modern physiologists. Thus the German physiologist, Pfluger, recognized the natural adjustments which lead toward the maintenance of a steady state of organisms when (1877) he laid down the dictum, "The cause of every need of a living being is also the cause of the satisfaction of the need." Similarly, the Belgian physiologist, Leon Fredericq, in 1885, declared, "The living being is an agency of such sort that each disturbing influence induces by itself the calling forth of compensatory activity to neutralize or repair the disturbance. The higher in the scale of living beings, the more numerous, the more perfect and the more complicated do these regulatory agencies become. They tend to free the organism completely from the unfavorable influences and changes occurring in the environment." Again, in 1900, the French physiologist, Charles Richet, emphasized the remarkable fact. "The living being is stable," he wrote. "It must be so in order not to be destroyed, dissolved or disintegrated by the colossal forces, often adverse, which surround it. By an apparent contradiction it maintains its stability only if it is excitable and capable of modifying itself according to external stimuli and adjusting its response to the stimulation. In a sense it is stable because it is modifiable—the slight instability is the necessary condition for the true stability of the organism."

Here, then, is a striking phenomenon. Organisms, composed of material which is characterized by the utmost inconstancy and unsteadiness, have somehow learned the methods of maintaining constancy and keeping steady in the presence of conditions which might reasonably be expected to prove profoundly disturbing. For a short time men may be exposed to dry heat at 115 to 128 degrees Centigrade (239 to 261 degrees Fahrenheit) without an increase of their body temperature above normal. On the other hand arctic mammals, when exposed to cold as low as 35 degrees Centigrade below freezing (31 degrees below zero Fahrenheit) do not manifest any noteworthy fall of body temperature. Furthermore, in regions where the air is extremely dry the inhabitants have little difficulty in retaining their body fluids. And in these days of high ventures in mountain climbing and in airplanes human beings may be surrounded by a greatly reduced pressure of oxygen in the air without showing serious effects of oxygen want.

Resistance to changes which might be induced by external circumstances is not the only evidence of adaptive stabilizing arrangements. There is also resistance to disturbances from within. For example, the heat produced in maximal muscular effort, continued for twenty minutes, would be so great that, if it were not promptly dissipated, it would cause some of the albuminous substances of the body to become stiff, like a hard-boiled egg. Again, continuous and extreme muscular exertion is accompanied by the production of so much lactic acid (the acid of sour milk) in the working muscles that within a short period it would neutralize all the alkali contained in the blood, if other agencies did not appear and prevent that disaster. In short, well-equipped organisms—for instance, mammalian forms—may be confronted by dangerous conditions in the outer world and by equally dangerous possibilities within the body, and yet they continue to live and carry on their functions with relatively little disturbance.

III

The statement was made above that somehow the unstable stuff of which we are composed had learned the trick of maintaining stability. As we shall see, the use of the word "learned" is not unwarranted. The perfection of the process of holding a stable state in spite of extensive shifts of outer circumstance is not a special gift bestowed upon the highest organisms but is the consequence of a gradual evolution. In the eons of time during which animals have developed on the earth probably many ways of protecting against the forces of the environment have been tried. Organisms have had large and varied experience in testing different devices for preserving stability in the face of agencies which are potent to upset and destroy it. As the construction of these organisms has become more and more complex and more and more sensitively poised, the need for more efficient stabilizing arrangements has become more imperative. Lower animals, which have not yet achieved the degree of control of stabilization seen in the more highly evolved forms, are limited in their activities and handicapped in the struggle for existence. Thus the frog, as a representative amphibian, has not acquired the means of preventing free evaporation of water from his body, nor has he an effective regulation of his temperature. In consequence he soon dries up if he leaves his home pool, and when cold weather comes he must sink to its muddy bottom and spend the winter in sluggish numbness. The reptiles, slightly more highly evolved, have developed protection against rapid loss of water and are therefore not confined in their movements to the neighborhood of pools and streams; indeed, they may be found as inhabitants of arid deserts. But they, like the amphibians, are "cold-blooded" animals, that is, they have approximately the temperature of their surroundings, and therefore during the winter months they must surrender their active existence. Only among the higher vertebrates, the birds and mammals, has there been acquired that freedom from the limitations imposed by cold that permits activity even though the rigors of winter may be severe.

The constant conditions which are maintained in the body might be termed *equilibria*. That word, however, has come to have fairly exact meaning as applied to relatively simple physico-chemical states, in closed systems, where known forces are balanced. The coordinated physiological processes which maintain most of the steady states in the organism are so complex and so peculiar to living beings—involving, as they may, the brain and nerves, the heart, lungs, kidneys, and spleen, all working cooperatively —that I have suggested a special designation for these states, *homeostasis*. The word does not imply something set and immobile, a stagnation. It means a condition—a condition which may vary, but which is relatively constant.

It seems not impossible that the means employed by the more highly evolved animals for preserving uniform and stable their internal economy (i.e., for preserving homeostasis) may present some general principles for the establishment, regulation and control of steady states, that would be suggestive for other kinds of organization—even social and industrial— which suffer from distressing perturbations. Perhaps a comparative study would show that every complex organization must have more or less effective self-righting adjustments in order to prevent a check on its functions or a rapid disintegration of its parts when it is subjected to stress.

And it may be that an examination of the self-righting methods employed in the more complex living beings may offer hints for improving and perfecting the methods which still operate inefficiently and unsatisfactorily. . . .

[17]

E. S. RUSSELL

The 'Drive' Element in Life*

If we look at living things quite simply and objectively we cannot but be struck by one feature of their activities, which seems to mark them off from anything inorganic. This is the active, persistent and regulatory nature of these activities. In this short article I shall try to illustrate and defend the thesis that there is common to all living things this basic element of directive striving, usually unconscious and blind, only rarely emerging into consciousness to become intelligently purposive. The master-end towards which the directive and persistent activities of the individual life converge is the completion of the life-cycle, including as a rule reproductive preparations for the repetition of the life-cycle in the ensuing generation. This thesis I stated on a former occasion in the following terms. Emphasizing the essentially *active* nature of life, I wrote: 'Structuro-functional wholeness or integrity, and specific structure, are actively built up and maintained in the course of development, chiefly by the morphogenetic and behavioural activity of cells or groups of cells. If this integrity is disturbed by injury or adverse environmental influences, it is, so far as possible, restored by appropriate physiological or morphogenetic activities on the part of the organism and its cells, so that the normal state is restored or a new adaptive norm of structure and function set up. The organism actively seeks out and selects the substances necessary for its metabolism, or draws them from its stores. It actively seeks in many cases its appropriate environment, and strives to maintain itself therein; it actively seeks in many cases a suitable ecological niche for its eggs and offspring. In all these ways, and in many others, the organism strives to persist in its own being, and to reach its normal completion or actualisation. This striving is not as a rule a conscious one, nor is there often any foresight of the end, but it exists all the same, as the very core of the organism's being.'[1]

* From *The British Journal for the Philosophy of Science*, Vol. I, no. 2 (August 1950), pp. 108–116, with the permission of the author, editor (Dr. A. C. Crombie), and the publisher (Thomas Nelson and Sons, Ltd.).

An array of facts was set out in the book containing the passage in justification of this thesis, and I shall not attempt to repeat or summarise them. Instead, I shall adduce some further instances in support, and then consider briefly what may be the relation between our own experience of striving and the unconscious drive-like, 'triebartig', character of organic activities, both morphogenetic and behavioural.

2

One aspect of the active striving nature of life is familiar under the guise of the 'struggle for existence'. All good observers of animals and plants in their natural surroundings, from Charles Darwin downward, have emphasized the strenuous character of the struggle for life and the struggle for reproduction. A classical example is the persistent growth towards the light of the trees and creepers in a tropical forest, vividly described by Hingston in the following passage : 'Like the trees, the lianas are also struggling to get upward. Too weak of themselves, they need the shoulders of others. Ever on the look out for some object to grip, they curl or twine themselves around their victims, or shoot forth roots that cling into the bark, or hook themselves to objects by curved spines, or stretch out arm-like projections that grip the sides of the stems and trunks. In the end by some contrivance or another they get up and free themselves into the light. They are in a new world and a transformation follows. The dried-up twisted leafless cables shoot out branches in every direction, a tangled mat develops with profusion of foliage, smothering the tree up which it has scrambled and extending into the mats and branches of its neighbours, covering perhaps a dozen of them with its leafy pall, and at last bursting into flower, the final purpose of its long climb.' [2] This example illustrates nicely the double purpose of the climber's struggle towards the light—to satisfy its own needs for growth and self-maintenance and to produce its seeds in suitable surroundings, in a word to complete or fulfil its normal life-cycle. It must be borne in mind that the struggle for existence and persistence is not primarily a struggle against other organisms, an internecine strife with neighbours, but essentially an individual struggle to obtain the means of life and to reproduce the race. There is inevitably competition, and the weak or unlucky go to the wall, but this is a consequence of the individual *conatus* of striving towards life and reproduction.

The active persistent nature of growth and development is particularly well marked in plants, and there are many familiar examples—the persistent and oft-repeated growth of the dandelion from a stubbed root, the way in which it forces itself up to the light through an inch or so of tarred foot-path, the shooting up of new branches from a truncated oak, the extraordinary way in which the roots of a birch or a pine burrow into and grip the most unpromising rock surfaces and afford precarious foothold for the tree. In his description of the Canadian scene in *The Transplanted*, Frederic Niven well illustrates this, when he writes, 'Still among boulders,

boulders as big as cottages, were a few trees here and there, trees that spread long roots out to great length, roots that gripped the rock claw-like, and took small hold on dust in their crevices'.

In animals the persistent and striving character of vital activities is shown most clearly in their behaviour, as in the drive to satisfy hunger or to mate. The strength of the sex drive is well known to us from personal experience, and the most casual observation of our domestic animals reveals the active, strenuous and continuing nature of their sexual and reproductive behaviour. Think of a dog pursuing a bitch in heat, or a broody hen intent on satisfying her drive to incubate a clutch of eggs. All this is familiar and obvious—so obvious that we are apt to forget its significance.

But in animals directive effort is manifest not only in their behavioural actions but also in their morphogenetic and physiological activities, which at all stages of the life-cycle maintain and restore norms of function and structure, and replace what is missing, as in the healing of wounds and in regeneration—within the limits of the possible. Such activities do not proceed smoothly and automatically, or with a machine-like rigidity towards a fixed end. They are, especially in difficult conditions, flexible, persistent and variable. This characteristic of persistency with varied effort is most conspicuous in behavioural action, of which many examples could be adduced. I have tried to summarise these special characteristics of organic directive activity as follows [3]—When the goal is reached, action ceases, but if it is not reached, action usually persists and is often varied, alternative modes of action being employed if the normal one fails to attain the goal. Accordingly the goal may be reached in different ways, the end-state or terminus of action being more constant than the mode of reaching it.

As the goals to which organic activities are directive and persistent are normally related to the main biological ends of development, self-maintenance and reproduction, the direction of these activities is towards the completion or fulfilment of the life-cycle. Life-cycle completion is indeed the master law governing all the activities of the organism, to which other laws of smaller scope, such as the law of need-satisfaction, are subordinate.

In normal conditions the activities of the life-cycle proceed in a stereotyped fashion, repeating in detail the life-cycle of previous generations, though not without active effort, as in an animal's struggle to obtain food or the growth-effort of a plant to reach the light. But when conditions are difficult, and especially whene there is operational interference by man, the stereotyped course of life-cycle activities is upset, and adaptive responses become necessary if norms are to be restored and the life-cycle completed. In many organisms, if not in all, such adaptive or directive reactions to unusual or even unprecedented situations are forthcoming, though in different degree in different organisms.

Even in the earliest stages of embryogeny, if differentiation has not proceeded too far, regulatory activities will lead to the production of a normal embryo from a half or a quarter of the segmenting egg. This in itself is perhaps not very remarkable, and may even be susceptible of explanation in dynamic terms, as Bertalanffy [4] maintains. But there are other phenomena of embryonic regulation which seem to prove the existence of a drive to restore normality from abnormal beginnings, even if the drive be not fully successful. A good example is that described by Holtfreter, who writes: 'Perhaps one of the most impressive illustrations of the puzzling complexity and at the same time of the "sensefulness" of the individuation process is provided by the following experiment. Several blastoporal lips from early gastrulae of *Amblystoma punctatum* were cut out and exposed for about 10 minutes to alkali, which caused them to disintegrate into a heap of single, amoeboid cells. The disorganisation was carried still further by stirring and intermingling the free cells by means of a glass needle. When the suspension fluid was subsequently neutralised, the cells reaggregated into one or several spherical bodies, the cellular arrangement of which was of course quite different from the original one in the gastrula. During the following days there occurred a certain amount of reorganisation, for instead of retaining their random distribution, the cells performed directed movements which led to their sorting out and regrouping into two germ layers; all mesodermal cells tended to disappear from surface positions and to slip into the interior of the bodies, while the endodermal cells, in competition with ectodermal cells, went to establish continuous, well oriented surface epithelia. The internal mass of mesoderm became further segregated into the distinctly separated tissues of notochord, somites and kidney. The latter formed long coils of nephric tubules provided with nephrostomes and surrounded by blood capillaries. The notochord cells, though not united into a single straight cord, were, on the other hand, not freely dispersed but appeared in the form of a continuous, slightly dendritic organ. Finally, the skeletal muscle cells were grouped into somites, the arrangement of which was, however, irregular.' [5] In this remarkable case, through directive cell-migrations, selective cellular adhesions and mutual inductive action, there was formed from quite abnormal beginnings an approximation to a normal organisation. The complex activities concerned have all the appearance of co-operative striving to reach a normal end in conditions quite unprecedented in the history of the race. The experiment recalls the somewhat similar phenomenon of the reconstitution of sponges from dissociated cells.

In many organisms the loss of a part of the body or of an organ leads to its replacement by regeneration, restoring thus the structuro-functional integrity which is necessary for continued life and the completion of the life-cycle. The activities concerned may be very complex, involving not a simple replacement but a complete remodelling of the remaining parts in such a way as to re-constitute a new whole, as in 'morphallaxis' in planarians and polychaets.

It is noteworthy that organs may be regenerated which are not likely to be lost or destroyed in the ordinary course of events, but have been removed experimentally by surgical operation. There is the classical case of the regeneration (from the upper edge of the iris) of the lens extirpated from the eye of certain species of newt, a case which led G. Wolff, who discovered it, to postulate the existence in living things of a primary, not evolved, power of 'purposive' or directive response. It has even been shown that in certain mammals, after the complete removal by surgical operation of the ovaries, new ovaries can be formed from non-ovarian tissues, and that this is followed in some cases by normal pregnancy.[6] Such a response to the loss of the ovaries could never have occurred in the whole history of the race.

Adaptive response, as in regeneration, compensatory hypertrophy and functional adaptation generally, is a phenomenon widespread in the organic realm, coming into play when the normal course of life-cycle activities is hindered or thwarted by unfavourable circumstances or by the experimental interference of man. It is shown in very varied degree, but the power is never completely absent.

In the life-cycle of most organisms adaptive response is directive towards satisfying the needs and restoring the norms of the individual itself, including its need for reproduction. In highly organised insect societies, however, adaptive response may serve the needs, not of the individual insect, but of the colony or 'social organism' as a whole. The late W. M. Wheeler, one of the best philosophical biologists, in the interesting parallel he drew between the organism and the insect society, well illustrated this remarkable fact. 'If the worker personnel be removed from a young ant colony', he wrote, 'leaving only the fertile queen, we find that this insect, if provided with a sufficiently voluminous fat-body, will set to work and rear another brood, or in other words, regenerate the missing soma (of the colony). . . . On the other hand, if the queen alone be removed, one of the workers will often develop its ovaries and take on the egg-laying function of the queen. In ants such substitution queens, or gynaecoid workers, are not fertilised and are therefore unable to assume their mother's worker and queen-producing functions. The termites, however, show a remarkable provision for restituting both of the fertile parents of the colony from the so-called complemental males and females'.[7] These complemental males and females are less developed forms of the 'royal' caste, and take on the reproductive functions of the true kings and queens when these are removed from the colony. In this way the maintenance, development and reproduction of the termite state is ensured.

How the needs of the hive are supplied in normal conditions by the directive activities of the worker-bees has been fully elucidated by the researches of K. von Frisch and his collaborators, and they have shown also in what a remarkable manner the workers overcome the difficulties in providing for these needs which they encounter when their normal procedure is drastically upset by experimental interference. In the ordinary course of events the workers go through a regular cycle of activities, which is closely correlated with the state of development of their salivary and wax glands. In the first period of a worker-bee's active life, up to about the 10th day, its main occupation is the care of the larvae, which it nourishes with the secretion from its highly developed salivary glands, together with honey and pollen which it draws from the storage cells in the combs. During its second period, from the 10th to the 20th day, the salivary glands atrophy, and the wax glands on the underside of the abdomen develop greatly. At this stage in the cycle it produces wax and builds cells as required, also it cleans the hive, stores the food brought in by the foraging workers, makes its first orientation flights, and for the last two or three days acts as a watcher at the threshold of the hive. In the third and last period of its life it takes on the duty of foraging for honey and pollen, and during this stage its wax glands atrophy.

By an ingenious method Rösch contrived to separate the young workers from the old gang; all the bees were first driven into one half of the hive (A) and shut off from the other half (B); then the hive was turned round 180°; the younger bees remained in half A, intent on their domestic duties, while the older bees flew off on foraging expeditions; when they returned they flew to their accustomed entrance which however led them into the B half of the hive only. Thus half A was inhabited by younger workers only, while half B was the home of the older bees. The half containing the young bees was accordingly without foragers, and food stores were soon used up. After a couple of days some of the bees lay starving on the bottom of the hive, and some of the larvae had been torn out of their cells and sucked to satisfy the food-need of the young bees. But on the third day a remarkable change in behaviour was observed. Bees of only one to two weeks in age went out foraging and came back laden with food, this in spite of the fact that their salivary glands were fully developed and their normal task was the feeding of the brood. The needs of the hive and not their stage of bodily organisation determined this adaptive modification of their normal behaviour; their salivary glands rapidly atrophied.

The older bees based on half B had been deprived of the younger stock that normally act as nurses and feeders of the larvae, but some of them that still had salivary glands in a functional state stepped into the breach and fed the young, retaining their glands in action long beyond the normal time. Here again the needs of the hive were attended to, rather than individual needs.

In another experiment by Rösch a hive was robbed of its building workers, and put in a situation where the construction of new comb became urgently necessary. The building of new cells was undertaken by bees that had passed the normal age for this task and whose wax glands were in course of disappearing. The remarkable fact came to light, through microscopical examination, that in these bees the fat-body had pressed itself up against the reduced wax glands and caused them to re-develop. K. von Frisch, from whose summary I take this account of Rösch's experiments, makes an interesting remark apropos of this last finding, to the effect that 'Man ist versucht, zu sagen: Der Wille regiert den Körper'.

But he cautiously adds, 'Doch wir wissen nichts vom Willen der Biene und lassen das Rätsel ungelöst'.[8]

3

We have now surveyed a number of examples, drawn from quite different fields, which illustrate what I have called the active, persistent and regulatory character of organic activities, as shown particularly in adaptive response, whether behavioural or morphogenetic. Now we as conscious subjects have direct and immediate knowledge or experience of this element of drive or striving towards biological ends which appears from objective evidence to be a characteristic common to all or many organic activities. We are part of Nature, and there must therefore be some relation between our experienced striving and that observed in other organisms. What then can be the relation between this experienced drive and the objective 'drive-character' of organic activities in general? Must we not think of them as two aspects—internal and external—of the same basic reality? Must we not postulate a general, supra-individual hormé or drive in life, after the fashion of Schopenhauer's 'Wille'? To do so would be to go beyond the bounds of science into the realm of metaphysical speculation. It is obviously impossible in a short essay to follow up and discuss this hormic theory of life, and I shall content myself with a few observations.

It is clear that there is nothing to be gained by trying to interpret morphogenetic and physiological activities in psychological terms such as are applicable to our own activity as conscious subjects. It is possible, within limits, to interpret the behaviour of animals in such terms, as Bierens de Haan [9] in particular has shown, but this mode of interpretation becomes increasingly doubtful and uncertain when we try to apply it to animals very different from ourselves, and appears highly hypothetical if applied to morphogenetic activities, though this attempt has been made by Agar.[10] Yet it seems certain that there is some element or factor in organic activities generally which cannot be a property of a purely physical system, and our only clue to its nature is that it must in some sense be psychological.[11] We know that we ourselves are psycho-physical unities, and certainly not purely physical systems, and we have every right to extend this conception to organisms in general.

We have a clue to the nature of directive activity in our own experience of striving. This is only a partial clue, and it is liable to be a misleading one, for our behavioural activity, which alone is directly known to us, is for the most part of a unique kind, not found elsewhere in the organic realm. It is often guided by conceptual thought; we pursue ends already explicitly present in consciousness, and our behaviour is to that extent intelligently purposive. But by no means all our behaviour-life reaches this purposive level; much of it is rooted in unconscious desires and impulses, closely related with our bodily and physiological state, as for instance in the hunger or the sex drive. Such instinctive and often unconscious drives we share with other animals, and these drives, we know, are not purely psychical but psycho-physical. We have therefore *some* direct insight into the nature of one form of directive activity, namely instinctive behaviour. Now there is, as I have pointed out in my *Directiveness of Organic Activities,* a close analogy between instinctive behaviour and directive activity in general. They have the same characteristics of persistency with varied effort towards reaching goals that are normally related to biological ends, without foreknowledge of those ends. The conclusion therefore seems reasonable that in directive activity generally, and not only in instinctive behaviour, there must be an element which we can conceive only as psychological, as a function of a psycho-physical organism.

As I have already said, this is not the occasion to discuss the very difficult question of the nature of organism and of directive activity. I have been concerned only to indicate a possible line of approach.

[18]

SIR CHARLES SHERRINGTON

Man On His Nature *

The physiologist has finer means now than ever before for asking the ways and doings of the brain. Electrical technique enables him to detect happenings in the brain which formerly he could not, and in that very part of the brain which evidence bespeaks as having correlation with the mind. In the pigeon suffering from beri-beri, along with dramatic relief of its symptoms by vitamin B_1, runs dramatic improvement of the impaired respiratory process in the brain (Peters). The roof-brain is more sensitive to shortage of oxygen than is the brain elsewhere. There is disturbance of thought and derangement of ideas. Barcroft, in the High Andes, observed disaptitude for arithmetic. Glucose, the typical physiological sugar, is urgently important to the brain. The brain draws it from the blood. It does not, as do some organs, take it into storage. It takes it to use it at once. Judged by its chemical turn-over the brain is not a homogeneous organ any more than it is as judged by its microscopical structure. In the roof-brain or cortex the need for oxygen is greater than in nearly every other part. Narcotics diminish the oxidation of sugar by the brain. When the quantity of sugar supplied to the brain by the blood-stream is less the

* From *Man On His Nature,* The Gifford Lectures (Cambridge University Press, 2d edition, 1951). Pp. 218–230 by permission of the publisher.

oxidative turn-over is less owing to the lack of oxidative food. Without vitamin B the brain cannot make proper use of glucose as a food. Thought and behaviour alter. If the conditions be prolonged, unconsciousness ensues, and if prolonged further the brain-cells are permanently damaged. But if not so prolonged when the normal supply of sugar is restored the brain-cells recover and thought and behaviour again become normal.

It is however by electrical means that the activity of nervous organs can be most intimately followed. Electrical potentials indicate nerve activity closely and quickly. The nerve-impulse—the process by which universally, and perhaps exclusively, nerve-cells communicate one with another—seems in essence electrical. Travelling impulses of less than a thousandth of a thousandth of a volt and lasting as they pass any spot, one/10,000th of a second only, are photographed or seen or listened to, and in their almost undistorted time-relations. They are fleeting and self-mending electrical leaks which move along the skin of the nerve-thread. Intensity of action does not increase an impulse but sets up successive impulses more quickly. When we speak of a nerve or of the brain as being at rest in the sense that nervous impulses are not travelling it, the expression 'at rest' stands simply for another and a steadier activity. The disturbance which we call 'action' can be thought of as rhythmic, and rhythmic at different rates. Its upset, which is 'action', is not an equilibrium, it cannot be maintained long. It spends a reserve which will have to be made good. It brings in its train 'fatigue'.

It may be objected that it is not nerve-impulses which are likely to tell us what we want to know of the brain. They are a concern of nerve-fibres. Nerve-fibres are merely the wires to and from the telephone-exchange. We want the activities of the exchange itself. Activity of the brain involves great numbers, not to say, vast numbers, of nerve-cells co-operating. Yet the means of securing that co-operation is by impulses via the nerve-fibres connecting cells. A large and an essential part of even the highest brain activity must therefore consist of nerve-impulses.

They come probably from the surface-sheet of the brain cells. The rhythm of the beat is not too quick to be easily distinguishable. But our consciousness knows nothing about it. Through all the ages no suspicion of it has dawned upon us. Not even when now told of it do we feel it. The seat of the rhythm is in the visual region of the brain; vision sees nothing of it. Yet with a shift of mind the beat is altered; to open the closed eyes immediately disturbs it. It is possible to upset the rhythm by trying, without opening the eyes, to see something. A flash of light on the eye and a whole series of waves can be picked up from the visual part of the brain.

.   .   .   .

Physiology has got so far therefore as examining the electrical activity in a 'mental' part of the brain when activity there is in normal progress. But has it brought us to the 'mind'? It has brought us to the brain as a telephone-exchange. All the exchange consists of its switches. What we wanted really of the brain was the subscribers using the exchange. The subscribers with their thoughts, their desires, their anticipations, their motives, their anxieties, their rejoicings. If it is for mind that we are searching the brain, then we are supposing the brain to be much more than a te'ephone-exchange. We are supposing it a telephone-exchange along with the subscribers as well. Does our admirably delicate electrical exploration vouchsafe us any word about them? Its finger is ultra-sensitive, but energy is all that it can feel. And is the mind in any strict sense energy?

The 'subject' whose eye opens and whose brain-waves then alter, experiences as the most significant fact of the moment the mental change that he now sees something whereas before he did not.

It is now some eighty years since the words of a great biological leader of his time to his hearers were 'the thoughts to which I am now giving utterance and your thoughts regarding them are the expression of molecular changes in that matter of life which is the source of our other vital phenomena' (T. H. Huxley).

In the training and in the exercise of medicine a remoteness abides between the field of neurology and that of mental health, psychiatry. It is sometimes blamed to prejudice on the part of the one side or the other. It is both more grave and less grave than that. It has a reasonable basis. It is rooted in the energy-mind problem. Physiology has not enough to offer about the brain in relation to the mind to lend the psychiatrist much help. It has occupied itself largely with what are called the lower levels of nervous action. Results of general value have emerged. The nature of the nerve-impulse, the properties of cell-contacts as one-way gates compelling one-way traffic on nerve-paths, the occurrence not only of action but of active suppression of action, the knowledge that intensity of action means not larger impulses but more frequent impulses, that impulse-effects can sum, or cancel, that there are places where impulses spontaneously arise. Much of this knowledge certainly applies to the brain, and to that part of it which interests us here, the roof of the forebrain. Every nerve-cell of the millions in it is clearly at a glance a nerve-cell. But nerve-cells as a class are elsewhere not specially concerned with mind. It is partly conjecture whether the properties of all these nerve-cells, their fibres, their cell-contacts (synapses), their cell-bodies, have rigidly those characters observed in the more accessible nerve-cells of the spinal cord and elsewhere. That the properties will not differ fundamentally from those elsewhere seems safe to suppose. Were for instance the one-way traffic along nervous paths which obtains in the spinal cord not to hold in the case of paths in the roof-brain, that would allow new possibilities of interaction which our present interpretation does not bargain for.

In one respect the highly specialized nerve-cells most studied, those of the spinal cord, fail as a type of nerve-cells in general. Their specialization for reflex action has reduced to vanishing point the feature of self-excitation. The rhythmic volleying of cell-groups in the roof-brain may be such self-stimulation. But self-firing in itself gives no presumption for correla-

tion between the roof-brain and mind. The roof-brain cells, whether because the latest and so less stereotyped in their ways than others of hoary
ancestral tradition, are more plastic and open to modification than the old.
They can attach old motor acts to fresh unwonted calls on them. They
can acquire new habits. Then, as counterpart to that, if we pass over to
'mind' they compose the organ which *par excellence* can learn.

A certain proportion of what we call living nature can learn. What is
commonly called the survival of the fittest turns partly on the capacity of
certain forms of life to learn. Not that what is learnt is inherited. But the
ability to learn favours survival and is heritable. A vast number, perhaps
the numerical majority, of animal forms cannot be shown unequivocally
to possess mind. But none the less the student of their behaviour finds
that while they 'seek' and prolong contact with some items of their surround, e.g. food, they 'avoid' or break off contact with other items, which
would harm them. Thus with the reflex action of the brain-less frog, a
morsel of paper wet with acid is pushed away (defence) by the mindless
limb or the limb is withdrawn from it (escape). This class of reflexes which
imply defence or escape are known as 'protective'. They are behaviour
which in higher forms of life where mind is recognizable have mental
accompaniment, and their mental accompaniment is 'pain'. The act and
the pain then make one integral reaction. In the spinal dog the limbs are
insentient; yet, if one foot tread on a thorn, it is at once held up out of
further harm while the other three legs run away. The protective reflex is
there, but the little wound causes no pain, because it has no nexus with
the mind. Again, in appendicitis, the muscles are characteristically
tightened over the inflamed part; thus protecting it and keeping it quiet.
This is reflex contraction, so automatic that the patient cannot even relax
it. It is quite separable from the pain, for ether inhalation will annul the
pain by paralysing the brain long before it annuls the contraction.

The protective reflexes are painful and innate. Their service we may
suppose has given them survival value. An acute psychical urge is 'pain'.
This urge reinforces and amplifies the measure of protection and relief
the pure reflex act affords. Being mental it develops the situation into a
mental situation involving perception and affect and imbuing it with
'time' and 'space', the attributes of mind. This mental reaction, like the
pure reflex it accompanies, is protective but comprising 'time' as it does
it is not indefinitely of *any* moment as is the reflex. Its 'pain' brands it
into the time-system of the finite mind as unpleasant and not to be repeated. It is a 'lesson'. 'The burnt child shuns the fire.' The experiments
of Thorndike and of Pavlov show how important this is in the methodology of training. It has a positive counterpart, training by reward.

Here our contact with it turns merely on two points. One is the
practically universal distribution through animal life of a special set of
receptor organs whose sole scope is that of making the animal react to
infliction of physical injury, and making it react either by 'defence' or
'escape'. This shows us that extraneous injury to life is taken by Nature

as part of the normal routine of life. This special set of so-called 'noci-ceptor' organs, which evokes protective movements, seems more widely broadcast in the animal series than is recognizable mind itself. It is found in animal forms where there is no evidence of mind. In animal forms however which partake of mind its noci-ceptor organs pertain to sentience, and provoke 'pain'. Physical pain is thus the psychical adjunct of a protective reflex. The only modality of sense which the noci-ceptor organ evokes is pain. Other of our sense-organs evoke their modes of sensation—sight, hearing, touch, cold, warmth, smell, bitter, sweet, and so on—without 'pain', but these injury-organs provoke pain and nothing but pain. They are pain-organs and are called so.

Their specific stimulus is, in the narrow sense, not specific at all, but in the biological sense it is specific enough. It is anything which does injury to the part it reaches. The little pain-organ so to say watches over the part at and immediately around where it is situate. Pain therefore is in the evolution of mind treated and provided for as part of the normal economy of animate nature; further it is the more developed the higher its organism in the scale of mind. It does not require much study of the pain-organs and their arrangement to show that the infliction of injury which they envisage and react to is in vast preponderance injury inflicted by other species of life. The infliction of injury by one species of life upon another is therefore treated by Nature as part of Nature's normal scheme.

The body has a special sense of its own injuries, drastically affecting the mind as to capture the mind's attention even to exclusion for the time being of all else. The development of this pain-sense has the interest that it illustrates the mental side of the organism as effectively for defence of the body. For all the evidence we have evolution draws no pragmatic distinction between the two. A mental event, pain, superadded to a reflex, the protective reflex, seems here to reinforce and amplify the physical act. The local reflex itself affords its limited protection and relief, e.g. by holding the part taut and quiet. But the 'pain' through the mind can enjoin keeping the whole body motionless though tense. In ourselves, social and sophisticated, it may provoke the train of action of 'calling in' the doctor. In short, under the rubric 'pain' we meet mind moving matter to help mind in mind's distress. Mind invoking the body to do something and, in spite of the eternal psycho-physical difficulty, effectively. 'Pain' seems to pay no heed to that old dilemma. My raging tooth drives me to the dentist.

The roof-brain is the nervous organ which *par excellence* can learn by experience, and it deals with final causes. One structural feature of it is so pronounced that, as a dry fact, it is impressive. Its cell-population is enormous. The numbers in our own brain-roof run to ten thousand millions (Judson Herrick). To microscope this nerve-mass is to be struck by a seemingly reckless profusion of nerve-cells. It is the reason of the greater size of the higher types of brain. In the dog it is larger than the whole of the rest of the nervous system taken together. In ourselves the relation is hugely increased further. It is out of all proportion to our bodily bulk. As old Laurent Joubert said [1] the brain of a man is larger than the brains of two oxen together. In the bygone geological world some of life's ancient shapes attained bodies 100 feet in length; but they had a forebrain not larger than a nut. Our forebrain is so large as to bulge out the contour of the head. Our forebrain is a monster forebrain. It is the ball-like top-end of us. It is an overgrown nerve-ganglion protected by a bony case. Our sophistication and prejudice may regard it as a thing of beauty. It symbolizes our prerogative, human mind, and in common belief contains it.

Of three aspects of mind broadly distinguishable, the affective, conative, and cognitive, one inference perhaps to be drawn from the human brain is that growth of cognitive processes makes wholesale demand on numbers of nerve-cells. We can understand how this might be if a principle such as the 'association' of old-time psychology be largely engaged in it. An automatic card-index on an enormous scale with copious cross-references may be asked for. This part of the brain is evidently cumulative in time. And so is knowledge. May it not be that there is a correlation between the two? Again, where intellectual activity is required it is as though a pressure-reservoir were kept at hand. This great many-celled spongework in the human roof-brain is something like a continuum from end to end furnished with perhaps a million discharging mouths. It might well provide reinforcement, and reinforce vicariously as occasion requires here or there. The cerebellum was once thought a reservoir-organ for reinforcing the motor powers of the cerebrum. Apart from that restricted strip whence electricity can evoke bodily movement, by far the greater part of the roof-brain is, as the phrase goes, 'silent', that is in response to electricity yields nothing detectable at all. There is the psychological theory that a general factor, g, enters into mental ability. Of this Spearman its author tells us that a permissible picture of it is as a 'power' which can be supplied to the mental factory from a general power-station and distributed to any required particular engine. Lashley would perhaps identify g with a 'mass-action' of the cortex of the brain.

The neural basis of affect we can suppose need not entail much neural superstructure. It might use chemical reinforcement. This lets us stress the roof-organ of the forebrain as especially cognitive, with below it the old kernel-organ of the forebrain especially related to 'affect'; and we remember that every cognition has, potentially at least, an emotive value; emotive, and, along with that, conative effort as a further factor. How do they hang together? What is the significance of their so doing? Not in man alone but infra-humanly in due degrees, no doubt less cognitive. What is the tie which conjoins these several aspects of mind so inseparably? What is it else than 'urge-to-live'? Human cognition may like the winged horse take at times its flights toward the stars and forget earth.

None the less it is harnessed to life's car, whose charioteer is 'urge-to-live' sublimed to 'zest-to-live'. It and its fellow-steeds, endeavour, will, emotion, passion or whatever else we call them pull under the same lash.

The student of the mind, for instance the practical psychiatrist at the mental hospital, must find the physiology of the brain still remote and vague for his desiderata on his subject. He may have hoped from it some knowledge which would serve to found the norm from which psycho-pathology could take its points of departure in this direction or in that. There is for instance the condition 'anxiety'. None is I suppose more far-reaching as a warper of the mind. But where does neuro-physiology con-tribute anything to the knowledge of the norm from which anxiety causes departure, and what has cerebral physiology to offer on the whole subject of 'anxiety'? The psychiatrist has perforce to go on his way seeking things more germane to what he needs. The mind is a something with such mani-fold variety, such fleeting changes, such countless nuances, such wealth of combinations, such heights and depths of mood, such sweeps of passion, such vistas of imagination, that the bald submission of some electrical potentials recognizable in nerve-centres as correlative to all these may seem to the special student of mind almost derisory. It is, further, more than mere lack of corresponding complexity which frustrates the comparison.

The mental is not examinable as a form of energy. That in brief is the gap which parts psychiatry and physiology. No mere running round the cycle of the 'forms of energy' takes us across that chasm. Perhaps that is what William Macdougall [2] was meaning when he exclaimed, 'medicine has nothing to learn from psychology nor psychology from medicine'.

The question of the relation between the working of the brain and the working of the mind is, we hear often, one improper to put. It is 'by nature insoluble', 'ignorabimus', 'the data at the present time are insufficient', or it is not of practical importance. The cogency of these grounds depends, I would think, partly on the purpose for which the question may be asked. It may serve 'pour préciser les idées'. And to do that may have urgency. Witness the training of the psychiatrist and the physiologist. Only *after* the question has been discussed can they go on their respective ways, as perforce they ultimately must, disappointed it may be, but wiser, if sadder, practitioners and men.

In such an impasse it seems permissible for the man in the street, such as myself, to outline to himself briefly, although he can do so but naïvely, the position. It was easy for the old classical *a priori* materialism to run rough-shod over mind. It used the term matter without any scien-tific delimitation of the concept. It was a doctrine which knew far less and spread itself far more than does the scientific study of matter, or energy, today. What is the reply when to the student of energy, in other words to the follower of Natural Science, there comes today someone who asks, 'Mind presents itself as thoughts, feelings, and so on. They are the out-come of the brain. The brain is matter, energy. Matter and energy can only be matter and energy. Therefore thoughts, feelings and so on are matter and energy. Therefore mind is matter and energy?' I trust I do no violence to the argument; I have no wish to do so. The reply by the follower of Natural Science of today, if I as a man in the street may guess it, will not be, even in trend, at all like that which Lucretius gave in a famous and vehement passage, about specially small and well-rounded atoms. Such materialism was merely a frame of mind. The materialist standpoint today is a scientific position. Its answer today is of a different order. As I surmise it, it would say: Thoughts, feelings, and so on are not amenable to the energy (matter) concept. They lie outside it. Therefore they lie outside Natural Science. If as you say thoughts are an outcome of the brain we as students using the energy-concept know nothing of it; as followers of natural science we know nothing of any relation between thoughts and the brain, except as a gross correlation in time and space.

In some ways this is embarrasing for biology. Biology cannot go far in its subject without being met by mind. Biology as its name says is the study of life. And biology is a branch of natural science. Natural science has studied life to the extent of explaining away life as any radically separate category of phenomena. The categories of living and lifeless as regards science disappear; there is no radical scientific difference between living and dead. Time was when to think and to breathe were on an equality as attributes of life. Now, living, so far as breathing, moving, assimilating, growing, reproducing, etc. amounts to life, has by natural science been accounted for—some might say, 'explained'. There is nothing in them which does not fall within the province of science. They are chemistry and physics. But though living is analysable and describable by natural science, that associate of living, thought, escapes and remains refractory to natural science. In fact natural science repudiates it as something outside its ken. A radical distinction has therefore arisen between life and mind. The former is an affair of chemistry and physics; the latter escapes chemistry and physics. And yet the occurrence of mind—recognizable finite mind—is confined to a certain particular field of chemistry and physics, namely, that of highly integrated animal lives. 'Thinking', in this its limited field of occurrence, appears as a phase of living. If, as is practical, we continue to subsume mind under life, we have to distinguish it as an activity of life selectively and uniquely apart from the rest. The psycho-physical difficulty places us in the position of empirics as to much. By ways which may be judged roundabout, we find ourselves at length pragmatically alongside of general commonsense opinion. That may be taken either as sanity or superficiality or perhaps both.

· · · · · · · ·

S. S. STEVENS

Psychology and the Science of Science *

The scientist has always been proud of his hard head and his tough mind. When William James (29) sat in judgment and divided the universe of temperaments into the tough- and tender-minded, the scientist knew where he belonged. He was happy to run with the goats, for he was an empiricist and he loved facts in all their crude variety. He was skeptical and cautious of word, and to "isms" of all kinds he was peculiarly unresponsive. The tender-minded were the rationalists. They had faith in intuition and were awed by the power of the mind. It was their opinion that by taking thought they could discover absolute principles of truth answering to the criteria of coherence and consistency and that, armed with these principles, they could legislate the bounds of science. They were the sheep whose wool shone white under the light of reason. They were most numerous in departments of philosophy.

Undoubtedly these two types are still with us, but it is the purpose of this review neither to shear the sheep nor tame the goats. Instead, its purpose is simply to invite attention to some recent developments in what we might call the Philosophy of Science.

The tough-minded scientist has always known that he could screen his integrity against the seductive pipings of the rationalist by ignoring philosophy. The tender-minded philosopher, gifted with his superior dialectic, has usually despaired at the stubborn naïveté of the scientist and has determined to leave the unrefined fellow to grovel alone, while he, the philosopher, calmly demonstrated the impossibility of proving anything by induction. Suddenly, however, we find, on the one hand, a coterie of philosophers plying us with what, if it is not science, is certainly not the brand of stuff we have ordinarily pigeonholed as philosophy; and, on the other hand, we are beset by a host of scientists of all disciplines campaigning for what, if it is not philosophy, is surely not the science we are used to.

The philosopher, Benjamin (3), says of these scientists:

* From S. S. Stevens, Psychology and the science of science, *Psychol. Bull.*, 1939, *36*, 221–263. Reprinted by permission of the author, the *Psychological Bulletin*, and the American Psychological Association.

They begin with science, they talk about science, and they end with science, yet they do not conform at all to the tradition of scientific writing. . . . Their repeated reference to philosophical issues tempts one to classify them with this group, yet the writings approach these problems in a new spirit and with a new method, which seem quite foreign to traditional philosophy.

And concerning the widespread groups of philosophers participating in this movement, Reichenbach (52) observes:

Though there is no philosophic system which unites these groups, there is a common property of ideas, principles, criticisms, and working methods. . . . It is the intention of uniting both the empiricist conception of modern science and the formalistic conception of logic . . . which marks the working program of this philosophic movement.

So numerous and insistent are the words of those who have been seized by the spirit of this movement that they swell the pages of several new journals—journals whose subject matter defies simple classification.[1] There are articles by philosophers, mathematicians, and scientists. But it is more than a mere scrambling of the sheep and the goats. A common spirit animates most of these writings. The common theme, despite its fundamental simplicity, despite differences of interpretation by newborn enthusiasts, and despite the disparagement of misunderstanding, is probably to be esteemed as a truly great advance in the Philosophy of Science, or the Science of Philosophy.

Numerous phrasings of this central theme have been cast by authors interested in various aspects of it, but they all assert essentially that *science seeks to generate confirmable propositions by fitting a formal system of symbols (language, mathematics, logic) to empirical observations, and that the propositions of science have empirical significance only when their truth can be demonstrated by a set of concrete operations.* There are thus two separate realms of discourse: the *formal* (or rational) and the *empirical*. It is the business of the philosopher to labor with the formal and discover and perfect the rules of the scientific language, and it is the business of the scientist to apply the formal symbolic model to the observable world in such a way that the concepts he generates will satisfy the rules of operational criticism.

Elementary as these notions may appear, the development of their implications has commanded the interest of both tough- and tender-minded. The movement has proved disastrous for metaphysics, challenging for logic, and salutary for science. Philosophers and scientists in essential agreement are astonishing enough, but here we have them pleading for a common method. In this strange harmony we are witnessing the birth of a new discipline: the Science of Science. It is a triumph for self-consciousness. The science-makers are asking themselves how they make science and are turning on that problem the powerful empirical weapons of science itself; while at the same time a tough-minded outcropping among the philosophers is carefully combing the metaphysics out of logic in order to investigate more easily the common linguistic structure of science. In this quest the philosophers, like the scientists, resort to empirical methods. Witness the spirit of philosophy as exemplified by Nagel (44):

> It is difficult for me to take seriously the various attempts made historically by philosophers to legislate to the sciences just what they can and cannot investigate . . . on the basis of a deductive theory of mind and nature. . . . Furthermore, it seems to me an integral character of skilled workmanship to insist upon the fact that no statement or proposal has any meaning apart from the methods which are or may be employed to establish or execute them.

In succeeding pages we shall see how operationism, beginning at one end in the laboratories of scientists, evolved an enterprise coördinate with that of Logical Positivism, Physicalism, and Scientific Empiricism which, beginning at the other end in the armchairs of philosophers, settled on the problem of the proper scientific use of logic. And we shall see how the natural issue of this mating came to make up the unifying principles of the Science of Science. We shall see how this movement concords with "behavioristics," which is a behavioristic psychology tuned up to keep pace with a fast-moving logical criticism. And finally, we shall see what the impact of this movement means for some specific problems in psychology, and what is indicated as the future rôle of psychology in this scheme.

Operationism

Ten years ago Professor Bridgman, the expert on high-pressure phenomena, wrote a book [2] called *The logic of modern physics* (11). It has been judged an excellent book, animated by the single idea that "in general, we mean by any concept nothing more than a set of operations; *the concept is synonymous with the corresponding set of operations.*" This dictum stands forth in what many have found to be objectionable nakedness, but, throughout more than 200 well-stocked pages, Bridgman demonstrates what he means by analyzing the operational meaning of the basic concepts of physics. There is nothing rationally a priori in his method (at least he honestly *tries* to exclude metaphysics). His introductory confession is: "The material of this essay is largely obtained by observation of the actual currents of opinion in physics." In this empirical spirit he observes the behavior of his colleagues and finds that what is considered an *explanation* "consists in reducing a situation to elements with which we are so familiar that we accept them as a matter of course, so that our curiosity rests." The reduction of the "situation" is made in terms of operations, but do we thereby arrive at exact and certain knowledge? No. "We never have perfectly clean-cut knowledge of anything, but all our experience is surrounded by a twilight zone, a penumbra of uncertainty, into which we have not yet penetrated," and consequently "no empirical science can ever make exact statements." The degree to which any of the laws of science wear the penumbrous halo can be told only by inspecting the operations which the laws are intended to generalize.

Bridgman's book is rich in example but poor in precept. That its author has occasionally been misunderstood has perhaps been due largely to this fact. The book gives numerous examples of operational method without prescribing explicitly what operational method is; it talks of "operations" without giving an explicit definition of the term; and it discourses on natural laws without pointing out how we get from particular operations to generalizations. In short, it is a thoroughly inductive enterprise, and the reader is often allowed to make the induction by himself. Nevertheless, the spirit of the book is unmistakable and its message is simple and powerful.

Philosophers rose to protest, or sometimes to defend, the notion of "operational meaning" because it assures the automatic elimination of even the choicest propositions of metaphysics: "If a specific question has meaning," says Bridgman, "it must be possible to find operations by which an answer may be given to it." No operations, no meaning! And so, as we have said, philosophers, and others, rose to protest. Finally, the pressure pushed Bridgman temporarily from his Harvard laboratory and on to the lecture platform at Princeton where he spoke what became another book: *The nature of physical theory* (13).

To say that this second book pleased all who were disciples of the first book is perhaps not quite true. The author had been able to say in his first book that fortunately he would "be able to get along with a more or less naïve attitude toward "psychology and epistemology, but in his second work he boldly lays hold on thought, language, and experience. Bridgman's discussion of these concepts was what the world had been waiting for, but once out of the well-charted sea of physics and adrift in epistemology, the author's bark, if we are to believe the critics, appears to have lost its rudder. One cannot avoid the impression that criticism of this second book has been of unmerited severity, but perhaps severe criticism is what must be expected by a man who challenges us with issues as vital as those proposed by Professor Bridgman. Objection has been made to such statements as: "In the last analysis science is only my private science." "What," asks editor Malisoff (35), "can an operationist mean by a 'last analysis'?" Bridgman says his purpose in sailing the epistemological waters is "to map out the possibilities and limitations of the human mind in dealing with the problems presented to it." "Our complaint," criticizes A. F. Bentley (6), "is not that he makes this inquiry, but that in it he employs all the bad devices he had ejected from physics." Some of his devices are assertions crutched on such terms as "essentially," "absolutely," and "intuitively." Nevertheless, Bridgman's critics agree that his discernment in physics remains as fine as ever—he is still simple, and hardheaded. In physics he is an operationist, and it is in physics that we should judge him, if we are to presume to do so.

Just as Bridgman had set out to apply and make explicit the principles by which Einstein shattered the physicist's notion of the absolute, so did others seize upon the opportunity to try out these principles in other fields. Psychologists, long self-conscious of their own self-consciousness, were particularly alert to this budding self-inspection on the part of the modern masters of physics. If the physicists could examine the methods of their science-making and evolve helpful principles, perhaps psychologists could do likewise. Such, at least, was the attitude of those who were happy to confess blindness to any fundamental dichotomy between the methods of psychology and physics.

OPERATIONISM IN PSYCHOLOGY

But psychology is more difficult than physics—at least psychologists often find it easier to get themselves into a mess in their field than physicists do in theirs. Of course, when the physicist strays into psychology, the result is apt to restore the psychologist's ego-level, but if the physicist fumbles it only serves to show that when doing open-field running among psychological concepts the critic must hold the ball more tightly. In view of the difficulty of keeping a grip on the operational principle, it is not surprising to find evidence of dissension among the psychological apologists [Professor Billes (7) calls them "apostles"]. In spite of much scattered writing, the case for operationism in psychology has perhaps never been adequately briefed, but a few of its consequences have been made explicit and some interesting applications have appeared.

We all remember Tolman's *Purposive behavior in animals and men* (61). Whatever dismay we may have felt at the superabundance of his glossary, the fact remains that in coining the words of his new language he appealed most directly and explicitly to experimental operations. The book is a monument in the methodology of definition. In much the same spirit, Professor Tolman has more recently prepared for us "an operational analysis of 'demands'" (62). In his own field of expertness we find McGeoch making a critical inquiry into the possibility of "learning as an operationally defined concept" (38). Boring treats of "temporal perception and operationism" (10) in a short, poignant demonstration of how a classical problem turns out to be specious when its defining operations are made explicit. Seashore and Katz propose to bring order to the chaotic discipline of abnormal psychology by "an operational definition and classification of mental mechanisms" (55). Lundberg, the sociologist, would do the same for the social sciences by replacing spineless intuitionism by "quantitative methods in social psychology" (34), the foundation for which would be concepts operationally defined. And finally, Kantor examines "the operational principle in the physical and psychological sciences" (30) and concludes that the principle, properly enlarged, can be employed to the psychologists' advantage. Now, these are not all of those who have taken notice of Bridgman's proposals. Nor do all these commentators see eye to eye with Bridgman or with each other regarding certain fundamentals. Furthermore, it is becoming alarmingly obvious that the phrases "operationally defined" and "operationally sound" are acquiring the sort of positive valence which leads to their being bandied about in indiscriminate fashion by writers who suppose that they can meet the operational test by announcing good intentions. Operationism is being threatened by its friends —largely, perhaps, because of the inherent difficulty of making a rigorous formulation of it.

What, then, are we to understand by operationism? All that any one man can do is to present his own version, and this I did in a series of articles in 1935 and 1936 (57, 58, 59). There are some points there which invite revision, but, in general, the sins appear to be those of omission. The statement there needs expansion, but obviously this review is not the place for it. A résumé is more in order.

First, however, it must be emphasized again that the development of operational principles is properly an empirical undertaking. What do the science-makers do? What methodology has the maximum survival value? When do propositions have empirical validity? In short, operational principles are induced generalizations rather than a priori fiats. They are therefore subject to the usual hazards and uncertainty of inductive propositions. This empirical aspect of operational criticism has never been sufficiently stressed, and it is not surprising that operationists have sometimes been regarded as self-appointed legislators who try to prescribe rather than discover.

These, then, are some of the generalizations which I propose as verifiable:

1. Science, as we find it, is a set of empirical propositions agreed upon by members of society. This agreement may be always in a state of flux, but persistent disagreement leads eventually to rejection. Bridgman does not agree to this social criterion of knowledge and it was against this notion that he aimed a part of his Princeton lectures (13). We must ask him, however, to produce the negative case. A physical law to which only Bridgman agreed would not be a part of physics—not, at least, until he won converts, and then there would be agreement.

2. Only those propositions based upon operations which are public and repeatable are admitted to the body of science. Not even psychology knows anything about private experience, because an operation for penetrating privacy is self-contradictory.

3. What becomes acceptable psychology accrues only when all observations, including those which a psychologist makes upon himself, are treated as though made upon "the other one." Thus, we make explicit the distinction between the experimenter and the thing observed. This distinction is obvious in physics; in psychology it is equally valid.

4. Although a particular experimenter may himself become the object of study by another experimenter, and he in turn by still another, at some

stage of such a regress an independent experimenter *must be* (i.e., is always) assumed. The recognition of this "experimenter-regress" unravels many knots in psychology.

5. A term denotes something only when there are concrete criteria for its applicability; and a proposition has empirical meaning only when the criteria of its truth or falsity consist of concrete operations which can be performed upon demand.

6. When we attempt to reduce complex operations to simpler and simpler ones, we find in the end that discrimination, or differential response, is the fundamental operation. Discrimination is prerequisite even to the operation of denoting or "pointing to," because whenever two people reduce their complex operations for the purpose of reaching agreement or understanding, they find that unless they can each discriminate the same simple objects or read the same scales they still will not agree. Agreement is usually reached in practice before these most elementary operations are appealed to.

7. There are two types of propositions: *formal* and *empirical*. The formal propositions are arrays of symbols without empirical reference. They are language, mathematics, and logic *as such*. Empirical propositions are those in which these arrays of symbols have been identified with observable events. Sometimes the two types of propositions intermingle and trouble results. For avoiding the obscurity of pseudo problems this distinction between the formal, syntactical model (symbols) and the operations for which it is made to stand is of prime importance. Hypotheses, for example, can be only formal statements—operationally empty—until they are demonstrated. . . . Within the formal realm we speak sometimes of mathematical operations, but here we mean the manipulation of symbols carried out according to certain conventional rules. These are not the operations of operationism.

Although we shall have more to say later about the contrast between the formal and the empirical, at this point we might do well to see how history occasionally sets them off from one another and thereby emphasizes their distinctive natures. Historically, the algebra of complex numbers (numbers of the form $x + iy$, where x and y are real numbers and i is the square root of -1) was developed from the purest of purely mathematical motives. The rules for the manipulation of these numbers (their addition, multiplication, division, etc.) were worked out in conformity with the conventional laws of ordinary algebra and interesting relations were discovered. Gauss, for example, set a landmark in algebra by proving that every algebraic equation in 1 unknown has a root and that all roots of such equations are complex numbers (see Bell, 2, p. 232). In Gauss's time these numbers were simply abstract symbols which could be combined according to the rules of the game we call algebra. They proved nothing about the empirical world or about science: they constituted, as they still do, a purely *formal* system. Then, with the advent of alternating electric currents, came also the need for a simple, effective "model" to represent electric circuits; and the electrical engineers discovered that if they let x stand for resistance, iy for inductive reactance, and $-iy$ for capacitative reactance, they could manipulate these symbols according to the rules of complex algebra and obtain new combinations of the symbols which they could then identify with some measurable aspect of an electric circuit. In other words, this formal system was found useful as a model, and out of its utility has grown the modern intricate theory of alternating currents. Therefore, when we can identify these complex numbers with various aspects of a circuit, we can say that the propositions containing these symbols are *empirical* propositions, testable by concrete operations.

These seven bald assertions about operationism are perhaps too brief to be convincing, but they may recommend the fuller development in the three papers already referred to. In the meantime we might profit by considering what operationism is not—still, of course, in only one man's opinion. Misunderstandings have been numerous and many of them could have been headed off had someone signaled what is non-operational. Let us, then, look at a few of operationism's contrasts.

What Operationism Is Not

1. It is obviously not a new school of psychology. Rosenzweig (53) presented an admirable argument to show that the schools of psychology are really more complementary than antagonistic, but he was worried about operationism. He should stop worrying.

2. It is not a set of rules telling how to be a bright and original scientist. It does not even tell how experiments should be carried out. It has no precepts. At the risk of breeding disappointment we must say of operationism, as James (29) said of pragmatism, that, "at the outset, at least, it stands for no particular results. It has no dogmas, and no doctrines save its method." Furthermore, its method is one which is applied *after* the scientific proposition has been made: it provides criteria for determining whether what *has been* said is empirically meaningful. In short, it tests inventions, but does not tell how to invent.

3. It is not opposed to hypotheses, theories, or speculation. It seeks merely to discover criteria by which these things may be detected and labeled. It is not opposed to poetry, art, or religion. It wants only to know the difference between these things and science. It wants to know under what conditions the consorting of science with metaphysics breeds pseudo problems. Scientists as people may be opposed to pseudo problems, but operationism's business, as a principle of criticism, is to discover them.

4. It is not a guarantee of agreement as to tastes or theories, but it points out how agreement as to facts is achieved by men capable of making the same fundamental discriminations. Operationism wants, most of all, to discover the bases of such agreement. What are the procedures which

compel agreement among those engaged in open-minded pursuit of science?
As to compelling agreement on tastes—that is probably a job in applied
eugenics.

5. It is not positivism. The blemish on positivism was that in its reaction against rational metaphysics it pretended to base *everything* in
science on experience. Operationism, however, acknowledges the rôle of
the rational methods of mathematics and logic—formal disciplines which
do not appeal to experience for verification, but only to conventions.
Science uses these formal systems as models for representing its data. To
deny them is to cure the disease by burying the patient.

When it is a matter of the significance of *empirical* rather than of
formal propositions, needless to say, operationism adopts an uncompromis-
ing positivistic attitude.

6. It is not behaviorism. Like positivism, behaviorism erred in denying too much. Operationism does not deny images, for example, but asks:
What is the operational definition of the term "image"? Of course there
are different behaviorisms, and some of the renovated brands are truly
operational. Tolman (63) has a variety which he dubs explicitly "operational behaviorism"—and perhaps it is. It is certain that the behavioristic
emphasis has served capably in blasting a path through subjectivity, and
without this path an objective Science of Science could not march.

7. It is not monism. It asks only whether any operational meaning
can be given the proposition that there is but one irreducible substance
or attribute. Can the truth or falsity of this proposition be put to experimental test? If not, we face a pseudo problem.

8. It is not dualism. Here again the problems raised are pseudo problems, because the propositions are not testable. As Bills (7) so aptly says,
"Parallelism would automatically reduce to a double-aspect formula,
because where two sets of defining operations coincide perfectly they become identical operationally." Of course there can be no quarrel, except
on the grounds of utility, with any arbitrary dividing or classifying of
facts, but pseudo problems can be avoided only provided we remember
that these classes are arbitrary.

The division of concepts into the categories of subjective and objective
is justifiable—if at all—only on pragmatic grounds, and only *provided*
both types of concept answer the operational test. Bills believes that
"mentalistic" concepts like percept, image, and idea can be operationally
defined. So do I. Kantor, however, is disturbed. He detects dualism. But
Bills "cannot agree with Kantor that there is any necessary dualism implied in Stevens' position." Neither can Stevens. If we admit to our store
of empirical science only those concepts which are operationally founded,
can we not classify them according to our purposes?

Kantor (30) would appear to supplant dualism with a kind of realism.
Now, realism is a metaphysical doctrine, and perhaps Kantor did not
intend a realism. Nevertheless, he appears to defend the proposition:
Nature is not the same as our knowledge of nature. Operationism must here

again pose its perhaps tiresome, but necessary, question: Can any operations be formulated which will either prove or disprove this proposition?
If not, it is operationally meaningless, however much "emotional meaning"
it may pack.

9. Finally, operationism is not pluralism. It should be apparent by
now that operationism is not consonant with any "ism" which asserts
something about the ultimate nature of reality.

THE PROBLEM OF GENERALITY

There is one more criticism we must take seriously before we continue.
It has been urged that operationism reduces to a vicious particularism;
that there is no provision for generalization; that instead of unification in
science a strict servility to the operational principle nourishes an ever-
expanding multiplicity of concepts. Here is what the critics say:

Margenau, in "Causality in modern physics" (36), which he addressed
to the philosophers, states that operationism "cannot be tolerated as a
general directive. For, in the first place, it would, if carried to its consequences, dissolve the world into an unmanageable variety of discrete concepts without logical coherence."

Lindsay, in "A critique of operationalism in physics" (32), says:
". . . logically the operational method . . . implies that each concept is
tied to a definite operation."

Lindsay and Margenau together, in their book, *Foundations of physics*
(33)—a book which has brought them merited high praise—state: "On the
basis of purely operational definitions, all concepts are strictly empirical
and isolated" (p. 412).

Bills, in his excellent address on "Changing views of psychology as
science" (7), says: "One of the ideals of scientific concept-makers is to
reduce all concepts to a few fundamental ones. . . . Yet this is not, by
any means, the likely outcome of operationally defined concepts. . . . For
there is no universal set of operations."

Waters and Pennington, in their careful criticism of "Operationism
in psychology" (64), assert: "The fact that the concept, for Bridgman, is
synonymous with a corresponding set of operations cannot be overemphasized. The slightest change in any aspect of a set of operations
would mean, therefore, a new concept and would demand, likewise, a new
symbol for its designation. A multiplicity of concepts could scarcely be
avoided."

Since Bentley (the critic, not the psychologist), in his flashy tirade
on "Physicists and fairies" (6), has a point to make here, we will let him
speak first. He refers to Lindsay and Margenau when he says: "By distort-
ing Bridgman grossly enough, either man can, of course, readily destroy
what he has distorted. Both men distort alike; first by insisting 'operations'
must be all hands and no mind; second by alleging that no operation in

this world can have anything to do with any other operation, not even with its own repetitions of itself."

Whether there is distortion or not, the fact that so many have pounced on this supposed snare in operationism means that the rules and procedure for generalizing from operations must sometime be made explicit. These rules obviously can be stated, because science does generalize, and operationism seeks only to discover how scientists do what they do.

The process of generalization proceeds on the basis of the notion of classes. All objects or events satisfying certain criteria we call members of a class and to that class we assign a name or symbol. Common nouns originate in precisely this fashion, and it is apparent at once that no empirical proposition is ever without some element of generality. Classification can proceed only when we have criteria defining the conditions for class-inclusion, and these criteria are essentially operational tests. Thus the statement, "Dobbin is a horse," asserts that Dobbin is a member of a class. This proposition is empirically meaningful only provided its truth or falsity can be demonstrated by concrete procedures. Does Dobbin satisfy the criteria of the class, *horse*? If he is a certain size and shape, is covered with hair, feeds on oats and hay, etc., we are happy to acknowledge him as a full-fledged horse. But how do we know he meets our tests? Here we resort to that fundamental operation we have already called discrimination. If we can discriminate crucial differences between Dobbin and other animals we have named horses, we reject Dobbin as something not horse. In other words, we "correlate" our discriminations—those made on Dobbin with those made on other objects—and the "goodness" of the correlation determines where we shall classify the beast.

It may be objected that we can always tell Dobbin from other horses, i.e., discriminate differences, but we still would resent the suggestion that he is not a horse. The answer is that a certain latitude is always allowed— we seldom resort to j.n.d.'s in a case like this—and the amount of the latitude determines the precision of the concept. As Bridgman has insisted, no concept is without its halo of uncertainty, its penumbra. No empirical class is ever watertight; we can always plague the taxonomist with the borderline case.

On the basis of elementary discriminations, then, we make our first rudimentary classes and in doing so we have made the first step toward generalization. From there we advance to form classes of classes [3] and to discover the relations between classes—always, at the empirical level, in keeping with operational criteria. Occasionally we find that from a certain point of view two classes satisfy the same criteria, or are related by a simple law, so that we are enabled to combine them into a more inclusive class under a more generic tag. Nevertheless, in all of these classifications and combinations the same simple rule is followed: We combine operations when they satisfy the criteria of a class; and the concept of that class is defined by the operations which determine inclusion within the class.

The matter can be illustrated by referring again to that example which appears to have been the jumping-off place for the critics: the concept of length. Bridgman's argument is that we measure the length of the table and the distance to a star by two different sets of operations and we have, therefore, two different concepts of length. True enough. And Bridgman proceeds thence to show that when dealing with very large distances or very minute ones, or with distances where velocities are involved, we do well to keep in mind the differences in our defining operations. However, in his concern for the perils of promiscuous class-matings he forgot to tell us when combining is legitimate. Length measured with a rod is different from length measured with a transit, but under certain statable conditions we can muster operations to determine the relation of these two sets of measurements, and, if they meet the proper criteria, we combine them to form a larger class defining length. Of course, if we had no operations for comparing the two lengths, we should have to veto their combination. In short, then, we can and do generalize the concept length, but we do it with operational sanction.

The Philosophical Movement

Just ten years ago, the year Bridgman published his *Logic of modern physics*, there appeared in Vienna a company of scholars bound together by mutual admiration and a common *Weltauffassung*—a scientific philosophy. Their discussions under the leadership of Professor Schlick accomplished a unitary enthusiasm which came to concrete form in the organization of *Der Wiener Kreis*.[4] The avowed intention of this "Circle" was to replace philosophy by the systematic investigation of the logic of science which, for Carnap, is "nothing other than the logical syntax of the language of science." There are but two kinds of acceptable propositions: *formal* and *empirical*. Formal propositions concern syntax. They state the rules and procedure for combining words or symbols and have no empirical reference. Empirical propositions are assertions about the observable world and their truth or falsity can be tested by means of observational procedures. Since metaphysics consists of statements not susceptible to empirical test, it is either an array of syntactical (formal) sentences or else it is technical nonsense. Mostly it is nonsense. Philosophy must be purged of it; and, once purged, it becomes the business of philosophy, says the Circle, to investigate the rules of the language we use in formulating our scientific propositions. The goal of such philosophical research is to provide a secure foundation for the sciences.

This movement was not, of course, without its antecedents. Its most immediate point of departure was the famous *Tractatus logico-philosophicus* (66) by Russell's pupil, Ludwig Wittgenstein. The *Tractatus* exhibited the close connection between philosophy and syntax; it made clear the *formal* nature of logic and showed that the rules and proofs of syntax should have no reference to the meaning (empirical designation) of symbols; and it showed that the sentences of metaphysics are pseudo propositions. But the roots of these notions can be traced even back beyond Wittgenstein. All who, like the positivists, struck out at metaphysics; all who, like Kant, sought to conciliate analytic (formal) methods with the synthetic (empirical); and all who, like the British empiricists, assaulted philosophy with logical weapons have something in common with the Vienna Circle. Hume, in particular, except when he was assuming the existence of a transempirical world, caught the spirit. He winds up his "Enquiries concerning human understanding" (28) with this counsel:

If we take in our hand any volume; of divinity or school metaphysics, for instance; let us ask, *Does it contain any abstract reasoning concerning quantity or number* [formal questions]? No. *Does it contain any experimental reasoning concerning matter of fact and existence* [empirical questions]? No. Commit it then to the flames: for it can contain nothing but sophistry and illusion.

A philosophy as distinctive as that of the Vienna Circle must inevitably become an "ism," and its disciples, Blumberg and Feigl (8), lost no time in introducing the Circle's program to American scholars under the title of "Logical Positivism." A. F. Bentley (5) promptly raised the question as to whether Logical Positivism is either logical or positive, but in spite of some obvious disadvantages, the name is not entirely unreasonable. Bentley, as his readers know, loves a *bon mot* and has a low threshold for alarm—he is aroused to criticism easily but not unpleasantly. The name Logical Positivism quite properly suggests the union of the formal and the empirical—a union which, in a well-ordered scientific household, is possible and legitimate.

Logical Positivism proposes to tell us how such a household should be run. A certain division of labor is required. The scientist, in his special field, continues to investigate the empirical relations among the variables he has at hand and these relations he represents by some form of symbolic language. The philosopher complements the scientist by probing the nature and the rules of this symbolic language. Statements about the empirical domain are called object-sentences; statements about language-forms are syntactical sentences. In any special science, such as psychology, both types of sentences frequently occur, because the psychologist must tell us not only about his facts, but also how he intends to use his words and symbols —he must provide his own definitions (see Appendix I).* The philosopher, on the other hand, can point out the logical implications of the psychologist's language and help him guard against the vicious combinations of the two types of sentences which lead to pseudo propositions.

Under this program it is not, however, the task of the philosopher to legislate for science. Science can use any logic it finds useful. Carnap (22), at this point, proposes a Principle of Tolerance to allay our fears: "It is not our business," he says, "to set up prohibitions, but to arrive at conventions." "*In logic,*" he continues, "*there are no morals.* Everyone is at liberty to build up his own logic, i.e., his own form of language, as he

* Omitted here.—Ed.

wishes. All that is required of him is that, if he wishes to discuss it, he must state his methods clearly, and give syntactical rules instead of philosophical arguments." Consequently, he who sets out to scrutinize the logic of science must renounce the proud claim that his philosophy sits enthroned above the special sciences. He works in the same field as the specialist, only with a different emphasis. He ponders the logical, formal, syntactical connections. He studies rules which are basically nothing other than conventions and matters of free choice. Hence the labors of the philosopher in that which is his only legitimate domain, the logic of science, are bound to be barren unless they are pursued in close coöperation with the special sciences.

Logical Positivism, then, seeks 1) to clarify the language of science, and 2) to investigate the conditions under which empirical propositions are meaningful. The language of science (including syntax, logic, and mathematics) consists of arrays of words or symbols which we assemble according to certain rules. The analytic propositions of syntax and mathematics are absolutely necessary and certain, once the rules of the game have been laid down. These propositions neither tell us anything about the empirical world, nor can they be confuted by experience. They can no more be proved "true" than can the conventional rules of the game of chess (see below). They simply record our determination to use words and symbols in a certain fashion.

Mathematics, under this view, is a completely rational and deductive system and nothing is contained in one formula which is not implicit in all formulas. This, to many, is a fearful thought. Poincaré (48) voiced his apprehension by asking: "If all the propositions it enunciates can be deduced one from the other by the rules of formal logic, why is not mathematics reduced to an immense tautology? . . . Shall we admit that the theorems which fill so many volumes are nothing but devious ways of saying that A is A?" The answer appears to be that regardless of how inventive mathematical discoveries may appear to be, they contain nothing not already implicit in the fundamental postulates of the system. The outcome of our symbol-juggling surprises and delights us and fills us with the illusion of discovery, simply because of the limitations of our minds. A man of sufficient intellect would disdain the use of logic and mathematics, for he would see at a glance all that his postulates and definitions implied. He would be aware of all possible discoveries under the rules. The rest of us, however, must continue to do our mathematics stepwise, proceeding from one tautological transformation to the next, and being surprised at the result.

The second aim of Logical Positivism—to discover the conditions of empirical meaning—leads to the notion that an object-sentence is one which is verifiable by means of some concrete procedure. At this point operationism and Logical Positivism are essentially indistinguishable and we shall say no more about them, except to note an error.

This is an error which the Logical Positivists themselves have acknowl-

edged and corrected (cf. Carnap, 21, p. 11), but since the slip was made in
what is commonly regarded as psychological territory, we had best have
a look at it. The Vienna Circle committed the all too common fallacy: It
claimed to find a difference between *knowledge* and *immediate experience*
(see Blumberg and Feigl, 8). Knowledge is communicable, but the immediately given is private and noncommunicable. This from the mouth of a
Logical Positivist! Indeed, by all the rules they have proposed, this
sentence is not a testable proposition, for how shall we demonstrate the
existence of the noncommunicable? But, as already indicated, the Logical
Positivists have not been stubborn about insisting that it makes sense to
talk of the private content of immediate experience as being different from
the discriminable and reportable relations between experiences. Their past
lapse in this regard is interesting only because it shows how easy it is for
even the well-intentioned to talk nonsense when they invade this field of
psychology. In "The operational definition of psychological concepts" (58)
I have tried to demonstrate that an empirical (operational) definition of
immediate experience is possible provided we note precisely what its advocates do when we ask them to indicate an example of it. Almost invariably
they point to a situation involving an elementary discrimination such as:
"I see red." Elementary discriminations, then, are what is meant by the
immediately given, and discriminatory reactions, of course, are public and
communicable.

PHYSICALISM

As thoroughgoing empiricists the Logical Positivists hold that all
meaningful scientific propositions are derived from experience. More precisely, all such propositions are reducible to *protocol-sentences*—sentences
relating to the simplest elements of experience. This notion, I take it, is
equivalent to the operationist's view that complex propositions are shown
to be meaningful when they can be reduced to simpler propositions for
which there are operational tests. The simplest propositions of all would
be those relating to elementary discriminations. Now, if all scientific
propositions are reducible in this fashion, including propositions expressed
in what is called *physical language,* it must follow that *all* propositions are
translatable into the physical language—a language similar to that of contemporary physics. This is the thesis of Physicalism.[5]

Physicalism was christened by Neurath (cf. 46). Contrary to what
the name suggests, it is not a metaphysical doctrine asserting that everything is physical, for such a proposition can have no testable meaning.
It is, on the other hand, a thesis relating to language: The physical language is a universal language of science and the individual languages used
in any subdomain of science can be equipollently translated into the
physical language. Innocent as this assertion about language may appear,
it is charged with far-reaching implications for psychology. In fact, the
examples used to illustrate Physicalism make it appear that the doctrine

was aimed directly against psychology—at least against the kind peddled by philosophers.

Physicalism makes it clear that the traditional but somewhat antiquated problem of psychophysical dualism is exclusively a problem of syntax. Using the common "material mode" of speech we might say: To every psychical state there is a corresponding physical state of the body and the two are lawfully connected. Couched in this form, such a sentence is a veritable gold mine for pseudo problems. Physicalism would throttle these problems by saying: All sentences purporting to deal with psychical states are translatable into sentences in the physical language. Two distinctly separate languages to describe physics and psychology are therefore not necessary. And in this assertion we have Physicalism's denial of metaphysical dualism. It is the Logical Positivist's way of saying that psychology must be operational and behavioristic.

The philosopher, Hempel (27), calls this kind of psychology *logical behaviorism*. It differs from the primitive American stamp in that it does not prescribe that research shall be limited to stimulus-response connections. It is not, properly speaking, a theory *about psychology* at all, but only a logical theory about psychological sentences. The psychologist may study anything he pleases, but any verifiable psychological proposition he may utter is equivalent to some proposition in the physical language. An operationist would certainly agree to this notion. In fact, an operationist would point out that this view is correlative with his own dictum that any meaningful psychological proposition, even though it pertains to a toothache, is reducible to public, concrete operations.

THE UNITY OF SCIENCE

How we get from Physicalism to the thesis of the *unity of science* is obvious indeed. If every sentence can be translated into the physical language, then this language is an all-inclusive language—a universal language of science. And if the esoteric jargons of all the separate sciences can, upon demand, be reduced to a single coherent language, then all science possesses a fundamental logical unity.

This idea of a unified basis for science, introduced into the Vienna Circle by the imaginative originality of Neurath, has launched a whole new movement in scientific philosophy. The newly-begun *International Encyclopedia of Unified Science* is tangible testimony to the vigor and seriousness of the enterprise.[6] Annual congresses provide a forum where the thesis is developed (Fifth Annual Congress . . . held at Harvard University, September 5–10, 1939); and out of this intellectual ferment there is emerging a substantial basis for an empirical and universal Science of Science. But before we inspect this newest of sciences—one which is obviously still warm in the womb of its philosophy-mother—let us look backward a few centuries.

How many men, since ancient Thales proposed that all is water, have dreamed the dream of a universal science is beyond a guess. The dream has taken many forms—mostly impracticable—for the history of science is a story of diversification and specialization proceeding almost geometrically with time. If there is unity in so much arborescence, where are we to find it? Certainly not in subject matter where differentiation is the rule. Perhaps, then, in method and logic.

In 1666 the twenty-year-old Leibniz (2) dreamed his own dream about the unity of science and recorded it in *De Arte Combinatoria*. He himself called it a schoolboy's essay, but in it he proposed to create *"a general method in which all truths of reason would be reduced to a kind of calculation. At the same time this would be a sort of universal language or script, but infinitely different from those projected hitherto; for the symbols and even the words in it would direct the reason; and errors, except those of fact, would be mere mistakes in calculation."* How long would it take to create this logistic? Leibniz thought a few chosen men could turn the trick within five years. But chosen men were not at hand and two centuries passed before the creation of a universal symbolic logic was even begun. Almost another century of labor has been needed to lay a foundation in logic and syntax so tangible that many men together could vision the unity of science.

Leibniz, though, if any single man, was father to the idea. He hoped for a universal logicalization of human thinking by means of a general calculus and a general terminology. He conceived a formal discipline to include a theory and art of forming signs to represent ideas and a general calculus giving a universal formal method of drawing consequences from the signs Then, if two men were to find themselves in disagreement as to anything except matters of observation, they would settle their argument by calculating the right answer. Leibniz' inspiration is perhaps not without its utopian aspect, but it cannot be denied that the modern logic of science has made progress towards Leibniz' goal.

Perhaps our progress has not always been of the sort that would have delighted the boy of twenty, for metaphysics was no triviality in 1666. Today, however, it is clear that the unhappy symphonies of pseudo propositions that are metaphysics have all too frequently thwarted our efforts at clarification. Logical analysis has unmasked metaphysics; at least that is one of the boasted achievements of the recent philosophical movement. Opinion will probably never be unanimous on this issue, but disclosure of the empirically meaningless aspects of metaphysics is intimately bound to the other advances claimed by the Logical Positivists. By way of review at this point, these are some of the achievements of the modern movement:

1. It has been demonstrated that a unified language of science is possible. The syntax of this language is to be discovered by careful analysis of linguistic usage in science. And what unity there is in science is to be found in the unity of its logic and syntax.

2. Linguistic analysis has revealed the all-important distinction between the *formal* and the *empirical* aspects of science. Formal science consists of

the analytic statements established by logic and mathematics; empirical science consists of the synthetic statements established in the different fields of factual knowledge.

3. The statements of logic and mathematics derive their validity from conventions, and, from the point of view of empiricism, they are materially empty and constitute a closed system of tautologies. Logic deals with language only—not with the objects of language. Likewise, mathematics deals with symbols—not with the objects which the symbols represent.

4. Empirical propositions have meaning when there exists a concrete procedure (a set of operations) for determining their truth or falsity. Empirical significance attaches only to testable or confirmable sentences.

5. What we have called the "truth" of an empirical proposition is something which can never be absolute. Repeated tests of an object-sentence can add to its probability but never clinch its certainty. Induction, as Hume pointed out, is not a watertight method of proving anything empirical.

6. The notion that all scientific sentences are translatable into a common form—the physical language—requires of psychology a behavioristic approach. Psychology so conceived is called *behavioristics*.

These alleged achievements of the philosophers have been attained in the same spirit professed by the operationists: an empirical study of the actual doings of science-makers. Little wonder, then, that the two groups, although differing in emphasis, have arrived at substantially the same generalizations. Furthermore, these studies investigating the science-makers are the beginnings of a Science of Science. Like all other sciences, this one began before it was founded. Its founding and christening are of very recent date. They coincide with the harvesting of its first fruits.

THE SCIENCE OF SCIENCE

These first fruits of the Science of Science, it would appear, are the positive advances of operationism, of Logical Positivism, and of all who have looked seriously into the rules under which science is created. Except for these fruits, of which many are still green and some may even turn out to be wormy, the Science of Science comprises little more than an optimistic program. The fullest account of this program is supplied by C. W. Morris in his excellent essay on the "Foundations of the theory of signs" (43).

Morris is a philosopher at Chicago, and many will want to ask: What good is a science in the hands of philosophers? The obvious retort is that all our major sciences passed their childhood in the mansion of philosophy and only after they had grown tough and empirical were they bold enough to desert the tender-minded parent. It may be that once again a band of curious men have turned up in some unsuspected corner a new science with which they will charm away a few hardy scholars and leave the parental mansion tenanted by the tender-minded.

Let us turn now to an outline of the scientific study of science. Morris calls it "Metascience" or "Scientific Empiricism." Morris is enthusiastically

full of new terms; in fact, a difficulty with his account is that he is overly
generous in his willingness to enrich our vocabulary. Much of his coinage,
however, is choice and merits more extensive circulation. Morris defends
the thesis that *it is possible to include without remainder the study of
science under the study of the language of science, because the study of
that language involves not merely the study of its formal structure but its
relation to the objects it designates and to the persons who use it.* Language is a system of signs or symbols and the general science of signs is
to be called *Semiotic.* Semiotic has a double relation to the other sciences:
It is both a science among the sciences and an instrument of the sciences.
It is not a "superscience" but rather a common science among the others.
Every scientist at some stage of his work must embody his results in
linguistic signs, and consequently he must be as careful with his linguistic
tools as he is in designing his apparatus or in making his observations. In
his enterprise, the scientist unites empiricism with methodological rationalism, and Semiotic studies how this marriage is consecrated.

The study divides itself into three dimensions or levels, which we shall
discuss in turn:

1. Syntactics is the study of the relation of signs to signs.
2. Semantics is the study of the relation of signs to objects.
3. Pragmatics is the study of the relation of signs to scientists.

Syntactics refers to the formal disciplines commonly called logic,
mathematics, and syntax, where the relation of signs to one another is
abstracted from their relation to objects and to users or interpreters. At
present this is the best developed branch of Semiotic, but in the field of
the logical syntax of language there is still great labor to be done. The
investigation of language from the syntactical point of view is at once
both complex and fruitful. It has been possible accurately to characterize
primitive, analytic, contradictory, and synthetic sentences, and to show
that many sentences which are apparently object-sentences (and so concern things which are not signs) turn out under analysis to be pseudo
object-sentences which must be interpreted as syntactical statements about
language. An astonishing number of the scientist's sentences are syntactical
in this sense. . . . They are propositions without material content.

Ayer (1, p. 63) gives us a "striking instance" of the way in which
propositions which are really linguistic are often expressed in such a way
that they appear to be factual. At first glance, the proposition, "A material
thing cannot be in two places at once," looks quite empirical, but critical
inspection shows that "it simply records the fact that, as a result of
certain verbal conventions, the proposition that two sense-contents occur
in the same visual or tactual sense-field is incompatible with the proposition that they belong to the same material thing." The proposition, then,
is a definition—it records our decision as to how we shall use the term
"material thing." As this example suggests, the scientist frequently couches

in the material idiom the propositions which he really intends as definitions, and thereby he tends unwittingly to generate pseudo problems out
of his use—or misuse—of signs.

Of course, science is not the only activity in which we use signs. The
artist, the musician, and the traffic cop are notable sign-users. What their
various signs express or designate concerns semantics; what the effect of
these signs is on society and the individual concerns pragmatics; but we
can also inquire under what rules the signs are made, combined, and transformed, and that is syntactics.

Semantics refers to the rules determining under what condition a
sign is applicable to an object or situation. Thus, the operational rule [7] laid
down by Bridgman for determining the meaning of a term is, I take it,
essentially a *semantical rule*. And the so-called "applicational definitions"
used by the Logical Positivists to state when a term shall apply to an
object come under this heading (cf. Blumberg and Feigl, 8). Within the
study of these rules belong all the problems relating to the correlation
between the signs which comprise a scientific treatise and the discriminable aspects of the physical world to which the signs are meant to apply.
The simplest semantical rule is that governing an *indexical* sign. Such a
sign designates what is pointed at at any instant. The denotation of the
sign is based upon the operation of pointing, which in turn, of course, involves an act of discrimination. We have already noted that discrimination
is the simplest and most basic operation performable.

Many of the problems of semantics belong to psychology. Morris sees
in the experimental approach made possible by behavioristics great promise for determining the actual conditions under which certain signs are
employed. Unfortunately, rules for the use of sign-vehicles are not ordinarily formulated by the users of a language; they exist, rather, as habits
of behavior, and semantics wants to know what these habits are and how
they come to be established. Many pertinent experimental studies have
already been made by psychologists seeking the conditions of concept
formation and judgments of similarity, but more are in order. Tolman's
discovery of sign-gestalts functioning in the life of the rat discloses semantics among the rodents, and Lashley's effort to discover what range of
patterns are considered equivalent by the rat when he uses them as signs
for food directs attention to the problem of functional substitutivity (to
use Professor Boring's term) among symbolic forms.

The game of chess is frequently suggested (cf. Carnap, 18, and Reichenbach, 52) as an example of a system of conventional formal rules applicable to concrete objects and situations. Perhaps at this point we can better
illuminate Semiotic by examining this ancient pastime. First let us consider a set of signs. We shall use 3 groups of symbols: 1) the letters a, b,
c. d, e, f, g, and h; 2) the numbers 1, 2, 3, 4, 5, 6, 7, and 8; and 3) certain
other signs such as Kt, B, Q, K, etc. Next we shall set up conventional
rules for manipulating these symbols by allowing only combinations in
which 1 sign from each of the 3 groups appears, such as, for example, Kt

c 4. This combination shall be transformable into other combinations, depending upon the first symbol, Kt. Thus:

$$\text{Kt } c \text{ 4} \longrightarrow \text{Kt } e \text{ 5.}$$

But we shall not be allowed to write:

$$\text{Kt } c \text{ 4} \longrightarrow \text{Kt } d \text{ 5.}$$

Now, when we have stated all the rules governing these signs, what do we have? Quite plainly, what we have is a formal system—a set of signs governed by syntactical rules. We are engaged in the pursuit of syntactics.

Anyone who is a chess player will have guessed by now that these syntactical rules were *abstracted* from the game of chess. The point is that we can abstract them in this way and study them with no reference to anything beyond themselves. On the other hand, we can use them as a "model" to describe chess. In order to use them in this way we proceed to set up *semantical rules*. We say: Let the letters stand for the rows and the numbers for the columns of a chess board; let Kt stand for a particular small object (called a knight) which sits on a square of the board; then define Kt c 4 as equivalent to the statement that there is a knight on the square of coördinates c and 4; and define Kt c 4 $\longrightarrow$ Kt e 5 as equivalent to the statement that the knight is moved from c 4 to e 5. These semantical rules are statements about the use of language—they merely record our decisions as to how we shall use certain signs—and as semantical rules they are not empirical propositions. (This distinction between semantical and empirical statements was not made sufficiently explicit in operationism, but it needs to be stressed.)

We create an empirical statement as soon as we say that Kt c 4 is true, i.e., that there is, in fact, a knight on c 4, because this statement can be operationally verified. We can look to see whether our knight is there on c 4, or elsewhere. If the knight is on c 4 the statement is confirmed as true and if the knight is not on c 4 the statement is unconfirmed and is false. On the other hand, the statement "Kt c a" can never be considered an empirical proposition, because this combination of signs violates the rules of syntax and is meaningless—it cannot be tested operationally.[8]

From our game of chess we can abstract still another dimension or aspect. We can ask: What is the relation of these rules to chess players? Is the game hard or easy? What is its place in society, etc.? Here we are broaching pragmatical questions.

Pragmatics, as a part of Semiotic, studies the relation of signs to scientists. Here belong the problems as to how the scientist, as a behaving organism, reacts to signs; how science, as a social institution, interacts with other social institutions; and how scientific activity relates to other activities. This, indeed, is the aspect of Semiotic most challenging to the psychologist. It is the problem of the interpretation of signs. What is their effect on the man who sees or hears them? How do they determine behavior? How are they used and abused in shaping human destiny? A nebulous problem, one might complain, and overwhelmingly complex. "Yes, but none the less real and pressing," must be the answer.

The term "pragmatics" obviously suggests the philosophy known as pragmatism. The word was deliberately chosen to be thus suggestive. (In Semiotic we should say that the *pragmatical* aspect of the word is one of suggestiveness.) Pragmatism, more effectively than ever before, directed attention to the relation of signs to their users and assessed this relation as an aid in understanding intellectual activities. Pragmatics, as part of Semiotic, pays tribute to the achievements of Peirce, James, Dewey, and Mead, but it must not be thought identical with pragmatism as a philosophy.

Both pragmatism and pragmatics agree that the interpreter of a sign-vehicle is an organism whose "taking-account" of the sign consists in a *habit to respond* to the vehicle as it would to the thing designated by the sign. We thus find the problem of pragmatics cast in such a form that it can be handled by behavioristics—we deliberately avoid talking about the subjective effects of signs unless these effects are disclosed by public operations. Not only do we react to the signs appearing in sober scientific propositions, but our habits of response carry over to situations where signs obey neither semantical nor syntactical rules. We are often delighted by senseless jingles and moved to strong emotions by what analysis shows to be gibberish. In propaganda, where syntax is usually not violated, but where semantical relations are sometimes distorted, the pragmatical effects (the induction of some form of behavior) may be profoundly disturbing. Clearly, psychology has a stake in the solution of all these problems arising in pragmatics.

One more facet of this many-sided problem deserves our interest. What Morris calls *descriptive pragmatics* occurs when a sign used by a person is employed as a means of gaining information about the person. The psychoanalyst studies dreams for the light they throw upon the dreamer, not to discover whether there are actually any situations which the dreams denote. Likewise, we may study the statements of newspapers and politicians, not as empirical propositions, but for their ability to disclose the faction whose interest is being served by this form of propaganda. And in much the same spirit, the psychiatrist inspects the signs used by his patient in order to diagnose an abnormality. The pragmatical aberrations found among the psychoses are extremely illuminating, for occasionally a patient lets his system of signs displace completely the objects they once stood for; the troublesome world of reality is pushed aside and the frustrated fellow gets his satisfaction in the domain of signs, oblivious to the restrictions of syntactical and semantical rules. The field of psychopathology thus holds great promise as a place to apply Semiotic and discover some of its laws.[9]

There can be no doubt that in the realm of human behavior the concept of sign holds a key place. And if, as the pragmatists contend, mental phenomena are to be equated to sign-responses, psychology bears an intimate relation to the science of signs. The theory of signs—being the co-ördinated disciplines of syntactics, semantics, and pragmatics—is the core of a unified science. "Indeed," exclaims Morris (43), "it does not seem fantastic to believe that the concept of sign may prove as fundamental to the sciences of man as the concept of atom has been for the physical sciences or the concept of cell for the biological sciences."

EPILOGUE

That then, in all too brief review, is the manner in which the Science of Science has been staked out. Whoever would probe the making of science can learn all the answers by inspecting thoroughly the language of science. The investigator must remember, however, that *this language is an intersubjective (public) set of sign-vehicles whose usage is determined by syntactical, semantical, and pragmatical rules.* By making the Science of Science coextensive with the study of the language of science we have set spacious bounds to this field of inquiry—there is ample room for a variety of talents, and to bring all the diverse areas under cultivation will require coöperation among the specialties.

Three features of this lusty embryonic science stand out with particular prominence.

First, the rational and the empirical elements in science are disentangled and then reassembled according to a straightforward, workable plan. The formal, rational, analytic, a priori, deductive side of creative thinking, which has always been so dear in the hearts of James's "tender-minded," neither rules nor is ruled by the empirical, synthetic, a posteriori, inductive wing. Neither side can be called a usurper when both are understood, for they are not even in competition. Their union is achieved, not after the manner of Kant, who held out for a bastard hybrid which he called the "a priori synthetic judgment," but in conformity with the relation of sign to object.

Secondly, it is proposed that in our study of the science-maker we begin with the *products* of his activity—his finished propositions—rather than with his "experiences" or any other phase of his earlier behavior. This is a sensible place to begin. If we were to study the manufacture of any product, such as automobiles, we should probably find it useful first to ascertain what an automobile is and then to discover the conditions under which it comes into being. Science manufactures sentences, and we, as curious mortals, ask: What is a sentence and how is it made? The *complete* answer to this question is the Science of Science.

Thirdly, does it not appear that the Science of Science must go directly to psychology for an answer to many of its problems? Is it not also plain that a behavioristic psychology is the only one that can be of much help in this enterprise? A sign has semantical significance when an organism will react to it as it would to the object which the sign supplants. The psychologist works out the laws under which different stimuli evoke equivalent reactions. Signs, as stimuli, can be combined and utilized extensively in the control and direction of behavior, both individual and social. The entire activity of the scientist as a sign-using organism constitutes, therefore, a type of behavior for which behavioristics seeks the laws. If there is a sense in which psychology is the propaedeutic science (cf. Stevens, 59), it is undoubtedly in its ability to study the behavior, *qua* behavior, of the science-makers.

Perhaps we are too close to this young Science of Science either to judge its value or see clearly how it came to be. We shall forego the value-judgment, since it would merely disclose the author's particular prejudice (already clear, no doubt), but an observation about the movement's immediate ancestry is not entirely out of order. It now appears, in retrospect, that the Science of Science emerged as the reasonable outcome of revolutions in the three major fields: physics, psychology, and philosophy. These revolutions occurred almost independently, but a general community of spirit among them led directly to extensive cross-fertilization. Operationism as a revolution against absolute and undefinable concepts in physics, behaviorism as a revolution against dualistic mentalism in psychology, and Logical Positivism as a revolution against rational metaphysics in philosophy were the three forces whose convergence into a common effort is effected by the Science of Science.

Finally, the purpose of this review has been to call the attention of those of us who are psychologists to the critical principles involved in scientific method as evolved in recent scientific and philosophic movements. We have had little to say concretely about psychology or its facts, and undoubtedly many will be impatient with so much non-experimental discourse. "Who cares about philosophy?" they will say. "What matters is the product of the laboratory." While such robust empiricism is admirable, we must ask the indulgence of these tough minds. We must ask them to bear with us while we inspect our logical tools as carefully as we do our other apparatus. And we must ask them to weigh the implications for psychology of this statement by Quine, the logician (49):

The less a science has advanced the more its terminology tends to rest upon an uncritical assumption of mutual understanding. With increase of rigor this basis is replaced piecemeal by the introduction of definitions. The interrelationships recruited for these definitions gain the status of analytic principles; what was once regarded as a theory about the world becomes reconstrued as a convention of language. Thus it is that some flow from the theoretical to the conventional is an adjunct of progress in the logical foundations of any science.

REFERENCES

1. Ayer, A. J. *Language, truth and logic.* London: Gollancz, 1936.
2. Bell, E. T. *Men of mathematics.* New York: Simon & Schuster, 1937.
3. Benjamin, A. C. *An introduction to the philosophy of science.* New York: Macmillan, 1937.

4. Benjamin, A. C. The operational theory of meaning. *Phil. Rev., N. Y.,* 1937, *46,* 644–649.
5. Bentley, A. F. The positive and the logical. *Phil. Sci.,* 1936, *3,* 472–485.
6. Bentley, A. F. Physicists and fairies. *Phil. Sci.,* 1938, *5,* 132–165.
7. Bills, A. G. Changing views of psychology as science. *Psychol. Rev.,* 1938, *45,* 377–394.
8. Blumberg, A. E. and Feigl, H. Logical positivism. *J. Phil.,* 1931, *28,* 281–296.
9. Boas, G. and Blumberg, A. E. Some remarks in defense of the operational theory of meaning. *J. Phil.,* 1931, *28,* 544–550.
10. Boring, E. G. Temporal perception and operationism. *Amer. J. Psychol.,* 1936, *48,* 519–522.
11. Bridgman, P. W. *The logic of modern physics.* New York: Macmillan, 1928.
12. Bridgman, P. W. A physicist's second reaction to Mengenlehre. *Scripta math.,* 1934, *2,* 3–29.
13. Bridgman, P. W. *The nature of physical theory.* Princeton: Princeton Univ. Press., 1936.
14. Bridgman, P. W. Operational analysis. *Phil. Sci.,* 1938, *5,* 114–131.
15. Brunswik, E. Psychology as a science of objective relations. *Phil. Sci.,* 1937, *4,* 227–260.
16. Bures, C. E. The concept of probability. *Phil. Sci.,* 1938, *5,* 1–20.
17. Campbell, N. R. *Physics: the elements.* Cambridge: Univ. Press, 1920.
18. Carnap, R. On the character of philosophic problems. *Phil. Sci.,* 1934, *1,* 5–19.
19. Carnap, R. *Philosophy and logical syntax.* London: Kegan Paul, 1935.
20. Carnap, R. Les concepts psychologiques et les concepts physiques sont-ils foncièrement différents? *Rev. Synthèse,* 1935, *10,* 43–53.
21. Carnap, R. Testability and meaning. *Phil. Sci.,* 1936, *3,* 419–471; 1937, *4,* 1–40.
22. Carnap, R. *Logical syntax of language.* London: Kegan Paul, 1937.
23. Dingle, H. *Through science to philosophy.* Oxford: Clarendon Press, 1937.
24. Einstein, A. On the method of theoretical physics. *Phil. Sci.,* 1934, *1,* 163–169.
25. Feigl, H. The logical character of the principle of induction. *Phil. Sci.,* 1934, *1,* 20–29.
26. Feigl, H. Logical analysis of the psycho-physical problem. *Phil. Sci.,* 1934, *1,* 420–445.
27. Hempel, C. G. Analyse logique de la psychologie. *Rev. Synthèse,* 1935, *10,* 27–42.
28. Hume, D. *Enquiries concerning the human understanding and concerning the principles of morals.* Oxford: Clarendon Press, 1902 (2nd ed.).
29. James, W. *Pragmatism.* New York: Longmans, Green, 1914.
30. Kantor, J. R. The operational principle in the physical and psychological sciences. *Psychol. Rec.,* 1938, *2,* 3–32.
31. Lewin, K. The conceptual representation and the measurement of psychological forces. *Contr. psychol. Theor.,* 1938, *1,* No. 4, 1–247.
32. Lindsay, R. B. A critique of operationalism in physics. *Phil. Sci.,* 1937, *4,* 456–470.
33. Lindsay, R. B. and Margenau, H. *Foundations of physics.* New York: Wiley, 1936.
34. Lundberg, G. A. Quantitative methods in social psychology. *Amer. sociol. Rev.,* 1936, *1,* 38–54.
35. Malisoff, W. M. The universe of operations (a review). *Phil. Sci.,* 1936, *3,* 360–364.

36. Margenau, H. Causality in modern physics. *Monist*, 1931, *41*, 1-36.
37. Margenau, H. Methodology of modern physics. *Phil. Sci.*, 1935, *2*, 48-72; 164-187.
38. McGeoch, J. A. Learning as an operationally defined concept. *Psychol. Bull.*, 1935, *32*, 688 (abstr.).
39. McGeoch, J. A. A critique of operational definition. *Psychol. Bull.* 1937, *34*, 703-704 (abstr.).
40. McGregor, D. Scientific measurement and psychology. *Psychol. Rev.*, 1935, *42*, 246-266.
41. Menger, K. The new logic. *Phil. Sci.*, 1937, *4*, 299-336.
42. Morris, C. W. Scientific empiricism. *Int. Encycl. unif. Sci.*, 1938, No. 1, 63-75.
43. Morris, C. W. Foundations of the theory of signs. *Int. Encycl. unif. Sci.* 1938, No. 2, 1-59.
44. Nagel, E. Some theses in the philosophy of logic. *Phil. Sci.*, 1938, *5*, 46-51.
45. Neurath, O. Historische Anmerkungen. *Erkenntnis*, 1930, *1*, 311-314.
46. Neurath, O. Physicalism: the philosophy of the Viennese Circle. *Monist*, 1931, *41*, 618-623.
47. Neurath, O. Unified science and its encyclopedia. *Phil. Sci.*, 1937, *4*, 265-277.
48. Poincaré, H. *The foundations of science.* New York: Science Press, 1913.
49. Quine, W. Truth by convention. In *Philosophical essays for Alfred North Whitehead.* New York: Longmans, Green, 1936. P. 90.
50. Rashevsky, N. Foundations of mathematical biophysics. *Phil. Sci.*, 1934, *1*, 176-196.
51. Rashevsky, N. Physico-mathematical methods in biological and social sciences. *Erkenntnis*, 1936, *6*, 357-365.
52. Reichenbach, H. *Experience and prediction.* Chicago: Univ. Chicago Press, 1938.
53. Rosenzweig, S. Schools of psychology: a complementary pattern. *Phil. Sci.*, 1937, *4*, 96-106.
54. Schlick, M. De la relation entre les notions psychologiques et les notions physiques. *Rev. Synthèse*, 1935, *10*, 5-26.
55. Seashore, R. H. and Katz, B. An operational definition and classification of mental mechanisms. *Psychol. Rec.*, 1937, *1*, 3-24.
56. Somerville, J. Logical empiricism and the problem of causality in social sciences. *Erkenntnis*, 1936, *6*, 405-411.
57. Stevens, S. S. The operational basis of psychology. *Amer. J. Psychol.*, 1935, *47*, 323-330.
58. Stevens, S. S. The operational definition of psychological concepts. *Psychol. Rev.*, 1935, *42*, 517-527.
59. Stevens, S. S. Psychology: the propaedeutic science. *Phil. Sci.*, 1936, *3*, 90-103.
60. Struik, D. J. On the foundations of the theory of probabilities. *Phil. Sci.*, 1934, *1*, 50-70.
61. Tolman, E. C. *Purposive behavior in animals and men.* New York: Appleton-Century, 1932.
62. Tolman, E. C. An operational analysis of 'demands.' *Erkenntnis*, 1936, *6*, 383-390.
63. Tolman, E. C. Operational behaviorism and current trends in psychology. *Proc. 25th Anniv. Celebr. Inaug. Grad. Stud.* Los Angeles: Univ. S. Calif. Press, 1936, 89-103.
64. Waters, R. H. and Pennington, L. A. Operationism in psychology. *Psychol. Rev.*, 1938, *45*, 414-423.

65. Weinberg, J. R. *An examination of logical positivism.* London: Kegan Paul, Trench, Trubner, 1936.
66. Wittgenstein, L. *Tractatus logico-philosophicus.* New York: Harcourt, Brace, 1922.
67. Woodger, J. H. *The axiomatic method in biology.* Cambridge: Cambridge Univ. Press, 1937.

[20]

DOUGLAS G. ELLSON [1]

Application of Operational Analysis To Human Motor Behavior *

1 THE SOURCE OF THE PROBLEM

A considerable amount of research on the effects of the characteristics of the task on motor behavior was performed during the recent war and interest in this field has persisted in many psychological laboratories. Most of this work should be classed as applied psychological research. It was stimulated largely by requests for data from engineers and designers of military, aviation, and other types of complex equipment which require highly skilled human operators. Very few of their questions concerning details of motor behavior could be answered on the basis of research performed prior to 1940, but a considerable body of data has accumulated since, most of it not yet published in the general literature. The wartime research was chiefly designed to obtain immediate answers to specific problems in the design of equipment. It included the determination of the effects of such variables as size, shape, and location of control knobs; friction, damping, and inertia of controls; operating radii of controls; and gear ratios upon the accuracy and speed of control movements. Post-war research has been concerned with similar variables, but it has utilized laboratory apparatus which provided better control of conditions than was possible with the modified service equipment chiefly used during the war.

As might be expected in a relatively new area, most of this research has been exploratory. The effects of stimulus variables (in this case, existing or conceivable design characteristics of machines) upon response characteristics (accuracy, speed, frequency, latency of movements, etc.) were investigated sometimes systematically, sometimes on the basis of more or less inspired hunches. In some cases data obtained in different experimental

* Reprinted from D. G. Ellson, The application of operational analysis to human motor behavior, *Psychol. Rev.,* 1940, *56,* 9–16. By permission of the author, the *Psychological Review,* and the American Psychological Association.

situations are supplemental; in other cases there is little indication of what factors determine apparently contradictory results. One investigation may indicate that increasing the radius of a crank produces greater accuracy in tracking. Another investigation indicates the reverse, but the differences in the two situations which may reconcile these two results are not apparent. When such contradictions exist, it is obviously impossible to predict the effect of a given variable in a new situation. A theoretical formulation is needed which will integrate the available data and indicate what variables are significant, but, so far, psychologists have not produced such a theory. Learning theory is too broad to be useful in this case since it has been concerned primarily with factors which determine the occurrence or nonoccurrence of a response and has not been extended to the details of response form which are important for the design of mechanical equipment.

II THE METHOD OF OPERATIONAL ANALYSIS

Although an adequate psychological theory has not been suggested, there is available a well worked out method of analyzing the characteristics of physical transmission systems which may be applicable to certain aspects of human motor behavior. This method, operational analysis, is widely used by engineers to predict the response of mechanical follow-up systems and electrical networks which are too complex to allow the computation of the performance of the whole from performances of individual components. In this and other ways this method represents a direct parallel in engineering of the behavioral approach in psychology. Its basic measurements are made on the input and output of a transmission system which correspond to the stimulus and response in a psychological organism. The relationships between input and output are the basic functions, and they may be investigated without reference to intervening mechanisms.

A simple example of a transmission system whose response to complex inputs may be predicted by means of operational analysis is a pendulum suspended from a support which can be moved horizontally. Movement of the support provides an input; movement of the bob is the output. For a particular pendulum the movements of the bob resulting from movements of the support of any complexity can be predicted with great accuracy on the basis of a relatively simple set of measurements. These consist of a determination of the output—the amplitude of the output oscillations and their phase shift (usually lag behind the input)—when the input is a series of sine form movements of a wide range of frequencies. The basic principles involved in predicting the pendulum movements can be utilized successfully in predicting the response characteristics of such varied mechanical and electrical transmission systems as levers, vacuum tubes, amplifying networks and complex servo or booster systems such as those used to move control surfaces in airplanes and to compute gun leads.

Fundamentally the principles of operational analysis are simple. The basic problem, as illustrated in the pendulum example, is the prediction of the response of a transmission system to a given, usually complex, input. The prediction is made by adding the outputs which the system produces in response to all of the components of the given input. The procedure involved may be represented as follows:

$$\text{Input}_1 \longrightarrow \text{Output}_1$$
$$\text{Input}_2 \longrightarrow \text{Output}_2$$

.

.

.

$$\text{Input}_n \longrightarrow \text{Output}_n$$
$$\text{Input}_x \longrightarrow \text{Output}_x$$

When (complex) $\text{Input}_x = \text{Input}_1 + \text{Input}_2 + \cdots \text{Input}_n$

Then: $\text{Output}_x = \text{Output}_1 + \text{Output}_2 + \cdots \text{Output}_n$

The conditions which must be satisfied in order to apply operational analysis are:

Condition 1. In any given application or experimental test, the components of the complex input must be known.

Condition 2. The outputs of the transmission system produced separately by the simple inputs included as components of a complex input must be known.

Condition 3. The transmission system must be 'linear.' A linear system is defined as one in which the outputs produced by simple inputs are additive when these inputs are added as components of a complex input.

For purposes of operational analysis complex inputs are usually broken down into either step function components (illustrated in Fig. 1) or sine wave components.

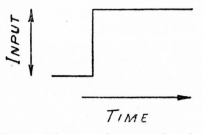

Fig. 1. Diagrammatic presentation of a step-function input.

It is possible mathematically to construct a single-dimension input of any complexity by adding (or integrating) either step functions or sine waves of suitable amplitude and time or phase relationship. Although it is possible to analyze inputs into other types of components, the step function and sine wave breakdown are more generally used since the mathematical procedures for handling them have been most completely developed. The term *frequency analysis* is applied to the type of operational analysis based on sine wave components. It is a highly developed analytical method used most widely with electrical circuits where the transmitted inputs are chiefly cyclical. Analysis by means of step function inputs may be more convenient experimentally when the complex inputs involved are slower or non-repetitive as in DC circuits and in certain mechanical transmission systems. However, the basic conditions listed above must be satisfied in order to apply operational analysis with any type of input breakdown.

The first condition, knowledge of the components of the complex input, is required in making specific predictions of outputs either for practical purposes or for making tests of linearity. In an input synthesized for experimental purposes the components will ordinarily be known. In other cases it may be necessary to determine the components of a given input by means of mathematical analysis.

To satisfy condition two, it is necessary to provide inputs which are the components to be used in the analysis and to measure the resulting output when each input is presented separately. For frequency analysis these components are sine waves of a single frequency. Theoretically the response to all possible frequencies must be determined, but in practice it is necessary to use only a limited range of frequencies. If the resulting output is in sine wave form, the output characteristics measured are 1) output amplitude as a percentage of input amplitude, and (2) phase shift (usually a lag behind the input). For step function (transient) analysis a single step function is introduced into the input, and the output is measured as a function of time following the introduction of the step.

To satisfy the third condition, linearity of the transmission system, it must be shown that the output produced by superimposing two or more component inputs is equal to the sum of the outputs obtained with each component separately. This implies the experimental verification of the unqualified hypothesis that outputs are additive, and as such, absolute proof could not be obtained from any finite set of experiments. Furthermore, all transmission systems are linear only within limits. Consequently, the question becomes: within what limits and under what conditions is the system linear? Again, this question can be answered specifically only for inputs and other conditions which are tested experimentally. In practice, this means that linearity or its limits will be determined in a finite number of experiments sufficient to satisfy the requirements of the experimenter.

A simple test of linearity under obviously limited conditions is to double the input to a system, or to multiply it by a constant. In a linear system this will result in doubling the output or multiplying it by the given constant. More general tests of linearity will include (a) the determination of the input-output functions for a step-function input or for a wide range of single frequencies as required by condition one, (b) the presentation of a variety of complex inputs, and (c) a comparison of the resulting outputs with those predicted from the appropriate input components. For frequency analysis, a wave analyzer may be used to determine

the components of the output and it may also be used to analyze the input
if the complex input is not synthesized from controlled components.

III USES OF OPERATIONAL ANALYSIS IN HUMAN ENGINEERING

Operational analysis is essentially a method of analyzing input-output
functions of transmission systems designed to make possible the prediction
of outputs when the input is known. One of its simplest applications is
indicated in the pendulum example given above; the characteristics of the
response to complex inputs is computed on the basis of empirical determinations of the response to a limited series of single-frequency sine form
inputs. Similarly, the fidelity with which a radio amplifier system will reproduce the human voice can be determined by measuring its response to a
sampling of single frequencies in the range of frequencies included in
speech. It may be found that a certain band of frequencies is amplified
relatively more than others, producing an unbalanced tone or emphasizing
high frequency static. This may be corrected by adding a second transmission system in the input or output circuit—a second amplifier or a filter
which counteracts the defects of the first amplifier by reducing the amplitude with which the overemphasized frequencies are transmitted.

If the response of a human 'transmission system' is linear as defined
above, then operational analysis may be utilized in order to design certain
machines which are controlled by human operators. When a man operates
a gunsight or controls the movements of an airplane or automobile, he may
be considered as one transmission system component of a larger system
which includes both the machine and its operator. If he over-responds or
under-responds to certain frequency components of the input (the movement of the target or the path he is attempting to follow), this distortion
may appear in his output (the movements by which he controls the machine).

As tracking errors or deviations from the path he is attempting to
follow, these errors may have other effects. In operating the machine component of the total man-machine transmission system, the output of the
man serves as input to the machine. If input frequencies distorted by the
human operator are matched by similar distortions of the same frequencies
by the machine he operates, then his tracking or control errors will be magnified. This condition has occurred in the operation of certain experimental
computing sights: the operator's tracking errors were magnified by a
factor of three or more in the output of the system. This was presumably
due to a matching of the frequency characteristics of the machine and its
human operators such that a phenomenon similar to resonance occurred.
It is obviously desirable for designers of such machines to know the frequency characteristics of potential human operators. If these characteristics
can be determined, it may not only be possible to avoid amplifying human
errors, but the machine may be designed so as to "filter out" much of
this error.

The example given above utilizes frequency analysis. There are many other applications of operational analysis in which a knowledge of the input-output functions of human transmission systems can be potentially used to stabilize the performance of a mechanism composed of a machine and its human operator.[2]

IV. APPLICABILITY OF OPERATIONAL ANALYSIS TO HUMAN MOTOR BEHAVIOR

Operational analysis applied to human motor behavior has two aspects. As a method for predicting certain characteristics of the performance of human operators of machines, it is potentially a powerful tool in human engineering. As a set of assumptions concerning the relationships between certain stimulus and response characteristics, it is a limited psychological theory which must be verified experimentally. Fundamentally the difference is small. Both the practical and theoretical value of the application of operational analysis to human behavior depend on the agreement of its predictions with observed data.

The type of motor performance to which operational analysis is most obviously applicable is tracking or pursuit responses, either direct or compensatory. In this situation there is a specific stimulus or input and a specific response or output, both of which may be measured in terms of characteristics which are adapted to operational analysis. Since a human being, qualitatively at least, is considerably different from any existing machine or electrical circuit, there are many factors which must be considered in determining whether the attempt to apply operational analysis is worthwhile. The first reaction of many psychologists to the suggestion that operational analysis may be applicable at all to human behavior would be to expect failure. Human behavior, in general, appears extremely variable and the determination of stable relationships between a response and the characteristics of any single stimulus has been difficult. In operational analysis the characteristics of the response are predicted from the characteristics of a very limited part of the total situation which may be affecting the organism at the time. However, it is possible that in certain laboratory and practical situations tracking behavior may be sufficiently well isolated by means of instructions and training that distracting factors may be ignored. This question can be answered only on the basis of experimental evidence. There are experiments in several laboratories at various stages of completion but not yet published which indicate a very high degree of constancy in tracking performance. Consequently, it seems desirable to attempt to apply operational analysis to this limited type of behavior.

The first step in applying operational analysis to any transmission system is to determine whether the system is linear or the limits of its linearity. The general procedures for doing this are indicated above. They are the same whether the system is an electronic amplifier or a human being operating a steering wheel. Since the human being is obviously far more complex than any transmission system to which operational analysis has previously been applied, it will be necessary to test linearity for many variations of the complex input and in many different situations. The first question, of course, is whether the human being is linear in *any* situation. Although little research has been done which is specifically applicable to this question, there are many general observations which indicate that a human being has some characteristics of a linear system. Time-and-motion engineers, for example, use as a working hypothesis the assumption that within certain fairly wide limits the time required for a movement is constant regardless of its extent. We know from general observation and some experimental evidence that a human being can adjust his rate of movement in a pursuit task to match the rate of stimulus movement within fairly wide limits. Errors are variable rather than constant. In both of these examples multiplication of the input amplitude has the effect of multiplying the output by the same factors, indicating that in a general way the requirements for a linear system are satisfied.

Taylor, Walker and Householder [3] performed an experiment in which they presented subjects with step-function target displacements of varying amplitudes. This experiment represents one of the simplest tests of linearity which may be performed with any transmission system. It uses the step-function as the basic input unit for operational analysis. The task is a direct pursuit problem in which the subject manipulates a stylus to follow a point which moves in one dimension. The response to an instantaneous movement of the point is shown schematically in Figure 2. A period

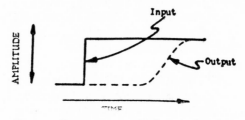

FIG. 2.   Response to a single step-function
input.

of no response (reaction time) is followed by a movement, roughly sine form, with an amplitude approximately equal to the input movement.

Taylor and his co-workers report that "the data indicate an approximately linear increase in rate of correction with increase in magnitude of displacement," which indicates that under these conditions at least the human subjects act as linear systems. This is true since a step-function of large amplitude is in effect a 'complex' input produced by adding step-functions of smaller amplitude. According to Taylor's statement, the addition of inputs results in a comparable addition of outputs as shown in Fig. 3.

Tests of linearity under different conditions may be made by means of other complex inputs such as those shown in Fig. 4.

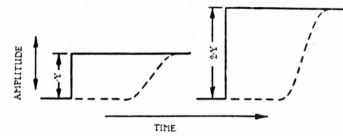

FIG. 3.   Change in response resulting from doubling the input amplitude.

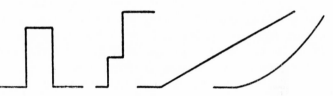

FIG. 4.   Complex inputs analyzable into step-function components.

Experimental tests of linearity using complex inputs such as those shown in Fig. 4 are in progress at Indiana University. Preliminary results indicate close agreement with the requirements of linearity.

If a human being acts as a linear system, it is quite possible that he may be a *different* linear system in different situations. This would mean that in a given situation, such as that presented in tracking by means of a hand wheel, his response to simple input components may be different from his response to the same simple input components in another situation, such as tracking by means of a lever, but that the output components obtained in each situation are additive in that situation. Another possibility is that the human transmission system, even though it may be linear, has different characteristics as a function of practice. This is almost certainly the case, but at present we do not know whether the processes of learning involve a change in the way in which response components are combined or a change in the components themselves. If a definite answer to this practical problem can be obtained, it will be of considerable importance for a theory of motor learning.

Operational analysis will also be concerned with individual differences. The problem here is somewhat similar to one introduced by learning. Are the differences between individuals due to their being different non-linear systems, that is, systems which combine response components differently or are they systems which combine different stimulus-response functions linearly? If it is found that all individuals are linear systems, it would be theoretically possible to construct selection tests for certain types of complex motor behavior on the basis of measurements of response to relatively simple stimulus input components. The score on such a test might resemble the specifications now given for electronic amplifiers.

v. SUMMARY

Recent development in military, aviation, and industrial equipment design has produced a need for specific information concerning characteristics of the motor behavior of the human operators of these machines. A considerable amount of research has been performed recently on the form of motor responses as a function of those characteristics of the task which are determined by design of machines. To date, no conceptual scheme has been presented which integrates the many isolated facts which have resulted from these experiments.

This paper calls attention to a method, *operational analysis*, which has been developed by mathematicians and engineers for the analysis of input-output relationships of electrical and mechanical transmission systems. This method, which permits the prediction of the response to complex inputs on the basis of a limited number of determinations of the response to simple input components is potentially applicable to certain aspects of human motor behavior. From a psychological point of view, the operational analysis method provides a ready-made, limited psychological theory which may be verified experimentally. The method is a direct parallel of the stimulus-response approach in psychology, which is concerned with the relationships between stimuli and responses rather than with intervening physiological mechanisms. Essentially it assumes that the motor response to complex changes in a stimulus input may be predicted from the addition or integration of responses of simpler components of this input. If this assumption is verified, aside from its value in application, it will provide a means for examining the nature of learning and individual differences in motor behavior.

[21]

L. L. THURSTONE

Multiple-Factor Analysis *

THE FACTOR PROBLEM

On the nature of science

This volume is concerned with methods of discovering and identifying significant categories in psychology and in other sciences. It is there-

* From *Multiple-Factor Analysis: A Development and Expansion of The Vectors of Mind* by Louis Leon Thurstone. The University of Chicago Publications in Biology and Medicine. The University of Chicago Press, 1947. Copyright, 1947, by The University of Chicago. Pp. 51–59 of Ch. I reprinted by permission of the author and the publisher.

fore of interest to consider some phases of science in general that bear on the problem of finding a methodology for a psychological science.

It is the faith of all science that an unlimited number of phenomena can be comprehended in terms of a limited number of concepts or ideal constructs. Without this faith no science could ever have any motivation. To deny this faith is to affirm the primary chaos of nature and the consequent futility of scientific effort. The constructs in terms of which natural phenomena are comprehended are man-made inventions. To discover a scientific law is merely to discover that a man-made scheme serves to unify, and thereby to simplify, comprehension of a certain class of natural phenomena. A scientific law is not to be thought of as having an independent existence which some scientist is fortunate to stumble upon. A scientific law is not a part of nature. It is only a way of comprehending nature.

A simple example is the concept "force." No one has ever seen a force. Only the movement of objects is seen. The faith of science is that some schematic representation is possible by which complexities of movement can be conceptually unified into an order. The error of a literal interpretation of a force vector as the pictorial representation of a corresponding physical entity is seen in the resolution of forces. If a particle moves with uniform acceleration in a certain direction, it is, of course, possible to describe the movement by one force, or by two, or by three or more coplanar forces. This resolution of a movement into several simultaneous and super-imposed movements is frequently done in order that a convenient and habitual reference frame may be retained. While the ideal constructs of science do not imply physical reality, they do not deny the possibility of some degree of correspondence with physical reality. But this is a philosophical problem that is quite outside the domain of science.

Consider, as another example, Coulomb's inverse-square law of electrical attraction. A postulated force is expressed as a function of the linear separation of the charges. Now, if the charges were to be personified, they would probably be much surprised that their actions were being described in terms of their linear separations. No one assumes that there is a string between the charges, but Coulomb's law implies that the length of such a string is to be used in our simplified scheme of comprehending the postulated charges. It is more likely that the whole space surrounding the charges is involved in the phenomena of attraction and that Coulomb's law is a fortunate short cut for representing approximately a part of the phenomena that are called "charges" and "attractions." It is not unlikely that all these entities will eventually vanish as such and become only aspects of an order more involved than Coulomb's law implies but not so chaotic as to individualize completely every moment of nature.

A science of psychology will deal with the activities of people as its central theme. A large class of human activity is that which differentiates individuals as regards their overt accomplishments. Just as it is convenient to postulate physical forces in describing the movements of physical objects, so it is also natural to postulate abilities and their absence as primary causes of the successful completion of a task by some individuals and of the failure of other individuals in the same task.

The criterion by which a new ideal construct in science is accepted or rejected is the degree to which it facilitates the comprehension of a class of phenomena which can be thought of as examples of a single construct rather than as individualized events. It is in this sense that the chief object of science is to minimize mental effort. But in order that this reduction may be accepted as science, it must be demonstrated, either explicitly or by implication, that the number of degrees of freedom of the construct is smaller than the number of degrees of freedom of the phenomena that the reduction is expected to subsume. Consider, as an example, any situation in which a rational equation is proposed as the law governing the relation between two variables. If three observations have been made and if the proposed equation has three independent parameters, then the number of degrees of freedom of the phenomena is the same as the number of degrees of freedom of the equation, and hence the formulation remains undemonstrated. If, on the other hand, one hundred experimentally independent observations are subsumed by a rational equation with three parameters, then the demonstration can be of scientific interest. The convincingness of a hypothesis can be gauged inversely by the ratio of its number of degrees of freedom to that of the phenomena which it has demonstrably covered. It is in the nature of science that no scientific law can ever be proved to be right. It can only be shown to be plausible. The laws of science are not immutable. They are only human efforts toward parsimony in the comprehension of nature.

If abilities are to be postulated as primary causes of individual differences in overt accomplishment, then the widely different achievements of individuals must be demonstrable functions of a limited number of reference abilities. This implies that individuals will be described in terms of a limited number of faculties. This is contrary to the erroneous contention that, since every person is different from every other person in the world, people must not be classified and labeled.

Each generalization in the scientific description of nature results in a loss in the extent to which the ideal constructs of science match the individual events of experience. This is illustrated by simple experiments with a pendulum, in which the mass, the period, and the locus of the center of gravity with reference to a fulcrum are involved in the ideal construct that leads to experimental verification. But the construct matches only incompletely the corresponding experimental situation. The construct says nothing about the rusty setscrew and other extraneous detail. From the viewpoint of immediate experience, scientific description is necessarily incomplete. The scientist always finds his constructs immersed in the irrelevancies of experience. It seems appropriate to acknowledge this characteristic of science, in view of the fact that it is a rather common notion that the scientific description of a person is not valid unless the so-called "total situation" has been engulfed. A study of people does not become scientific because it attempts to be complete, nor is it invalid because it is restricted. The scientific description of a person will be as incomplete from the viewpoint of common sense as the description of other objects in scientific context.

The development of scientific analysis in a new class of phenomena usually meets with resistance. The faith of science that nature can be comprehended in terms of an order acknowledges no limitation whatever as regards classes of phenomena. But scientists are not free from prejudice against the extension of their faith to realms not habitually comprehended in the scientific order. Examples of this resistance are numerous. It is not infrequent for a competent physical scientist to declare his belief that the phenomena of living objects are, at least in some subtle way, beyond the reach of rigorous scientific order.

One of the forms in which this resistance appears is the assertion that, since a scientific construct does not cover all enumerable details of a class of phenomena, it is therefore to be judged inapplicable. Since the analysis of cell growth by mathematical and physical principles does not cover everything that is known about cells, the biologist judges the analysis to be inapplicable. Since no mathematical analysis that can be conceived would cover all the subtle mysteries of personality, this realm is frequently judged to be outside the domain of rigorous science. But physical scientists accept rigorous scientific analyses about physical events that leave fully as much beyond the scientific constructs. Every explosion in the world has been different from every other explosion, and no physicist can write equations to cover all the detail of any explosive event. It is certain that no two thunderstorms have been exactly alike, and yet the constructs of physics are applied in comprehending thunder and lightning, without any demand that the detail of the landscape be covered by the same scientific constructs.

The attitudes of people on a controversial social issue have been appraised by allocating each person to a point on a linear continuum as regards his favorable or his unfavorable affect toward the psychological object. Some social scientists have objected because two individuals may have the same attitude score toward, say, pacifism, and yet be totally different in their backgrounds and in the causes of their similar social views. If such critics were consistent, they would object also to the statement that two men have identical incomes, for one of them earns while the other one steals. They should also object to the statement that two men are of the same height. The comparison should be held invalid because one of the men is fat and the other is thin. This is again the resistance against invading with the generalizing and simplifying constructs of science a realm which is habitually comprehended only in terms of innumerable and individualized detail. Every scientific construct limits itself to specified variables without any pretense of covering those aspects of a class of phenomena about which it has said nothing. As regards this characteristic of science, there is no difference between the scientific study of physical events and the scientific study of biological and psychological events. What is not generally understood, even by many scientists, is that no scientific law is ever intended to represent any event pictorially. The law is only an abstraction from the experimental situation. No experiment is ever completely repeated.

There is an unlimited number of ways in which nature can be comprehended in terms of fundamental scientific concepts. One of the simplest ways in which a class of phenomena can be comprehended in terms of a limited number of concepts is probably that in which a linear attribute of an event is expressed as a linear function of primary causes. Even when the relations are preferably non-linear and mathematically involved, it is frequently possible to use the simple linear forms as first approximations. A well-known example of this type of relation is that in which the chroma of a spectral color is expressed as a linear function of two arbitrarily chosen primaries. If two spectral colors are chosen arbitrarily for use as primaries, it is possible to express any intermediate color as a linear function of the two arbitrarily chosen primaries. The coefficients of the two terms of this linear function represent the angular sizes of the two sectors into which a color rotator is divided. When the rotator is spun, the intermediate color is seen. But here, as elsewhere in science, although the chroma of the resulting color is expressed in terms of the linear function of the arbitrary primaries, it does not follow that the saturation and the gray-values are expressed by the same law. There is still debate about which colors are to be considered primary. This question can be settled only by discovering that a certain set of primaries gives the most parsimonious comprehension of some phase of color vision. A parallel in the delineation of human traits is their description, in first approximation, as linear functions of a limited number of reference traits. The final choice of a set of primary reference traits or faculties must be made in terms of the discovery that a particular set of reference traits renders most parsimonious our comprehension of a great variety of human traits.

The Purpose of Factor Analysis

A factor problem starts with the hope or conviction that a certain domain is not so chaotic as it looks. The range of phenomena that is represented in any factor analysis will be referred to as its *domain*. If a particular investigation is limited to measurements in visual perception, it is likely that auditory effects will be outside of its domain. The factorial methods were developed primarily for the purpose of identifying the principal dimensions or categories of mentality; but the methods are general, so that they have been found useful for other psychological problems and in other sciences as well. Factor analysis can be regarded as a general scientific method. Since the methods were developed especially for the solution of psychological problems and since the new methods have been used so far mainly on psychological problems, these will be used for most of the examples in this text. Some of the principles can be illustrated to best advantage in terms of simple mechanical or geometrical examples; and these will be used occasionally, especially when it is desired to illustrate a logical principle without involving the distractions of controversial or nebulous subject matter.

The factorial methods were developed for the study of individual differences among people, but the individual differences may be regarded as an avenue of approach to the study of the processes which underlie these differences. If a process is invariant in all its characteristics in an experimental population of individuals, then there exist no individual differences as regards such a process, and it cannot be investigated by factorial means.

Thus, if we select an experimental population of individuals who are all equally good or equally bad in some form of visual perception, then we cannot expect to identify or differentiate such processes by factorial methods. It is only to the extent that the individuals of an experimental population exhibit individual differences in a process and its effects that these effects can become accessible to investigation by factorial methods.

When a particular domain is to be investigated by means of individual differences, one can proceed in one of two ways. One can invent a hypothesis regarding the processes that underlie the individual differences, and one can then set up a factorial experiment, or a more direct laboratory experiment, to test the hypothesis. If no promising hypothesis is available, one can represent the domain as adequately as possible in terms of a set of measurements or numerical indices and proceed with a factorial experiment. The analysis might reveal an underlying order which would be of great assistence in formulating the scientific concepts covering the particular domain. In the first case we start with a hypothesis that determines the nature of the measurements that enter into the factorial analysis. In the second case we start with no hypothesis, but we proceed, instead, with a set of measurements or indices that cover the domain, hoping to discover in the factorial analysis the nature of the underlying order. It is this latter application of the factorial methods that is sometimes referred to as an attempt to lift ourselves by our own boot straps, because the underlying order in a domain can be discovered without first postulating it in the form of a hypothesis. This is probably the characteristic of factor analysis that gives it some interest as a general scientific method.

Factor analysis is not restricted by assumptions regarding the nature of the factors, whether they be physiological or social, elemental or complex, correlated or uncorrelated. For example, some of the factors may turn out to be defined by endocrinological effects. Others may be defined in biochemical or biophysical parameters of the body fluids or of the central nervous system. Other factors may be defined by neurological or vascular relations in some anatomical locus; still other factors may involve parameters in the dynamics of the autonomic nervous system; still others may be defined in terms of experience and schooling. Factor analysis assumes that a variety of phenomena within a domain are related and that they are determined, at least in part, by a relatively small number of functional unities or factors. The factors may be called by different names, such as "causes," "faculties," "parameters," "functional unities," "abilities," or "independent measurements." The name for a factor depends on the context, on one's philosophical preferences and manner of speech, and on how much one already knows about the domain to be investigated. The factors in psychological investigations are not ordinarily to be thought of as elemental things which are present or absent, like heads or tails in the tossing of coins.

The exploratory nature of factor analysis is often not understood. Factor analysis has its principal usefulness at the border line of science. It is naturally superseded by rational formulations in terms of the science involved. Factor analysis is useful, especially in those domains where basic and fruitful concepts are essentially lacking and where crucial experiments have been difficult to conceive. The new methods have a humble role. They enable us to make only the crudest first map of a new domain. But if we have scientific intuition and sufficient ingenuity, the rough factorial map of a new domain will enable us to proceed beyond the exploratory factorial stage to the more direct forms of psychological experimentation in the laboratory.

In a domain where fundamental and fruitful concepts are already well formulated and tested, it would be absurd to use the factorial methods except for didactic purposes to illustrate factorial logic. In such situations there are available more direct methods of investigating rival hypotheses. In the relatively young sciences and in the new domains of the older sciences, the factorial experiments will be useful. It seems quite likely that the new methods will be applied with profit in the field of meteorology, but it is not likely that they will ever be used in classical mechanics.

In factorial investigations of mentality we proceed on the assumption that mind is structured somehow, that mind is not a patternless mosaic of an infinite number of elements without functional groupings. The extreme, opposite view would be to hold that mind has no structure at all. In the interpretation of mind we assume that mental phenomena can be identified in terms of distinguishable functions, which do not all participate equally in everything that mind does. It is these functional unities that we are looking for with the aid of factorial methods. It is our scientific faith that such distinguishable mental functions can be identified and that they will be verified in different types of experimental study. No assumption is made about the nature of these functions, whether they are native or acquired or whether they have a cortical locus.

In order to illustrate the method, let us consider a set of gymnastic stunts that might be given to a group of several hundred boys of comparable age. A factor analysis starts with a table of intercorrelations of the variables. If there were twenty different stunts, we should have a square 20 × 20 table showing the correlation of every performance with every other performance. Our question now is to determine whether these relations can be comprehended in terms of some underlying order, which is simpler than the whole table of several hundred experimentally determined coefficients of correlation. Let us suppose that some of the stunts require principally strength of the right arm, that others require principally a good sense of balance, that still others require speed of bodily movement. Several tests that require good sense of balance might not require arm strength, while those which require a strong arm might require very little bodily balance. We might then find that the correlations can be comprehended in terms of a small number of functional unities, such as sense of balance, arm strength, or speed of bodily movement. Each of the gymnastic tests might require one or several of these functional unities; but it is not likely that every test will require every one of the functional unities that are represented by the whole set of gymnastic tests. A factorial analysis would reveal these functional unities, and we would say that each of them is a primary factor in the battery of tests. Now, if we should take any one of these functional unities, such as sense of balance, and represent it in a new set of twenty tests of great variety which all required bodily balance, we might find that there are really several primary factors involved in this domain. For example, there might conceivably be a separate balancing factor for each of the semicircular canals, or there might be some other breakdown of the balancing factors that would be revealed in an extensive study of balancing tests.* A new set of more refined primary factors might be found within the domain of bodily balance. This process might continue with the factorial investigation of more and more restricted domains, as long as the functional unities continued to be difficult to conceive in direct experimentation. Eventually, the factorial methods, which are essentially exploratory, would yield to the reformulation of a problem in terms of the fundamental rational constructs of the science involved. It is not unlikely that factorial analyses will point the way in the work of inventing significant and fundamental scientific concepts.

Let us consider, next, an example in the sensory and perceptual fields. Let us start with a set of twenty perceptual tests involving several of the modalities. Some of the tests might require visual acuity; others would require keen discrimination of rhythm; still others might require speed of perception. Each of the perceptual tests might involve one or more of these functional unities; but few would require all these functions. Some of the tests, for example, might not depend on visual acuity. In this simple case we should not be surprised to find factorially the primary functional unities that are obvious at the start.

If we turn to the more central functions that are involved in the intellectual and temperamental differences among people, it seems reasonable to suppose that here also we may expect to find functional unities that will some day be as obvious as the sensory and perceptual unities are obvious to us now.

---

* Several such factors might appear in the place of specific variance and uninterpreted common-factor variance in the earlier studies.

Our work in the factorial study of the human mind rests on the assumption that mind represents a dynamical system which can eventually be understood in terms of a finite number of parameters. We have assumed, further, that all these parameters, or groups of parameters, are not involved in the individual differences of every kind of mental task. Just as we take it for granted that the individual differences in visual acuity are not involved in pitch discrimination, so we assume that in intellectual tasks some mental or cortical functions are not involved in every task. This is the principle of "simple structure" or "simple configuration" in the underlying order for any given set of attributes.

Observation and educational experience lend plausibility to the conception that the mental abilities are determined by a great multiplicity of causes or determiners and that these determiners are more or less structured or linked in groups. This multiplicity of determiners can be thought of as a field of elements in which all are not equally closely linked. Some elements may be quite independent in their actions, while others may be rather closely associated. The factors are probably functional groupings, and it would be a distortion to assume that they must be elemental. We know precious little about the determiners of human talent and temperament, and we should not impose upon our thinking an unnecessarily rigid causal frame.

If we grant that men are not all equal in intellectual endowment and in temperament and if we have the faith that this domain can be investigated as science, then we must make the plausible and inevitable assumption that individual differences among men can be conceived in terms of a finite number of traits, parameters, or factors. Some of the factors may be found to be anatomically determined; others will be physiological; while others will be defined, at first, in experiential, educational, and social terms. As scientists, we must believe that a set of categories can be found for the understanding of mentality, which have, by their simplicity, a prior claim on our conceptual formulations.

· · · · · · · · ·

PSYCHOLOGICAL IMPLICATIONS OF FACTOR ANALYSIS *

Factor analysis originated in an epoch-making paper by Spearman in 1904. Spearman probably saw important implications in that paper but it seems doubtful whether he could have realized at that time the superstructure that was to be built on his first observations on what he called hierarchy. For a quarter of a century the journals were full of controversy about Spearman's single-factor theory of intelligence. His hypothesis and his uni-dimensional methods were extended to the n-dimensional case in 1930. In the last seventeen years, multiple-factor analysis has seen a very

* Presidential address, American Psychological Association, Division on Evaluation and Measurement, Detroit, September 9, 1947. Reprinted from L. L. Thurstone, Psychological implications of factor analysis, *Amer. Psychol.* 1948, *3*, 402–408. By permission of the author, the *American Psychologist*, and the American Psychological Association.

fast development so that even in this short period there have been published several thousand papers on multiple-factor theory and experimental results.

Our purpose here is to review some psychological implications of multiple-factor analysis and to make only incidental reference to the factorial methods as such. It is time that we take stock more frequently of how the factorial methods are affecting psychological concepts, and how these in turn affect the development of appropriate factorial methods. It should be emphasized that factor analysis is a scientific method that must be adjusted to each problem. It is not merely a satistical method, and it is not a routine that can be applied fruitfully to every correlation table in sight.

In the light of a good deal of experience with the factorial methods, we should be able to give students a few practical suggestions. In the Psychometric Laboratory at Chicago, we spend more time in designing the experimental tests for a factor study than on all of the computational work, including the correlations, the factoring, and the analysis of the structure. If we have several hypotheses about postulated factors, we design and invent new tests which may be crucially differentiating between the several hypotheses. This is entirely a psychological job with no computing. It calls for as much psychological insight as we can gather among students and instructors. Frequently we find that we have guessed wrong, but occasionally the results are strikingly encouraging. I mention this aspect of factorial work in the hope of counteracting the rather general impression that factor analysis is all concerned with algebra and statistics. These should be our servants in the investigation of psychological ideas. If we have no psychological ideas, we are not likely to discover anything interesting because even if the factorial results are clear and clean, the interpretation must be as subjective as in any other scientific work.

Another hint for the student is that he usually tries to accomplish something too ambitious in his first factorial studies but that is also typical in the formulation of other thesis subjects. A factorial study is more likely to give convincing findings if it covers a restricted domain with only enough measures of known factorial composition to serve as a linkage between the factors that are already known and the factors that we hope to discover or isolate.

Most of the factorial studies that have been done so far have been concerned with the cognitive domain. Previous work had discovered a number of group factors such as the verbal, the numerical, and the visual. These were more clearly revealed by the more powerful multiple-factor methods. The further breakdown of the cognitive intellective functions into primary factors has revealed that the cognitive field represents a large number of functional unities or factors. We no longer speak of "the" verbal factor as if it were unitary. At least three verbal factors are known and several additional verbal factors are clearly indicated. One of these verbal factors has been denoted V and it represents facility in understanding verbal material.

Another verbal factor has been denoted Word Fluency W and it represents facility in finding words to represent restricted context. A third verbal factor F represents ideational fluency with words. There is indication that a naming factor exists which is independent of the three that have been mentioned. In some forms of aphasia we seem to be dealing with patients who have one or more of these verbal factors intact while they are lacking in other verbal factors. Without understanding the differences between the several distinct verbal factors, one is at a loss to understand why the patient can do certain verbal tests while he fails on other verbal tests. This field should be experimentally investigated more intensively in the light of factorial results.

The ability to memorize has been found to be a primary factor that is independent of other cognitive functions. Incidental memory seems to be an ability that is distinct from the ability to memorize intentionally. There is good indication that auditory memory is not the same ability as visual memory.

One of the most important of the primary abilities is that of visualizing space which has been denoted the Space factor S. It is involved in all thinking about solid objects and flat objects in space.

The perceptual functions have been broken down into a number of distinct primary factors. Among the most interesting are those which represent facility in perceptual closure in which there are very large individual differences. Perceptual closure has been found in a battery of visual tests and also in a battery of twenty-eight auditory tests that were specially designed for factorial analysis. It is a curious circumstance that we do not yet know whether the closure factor in visual material is the same as the closure factor in auditory material. In order to solve that problem, it will be necessary to include both visual and auditory tests of closure in the same factorial analysis. It will then be interesting to ascertain whether perceptual closure is a primary factor that transcends the visual and auditory modalities. If so, then closure is a central factor that may be of considerable importance in the human intellect. On the other hand, it may be found that closure is represented by two or more factors that are specific for each modality. An extensive study of perceptual abilities has recently been carried out by Harold P. Bechtoldt.

It is not our purpose here to summarize all of the primary factors that have been identified but only to describe the general nature of these findings.

When we consider the increasing number of distinct functional unities into which the field of cognition is being divided, we find that it is necessary to revise very fundamentally our notions about general intelligence. Factorial results make it imperative that we describe each individual in terms of a profile of mental abilities instead of by a single index such as the I.Q.

With further progress in this field we shall have a profile for each person with a very large number of columns. It is our present belief that if we knew the twenty most important primary factors we should be able to undertake educational and vocational counseling with more confidence than at present. Even in the present state of knowledge with about ten of these factors identified, we certainly can do much better in appraising the intellective assets of a person than by the older methods by which each person was described in terms of a single I.Q.

Factorial work raises interesting questions about the general intellective factor of Spearman. According to his hypothesis, general intelligence is mediated by a central intellective factor which he denoted "g." This hypothesis has been the subject of much controversy in the last forty years. When the multiple-factor methods began to isolate quite a number of primary factors in the cognitive domain, it looked at first as if the Spearman single-factor hypothesis would have to be discarded but that does not seem to be necessary. It was found that the primary factors of cognition were positively correlated. For adults, most of these correlations are under +.30. When the positive correlations between the primary factors are examined factorially, there appear second-order factors, and the most conspicuous of these second-order factors agrees well with Spearman's hypothesis. Here we have a clue to an interpretation that may unify the early work of Spearman and the later work with multiple-factor analysis. The interpretation that seems plausible at this time is that the primary factors represent different kinds of mental facilities such as several kinds of memory, several kinds of perceptual closure, several visualizing factors, and several verbal factors. These primary abilities may be regarded as media for the expression of intellect and people differ markedly in the effectiveness with which they can express themselves in these different media. The second-order factors may represent parameters that are more central in character and more universal in the sense that they are not determined by the efficiency of each modality or imagery type. The first-order primary factors may be regarded as separate organs, in a general sense, while the second-order or general factors represent parameters which influence the activities of the several organs or primary factors. The general factors may then be expected to have no particular locus whereas some of the primary factors may eventually be rather definitely localized.

This attempt to unify Spearman's work with the later multiple-factor work seems to be plausible in terms of the findings of recent factorial studies but it should not be taken very literally. We can make only a tentative sketch of the underlying order at this early stage of knowledge of the organization of human intellect. If Spearman's general intellective factor is the same as the second-order inductive factor, then we can now determine that general factor uniquely. That is something which Spearman was never able to do. I have spoken of second-order factors in the plural. The reason is that we seldom find a single second-order general factor which would be indicated by Spearman's original hypothesis. Such complications are to be expected with the development of any science and it should not be interpreted as a discredit to Spearman's early work on which all of us have built.

In introducing our speculation about the relation of Spearman's general intellective factor "g" to later multiple-factor studies, we have noted that the primary factors are positively correlated. This also introduces a conflict between our statistical habits and psychological judgment. Some students of factorial theory bring to this subject their statistical habits and they sometimes insist that factors must be uncorrelated in order to be meaningful and useful. This is a curious situation. We deal all the time with meaningful measures that are correlated such as height and weight, but when we turn to the mental abilities, we are told that we must force them to be uncorrelated. Scientific judgment dictates that we report the correlations between primary factors as they are actually found, irrespective of statistical convenience. The correlated abilities are represented in factor analysis by oblique reference axes. This is not so convenient as a coordinate system in which all of the axes are at right angles.

Psychological studies of aptitudes frequently refer to such categories as mechanical aptitude, artistic aptitude, and musical aptitude. We shall describe briefly a current study of mechanical aptitude as an illustration of the psychological aspects of factorial analysis. It is rather common to hear mechanical aptitude referred to as if it were a single entity but it is our hypothesis that mechanical aptitude is a complex of abilities rather than a single unitary trait. It also seems plausible that we are dealing here with a rather restricted number of abilities. It is our job now to try to discover how many important abilities are involved in the complex known as mechanical aptitude and what those abilities are. Further, we make the hypothesis that mechanical aptitude is mostly in the head. It is not uncommon to hear this type of talent described as if it were in the finger tips, even associated with a certain amount of stupidity and a willingness to get one's hands dirty. In fact, it is rather common in the public schools to send the verbally slow learners into technical schools with the idea that if a boy is sufficiently stupid, he may become a good machinist. This is one of the educational blunders of our generation. It is our hypothesis that when a mechanic inspects a piece of machinery that is misbehaving, and when he diagnoses what is wrong with it, he is using his head and only incidentally his hands. Musical talent is also a complex that is not confined to finger dexterity. The psychological problem in the current study is to discover, if possible, what cognitive primary functions are involved in mechanical aptitude. If we could solve that problem, we might make a contribution of importance to education as well as to industry.

In the current study of this problem, we have made some tentative hypotheses which are in turn represented by differentiating tests that were specially designed for the purpose. One hypothesis which will almost certainly be sustained, as it has been in previous studies of this problem, is that mechanical aptitude consists in some large part of the space factor S, namely, the ability to think about objects in two-dimensional and in three-dimensional space. There are tremendous individual differences in this ability to visualize space, and in an educated audience we could find a fairly large proportion of individuals who, although otherwise gifted, are very poor in this ability. The tests by which this factor has been identified all involve the visualizing of objects that are stationary. In dealing with mechanical problems, one must be able to think of objects in motion. Their relative motions have definite restrictions that are studied in a separate discipline known as kinematics. We might therefore add another psychological hypothesis, namely, that there exist one or more abilities that are revealed in the ability to think about solid objects in motion as distinguished from thinking about them when they stay still. Another hypothesis about this group of aptitudes is that the ability to remember visual form has some part in mechanical aptitude. Still another hypothesis is that the perception of fine detail is involved. Perhaps one of the most fruitful hypotheses is that mechanical aptitude involves non-verbal reasoning.

When a list of hypotheses has been assembled, the next step is to invent a set of experimental tests which shall be crucially differentiating among the hypotheses. When that has been done, the tests are prepared and tried out for suitable time limits and performance instructions. Then they are given to several hundred individuals who are known to differ widely in mechanical aptitude. There is no need to represent the general population. In fact, it is wasteful to assemble a group of experimental subjects so as to represent the general middle range. It is better to include extremes of all available types in the experimental group. It will generally be found that all this work requires more time than the computational work that follows.

Similar studies should be undertaken in the fields of artistic aptitude and of musical aptitude in the hope of determining the dimensionalities of these fields. It has been our experience that no domain is completely determined in a single factor study because every study raises more psychological problems than it answers, but this is the natural course of science.

When a factorial analysis has been completed, one is tempted to try to interpret all of the common variance in terms of common factors, but it usually happens that some of the factors are indeterminate while some of them are clear and easily interpreted. It should be pointed out that a factorial study can make a major scientific contribution to our understanding of mind, even if it does not attempt to identify all of the common factors clearly. An important contribution can be made even if only one new factor is isolated and psychologically described even if all of the rest of the variance remains an unknown muddle. Such results depend on the structure that happens to be found in the factorial battery that is assembled to represent a domain, and every factor study is in this sense a gamble.

The inheritance of mental abilities has been investigated on 150 pairs of identical and fraternal twins. They were given forty psychological tests, including both group tests and individual performance tests. It was found that the identical twins were more nearly alike than the fraternal twins.

Their differences were especially marked in the visualizing factors. It was found that spelling ability was one of the most conspicuous in differentiating the identical from the fraternal twins. The ability to learn spelling seems to be quite independent of most other abilities and it should be investigated to determine its relations to the primary factors.

One of the most important implications of factorial work is the breakdown on the line of demarcation between intellect and temperament. It is becoming increasingly evident that these two domains are not so completely separated as they have frequently been assumed to be. For example, the primary factors that identify perceptual closure are certainly cognitive in character and yet they seem to be definitely related to temperamental characteristics as well. In this connection the recent work of Dr. John G. Lynn is of special interest. He gave some tests of primary mental abilities to psychiatric patients and he noted in particular those patients who were relatively much better gifted in the space factor than in the verbal factors. He noted also the opposite extreme, namely, those patients who were much better gifted in the verbal factors than in the space factor. He found interesting differences in the symptoms of these two groups of patients. For example, he found that among the patients who were much higher in the space factor than in the verbal factors, there were no hallucinations. This field calls for very intensive study so that we may know more definitely the relations between the emotional symptoms and the relative strengths of the cognitive primary factors. Other studies of normal subjects have shown indication of temperamental differences between those who excel in the visualizing factors and those who excel in the verbal factors.

Factorial work is customarily based on experimental populations of several hundred subjects and the primary factors are isolated, ordinarily, on populations of normal subjects. I should like to suggest a parallel form of experimentation that should give results consistent with the factorial experiments. It is well known that among feeble-minded subjects we find occasionally conspicuous cases in which one or more abilities remain intact and even of superior quality while the subject is otherwise so poorly endowed mentally that he must have institutional care. I believe that significant studies could be made of single subjects in order to clarify our understanding of the primary mental abilities. For example, a single patient might be found who excels on a few similar tests while he fails hopelessly on the rest of them. Now, the investigator should alter slightly the several tests which the patient can do in order to determine just what characteristics must be retained in order for the patient to be able to do the task and just what characteristics of the test are associated with his failures. The investigator would have to try a large number of slight variations in the tests in order to be able to draw a sort of psychological map, as it were, to show just what the patient can do and what it is that he fails to do. If it can be assumed that one or a few of the abilities are intact in the patient, then we might be able to determine from the successive performances of a single patient just what each primary factor involved. The results should then be verified factorially by a study of normal subjects. I am calling attention to this type of inquiry in order to show again the intimate relations between factorial experiments and psychological hypotheses. We must not regard factor analysis merely as a toy for the statisticians to play with. It is a scientific method that should be useful in testing hypotheses in experimental, clinical, and social psychology.

[22a]

GARDNER MURPHY

Gestalt and Field Theory *

GESTALT

Nature is neither kernel nor shell; she is everything at once.

GOETHE

As one dips into the works of psychologists in any period from the pre-Socratic to the present, one may run upon phrases which deny the possibility of explaining wholes by a study of their constituent parts. It is therefore a futile and fruitless enterprise to try to specify who first got hold of the general principle of Gestalt psychology; and it is peculiarly futile to try to guess which of the Gestalt writers were influenced, consciously or unconsciously, by this or that earlier formulation of doctrines of wholeness or structure.

It is, however, worth while to note that relationships or modes or organization are repeatedly stressed by early Greek thinkers, many of whom decried the tendency to find a primordial stuff of which the world was made, and looked rather for a law of arrangement, a principle of synthesis or order. In general, the Pythagorean answers were the most successful, and in general the history of science has shown them to be the most generally followed by men of other eras. It was, in other words, the mathematical approach to the problem of structure or organization that stood in the most fruitful and dynamic opposition to the various types of atomism or elementarism. The Platonists, of course, had taken over with enthusiasm the emphasis upon mathematics as a clue to structure, and Platonism contains many passages which may reasonably enough be regarded as foundation stones for a Gestalt theory.

In modern times—to remind the reader of a few examples already

* Reprinted from *Historical Introduction to Modern Psychology* by Gardner Murphy. Revised edition, 1949. Copyright, 1949, by Harcourt, Brace & Co., Inc. Pp. 284–300. By permission of Harcourt, Brace & Co., Inc. and the author.

quoted—Hartley had pointed out that tastes and smells may not only combine in such a way as to give new qualities, but may be experienced in such a way that the original elements are no longer observable at all (page 33).[1] The elements are literally lost to view. John Stuart Mill had later made a profitable use of this conception (page 104).[2] Alexander Bain stated expressly that this principle applies not only to momentary wholes, but to the flow of experience as well (page 196).[3] There is no starting or stopping; there is constantly a dynamic readjustment in the structure of a complex experience which makes mechanical types of analysis peculiarly unfruitful. William James was positively obsessed with this problem, of course, and returned to it on every possible occasion (page 196).[4] The best known of his philippics against the atomistic view is the discussion of the "psychologist's fallacy," which is simply the assumption that when one has reduced a complex to its supposed parts, the parts must have been there all the time and must have been the real key to the complex. James seldom worked out his position from an initial protest to the calm and positive assertion of a system; in fact, one feels that he would have knocked the system down if he had ever succeeded in building one. But in so far as Gestalt psychology is a protest against elementarism or atomism, this celebrated passage of James's is a clear enough forerunner. Not to tire the reader with countless examples of other forerunners, we may finally note Henri Bergson's expression of the evolutionary outlook at the turn of the century in his comment that the perceptual whole which we experience on a starlit night includes an integration of everything from the stars we observe to the brain processes which go on during the event.

But we must get down to much more specific and clear-cut examples of immediate forerunners of the German Gestalt psychology which took shape in 1912. Here we may follow Helson in noting the importance of Mach,[5] who grappled so brilliantly with the "analysis of sensations" in the eighties. While Mach had come to the conclusion that the world of sensations with which the physical scientist deals as he takes note of lights, sounds, and temperatures, is identically the same world of lights, sounds, and temperatures with which the psychologist is concerned, he did note certain relational problems which seemed to disturb the symmetry of this beautiful analysis. He noted, for example, that the arrangement of elements—say, for example, the arrangement of lines in geometrical figures—causes the emergence of different totals which are reported as squares, diamonds, and so on. He had therefore resorted (page 226)[6] to the doctrine that there are "sensations of space," sensations which, while not pointing directly to the elements of the original experience, must be taken jointly with them if we are to explain the structured total.

This tour de force was followed a few years later by the more radical and adequate formulation of Von Ehrenfels (page 226).[7] In a paper in 1890 Von Ehrenfels noted that melodies must consist of something other than a sequence of tones, since obviously one sings or recognizes the melody in other keys; and indeed (with the very dubious exception of instances of absolute pitch) one makes no absolute use at all of specific tonal *elements* which enter into the melody. One may, moreover, encounter the same "element" (say middle C) in different melodies played in different keys, and find that they differ utterly. If we can have the same elements and get a different result, and have different elements yet get the same result, where are we with regard to the reduction of experience to fixed components? Von Ehrenfels went on to conclude that over and above various sensory ingredients there must be qualities belonging to organized forms, and coined the term "form quality"—*Gestaltqualität*—to describe that which a melody or a painting or a sonnet possesses which is not given in the component tones, colors, or words. Though this is more like a real psychological theory than is Mach's, it is extraordinary that Von Ehrenfels did not really undertake to solve, any more than did Mach, the question of what to do with the *new* elements—in this case new qualities—which he had thrown into the picture. One might accuse both Mach and Von Ehrenfels of buttressing up a tottering elementarism by throwing new elements into the situation, rather than by noting the nature of the architectural problem. If there are sensations of space, then what is the relation of the sensation of space to the other sensations already present? So also with regard to Von Ehrenfels: As we specify *qualities* to be added to sensory *elements*, why do we not need to specify other qualities which result from the relations of the first qualities to the sensory elements? If qualities or relations of any sort *between elements* are to be added to primary elements, do we not find ourselves lost in an infinite regressus? Indeed, if there are form qualities which go with certain sequences of tones (melodies), these must candidly be regarded as new elements in experience.

Moreover, the Von Ehrenfels solution makes one begin to wonder whether it means anything to say that *the same melody* sounds differently in different keys. Just what do we mean by "the same"? If a voice on one occasion, a violin on another occasion, carry an air, and we note the same form quality, we have the quality reappearing when no one of the original elements is there, a resultant without any component forces. Our problem has not really been solved; all we have done is to name a quality given by each structural total so that to all intents and purposes their number is unlimited. If it is replied that this is a new structural conception, one may simply note that unless form can be more fully defined, one has no more help in explaining and predicting the outcome of a new combination of ingredients than one would have if one simply let the ingredients try to do their own work without such aid. Certainly the Von Ehrenfels principle is an honest recognition of a grave difficulty, and there can certainly be no quarrel with its statement of the facts; perceptual wholes are not made up of the kinds of sensory elements that had traditionally been described as their ingredients. But just what form actually is and what its laws are remain indeterminate.

WERTHEIMER

That is where the problem stood during the time of the Würzburg investigations of attitude and thought, described above. Eagerly prosecuting such studies of higher mental processes, Max Wertheimer and two of his experimental subjects, Wolfgang Köhler and Kurt Koffka, came upon a radically different way of viewing the whole problem. It was Wertheimer's formulation of what occurred that led in Frankfurt in 1912 to the formal inauguration of the Gestalt psychology—the psychology of form.

The problem was the perception of motion. When light is thrown through a small slit placed vertically, and a moment later through a slit inclined 20° or 30° to the right, the interval separating the two presentations may be so chosen that the shaft of light appears to *fall* from one position to the other. Wertheimer proceeded to work out quantitatively those time relations which would give (1) two simultaneous illuminated slits, (2) the experience of motion from A to B, and (3) the sense of temporal succession, the first being followed by the second, but no movement being involved. The central problem was the nature of the experience of movement, the phi phenomenon.

Now a rather good elementaristic explanation of movement had been developed by Lotze some fifty years earlier (page 147).[8] For Lotze, the visual perception of motion depended upon the sequential stimulation of points on the retina, and hence the sequential stimulation of brain regions; a moving object caused a track of light to be made upon the retina. If, however, there is no such track of light when the eye is stationary while being stimulated successively by two lights as in the Wertheimer experiment with the phi phenomenon, Lotze's interpretation collapses. The perception of motion, argued Wertheimer, is an experience organically different from the perception of stationary lights, and no kind of serial arrangement of static stimulating points can give us this unique type of experience. The very essence of the experience is the manner in which temporal organization of two stimulations occurs. Wertheimer developed, therefore, the conception of "cross-processes" in the brain, dynamic *interactions* between the various cortical excitations which follow from the two stimulations.

Not being content with the insistence upon the reality of the experience of motion as something dynamically distinct from the awareness of position and of temporal succession of such positions, Wertheimer proceeded at once to a reformulation of the theory of wholes and parts. Just as Fechner had protested against the procedure of the philosopher from above to below (cf. page 92),[9] so Wertheimer protested against the general modern scientific movement from below to above. We shall never achieve an understanding of structured totals by starting with the ingredient parts which enter into them. On the contrary, we shall need to understand the structure; we shall need to have insight into it. There is then some possibility that the components themselves will be understood.

This leads immediately to two laws which follow inevitably if the relation of whole to parts has been properly stated. The first is the law of membership character. The tones in a melody do not have their several fixed qualities, to which a form quality is somehow added; rather, each such tone manifests qualities which depend upon the place of the tone in the context. Such attributes, depending on the place of an identifiable component in a structure, permit no use of the conception of elements which when compounded into totals remain what they were before. Similarly, a patch of color in a landscape, far from being an ingredient in a total, depends for its value upon the context which nature, or the artist, supplies; we are working from above rather than from below. The Gestaltist insists that the attributes or aspects of the component parts, in so far as they can be defined, are defined by their relations to the system as a whole in which they are functioning.

A simple laboratory demonstration is offered by a red cross on a gray field which after twenty seconds' fixation in fair light will elicit a green border (according to the familiar dynamics of contrast, page 141).[10] Cut out, however, a tiny notch in one of the arms of the cross. What color will the space within the notch yield to our observation? Green, says the traditional elementarist theory, for it is a part of the gray border which must take on a contrasting hue. Red, says the Gestaltist, for a cross is one of those organized wholes which forces the component materials within it, as a result of membership character, to take on the attributes supporting the structure. The Gestaltist predicts more accurately than the elementarist what will actually occur.

Proceeding further, however, Wertheimer noted that there are certain directions in which one can predict the emergence of structured wholes. Instead of simply saying with Von Ehrenfels that there is always something more than the parts, Wertheimer notes that if unstable equilibrium and unstable structure are given, which manifest certain types of inner relationships, one can predict from a knowledge of the laws of structure what kind of organization must supervene. It will be that kind of organization which is most orderly, most comprehensive, most stable, most free of the casual and the arbitrary; in a single word, that which is most good. Goodness, or as he preferred to say, *Prägnanz*, is the dynamic attribute or self-fulfillment, intrinsic in all structured totals. Glancing back at the example of the notched cross, one sees immediately that the stable, rugged, definite outlines of the arms have a far higher degree of *Prägnanz* than the chaotic, and one might even say rather irrational, lines of the notch, which disturb the simple, orderly, and stable pattern presented. These two laws, the law of membership character and the law of *Prägnanz*, are typical of many which rapidly evolved in Wertheimer's thinking. They are in general representative of Gestalt laws as a whole, laws in which one works not with an infinite number of tiny particles arranging themselves more or less independently, but with a limited, finite number of possible modes of stable organization, which because of their orderly, rationally intelligible form are capable of being discovered, and their dynamics understood.

The first task of the perceiver, then, is not to create, but to apprehend the order and meaning which is there objectively in the world. This is, so far, essentially like Platonism. There are, however, many forms or structures to be found, not all of which are of equal relevance to the perceiver. Just as perception moves from the incomplete toward that which is more nearly complete, so there is continuous dynamic selection and integration of forms. We have thus a direct transition from the psychology of perception to the psychology of thought, without involving the need of any essentially different principles. We need to grasp, first of all, the order lying in nature and waiting for our apprehension; and second, that internal order which the thinker manifests as he passes from one to another orderly form, creating new order in the succession and in the integration. The psychology of thinking already implicit in Wertheimer's earlier work became more and more important both in his own work and in that of his pupils. It was the process of thinking which intrigued Köhler (page 291)[11] in his comparison of men with apes. It was thinking which intrigued Koffka (page 291)[12] as he first ventured to conceive of educational psychology as the successive realization of levels of complexity, growing out of the capacity of the individual to move ever toward higher integrations rather than simply to acquire piecemeal one new response at a time. It is not in any sense accidental that during those last years of his life, when Wertheimer was endlessly burdened with the task of adapting to a new environment (after 1933 he taught at the New School for Social Research in New York), the book upon which he labored was a book on productive thinking.[13]

The basic conception which runs through this struggle to lay bare the dynamics of thought was the conception of *recentering*; the discovery of new forms of figure-ground organization in which an inadequate and ultimately disorderly mode of centering or focusing is thrust aside in favor of a newly recentered pattern—insightful and correct in the sense of mediating contact with reality, because the center as apprehended by the observer corresponds with a natural center in the objective event waiting for such discovery.

From the new viewpoint the entire domain of cognitive processes—processes of perception, learning, thinking, imagining—was to be systematically redefined in terms of the conception of Gestalt. In practice, moreover, cognitive phenomena were to be studied alongside the phenomena of affect. Emotion came to be viewed, for example, as a response involving the entire living system, rather than as a local response of the midbrain, after the manner of Walter Cannon (page 383).[14] And impulse, instinct, and will were treated ultimately as processes involving the entire community of various aspects of a bodily tension system, and presenting no possibility that a segmental act of impulse or will could be mapped out and independently studied.

Koffka and Köhler

The new doctrine, formulated by Wertheimer, was blazoned forth by Koffka and Köhler. They were younger than Wertheimer, and infinitely more ready to systematize publicly what was daily being discovered in hundreds of fresh little experiments and communicated by Wertheimer to his friends by word of mouth. Fortunate indeed for the spread of the Gestalt doctrine was the series of circumstances which led Koffka and Köhler into the public eye. Marooned in the Canary Islands during World War I, Köhler had carried out a series of ingenious studies to test the Thorndike hypothesis that animal learning depends simply upon trial and error and upon the stamping-in of the correct responses. Working with the anthropoid apes at the Teneriffe research station, Köhler presented a series of simple problems in which the animal had to discover a way of reaching a suspended banana by placing boxes underneath it and climbing up on them, or by fitting together sticks which, when thus fitted together, would make it possible to reach the food. Köhler strove to demonstrate that apes, no less than men, come to solutions all at once by a process of integration or insight, in which not a series of separate clues taken in series, but an integrated system of clues, is responded to all at once. His reports appeared in German in 1917–24; in English in 1928, under the title of *The Mentality of Apes* (a translation of the German title would read *Intelligence Tests on Anthropoid Apes*).[15] (Although he had in the meantime written an erudite mathematical study of physical forms [16]—that is, the objective and measurable systems of forces which require consideration as systems rather than as agglomerations of particles—the volume became known only sporadically, and much later.) Koffka had in the same years published a systematic educational psychology which also soon became known. It was entitled *The Growth of the Mind* (1921; English translation, 1924). The thesis of the volume is that growth is the progressive realization of forms rather than a matter of accretion.

Though Koffka's survey article "Perception: An Introduction to the Gestalt-Theorie" had appeared in the *Psychological Bulletin* in 1922, the viva-voce introduction of Gestalt psychology into the United States occurred at the Christmas meetings of the American Psychological Association in that year, through a paper read by R. M. Ogden. The response was hesitant and uncertain; one heard the comments: "What is this Gestalt psychology?" "Is it just one more foggy German philosophy?" It soon became very evident, however, that masses of experimental materials, highly ingenious and challenging, were waiting to be assimilated along with the new theory. Through extraordinary good fortune for the movement, both Koffka and Köhler were soon available to explain, at every interested American university center, what the new movement was all about, and to show its revolutionary implications. The vivid personalities and good-tempered debating tactics of Koffka and Köhler led quickly to a widening interest in the new school, and soon everybody was taking Gestalt psychology in his stride.

The Spread of Gestalt Psychology

There is no doubt that the enthusiasm over Watson's behaviorism as a system was a factor challenging all his opponents to discover a counter-system which had the same vitality. It was also no doubt true that the various experimental studies being carried out in laboratories charged with the maintenance of the introspective tradition called loudly for some vivid systematization that would give them the crisp and compelling form which was felt to be wanting in Titchener's rather cold and arid system. Integrations of Gestalt psychology and behaviorism were likewise attempted. In the same period appeared J. R. Kantor's organismic psychology,[17] in which the interdependence and formal unity of all organic responses is noted, but with an emphasis upon objectivism.

The Gestalt psychology became domiciled not only in American theory, but also in American laboratories. In the United States, however, it remained primarily a psychology of the cognitive processes. Those implications already noted which bore upon affective and conative processes were in this same period between the two world wars carried forward in Germany, notably at the universities of Frankfurt and Berlin. In the late twenties, Rudolf Arnheim,[18] for example, introduced Gestalt theory into the field of personality research by showing that fragments of handwriting containing the various clues which are supposedly used in gauging personality did not in fact serve any such purpose, but that the intact handwriting, with half a page or so to work with, could nevertheless give (even to a naïve observer) some capacity to tell which one of a group of scripts had been produced by a given individual. Werner Wolff was likewise beginning a series of experiments in this same period, to be continued later in Spain and in the United States,[19] in which photographs of posture, the hands, and the profile, and motion pictures of the moving body, were to be matched against one another and against personality sketches, demonstrating that when rather large and well-organized expressions of individuality are available, even the naïve judge attains a score significantly better than chance expectancy. In Wolff's case, the Gestalt principles were integrated with psychoanalytic principles, in the sense that unconscious dynamics was given a large place. The subject, for example, failed frequently to recognize his own expression, though dealing competently with the expressions of other persons, as if he were unable to accept certain aspects evident to other people regarding his own personality expression.

By the mid-thirties Gestalt psychology had become a complete system, with all the cardinal areas and problems of psychology undergoing redefinition in terms of the theory of form. These doctrines were coming into applied psychology, likewise notably into psychiatry and education, and were being heard of and used by social scientists such as anthropologists and sociologists. In 1933 the movement was solidly established in Germany and in the United States (hardly known elsewhere). It then became centered in the latter country, owing to the departure from Germany of Wertheimer and numerous other proponents of Gestalt doctrines, and owing, upon their arrival in the United States, to the appeal of the message which the expanding group of laboratory and clinical people brought to these shores. One encountered, particularly on the Eastern seaboard, dozens of young research psychologists who had learned to think in Gestalt terms, and who could talk interestingly, in or out of academic situations, regarding the promise of this approach; likewise, literally hundreds of clinical workers who had combined the Gestalt approach with psychoanalytic concepts in one guise or another. Gestalt psychology, then, came to be a vital new phase of American psychology, rapidly moving West as the doctrines were published and distributed in American journals, and as the eager young refugees themselves showed what a difference it made whether one did or did not utilize these new ideas.

It is not meant to imply that Gestalt psychology disappeared in Germany, or that it won an uncontested triumph in the United States. What happened in Germany after the departure of the leader and many of his followers was that the general emphasis upon wholeness and structure (which, as we saw, had been increasing for several decades) went on increasing, and that various types of applied psychology, such as graphology and the Rorschach method (already saturated with theories of wholeness), were given a larger and larger place in the various types of clinical assessment of individuals. German psychological warfare itself made extensive use of personality testing based upon various theories of structure. That was, however, at best a rather diluted form of Gestalt psychology, when it was Gestalt psychology at all; and the amount of original experimental work done under the egis of such studies of wholeness was apparently trivial. Gestalt psychology was reduced to a very minor position in the German university system. As far as we can judge at this time, the isolation of German and Austrian scholars from those of other countries has in general impeded the recovery that might be expected since the downfall of the Nazi system, and one must conclude that the restoration of serious and systematic efforts along the lines defined by Wertheimer will prove to be a matter of some years.

In the United States, the most general tendency, except among German-trained scholars who came here as complete adherents to the system, was to regard Gestalt psychology as an interesting and valuable, but not a final or complete, solution to primary problems. Sometimes the theory was diluted to mean simply that there must always be a consideration of the multiplicity of factors working toward any given response; sometimes it was meant to signify a study of relationships obtaining between various stimuli present in the stimulus field, or various responses going on successively or simultaneously (so much, of course, any associationist would have granted). Sometimes it came nearer to the Wertheimer doctrine by emphasizing membership character and the futility of dissecting out supposedly independent elements. Occasionally it meant going the whole way, insisting that conscious or behavioral responses are intelligible only as structures or systems, and that all aspects or phases of such wholes, with their membership character, express cross sections in a dynamic flow oriented toward the completion of some purposive act.

If such a characterization is at all adequate, it means that in general Gestalt psychology has been gratefully received and grafted upon existing systems, but that it has not, except here and there on a very small scale, been espoused by American psychology as a final or fundamental solution of psychological problems.

Particularly characteristic of American psychology has been the effort, through countless experiments and clinical observations, to show that *both* piecemeal *and* organized responses occur—just as, in response to behaviorism, the prevalent tendency has been to say that both consciousness and behavior need to be studied. Typical of dozens of studies is Durkin's generalization that in problem-solving,[20] the responses made by her subjects ranged all the way from (a) blind poking about until pieces happened to fall into a correct position to (b) those responses in which a large number of separate pieces suddenly seemed to leap together into one meaningful and adequate total. There are, then, according to Durkin, and a great many of the middle-of-the-roaders, not only two basic ways of thinking—the associationist way and the insightful way—but all the theoretical possible intervening points on a continuum.

That aspect of Gestalt psychology which seems to this writer to be most fundamental and at the same time most incompletely worked out is the definition of membership character. At times one discovers in the Gestalt literature the conception that all the elements or component parts of a total need to be seen in their interrelations in order to understand the structure. On another page, however, one discovers that there *are* no elements or component parts. Each aspect or phase of the total manifests those attributes which each must possess if it is to stand at a particular point and function in a particular role; attributes which belong *to the elements themselves* are not definable. If this second statement is true, then obviously the first is far from the mark. Surely if membership character in so fundamental a sense dominates not only the locus but the very character of every ingredient, then there are no parts or elements or components, and it means nothing to say that the relations between them must be studied. The Gestaltist sometimes tries to have his cake and eat it too as he maintains that there are components which enter into structures and also that there are no components. The issue seems to stand about as it stood twenty years ago. The theory of membership character and the whole ultimate theory of the atomic or nonatomic character of psychological events remains unresolved—both as to clear theoretical treatment and as to answers from crucial experiments.

Yet every nook and cranny of psychology has been invaded with the conception of structure, or system, or interdependence; every theoretical system today either rejects atomism or admits its incompleteness, or at least apologizes for it. So huge a tidal wave cannot be "met" by a counter-movement of any sort; it will have its effect. Since in general the trend is clearly in accord with general trends in physics toward fields and whole-ness, and general trends in biology toward the actualization of evolutionary patterns involving the interdependence of organs, of whole individuals, and of species, this movement in psychology is fully in the modern spirit.

REFERENCES

Ellis, W. D., *Source Book of Gestalt Psychology*, Sather Gate Book Shop, Berkeley, Calif., 1938.
Hartmann, George W., *Gestalt Psychology*, Ronald Press, 1935.
Heidbreder, Edna, *Seven Psychologies*, Century, 1933.
Koffka, Kurt, *Principles of Gestalt Psychology*, Harcourt, Brace, 1935.
Köhler, Wolfgang, *Gestalt Psychology*, Liveright, 1929; rev. ed., 1947.
Petermann, Bruno, *The Gestalt Theory and the Problem of Configuration*, Harcourt, Brace, 1932.
Wertheimer, Max, *Productive Thinking*, Harper, 1945.
Woodworth, Robert S., *Contemporary Schools of Psychology*, rev. ed., Ronald Press, 1948.

FIELD THEORY

. . . practically all developmental phenomena exhibit field-like characters.
PAUL WEISS

From time to time reference has been made in this volume to the grow-ing tendency of nineteenth-century science to become suspicious of ele-ments or atoms, and to doubt whether the method of analysis into such irreducible bits could ever prove satisfactory in the explanation of ob-served phenomena [cf. p. 207 above]. Wertheimer's theory [p. 210 above] reflected this tendency, and field theory in psychology is sometimes re-garded as its parthenogenetic child. But this view is not really sufficient; there was another parent. It may be worth while to look more directly for a moment at the outcome of such skepticism about irreducible elements, and at the form in which a new conception of scientific method was devel-oped.

Newtonian physics had assumed infinitely divisible material bodies operating upon one another through gravitation, and through certain other secondary forces such as magnetic attraction and repulsion. Ultimately, as Einstein and Infeld have put it, the world was a question of "pushes and pulls." If one fully understood the location, the mass, the velocity, and so on of material particles, one could predict what would occur when a num-ber of them interacted. This mode of thinking proved to be fairly adequate until well beyond the middle of the nineteenth century. The study of electromagnetism, however, gave rise in time to more and more misgivings.

It was evident that a particle moving in a given direction might cause another particle to move in a direction other than that of the supposed direction of the "push." Indeed, one could not sharply localize the region in which the energy of a moving particle was expressed; it became necessary to think in terms of regions or fields through which electromagnetic forces were spread. Such fields are not aggregates of the effects generated by separate particles, each pulling and pushing in classical fashion, but must be seen in terms of new structural entities within which the behavior of individual particles may be predicted. Specifically, Clerk Maxwell, in 1875, in his studies of the distribution of electromagnetic forces, found it possible to formulate equations which no longer regarded fields as in any way the end results of distinct, individual particles, but as entities to be directly observed and mathematically treated in their own right. The era of atomism began to come to an end and particles began to be understood as aspects of field relationships.

This way of thinking invaded biology in the period between the two world wars, notably in the long series of brilliant investigations in embryology by the German investigator Spemann and his pupil and coworker Paul Weiss. It began to be evident in their studies, for example, that the various component parts of the embryonic body and of the maternal body surrounding it could not be regarded in mosaic fashion, but required the full utilization of a field theory in which chemical, thermal, and other factors were viewed as operating within a unitary matrix or field. In the effort to predict, for example, when and where a nose or an eye would appear, no system was really adequate which made use of small areas considered piecemeal; and within the living system no part could be defined in terms of what it would be were it outside the system. One transplants a few undeveloped cells into an eye socket and they become eye material; one transplants a few more into an ear region and they become ear material; but if one tries to achieve a compromise result, each cell will become completely the one or the other, not a mosaic agglutination of aspects of the two. There are thus major fields, and minor fields within them, but nothing to remind one of the juxtaposition of fragments, as was supposed in the Newtonian system.

It is within this frame of reference, notably the developments in physics, that one must understand the development of field theory in psychology. The movement began when modern physics invaded the Gestalt psychology. Indeed, as early as 1920 Köhler, in a volume dealing with "physical Gestalten," studied those distributions of energy in which field principles were evident [p. 213 above]. He specifically called attention to those experiments in physics in which the local event is determined by the entire context; in which it is impossible to specify any detail which, defined in and for itself, can then be placed in the total situation and be found to remain what it was before. So far, this gave background for Gestalt psychology; Köhler was describing Gestalten in the physical world which were analogous to perceptual responses.

KURT LEWIN

In this period the young student of mathematics and physics Kurt Lewin, who had recently returned from army service, became a vigorous and intensely creative member of the Gestalt group at the University of Berlin. He rapidly qualified himself for the role of colleague of the three senior Gestaltists already named: Wertheimer, Köhler, Koffka. At Berlin he carried out a series of studies of the dynamics of memory, in which he showed that items are linked together in memory not by virtue of "association," but by virtue of the way in which each word or nonsense syllable expresses the field organization of the experimental task as a whole (cf. page 280).[21]

But feeling a need for a fuller utilization of what the physicists were doing, he began to think of psychological problems more and more in terms of events occurring in a kind of space which had something in common with physical space, and to think of psychological activity as a progression from one point to another within this life space, or psychological space. Here he felt the need for more adequate mathematical tools, and gave himself intensely to that branch of mathematics which deals with such types of space as are of interest for their own intrinsic spatial attributes and not for their quantitative relationships. He found what he needed in the branch of mathematics known as topology, in which one is concerned with regions and their boundaries and subdivisions, the modes of progression which are possible within them, and the possibility of transformation of such portions of space as a result of weakening or strengthening barriers. Instead of the formal quantitative laws of the individual organism conceived as a biological system, we find ourselves confronted with *psychological motion toward goals within defined regions of life space*.[22]

Our interest in quantitative problems here becomes secondary; our interest turns rather to goals toward which psychological motion occurs, the tension systems or needs which appear as vectors expressing such motion, the barriers which interfere with it, the subdivisions into subregions of life space which occur (as in the absent-minded or the dissociated), the new integration which may occur under therapy, and so on. He thus simultaneously solved two problems: first, that of transferring the field mode of thought into psychology; and second, the problem of representing graphically rather than verbally the nature of psychological impulsions, the resistance to such impulsions, and the resulting transformations in movement toward goals.

KURT LEWIN

Field Theory and Experiment in Social Psychology *

The sociologists, I suppose, have reason to be satisfied with the recent trends in psychology. Traditionally, most psychologists seem to have felt more or less obliged to emphasize the biological character of the individual, to believe in the reality of physical and physiological processes, but to be rather suspicious of social categories and to regard as mystic those who claimed that social facts were as real as physical ones.

Recently, however, a growing number of psychologists seem to have abandoned this view. They seem to be persuaded that social facts are equally or even more important for psychology than the so-called "physiological facts." These psychologists recognize that the child from his first day of life is objectively a part of a social setting and would die within a few days if he were to be withdrawn from it. Also, the so-called "subjective" psychological world of the individual, his life-space, is influenced in a much earlier stage by social facts and social relations than anyone would have expected a few decades ago. Already, at a few months, the child seems to react to another person's smile and voice in a rather specific way. It is probably safe to say that the child is able to perceive and to distinguish the friendliness and unfriendliness of another person at an earlier age than he is able to distinguish the pattern of physical lines in a countenance which expresses these social attitudes.

Beginning with this early age, the child's behavior is molded in every respect by his social situation. Of course, his morale, his religion, and his political values are determined by his being a part of, and reacting to, the society in which he lives. If one considers the findings of cultural anthropology and of experimental psychology, one can, I think, establish evidence that social influences enter every action of the individual, even actions which seem to have nothing to do with society.

Human behavior is either a directed action or an emotional expression.

* From K. Lewin, "Field theory and experiment in social psychology: concepts and methods," *Amer. J. Soc.*, 1939, *44*, 868–896. Pp. 868–884 reprinted in part; by permission of the University of Chicago Press.

Experimental psychology has shown that the formation of goals depends directly upon the laws which govern the level of aspiration, particularly upon the effect which success or failure has in raising and lowering the level of aspiration (3, 5, 7). These experiments make it evident that the level of aspiration is greatly influenced by such social facts as the presence or absence of other persons or by the competitive or noncompetitive character of the situation. It has been shown, too, that the goal-setting depends upon certain ideal goals, upon what the sociologists call the "ideology" of the person. Cultural anthropology proves that these ideologies vary extremely among different cultures. As to the emotional expression, experiments have shown that, for instance, the emotional reaction to failure can be changed to a great extent by appropriate praise or change in social atmosphere (3, 8). This substantiates the general thesis that the management of tension (4) by the individual depends upon his particular social and cultural setting.

From this it should be apparent that experimental psychology is instrumental in helping the sociologists to realize their most ardent dream: the demonstration of the fundamental, direct, and widespread effect of social facts on behavior.

There is a growing number of psychologists who emphasize the "historical," social side of psychological facts; and even the hard-boiled believers in a stimulus-reaction psychology show a peculiar interest in getting as much of, and as close to, social facts as they can. I believe there is no longer any need for the traditional opposition between psychologists and sociologists in this basic issue.

I

Unfortunately, this insight into the social dependency of behavior does not end the problem for the psychologist. His problems rather begin here. For the sociologist, too, they should begin here. Psychology, including social psychology, cannot possibly be satisfied with any "generalities" (however correct they may be). It has to judge scientific concepts and theories largely by their ability or inability to handle problems of dynamic interdependence and to handle them in a manner sufficiently specific to attack the concrete tasks of the laboratory or the clinic.

Of course, for hundreds of years the belief was prevalent that personality, will, and emotion were not subject to strict laws and that they could not be studied experimentally. A similar view is traditionally strong in sociology. In the long run, however, *dira necessitas* is bound to be stronger in both sociology and psychology than those metaphysical prejudices, and sociology seems to be ready now for important steps away from these prejudices. Psychology as a science might be said to be somewhat more advanced technically and conceptually, at least in some of its areas. However, on the whole, and particularly in regard to social psychology, it, too, is facing the task of developing a general approach which offers specific conceptual tools for solving the concrete problems of a vast and diversified area.

Social psychology indicates, probably better than any other part of psychology and of sociology, what is needed. Its progress depends upon an overcoming of certain major difficulties, which include at least the following:

a) The integrating of vast areas of very divergent facts and aspects: the development of a scientific language (concepts) which is able to treat cultural, historical, sociological, psychological, and physical facts on a common ground.
b) The treating of these facts on the basis of their interdependence.
c) The handling of both historical and systematical problems.
d) The handling of problems related to groups as well as to individuals.
e) The handling of all "sizes" of objects or patterns (social psychology has to include problems of a nation and its situation, as well as of a play group of three children and their momentary struggle).
f) Problems of "atmosphere" (such as friendliness, pressure, etc.).
g) Experimental social psychology will have to find a way to bring the large-size patterns into a framework small enough for the technical possibilities of experimentation.

The variety of facts which social psychology has to treat might really seem frightening to even a bold scientific mind. They include "values" (such as religious and moral values), "ideologies" (such as conservatism or communism), "the style of living and thinking," and other so-called "cultural" facts. They include sociological problems, i.e., problems of group and group structure, their degree of hierarchy and type of organization; or such problems as the difference between a rural and an urban community, their rigidity or fluidity, degree of differentiation, etc. They also include so-called "psychological" problems, such as the intelligence of a person, his goals and fears, and his personality. They include such "physiological" facts as the person's being healthy or sick, strong or weak, the color of his hair and of his complexion. They include, finally, such "physical" facts as the size of the physical area in which the person or a group is located.

It is utterly fruitless and merely a negative scientific treatment to put these facts into classificatory pigeonholes, however accurately built and fitted they may be. It is widely accepted today that we need positive means of bringing these various types of facts together in such a way that one can treat them on one level without sacrificing the recognition of their specific characteristics. The problem of adolescence which we will discuss as an example shows, I think, particularly clearly that a way must be found to treat bodily changes, shift of ideology, and group-belongingness within one realm of scientific language, in a single realm of discourse of concepts. The question is "How can that be done?"

Behaviorism has tried to answer this question by interpreting everything as a conditioned reflex. One of the main reasons for the appeal of such approach is the same as that which lies behind the popular appeal of the "unity of science" idea: namely, it appeared to put every problem on a "physiological" basis (although in fact it did not), and in this way it seemed to promise integration of the divergent facts on one level.

Today most research workers in sociology and social psychology will agree that the program of describing and explaining sociopsychological processes by concepts and laws of physics or physiology might at best be something to talk about as a distant possibility for a speculative philosopher. But such a way would definitely not be a realistic research program for attacking the sociopsychological problems of today. On the other hand, to elaborate on the "fundamental differences" between physics, sociology, and psychology and to rest satisfied with such distinctions is no help either.

To discuss these problems adequately would involve a more thorough treatment of certain questions of comparative theory of science than is possible here. As far as I can see the solution lies in the direction (a) that a science should be considered a realm of problems rather than a realm of material; (b) that the different realms of problems might necessitate different universes of discourse of constructs and laws (such as those of physics, aesthetics, psychology, and sociology); and (c) that any one of them refers more or less to the same universe of material.

For any practical purpose of research—and that, after all, is what counts—sciences like sociology or psychology should feel fully free to use those types of constructs which they think most adequate for handling their problems; and they should attempt to find the integration we have discussed on their own level. They should not feel obliged to use constructs of another science merely out of philosophical reasons (e.g., because some philosophies or popular metaphysics apply "true reality" to physical entities only). On the other hand, feeling confident in their own right, those sciences do not need to be afraid of using methods or concepts (e.g., mathematical concepts) which might or might not have similarities with those of other sciences.

The field-theoretical approach is intended to be a practical vehicle of research. As is true with any tool, its characteristics can be understood fully only by the use of it in actual research. Therefore, instead of stating general methodological principles *in abstractum,* I prefer to discuss the problem of adolescence and the definition of a social group as an illustration. Our purpose in discussing them is not the proving of certain facts or theories (which might or might not be fully correct) but to survey certain major aspects of the field-theoretical approach. In discussing these examples I will therefore, from time to time, point to similar aspects in other problems. A forthcoming article by Mr. Lippitt (12) offers a more detailed example of actual research.

II

We have chosen the problem of adolescence because the changes in behavior which are supposed to be characteristic for this period seem, at first sight, to give excellent backing to a biological view in sociology. Obviously, adolescence has something to do with sexual hormones and with certain periods of bodily growth. The more recent treatments of the problem of adolescence, however, seem to emphasize its social aspect. They point particularly to the fact that the behavior typical for this age is rather different in different societies (2, 14). Considerable argumentation has been advanced for and against both views.

However, in regard to the problem of adolescence, as in relation to other social and psychological problems, it does not help much to argue whether adolescence is a biological or psychological effect. It does not help very much either to try to describe, on a statistical basis, to what degree this problem is biological or psychological in nature. Even if an answer could be found, it would be of as little value as, for instance, the determining of the degree to which heredity and environment affect intelligence. We still would not have gained any insight into the way in which bodily and social factors are working together and against each other, integrating the concrete behavior of the adolescent. It would seem to be more fruitful to start with an analysis of the setting in a concrete case. This case should be chosen not so much according to the frequency of occurrence as according to the amount of insight it offers into a constellation which is typical at least for a part of the setting in question.

In regard to the problem of adolescence, it might be helpful to refer first to cases which show the so-called "typical" difficulties of adolescent behavior. A field-theoretical analysis of such a situation should give some hints as to what conditions would increase or decrease these symptoms.

The period of adolescence can be said to be a period of transition. It seems to imply, at least under certain circumstances, a more rapid or deeper shift than the period before. After the rather important changes around the age of three years, often a more stable situation has arisen. Maybe minor crises have come up; but particularly in cases where the adolescence is characterized by special disturbances, a relatively quiet or stable time might have preceded it. If one tries to characterize the nature of the transition, one can point to several aspects.

a) One can view adolescence as a change in group-belongingness. The individual has been considered by himself and by others as a child. Now he does not wish to be treated as such. He is ready to separate himself from things childish and to try seriously to enter adult life in manners and in outlook on occupation, as on life in general. Any change in belongingness from one group to another is of great importance for the behavior of the person; the more central for the person this belonging is, the more important is the change. A shift in group-belongingness is a "social locomotion." That means it changes the position of the person concerned.

.   .   .   .

. . . The similarities between the position of the members of the underprivileged minority and the adolescent and between their behavior seems to me so great that one might characterize the behavior of the marginal members of the minority group as that of permanent adolescence.

We might sum up our discussion of the adolescent in the following manner:

a) The basic fact concerning the general situation of the adolescent can be represented as the position of a person during locomotion from one region to another. This includes (i) the widening of the life-space (geographically, socially, and in time perspective [. . .] and (ii) the cognitively unstructured character of the new situation.

b) Somewhat more specifically, the adolescent has a social position "between" the adult and the child, similar to a marginal member of an underprivileged minority group.

c) There are still more specific factors involved in adolescence, such as the new experiences with one's own body, which can be represented as the baffling change of a central region of the established life-space.

From this representation one can derive conceptually:

I. The adolescent's shyness, sensitivity, and aggressiveness, owing to unclearness and instability of ground (follows from *a, b,* and *c*).

II. A more or less permanent conflict between the various attitudes, values, ideologies, and styles of living (follows from *b*).

III. Emotional tension resulting from these conflicts (follows from *a, b,* and *c*).

IV. Readiness to take extreme attitudes and actions and to shift his position radically (follows from *a, b,* and *c*).

V. The "adolescent behavior" should appear only if the structure and dynamic of the field is such as represented by *a, b,* and *c*. The degree and particular type of behavior should depend upon the degree of realization of this structure and upon the strength of the conflicting forces. Above all, the degree of difference and of separation between adults and children which is characteristic for a particular culture is important; also, the extent to which the particular adolescent finds himself in the position of a marginal man. According to field theory, actual behavior depends upon every part of the field. It follows that the degree of instability of the adolescent should be greatly influenced also by such factors as general stability or instability of the particular individual.

REFERENCES

1. Brown, J. F. *Psychology and the social order.* New York: McGraw-Hill. 1936.

2. Cole, Luella. *Psychology of adolescence*. New York: Farrar & Rinehart, 1936.

3. Fajans, Sara. Erfolg, Ausdauer und Aktivität beim Säuglings und Kleinkind: Untersuchung zur Handlungs- und Affektpsychologie XIII (Success, perseverance and activity in the infant and young child: Studies in the psychology of action and emotion XIII). Ed. Kurt Lewin. *Psychol. Forsch.*, 1933, *17*, 268-305.

4. Frank, L. K. The management of tensions. *Amer. J. Sociol.*, 1928, *33*, 705-736.

5. Frank, L. K. Time perspective. *J. soc. Philos.*, 1939, *4*, 293-312.

6. Jack, Lois M. An experimental study of ascendant behavior in pre-school children, in Lois M. Jack, Elizabeth M. Manwell, Ida G. Mengert, and others. Behavior in the preschool child. *Univ. Ia. Stud. Child Welf.*, 1934, *9*, No. 3.

7. Jones, H. E., Conrad, H. S., and Blanchard, M. B. Environmental handicap in mental test performance. *Univ. Calif. Public Psychol.*, 1932, *5*, No. 3.

8. Keister, Mary E. The behavior of young children in failure: An experimental attempt to discover and to modify undesirable responses of preschool children to failure. *Univ. Ia. Stud. Child Welf.*, 1937, *14*, No. 4.

9. Lewin, K. The conceptual representation and measurement of psychological forces. *Contr. psychol. Theor.*, 1938, *1*, No. 4.

10. Lewin, K. Bringing up the child. *Menorah J.*, 1940, *28*, 29-45.

11. Lewin, K. *Principles of Topological psychology*. New York: McGraw-Hill, 1936.

12. Lippitt, R. Field theory and experiment in social psychology. *Amer. J. Soc.*, 1939, *45*, 26-49.

13. Murphy, Lois B. *Social behavior and child personality: An exploratory study of some roots of sympathy*. New York: Columbia Univ. Press, 1937.

14. Reuter, E. B. The sociology of adolescence. *Amer. J. Sociol.*, 1937, *43*, 414-427.

15. Wiehe, F. Die Grenzen des Ichs. Reported from the manuscript in Kurt Lewin, *A dynamic theory of personality*. New York: McGraw-Hill, 1935, 261-264.

[22c]

EDWARD CHACE TOLMAN

Physiology, Psychology, and Sociology *

I would define physiology as a study of the laws determining the *activities* of muscles and glands; I would define psychology as a study of the laws determining the *behavior* of whole organisms; and I would define

* From *Psychological Review* (May, 1938). Excerpts from this article are reprinted here. By permission of the author, the *Psychological Review*, and the *American Psychological Association*. Also, of Edward Chace Tolman, *Collected Papers in Psychology*, University of California Press, 1951, Ch. 14.

sociology as the study of the laws determining the *conduct* of groups of organisms.[1]

Accepting these definitions, one's first reaction concerning the interrelations of the three sciences would be to think of physiology as the most basic, psychology as the next most basic, and sociology as the least basic—or, in other words, to conceive the facts and laws of psychology as dependent upon those of physiology and the facts and laws of sociology as dependent upon those of psychology. But the thesis that I am actually going to try to uphold here is the reverse and, at first sight, seemingly absurd one, to wit: that the facts and laws of psychology are, rather, in some part dependent upon those of sociology and that the facts and laws of physiology are similarly in some part dependent upon those of psychology.

It was the Gestalt psychologists who first brought it home to psychologists in America that even within the confines of a single science, such as psychology by itself or physics by itself, the whole can often be said to govern its parts quite as truly as the parts may be said to govern the whole. Hence what I am going to argue for is, in a sense, merely a further extension of this Gestalt doctrine to be applied to the interrelationships between the three successively larger science of physiology, psychology, and sociology. . . . Further, it has been assumed that each of these sciences operates with three classes of variable, to wit, *independent variables, intervening variables,* and *dependent variables.*

Independent variables are to be defined as those which the science in question manipulates in direct experimental (or historical) fashion and which it assumes as the ultimate causes of its phenomena. . . . The final *dependent variables*—i.e., "the group conduct," the "individual behavior," and the "physiological activities"— . . . are (those) ultimately to be predicted and, so far as possible, controlled. . . . And lastly, the *intervening variables* are to be conceived as further constructs which each science finds it helpful to invent and to introduce as explanatory steps between the independent variables, on the one hand, and the final dependent variables, on the other. . . . Finally, it must be noted that for each science, there (are) two sets of functions, viz.: f_2 functions whereby the intervening variables result from the independent variables and f_3 functions [2] whereby the final dependent variables result from the intervening variables.

[Professor Tolman uses as an illustration of *group conduct* (Group G) "the carrying out of a marriage and wedding by a middle-class American social and religious group" some twenty or thirty years ago; this *group conduct, the individual behavior* (C) of a young man in "going to this wedding," and the *physiological activity* of this young man, are all analyzed on three levels respectively in a diagram omitted here.]

. . . Let us consider, now, the independent and the intervening variables at each of the three levels.

Sociology.—Turn to . . . the independent variables for sociology. They are the geographical, historical, racial,[5] economic, technological and political factors which underlie and condition Group G and its conduct. They are the ultimate determiners of this group and of such particular conducts carried out by it as that of the present marriage and wedding. It is these geographic, historical, racial, economic, technological, and political causes which would have to be changed if Group G were to be other than it is and if it were not to "go in for" this present marriage and wedding.

In attempting, however, to work out the functional connection between these ultimate determiners and any final group conduct, the social scientist is led to construct certain hypothetical "intervening variables." That is to say, instead of attempting to state at once the complete (f_1) functional connections between any given conduct (such as the present wedding), and such geographical, historical, racial, economic, technological, and political causes, a sociologist today seems to find it more feasible to trace such conducts back, first (f_3 function), to a set of "intervening variables" such as the customs, taboos, religious and sex mores, types of family-organization, "statuses," [7] "sociometric forces," [8] art and architecture, local geography, etc. of the given group. A most useful single term to cover these intervening variables would seem to be that of the "culture pattern" suggested by Benedict (1). Only after having invented this intervening variable of the culture pattern, does the sociologist attempt to find a further set of laws or functions (f_2) to connect such a culture pattern to the final independent variables of geography, history, genetics, economics, technology, and politics. The social sciences break up the total relation into two successive steps—the f_2 laws and the f_3 laws. The f_3 laws as now stated seem to be relatively simple. They are hardly more than descriptive exemplifications of the culture patterns. The f_2 laws, on the other hand, are hardly known at all. Anthropologists and sociologists are apparently as yet finding great difficulty in saying much of anything with regard to the f_2's.[9]

Psychology.—Turn now to psychology. The sort of independent variables, which, as psychologists, we assume as determinative of the behavior of the individual C, I have located [in the diagram, omitted here] directly under the sociological intervening variables for the group as a whole. These psychological independent variables are: "maintenance schedules" (*re* food, sex, sleep, etc.), "environmental object-patterns," "heredity," "training," and "age," etc. . . . In short, the culture pattern of the group appears to be a whole which is made up of the maintenance schedules, the environmental object patterns, the heredities, the previous trainings, the ages, etc. of all the various individuals within the group. But, if this be correct, then it appears that the psychologist's independent variables are not in any final sense independent and absolute. They are always immersed in a "field" constituted by the "cultural pattern" of the whole group. They cannot be manipulated independently of this field.

Further, it is to be stressed that such a field—such a culture-pattern—is a relatively interconnected whole. Hence any experimental variation that the psychologist attempts to make in any one independent variable is

almost surely bound to produce at the same time uncontrolled and un-
wanted changes in others of the independent variables also acting upon the
given individual. Or, in short, psychology here comes up against two sorts
of difficulty:

First, psychologists cannot study the f_2 function issuing from some
one independent variable—for example, sex maintenance schedule—for
some one individual without danger of at the same time affecting, even
though only in some slight degree, the sex *mores* of the whole group. And
such a change in group *mores* will react back upon and affect all the other
independent variables (e.g., the environmental object pattern of persons
and things) also acting upon this same individual. Any one independent
variable for any one individual is, in short, always part of a whole inter-
connected sociological field. And the laws found for any one such independent variable will always thus be colored by the latter's interconnections with all the other variables in this field.

And secondly, even if psychology surmounts, to some extent, the above
difficulty and tears the effects of the separate independent variables apart,
it will still remain true that the laws for individual behavior which psychology finally arrives at will be laws holding, so far as we can be certain,
only within the given culture in which they have been found. Only by
studying psychology within many cultures would it eventually be possible
to arrive at a pure psychology—a psychology which one could be certain
would hold for all cultures.[10] . . .

Physiology.—But turn now to the physiological level. Its relation to
the psychological (behavioral) level above is one of parallelism. . . .

Consider, first, the independent variables. Corresponding and parallel
to the independent variables as identified by the psychologist, the physiologist finds patterns of present and past *stimuli* (exteroceptive, intero-
ceptive, and proprioceptive) plus such and such neural and biochemical
make-ups. That is to say, stimuli and neural and biochemical make-ups
are to be conceived as being the same events and processes which the
psychologist calls maintenance schedules, past and present environmental
object patterns, heredity, training, age, and the like. The difference is one
of language and size of descriptive unit. But any "operational" change
made in the one set of entities will always be accompanied by some corresponding change in the other parallel set of entities.

Look next at the intervening variables. Here also we find a parallelism. For the physiologist the intervening variables are spatially, temporally, electrically, and perhaps also chemically, identifiable excitations
within the nervous system.[14] But these can be considered as parallel to
the psychologist's "intervening variables" of demands, perceptions, and
hypotheses. Further, just as the larger demands, perceptions, and hypotheses, which are determinative of the total behavior of "going to the
wedding" are to be conceived as containing within themselves subordinate
demands, perceptions, and hypotheses occurring at moments K, L, M, etc.,
so here at the physiological level the larger set of neural excitations must

be supposed to contain within themselves distinguishable narrower more momentary patterns of excitation.

What the above means is that before studying the laws governing any relatively small group of physiological activities (muscle contractions and gland secretions) such as those at moment M, we have to note, first, that such a minor group of physiological processes occurs only within a larger matrix of processes. Hence the laws which we, as physiologists, discover for the minor process probably hold within the specific larger matrices in which they have been studied. And this limitation the physiologist (or at least the psychologist who poses as physiologist) is apt to forget. . . .

And so we come to the second half of our original thesis—namely, that (at any rate, today, *in the present stage of the two sciences*) psychology tends to be in large part ancillary to physiology.[15]

In conclusion let me briefly recapitulate:

1. *Sociology versus psychology.*—It has appeared that we cannot (at least in the case of society-forming animals such as human beings) study psychology—i.e., the *behavior* of individuals—save within larger sociological wholes. The intervening factors determining the *group conduct* act as a "field" [16] determinative of the independent variables acting upon the individuals within the group. And this makes for two kinds of difficulty or limitation for psychology:

a. The field presented by the social group tends to cause interfunctional relations between the psychologist's independent variables.

b. Even if it prove in some measure possible to get around this first difficulty, there is still a second difficulty in that (having studied the f_2 and f_3 functions within merely one social group) we shall still have to study them over again within other different types of social group. For in such other types of group the independent variables of "maintenance-schedule," "environmental pattern," etc. may take on quite other and wholly new values, the effects of which cannot be extrapolated from the findings for the first type of group.

In a word, we are forced to conclude that sociology is to a surprising degree ancillary to psychology. (See note 15 on meaning of "ancillary.")

2. *Psychology versus physiology.*—Psychology and physiology are parallel sciences—(i.e., a behavior-physiological parallelism, not a psychophysical parallelism). From a purely theoretical point of view neither, therefore, would seem ancillary to the other. We note further, however, that for both sciences there appeared to be the difficulty that any relatively limited behavior (or correlated set of physiological activities) is practically always immersed in a "field" constituted by a larger behavior (or larger set of correlated physiological activities). And this presents a difficulty analogous to that as between psychology and sociology. For it appears that to study any small behavior we have to know the larger behavior that this smaller one is immersed in; and similarly, to study any smaller group of physiological activities we have to know the larger group of physiological activities.

And it also appears, further, that psychology is, today at any rate, here in perhaps the better position. For today it seems easier and more feasible to identify and control the larger circumambient processes in psychological rather than in physiological terms.

Hence we must conclude that (*practically speaking*) psychology today is also in some considerable degree ancillary to physiology.

REFERENCES

1. Benedict, R., *Patterns of culture*. New York: Houghton Mifflin, 1934.
2. Brown, J. F., *Psychology and the social order*. New York: McGraw-Hill, 1936.
3. Lewin, K., *A dynamic theory of personality*. New York: McGraw-Hill, 1935.
4. Linton, R., *The study of man: an introduction*. New York: Appleton-Century, 1936.
5. Mead, M. (editor), *Cooperation and competition among primitive peoples*. New York: McGraw-Hill, 1937.
6. Moreno, J. L., *Who shall survive? A new approach to the problem of human interrelations*. Washington, D.C.: Nervous and Mental Disease Publishing Co., 1934.
7. Tolman, E. C., *Purposive behavior in animals and men*. New York: Century Co., 1932.
8. ————, "Psychology vs. immediate experience," *Philos. Science* 2 (1935), 356–380.
9. ————, "Operational behaviorism and current trends in psychology," *Proc. 25th Anniv. Celebration Inaug. Grad. Studies*, Los Angeles, University of Southern California, 1936, pp. 89–103.
10. ————, "The determiners of behavior at a choice point," *Psychol. Rev.*, 45 (1938), 1–41.

[Also cf. Edward Chace Tolman, *Collected Papers in Psychology*. Berkeley and Los Angeles: University of California Press, 1951.]

[23a]

SIGMUND FREUD

The Origin and Development
of Psychoanalysis

Fifth Lecture *

Ladies and Gentlemen: With the discovery of infantile sexuality and the tracing back of the neurotic symptoms to erotic impulse-components we have arrived at several unexpected formulae for expressing the nature

* Last of five lectures published in *American Journal of Psychology*, vol. XXI (April, 1910).

and tendencies of neurotic diseases. We see that the individual falls ill when in consequence of outer hindrances or inner lack of adaptability the satisfaction of the erotic needs in the sphere of reality is denied. We see that he then flees to sickness, in order to find with its help a surrogate satisfaction for that denied him. We recognize that the symptoms of illness contain fractions of the sexual activity of the individual, or his whole sexual life, and we find in the turning away from reality the chief tendency and also the chief injury of the sickness. We may guess that the resistance of our patients against the cure is not a simple one, but is composed of many motives. Not only does the ego of the patient strive against the giving up of the repression by which it has changed itself from its original constitution into its present form, but also the sexual impulses may not renounce their surrogate satisfaction so long as it is not certain that they can be offered anything better in the sphere of reality.

The flight from the unsatisfying reality into what we call, on account of its biologically injurious nature, disease, but which is never without an individual gain in pleasure for the patient, takes place over the path of regression, the return to earlier phases of the sexual life, when satisfaction was not lacking. This regression is seemingly a twofold one, a *temporal*, in so far as the *libido* or erotic need falls back to a temporally earlier stage of development, and a *formal*, since the original and primitive psychic means of expression are applied to the expression of this need. Both sorts of regression focus in childhood and have their common point in the production of an infantile condition of sexual life.

The deeper you penetrate into the pathogenic of neurotic diseases, the more the connection of neuroses with other products of human mentality, even the most valuable, will be revealed to you. You will be reminded that we men, with the high claims of our civilization and under the pressure of our repressions, find reality generally quite unsatisfactory and so keep up a life of fancy in which we love to compensate for what is lacking in the sphere of reality by the production of wish-fulfillments. In these phantasies is often contained very much of the particular constitutional essence of personality and of its tendencies, repressed in real life. The energetic and successful man is he who succeeds by dint of labor in transforming his wish fancies into reality. Where this is not successful in consequence of the resistance of the outer world and the weakness of the individual, there begins the turning away from reality. The individual takes refuge in his satisfying world of fancy. Under certain conditions it still remains possible for him to find another connecting link between these fancies and reality, instead of permanently becoming a stranger to it through the regression into the infantile. If the individual who is displeased with reality is in possession of that *artistic talent* which is still a psychological riddle, he can transform his fancies into artistic creations. So he escapes the fate of a neurosis and wins back his connection with reality by this round-about way. Where this opposition to the real world exists, but this valuable talent fails or proves insufficient, it is unavoidable that the *libido*, following the origin of the fancies, succeeds by means of regression in revivifying the infantile wishes and so producing a neurosis. The neurosis takes, in our time, the place of the cloister, in which were accustomed to take refuge all those whom life had undeceived or who felt themselves too weak for life. Let me give at this point the main result at which we have arrived by the psychoanalytic investigation of neurotics, namely, that neuroses have no peculiar psychic content of their own, which is not also to be found in healthy states; or, as C. G. Jung has expressed it, neurotics fall ill of the same complexes with which we sound people struggle. It depends on quantitative relationships, on the relations of the forces wrestling with each other, whether the struggle leads to health, to a neurosis, or to compensatory over-functioning (*Ueberleistung*).

Ladies and Gentlemen, I have still withheld from you the most remarkable experience which corroborates our assumptions of the sexual impulse-forces of neurotics. Every time that we treat a neurotic psychoanalytically, there occurs in him the so-called phenomenon of *transfer* (*Uebertragung*), that is, he applies to the person of the physician a great amount of tender emotion, often mixed with enmity, which has no foundation in any real relation, and must be derived in every respect from the old wish-fancies of the patient which have become unconscious. Every fragment of his emotive life, which can no longer be called back into memory, is accordingly lived over by the patient in his relations to the physician, and only by such a living of them over in the "transfer" is he convinced of the existence and the power of these unconscious sexual excitations. The symptoms, which, to use a simile from chemistry, are the precipitates of earlier love experiences (in the widest sense), can only be dissolved in the higher temperature of the experience of transfer and transformed into other psychic products. The physician plays in this reaction, to use an excellent expression of S. Ferenczi, the rôle of a *catalytic ferment*, which temporarily attracts to itself the affect which has become free in the course of the process.

The study of transfer can also give you the key to the understanding of hypnotic suggestion, which we at first used with our patients as a technical means of investigation of the unconscious. Hypnosis showed itself at that time to be a therapeutic help, but a hindrance to the scientific knowledge of the real nature of the case, since it cleared away the psychic resistances from a certain field, only to pile them up in an unscalable wall at the boundaries of this field. You must not think that the phenomenon of transfer, about which I can unfortunately say only too little here, is created by the influence of the psychoanalytic treatment. The transfer arises spontaneously in all human relations and in the relations of the patient to the physician; it is everywhere the especial bearer of therapeutic influences, and it works the stronger the less one knows of its presence. Accordingly psychoanalysis does not create it, it merely discloses it to consciousness, and avails itself of it, in order to direct the psychic processes to the wished-for goal. But I cannot leave the theme of transfer without stressing the fact that this phenomenon is of decisive importance to convince not only the patient, but also the physician. I know that all my adherents were first convinced of the correctness of my views through their experience with transfer, and I can very well conceive that one may not win such a surety of judgment so long as he makes no psychoanalysis, and so has not himself observed the effects of transfer.

Ladies and Gentlemen, I am of the opinion that there are, on the intellectual side, two hindrances to acknowledging the value of the psychoanalytic viewpoint: first, the fact that we are not accustomed to reckon with a strict determination of mental life, which holds without exception, and, second, the lack of knowledge of the peculiarities through which unconscious mental processes differ from these conscious ones with which we are familiar. One of the most widespread resistances against the work of psychoanalysis with patients as with persons in health reduces to the latter of the two moments. One is afraid of doing harm by psychoanalysis, one is anxious about calling up into consciousness the repressed sexual impulses of the patient, as though there were danger that they could overpower the higher ethical strivings and rob him of his cultural acquisitions. One can see that the patient has sore places in his soul life, but one is afraid to touch them, lest his suffering be increased. We may use this analogy. It is, of course, better not to touch diseased places when one can only cause pain. But we know that the surgeon does not refrain from the investigation and reinvestigation of the seat of illness, if his invasion has as its aim the restoration of lasting health. Nobody thinks of blaming him for the unavoidable difficulties of the investigation or the phenomena of reaction from the operation, if these only accomplish their purpose, and gain for the patient, a final cure by temporarily making his condition worse. The case is similar in psychoanalysis; it can lay claim to the same things as surgery; the increase of pain which takes place in the patient during the treatment is very much less than that which the surgeon imposes upon him, and especially negligible in comparison with the pains of serious illness. But the consequence which is feared, that of a disturbance of the cultural character by the impulse which has been freed from repression, is wholly impossible. In relation to this anxiety we must consider what our experiences have taught us with certainty, that the somatic and mental power of a wish, if once its repression has not succeeded, is incomparably stronger when it is unconscious than when it is conscious, so that by being made conscious it can only be weakened. The unconscious wish cannot be influenced, is free from all strivings in the contrary direction, while the conscious is inhibited by those wishes which are also conscious and which strive against it. The work of psychoanalysis accordingly presents a better substitute, in the service of the highest and most valuable cultural strivings, for the repression which has failed.

Now what is the fate of the wishes which have become free by psychoanalysis, by what means shall they be made harmless for the life of the individual? There are several ways. The general consequence is, that the wish is consumed during the work by the correct mental activity of those better tendencies which are opposed to it. The repression is supplanted by a condemnation carried through with the best means at one's disposal. This is possible, since for the most part we have to abolish only the effects of earlier developmental stages of the ego. The individual for his part only repressed the useless impulse, because at that time he was himself still incompletely organized and weak; in his present maturity and strength he can, perhaps, conquer without injury to himself that which is inimical to him. A second issue of the work of psychoanalysis may be that the revealed unconscious impulses can now arrive at those useful applications which, in the case of undisturbed development, they would have found earlier. The extirpation of the infantile wishes is not at all the ideal aim of development. The neurotic has lost, by his repressions, many sources of mental energy whose contingents would have been very valuable for his character building and his life activities. We know a far more purposive process of development, the so-called *sublimation (Sublimirung)*, by which the energy of infantile wish-excitations is not secluded, but remains capable of application, while for the particular excitations, instead of becoming useless, a higher, eventually no longer sexual, goal is set up. The components of the sexual instinct are especially distinguished by such a capacity for the sublimation and exchange of their sexual goal for one more remote and socially more valuable. To the contributions of the energy won in such a way for the functions of our mental life we probably owe the highest cultural consequences. A repression taking place at an early period excludes the sublimation of the repressed impulse; after the removal of the repression the way to sublimation is again free.

We must not neglect, also, to glance at the third of the possible issues. A certain part of the suppressed libidinous excitation has a right to direct satisfaction and ought to find it in life. The claims of our civilization make life too hard for the greater part of humanity, and so further the aversion to reality and the origin of neuroses, without producing an excess of cultural gain by this excess of sexual repression. We ought not to go so far as to fully neglect the original animal part of our nature, we ought not to forget that the happiness of individuals cannot be dispensed with as one of the aims of our culture. The plasticity of the sexual-components, manifest in their capacity for sublimation, may cause a great temptation to accomplish greater culture-effects by a more and more far reaching sublimation. But just as little as with our machines we expect to change more than a certain fraction of the applied heat into useful mechanical work, just as little ought we to strive to separate the sexual impulse in its whole extent of energy from its peculiar goal. This cannot succeed, and if the narrowing of sexuality is pushed too far it will have all the evil effects of a robbery.

I do not know whether you will regard the exhortation with which I close as a presumptuous one. I only venture the indirect presentation of my conviction, if I relate an old tale, whose application you may make yourselves. German literature knows a town called Schilda, to whose inhabitants were attributed all sorts of clever pranks. The wiseacres, so the story goes, had a horse, with whose powers of work they were well satisfied, and against whom they had only one grudge, that he consumed so much expensive oats. They concluded that by good management they would break him of this bad habit, by cutting down his rations by several stalks each day, until he had learned to do without them altogether. Things went finely for a while, the horse was weaned to one stalk a day, and on the next day he would at last work without fodder. On the morning of this day the malicious horse was found dead; the citizens of Schilda could not understand why he had died. We should be inclined to believe that the horse had starved, and that without a certain ration of oats no work could be expected from an animal.

[23b]

ERNST KRIS

Validation of Psychoanalytic Propositions *

The word *psychoanalysis* will be used in the context of this paper [1] to designate a body of hypotheses. I shall speak of *the psychoanalytic movement* in order to designate a social force, consisting mainly of the association of individuals who believe in the truth of these propositions, and who wish to propagate their acceptance, sometimes, especially early in this century, in an attitude of opposition to current social values. I shall speak of *psychoanalytic therapy* in order to designate a therapeutic technique, and of *psychoanalytic observation* in referring to the investigatory value of the *psychoanalytic interview*: the regular and frequent association of subject and observer, patient and therapist, over long stretches of time and under special rules of procedure.

Psychoanalytic hypotheses are derived from this interview situation, which is, at the same time, the most important testing ground for their validity. This leads to the crucial question of how reliable this observational method is in which the observer fulfills a threefold function: he records the behavior of his subject, he judges his own reactions to this behavior, which are part of the record, and he acts in order to produce changes in his subject. The lack of precision that results from such triple involvement of the observer is a cause for discomfort to the scientist. But there also are other grounds for discomfort: some lie in the development

* From E. Kris, The nature of psychoanalytic propositions and their validation. In S. Hook and M. R. Konvitz (eds.), *Freedom and Experience, Essays Presented to Horace Kallen.* Ithaca, N. Y.: Cornell University Press, 1947. Reprinted by permission of the author, the editors and the publisher.

of psychoanalysis, and others are connected with the subject matter with which the propositions deal.

Psychoanalysis has developed outside institutionalized science and has been carried forward almost exclusively by the psychoanalytic movement. For over forty years professional associations of psychoanalysts have provided the necessary facilities for all those who have wished to study psychoanalysis and its applications; mainly they have provided facilities for the training of psychiatrists in the handling of psychoanalytic therapy. Even at the present time, when psychoanalytic propositions are permeating various psychological systems and are forming the hard core of psychiatry, psychoanalysis is taught at but few medical schools and only in exceptional cases in other departments of American universities. It seems that some of the—admittedly more superficial—difficulties with which many scientists are faced in their first contact with psychoanalysis have to do with this state of affairs. There is, for instance, a lack of trained clarifiers, who might properly co-ordinate the various propositions with each other or try to eliminate the inequities of language in psychoanalysis. As examples of such inequities one may mention that definitions of terms are sometimes unsatisfactory, that even their translation from German into English is not always fortunate; that in psychoanalytic writings metaphors tend to obscure the meaning of statements; and that such usages are ingrained by the fact that a generation of scientists adopted what now seem understandable as the peculiarity and privilege of one genius (28).

No other large body of hypotheses in recent science reveals to a similar extent the influence of one investigator. This has a number of consequences of varying significance. In the present context we refer to one of these consequences only: terminology and constructs of psychoanalysis reflect ideas and connotation dominant in Freud's formative years, i.e., in the 1870's and 1880's. Many interacting influences have to be considered: the humanist tradition in European education of the period, the concepts of "classical" neurology, the impact of twenty years of experiments and clinical work in the physicalist physiology if the school of Helmholtz and Du Bois-Reymond (5) and finally the influence of evolutionism, both Darwinian and Lamarckian. It has been argued that since some of the concepts of psychoanalysis are derived from overaged connotations, for instance, from the mechanistic psychology of Herbart and his followers (10), psychoanalysis itself is either in general overaged or, more specifically, limited to the viewpoints which originally suggested the terms used. The argument is clearly fallacious (24). The concepts borrowed from other sciences gained a new meaning in the new context: if in psychoanalysis reference is made to "associations"—mainly to the "free associations" of the subject—this has little to do with the traditional associationism of the nineteenth century. On the contrary, it seems that, historically speaking, the method of free associations has suggested some of the early criticism of the older association theories. Or, to use an even more significant example, Freud borrowed the term regression from brain pathology, but

Freud's and not the neurological meaning of the term has found entrance in modern psychopathology and psychology. While it seems possible that the reverberations of overaged connotations attached to some of the psychoanalytic terms and constructs might act as a factor delaying their understanding or impeding communication, this origin does not affect their function. And in the present context we are interested in this function. How well do the constructs of psychoanalysis permit the establishment of a systematic set of propositions that review present knowledge, and how well do they function in suggesting "new" propositions that can be empirically tested—empirically tested in spite of the great number of independent variables? [2]

The subject matter of psychoanalysis was new within science when Freud started on his investigation; it is new and bewildering even today. That subject matter is human behavior viewed as conflict. Before Freud it had been the exclusive province of intuitive insight, religious, poetic, or philosophic: these had created the various patterns of "the image of man" around which philosophy and the arts of Eurasian civilization have centered throughout the ages. And rapid changes of that image were under way in the outgoing nineteenth century, in the age of Darwin, Nietzsche, Dostoievsky. The relation of psychoanalysis to this world of thought has not yet been satisfactorily investigated, a study that will clearly be one of the major assignments of a future biographer of Freud. Suffice it to say here that a distinction between tangible influences of contemporary intellectual movements on Freud's thought and between "mere" similarities of his approaches to that of others working in other fields cannot always be made. However, the coincidences are often astonishing—no less astonishing and unexplored than the rapidly spreading influence that Freud's thought has exercised on the intellectual life of the twentieth century. To give only one example: The method of free association, one of the main avenues of exploration in psychoanalytic observation, has so clearly influenced literary fashions of the twentieth century that one has been inclined to assume that the "stream of consciousness," as a medium of poetic expression, was derived from it. And yet that very medium was used in France in 1887 in Edouard Dujardin's novel *Les Lauriers sont coupés* (31), several years before Freud ever applied the method of free association in his explorations. There is no evidence that Freud ever read Dujardin's novel, and there hardly need be any. Both Freud's approach and some of the literary currents of the second half of the nineteenth century are part of a general trend in the history of ideas, that tended ever increasingly to pay tribute to the manifestations of psychopathology. The quest for the first relevant traces of this interest within science leads to the French psychiatrists of the nineteenth century, who stimulated Freud's interest in the new field (38).

Freud's first reaction to that field was similar to that through which many students of later generations including our own have passed and are passing. When, at the age of thirty, he first had contact with the study of neurosis, he reacted by a partial withdrawal. After his return from Paris, where he had studied with Charcot in 1886, and from Nancy, where he had worked with Bernheim in 1888, he renewed his interest in physiology and brain pathology. His studies on aphasia (14), one of the first attempts at a functional approach in neurology—functional as contrasted to traditional localizationism—were written in these years of retreat; Freud's interest and publication in the field of neurology continued until the end of his fourth decade.[3] When, at the age of almost forty, he published his first psychoanalytic case histories, he confessed to a feeling of *discomfort*. He who had been trained in the school of experimental sciences was writing what read like a novel. Not personal preference, he said, but the subject matter forced such presentation on him (15). We may add that one particular property of the subject matter was responsible: the property that led to the discovery of the importance of the individual's past in relation to society, to primary and secondary groups—the clinician's role as life historian and social historian—drove him toward the novelist.

Psychoanalytic constructs and assumptions are designed to cope with this difficulty and to make the scientific study of human conflict possible. In the present context it suffices briefly to characterize some of these constructs. The first step in the formation of Freud's theories led to an application of the dynamic concepts of Herbartian psychology to the study of conflict in general, in all areas of human behavior, but especially to the already familiar problems of the stages of awareness, i.e., to the then current ideas concerning conscious and unconscious mental processes. Consequently, "unconscious" became a dynamic attribute, instead of a merely descriptive one; and a special term, "preconscious," was introduced to designate processes that are only descriptively unconscious. The dynamic concepts are supplemented by assumptions dealing with the nature of psychic energy and its somatic source in basic drives and needs; and by specific assumptions that deal with the general principles regulating the functioning of the psychic apparatus in its relation to discharge of tension and its postponement. All these assumptions are characterized by their relation to physiology. Contrary to the tradition of German psychology and psychopathology of the late nineteenth century, Freud kept at a safe distance from making too close a link between psychological and physiological assumptions. He borrowed this approach from French psychiatrists: "The clinical observation of the French [psychiatrists]," he writes in 1892, in his introduction to the German translation of Charcot's *Leçons du mardi*, "gains undoubtedly in independence, since it relegates physiological viewpoints into a second plane . . . not by omission, but by an intentional exclusion, that it considered to serve a purpose." Freud himself never loses sight of this second plane. When after many tentative formulations he developed his structural model of the psychic apparatus, in his assumptions regarding the development of the psychic organizations during ontogenesis, the Id, the Ego, and the Superego, he defined these organizations as physiologists define organs, i.e., he defined them by their functions (28). While neither Freud nor the majority of later workers in the field find it advisable to

establish strict correlations between these functions and certain parts of
the nervous system, such lack of correlation is considered provisional.
Freud explicitly assumed that the time would come when psychological
constructs would be replaced by physiological or biochemical constructs.[4]

The constructs of psychoanalysis here briefly characterized have in
the course of forty years been repeatedly revised. Sometimes so radically
that older propositions were—silently—superseded by newer ones. As a
consequence, the student who wishes to familiarize himself with the system
of propositions has to study its history. No fully satisfactory comprehensive
statement on the system itself is known to me. This is one of the reasons
why random quotations from psychoanalytic writings are of particularly
dubious value. A young American scholar has recently pointed to the fact
that much confusion about what is believed to be a psychoanalytic proposition is due to the exclusive acquaintance with one or the other phase in
the development of hypotheses as embodied in Freud's writings (31). This
state of affairs is symptomatic of the social setting in which psychoanalysis
is developing; the interest of psychiatrists who alone have access to the
full set of observational data can hardly be expected to center on problems
of semantic and systematic clarification, at a time when the rapid advance
of clinical insight attracts their attention. A time lag exists between their
insight and their theoretical formulations and even between clinical experience and published case histories; the clinical tradition, at the present
time, is richer and both more concrete and more precise than the psychoanalytic literature tends to reveal. Since the evidence on which the handling
of psychoanalytic therapy rests is on the whole convincing to those who
apply it, the need for systematic clarification presents itself mostly when
controversial issues arise among those who work with his therapy.

There are obviously many reasons why such controversies have been
frequent since, early in the century, Freud gained his first collaborators;
and there are obviously many reasons why they should have taken the
specific form of "splits" of what we here call the psychoanalytic movement. One of these reasons, however, is directly relevant in the context of
the present paper: it is the elusive nature of the subject matter (52). The
fact that there are many psychoanalytic propositions that have not yet
been verified by procedures used in science seems to explain why controversies tend on the whole to be less fruitful and less centered on essential
issues than they otherwise might be. Whatever the incentives to controversy, unverified propositions are readily taken as training ground by those
polemically inclined.

Not all propositions currently included in psychoanalysis can be made
subject to verification. To mention only two examples: The large set of
propositions which accounts for human behavior in using phylogenetic
assumptions frequently implies another purely biological proposition, the
inheritance of acquired characteristics; and so long as there is no reason to
consider this proposition verified by biologists, it seems appropriate to
exclude psychoanalytic propositions based on it. Similarly, Freud's assump-

tion of a drive toward death ("death instinct") as a propensity of living matter should not be used in establishing empirical propositions, so long as the implied biological assumption has not been tested—the assumption, namely, that living matter tends toward extinction even when chemical self-intoxication is eliminated. Psychoanalysis as a science cannot, I believe, directly deal with these propositions; moreover, their value for the formulation of other empirical propositions can be seriously questioned.[5] Their place in Freud's thinking, however, and their immensely stimulating effect is a matter of great concern to those interested in the history of ideas.

In turning to the problem of validation of psychoanalytic propositions, I shall distinguish validation provided by psychoanalytic observation from other "objective methods" (48) of verification. In discussing the latter, I shall distinguish experimental procedures from observational evidence.

The validation of psychoanalytic propositions through psychoanalytic observation can in this context only briefly be characterized; any attempt to do so must start with the exclusion of what one might expect to be the most convincing test: the success of psychoanalytic therapy. This therapy operates with a number of agents. In many cases it remains to some extent doubtful which of these agents has produced the desired change; even if the probability is great that one particular agent can be made responsible, evidence is as a rule difficult to establish. However, this limitation does not seriously restrict our discussion since, apart from the question of the effectiveness of psychoanalytic therapy, the psychoanalytic interview provides a setting of experimental character through its rules of procedure; it covers an area and makes data accessible that are otherwise not observable under conditions of comparably relative precision.[6] Not only does the total course of the association between observer and subject provide an experimental setting and permit the testing of long range predictions; each interview provides potentially a number of opportunities for the testing of forecasts. Each one of the manifold reactions of the subject to the interventions of the observer can be described as a reaction to a deliberately introduced change in the situation between observer and subject. The reactions of acknowledgment to any interpretation given, for instance, that of sudden insight combined with the production of confirmatory detail or substitute reactions of a variety of kinds, frequently—but not always—permit confirmation or falsification of the hypotheses on which the given intervention was based. It seems appropriate to discuss the simplest example of such confirmatory evidence: the interpretation has removed obstacles to recall; the forgotten memory can take its place within awareness. It is naturally not assumed that in such cases the interpretation "produced" recall; rather the situation existing previous to the interpretation, the one which "suggested" the interpretation, must be described as one of incomplete recall (and, therefore, as in some measure similar to the situation in which the memory trace was laid down). Interpretation, therefore, acts here as a help in completion. Incomplete recall had announced itself by a variety of signs in the individual's behavior. The subject may have acted in relation to an actual rival as he once acted toward a sibling, and the interpretation of the observer merely translated the nonverbalized into verbalized response, unconscious repetition into conscious recollection. The similarity of the situations to which we here refer need exist only in the meaning of the situation to the subject, for instance, in the dynamic structure of the constellation in his life, as this constellation may have been modified by previous interview situations. The frequency of such experiences during analytic observation is in part due to the rules of procedure. They are designed to bring about the experience of similarity of present and past. Thus in many instances the personal relation to the observer is experienced as "similar" to the relation to one or another member of the subject's primary group—we here refer to rules concerning the relative anonymity and passivity of the observer during the interview situation. In saying that the subject exhibits behavior similar to earlier behavior patterns, behavior that would, as it were, be appropriate in another context, we refer to a large number of behavioral details, actions in life as well as during the interview, dreams, and verbalizations that follow the process of free association. In order to eliminate a number of problems concerning the reliability of confirmations of reconstructions by recall of the subject, it seems appropriate to mention that in a considerable number of instances in which interpretation was used to reconstruct the past, or, as one might say, to "predict the past" (27), objective verification of the reconstruction was possible. Inquiries in the environment of the subject and for recollections of members of his family brought confirmations of astonishing details. Thus Marie Bonaparte (7) reported a case in which confirmation was obtained for a reconstructed experience that occurred in the second year of life; the reconstruction was largely based on one dream. At least one subject, the psychologist E. Frenkel-Brunswik, has published an account from her own experience under psychoanalytic observation. From her behavior, and from associations about her two sisters, the analyst had interpreted what he called a "Cordelia motive." He suggested to her that she was displaying in her life the role of Cordelia, the youngest daughter of King Lear. To her answer that she had read most of Shakespeare's dramas but not *King Lear*, the analyst replied that Cordelia was the best and most generous daughter of King Lear, who nevertheless preferred his other two daughters because of their flattering attitudes. Such an interpretation was at that time refused by the author rather emotionally. Later it was received somewhat more favorably. But she was still very surprised when much later she discovered, in looking through old notes, that at the age of about fifteen she had copied the entire role of Cordelia. Thus she must at that age have been very much concerned with the fate of Cordelia, with whom she probably had identified, later repressing not only this identification but also all other memory of the play.

The confirmation of reconstructions by objective evidence played a considerable part in the early history of psychoanalysis, at a time when Freud was constantly experimenting with new propositions. From as yet unpublished notes it appears that he felt considerably encouraged as to the validity of his theories on dream interpretations when the interpretation of one of his own dreams led to the reconstruction of an experience in his third year of life, which was subsequently confirmed by a recollection of his mother.

But even without the support of objective confirmation psychoanalytic observation has in many instances been able to decide between alternative propositions. Thus the hypothesis that there was a regular or extremely frequent occurrence of actual seduction by adults in the childhood of individuals who later in life develop hysterical symptoms, or a regular or frequent correlation between the severity of the birth experience to incidence of neurosis in the adult, was falsified by this procedure.

A survey of the body of psychoanalytic propositions reveals, however, that in other instances psychoanalytic observation does not provide criteria for verification. Observers using the same proposition claim different results; and even when they submit their data to each other, no decision can be reached. The number of variables and the fact that no repetition of the experimental procedure under comparable conditions is feasible, limit in these cases the possibility of decision. This is, for instance, true of propositions suggested by M. Klein (36) and S. Isaacs (33), concerning earliest reactions of the infant to deprivation.[7] They claim, for instance, that in earliest infancy, at the age of a few months, the child reacts with self-punitive tendencies to the extraordinarily intense destructive impulses that it feels against an environment imposing even slight and unavoidable frustrations. I select this instance since it is typical of a large number of other propositions that are indispensable in psychoanalysis: they deal with reactions of the child during the preverbal stage or during the earliest stages of development of its verbal faculties; propositions which will tend to remain controversial unless verified by objective methods. It should be added that they are not the only propositions of which it is true that a decision cannot be reached. Briefly, if we speak of verification of psychoanalytic propositions by objective methods, we do so not in order to make psychoanalytic propositions "respectable" in science, or in order to establish unity in the field of psychology, but because sooner or later the ever more precise empirical test becomes an essential element in the development of any system of scientific propositions. In the development of psychoanalysis this moment seems to have arrived.

Validation of psychoanalysis by experimental procedure has been the preoccupation of individuals and groups of writers over many years, in certain areas (relation of dream formation to percepts, symbolism in dreams) for over thirty years. The interest in this approach is so rapidly growing that recent bibliographies, though incomplete (47, 48), enumerate several hundred contributions, and "experimental psychoanalysis" has come to be considered "a field of its own." The importance of this trend in experimental psychology can hardly be over-estimated. The walls that a generation ago separated the psychological laboratory from "life" have been pierced; the relevance of the problems investigated has increased; experimental work is gradually moving from a concern with peripheral factors determining human behavior to the central problems, on which man's existence depends. That movement is—naturally—slow, but it is effective. And from the experimental setup there leads a way to test-situations and test-procedures and their ever wider application in techniques of welfare and social control.

Through this trend in experimental psychology the isolation of psychoanalysis from other systems and approaches in psychology has been considerably reduced. Furthermore, a number of psychoanalytic propositions have gained wide recognition and are moving rapidly into the area of common-sense psychology. This corresponds to a regular sequence: the greater familiarity with some psychoanalytic propositions leads to their becoming part of "what one always knew."

Before discussing the significance of these experiments for the verification of psychoanalytic propositions it seems appropriate to introduce a distinction applicable to the most frequently tested and most relevant psychoanalytic proposition (27). Psychoanalysis describes processes of conflict solution in their time sequence. It seems, therefore, necessary to organize psychoanalytic propositions according to two viewpoints: according to whether or not they deal with dynamic or genetic (ontogenetic) interrelations. "Dynamic propositions are concerned with the interaction of forces and the conflicts within the individual and with their reaction to the external world at any given time or during brief time spans. Genetic propositions describe how any condition under observation has grown out of an individual's past extended through his total life span. If we take as examples of dynamic propositions defense against danger and reaction to frustration, genetic propositions state how defense and reaction come into being and are used in an individual's life." A survey of the vast number of experiments dealing with reactions to frustration indicates that they frequently test only dynamic propositions. They are concerned "with the field conditions as they exist here and now" and view the subject "who is a product of his past experiences as a static part of the field conditions" (45).[8] Thus Dollard and his collaborators (9) have ably dealt with the proposition that frustrations sometimes lead to aggression; Barker, Dembo, and Lewin (1) with that asserting that frustration sometimes results in primitivization of behavior, in what Freud called ego-regression Both investigations have convincingly verified psychoanalytic propositions. However, these propositions are of a general kind, and the question arises under what condition an individual will react to frustration either with aggression or with regression or with another mechanism of defense. Dynamic propositions alone cannot answer the question. An example may illustrate the reasons: Lewin and his collaborators investigated the reaction of children when suddenly deprived, but still in view, of highly desirable toys. Let us transfer this laboratory situation into life: "When children visit department stores with their mothers, they are in an almost equally tantalizing situation. What will their reaction then be? It will depend on what meaning the 'You can't have it' and the 'It is too expensive' gains for the child, by the way in which the mother puts it to him. This depends on a variety of factors: on the child's relation to the mother; on the mother's own relation to similar present and past experiences; and how, in the child's own previous development, tolerance for deprivation in general and for certain specific deprivations has developed" (27).

This comparison is not meant as a criticism of the laboratory technique; it is only an attempt to characterize the limitations of the predictions that can be based on experiment. Lewin and his collaborators can naturally not generalize "to what kind of frustration and under what circumstances a child will respond with regression" instead of with a different mechanism. However, when the data available cover the individual's past, when both dynamic and genetic propositions are applied, such forecast frequently becomes possible. Thus, in order to prognosticate the child's behavior in the department store, data on both the mother and the child's past experience are essential, detailed data that hardly ever are assembled outside of psychoanalytic observation.

Other experimental approaches have been singularly successful in studying genetic propositions. The experimenter can view life as a series of learning processes (4, 42). The outstanding example of an experimental setup of this kind is J. McV. Hunt's article on "The Effect of Infant Feeding Frustration upon Adult Hoarding in the Albino Rat" (32). He found that the experience of frustration in infancy modifies adult behavior under two conditions: first, that the frustration be experienced at a certain early point during the maturational sequence, and second, that the adult animal be exposed to frustration experiences. The behavior of the satiated animal cannot be said to have been modified; nor will the behavior of the adult animal exposed to frustration be modified if the infantile frustration was experienced at a late period of maturation. This experiment reproduces not only the general proposition that under certain conditions frustration modifies subsequent behavior but also the specific interrelation between experience and predisposition, which is part of all genetic propositions in psychoanalysis. Any experience, it is contended, will become effective only if the child meets it at a given moment of his development.[9]

The value of experiments such as those of Hunt's and of a limited number of similar ones by O. H. Mowrer (41) and D. M. Levy (39) is self-evident: they have succeeded in demonstrating experimentally the validity of genetic propositions of psychoanalysis in an incontrovertible manner.

Whatever gratification one feels at such results is somewhat reduced by the fact that the proposition verified is a good deal removed from the area in which, from the point of view of psychoanalysis, verification of propositions is most urgently needed. To remain in the province covered by Hunt's experiment, we would wish to know what constitutes frustration to the human child, when does what kind of experience act how on what kind of children in what kind of environment—variables in whose effects psychoanalysis is equally interested and whose interrelations are tentatively covered by psychoanalytic propositions, which, as a rule, cannot be verified by experimental procedure.

The use of animal experiments reaches its limit when propositions are so specific that they apply to one species only, to the human animal. The limit of experiments with humans rests on the fact that the laboratory cannot as a rule reproduce dangers or basic needs with which the genetic propositions of psychoanalysis deal.

A number of authors have contested this point and have claimed that the difference between quasi needs and "true needs" can be neglected; the study of human motivation can, they suggest, be exclusively based upon investigations of behavior determined by quasi needs. Lewin (40), who has advanced this view, argues that tensions of low and high intensity are only quantitatively and not qualitatively different; that the fact of this quantitative difference cannot affect the laws in question. Henle (29), who has more recently elaborated on Lewin's views, argues that experiments in a variety of fields have proved that Lewin's contentions are correct. None of these experiments seem entirely convincing; but one of Henle's examples encourages a more detailed discussion. Henle claims that Freud's analysis of the psychopathological phenomena of everyday life, of slips of the tongue, and parapraxes have shown that in an area where tensions of low intensity operate, phenomena come into being that clearly follow the same principles as the symptom formation in neurotic behavior, i.e., phenomena of great intensity.

Henle's argument is misleading. Not only is it worth remembering that not all essential propositions concerning the formation of the neurotic symptom apply to parapraxes (the theory of symptom formation was known to Freud when he hit upon the explanation of parapraxes, and it is doubtful whether a reversal of the sequence could have led to equally satisfactory results); but also the assumptions that the conflicts that lead to parapraxes are necessarily or typically of low intensity is entirely unwarranted. Evidence to the contrary is rather suggestive. But I should like to introduce a different kind of argument. Assuming that even in some cases the intensity of the conflict that leads to parapraxes be low, the nature of the conflicts remains significant. The conflict is of the same kind as the conflict that leads to symptom formation in neurosis; it may involve libidinal and aggressive impulses, love, hate, guilt, and anxiety, and the part played by the three psychic organizations may be in details comparable to that observable in symptom formation.

The quasi needs of the laboratory investigations are of a different kind. There is no doubt that, as Zeigarnik (54) and a host of experimenters since the publication of her paper have shown, the need to complete an uncompleted task exists. But that need is of a very specific kind; [10] seen from the point of view of the psychoanalyst, it is a complex desire in which, however, two elements, that of avoiding failure, or that of feeling unsatisfied because one has not complied with a task, seem to predominate—impulses in which the Ego and the Superego are predominantly involved; as a rule no Id impulses are either frustrated or gratified. Consequently, the conflict that arises when the impulse to complete is frustrated can hardly be compared to conflicts that may arise when the impulse to complete an action with aggressive or libidinal connotation is impeded. In these cases the impediment, whether external or internal, is frequently experienced as a threat and the individual frequently reacts with anxiety. The difference in the situations here referred to, which Lewin described as one of mere quantitative character, can be demonstrated in terms of physiological reactions: the bodily changes (Cannon) attending anxiety states are different in kind and not in degree from other and lower tension states in the organism; their closest relative is the state of rage. Considerations of this kind must be taken into account in discussing the relation of quasi needs of the laboratory to the true needs of life and when evaluating the bearing of certain types of experiments.

It should here be added that experimental approaches to the study of "true" conflict situations have repeatedly been attempted. They were initiated by H. A. Murray (43) who, in his paper on "The Effect of Fear upon Estimates of the Maliciousness of Other Personalities," clearly demonstrated the working of projection. Murray's method has been elaborated by others (cf. 23), and experimentation in this area is rapidly developing. The preliminary reports of various wartime setups for the selection of specialized personnel, where subjects were exposed to considerable strain, seems to indicate that the "paper and pencil" experiments are finding rivals in controlled observation of individuals exposed to real or almost real threat situations.[11]

And yet it seems doubtful whether any experimental method will ever be able to rival the confirmation of psychoanalytic hypotheses concerning human reaction to danger that can be obtained by carefully controlled data of observation. To quote a recent example (37): the fantastic prediction that bombing of civilians in the Second World War would produce mass neuroses was made by those who were unaware of psychoanalytic propositions. The result of bombing surveys, however, confirmed the latter; they state that an individual's reaction to objective danger in a clearly structured situation—under adequate leadership and morale—will depend on the state of inner tension of the individual. All surveys on reaction to bombing in England (53) have shown that pathological reaction was maximized with one group of citizens, the adolescents, i.e., with those whose level of adjustment is for biological reasons least stable and in whose life conflict is supreme. Some surveys (cf. 8) have been interpreted (37) as showing that a similar peak of the curve existed for the age groups 3–5, in which another set of psychoanalytic propositions locates a high propensity to anxiety. Verifications of this kind seem particularly significant since they are based on data selected for other purposes.

The limitations of the laboratory to quasi needs (and quasi dangers) seriously restrict the area of propositions that can be experimentally verified. In fact, up to the present, experimental approaches have been more successful in dealing with propositions concerning substitution [12] than they have been with propositions concerning repression (45, 27). The child represses an experience because the remembrance would entail conflicts of "too great intensity" in the presence of what to the child are vital threats. Situations of this type can hardly be reproduced by the experimenter, but they can be successfully studied by trained observers of behavior, who live in close contact with the child. The ideal of an intense study of the child by a team of participant observers of many skills is as yet unfulfilled, partly for organizational reasons. The communication between "academic" and "psychoanalytic" studies of child development is very incomplete. Quotation marks are used to indicate the spurious character of a division according to which one group of observers would be mainly interested in maturational aspects, the other, the psychoanalytic observer, in the "emotional" or "social" aspect of the child's life,[13] a division of interests which is bound to reduce the value of both sets of findings. In fact, observation has been most meaningful when it covers many areas at the same time and tends to illustrate how all sides of the child's personality are interdependent. The observations by A. Freud and D. Burlingham in a wartime nursery in London may be quoted as outstanding examples (12, 13). Similarly, the investigations of R. Spitz (50) on hospitalism have produced quantified data demonstrating how lack of stimulation by mother or mother-substitute may seriously and under certain conditions irreversibly affect the total development of the infant. In both these investigations the plan to verify psychoanalytic propositions has led far afield: the investigators have not only been able to decide between alternative hypotheses but, what is even more essential, to suggest new ones. The requirements of scientific procedure would suggest that observation of this kind should not be limited to random groups but to representative samples, that it should be conducted over long periods of time, and that studies of child development should be extended and should form the substance of systematic studies in life histories.

Data cannot be restricted to any one cultural or subcultural area. The study of the "nursery" as a matrix of civilization has gained considerable impact from the fieldwork of anthropologists who followed the lead of the genetic propositions of psychoanalysis (Bateson, Erikson, Mead, and others) or used these propositions in their interpretation of anthropological data on child-rearing (21, 22; 34, 35). While advance in this area has been rapid, one other possible field of elucidation has been neglected: the study of identical twins, which would permit access to factors of heredity.[14]

In speaking of validation of psychoanalytic hypotheses by psychoanalytic observation, experimental procedure, and systematic observation, I may have unwittingly conveyed the impression that psychoanalysis is a complete system of propositions, or one near completion. Both impressions would be equally misleading. While psychoanalysis covers a wide area, the closer one investigates the interrelation of propositions, the more "the gaps" hit one's eye; the more does it become evident that however suggestive is the sketch at which one looks, a sketch it is, richer in some parts, more general and painted with a broader brush in others.

Psychoanalysis is not static. Out of psychoanalytic observation a stream of new propositions constantly emerges; the increased number of workers, the changing conditions of observation, such as those of wartime, advances in neighboring fields, but most of all an ever more careful evaluation of the data obtained by psychoanalytic observation are all reflected in psychoanalysis. Hence the quest for verification refers to "old" and "new" propositions alike.

It cannot be a static process; it must be dynamic and continuous. Finally I would venture the forecast that the gradual amalgamation of psychoanalysis with other sciences, mainly with psychology and psychiatry, will find its expression in the institutions of higher learning. The psychoanalytic movement will yield its function to institutionalized science—for better or worse; there are advantages and serious dangers implied in this development. The tradition of courageous exploration that lives on in psychoanalysis may be well lost in this transformation.

REFERENCES

1. Barker, R.; Dembo, Tamara and Lewin, K. Frustration and aggression, an experiment with young children. *Univ. Ia. Stud. Child Welf.*, 1941, *18*.
2. Bateson, G. Cultural determinants of personality. In J. McV. Hunt (Ed.), *Personality and behavior disorders*, Vol. II. New York: Ronald Press, 1944.
3. Bateson, G. and Mead, Margaret. *Balinese character, a photographic analysis*. New York: N. Y. Acad. Sci., 1942.
4. Bergmann, G. Psychoanalysis and experimental psychology. A review from the standpoint of scientific empiricism. *Mind*, 1943, *52*, 122–140.
5. Bernfeld, S. Freud's earliest theories and the school of Helmholtz. *Psychoanal. Quart.*, 1944, *13*, 341–362.
6. Bion, W. R. The leaderless group project. *Bulletin of the Menninger Clinic*, 1946, *10*, 77–81.
7. Bonaparte, Marie. Notes on the analytical discovery of a primal scene. *Psychoanal. Stud. Child*, 1945, *1*, 119–125.
8. Burt, C. *Under fives in total war*. London: Brit. Psychol. Assoc., 1941.
9. Dollard, J.; Doob, L. W.; Miller, N. E.; Mowrer, O. H.; and Sears, R. R. *Frustration and aggression*. New Haven: Yale Univ. Press, 1939.
10. Dorer, M. *Die Historischen Grundlagen der Psychoanalyse*. Leipzig: Meiner, 1932.
11. Erikson, E. H. Childhood and tradition in two American Indian tribes. *Psychoanal. Stud. Child*, 1945, *1*, 319–350.
12. Freud, Anna and Burlingham, Dorothy T. *War and children*. New York: Medical War Books, International Univ. Press, 1943.
13. Freud, Anna and Burlingham, Dorothy T. *Infants without families*. New York: Medical War Books, International Univ. Press, 1944.
14. Freud, S. *Zur Auffassung der Aphasien, eine kritische Studie*, 1891.
15. Freud, S. and Breuer, J. Studies in hysteria. *Nerv. Ment. Disease Monogr.*, New York, 1947.
16. Freud, S. Inhaltsangabe der wissenschaftlichen Arbeiten des Privat-

dozenten Dr. Sigmund Freud (1877-1897). *Int. Z. Psychoanal., Imago,* 1940, *25.*

17. Freud, S. Character and anal erotism. *Collected papers,* Vol. II. London: Hogarth, 1924.

18. Freud, S. *Beyond the pleasure principle.* London: Hogarth, 1922.

19. Freud, S. New introductory lectures. In *Autobiography* (Trans. by J. Strachy). New York: Norton, 1935.

20. Glover, E. Examination of the Klein system of child psychology. *Psychoanal. Stud. Child,* 1945, *1,* 75-118.

21. Gorer, G. Themes in Japanese culture. *Trans. N. Y. Acad. Sci.,* 1943, *5,* 106-124.

22. Gorer, G. *Japanese character structure and propaganda.* Mimeographed memorandum, Committee on Intercultural Relations, New York, 1942.

23. Harrower, M. and Grinker, R. R. The stress tolerance test. Preliminary experiments with a new projective technique utilizing both meaningful and meaningless stimuli. *Psychosom. Med.,* 1946, *8,* 3-15.

24. Hartmann, H. *Grundlagen der Psychoanalyse.* Leipzig: 1927.

25. Hartmann, H. Ein Experimenteller Beitrag zur Psychologie der Zwangsneurose. (Ueber das Behalten erledigter und unerledigter Handlungen.) *Jahrbücher für Psychiatrie und Neurologie,* 1934. *50.*

26. Hartmann, H. Psychiatrische Zwillingsprobleme. *Jahrbücher für Psychiatrie und Neurologie,* 1934, *51.*

27. Hartmann, H. and Kris, E. The genetic approach in psychoanalysis. *Psychoanal. Stud. Child,* 1945, *1,* 11-30.

28. Hartmann, H.; Kris, E. and Loewenstein, R. Some comments on the formation of psychic structure. *Psychoanal. Stud. Child,* 1946, *2.*

29. Henle, Mary. The experimental investigation of the dynamic and structural determinants of substitution. *Contr. Psychol. Theor.* 1942, *2,* No. 3.

30. Hermann, I. Die Psychoanalyse als Methode. *Imago,* Leipzig, 1934, *1.*

31. Hoffman, F. J. *Freudianism and the literary mind.* Baton Rouge: Louisiana State Univ. Press, 1945.

32. Hunt, J. McV. The effect of infant feeding frustration upon adult hoarding in the albino rat. *J. abn. soc. Psychol.,* 1941, *36,* 338-360.

33. Isaacs, Susan. *The psychological aspects of child development.* London: Evans, 1935.

34. Kardiner, A. *The individual and his society.* New York: Columbia Univ. Press, 1939.

35. Kardiner, A. *Psychological frontiers of society.* New York: Columbia Univ. Press, 1945.

36. Klein, Melanie. *Psychoanalysis of children.* London: Hogarth, 1932.

37. Kris, E. Danger and morale. *Amer. J. Orthopsychiatry,* 1944, *14,* 147-156.

38. Kris, E. Review of Hoffman, *Freudianism and the literary mind. Psychoanal. Quart.,* 1946, *15,* 226-234.

39. Levy, D. M. Experiments on the sucking reflex and social behavior of dogs. *Amer. J. Orthopsychiatry,* 1934, *4,* 203-224.

40. Lewin, K. The conceptual representation and the measurement of psychological forces. *Contr. Psychol. Theor.,* 1938, *1,* No. 4.

41. Mowrer, O. H. An experimental analogue of "regression" with incidental observations on "reaction-formation." *J. abn. soc. Psychol.,* 1940, *35,* 56-87.

42. Mowrer, O. H. and Kluckhohn, C. Dynamic theory of personality. In J. McV. Hunt (Ed.), *Personality and behavior disorders,* Vol. I. New York: Ronald Press, 1944.

43. Murray, H. A. The effect of fear upon estimates of the maliciousness of other personalities. *J. soc. Psychol.*, 1933, *4*, 310-329.
44. Piaget, J. *The moral judgment of the child*. New York: Harcourt, Brace, 1932.
45. Rapaport, D. Freudian mechanisms and frustration-experiments. *Psychoanal. Quart.*, 1942, *11*, 503-511.
46. Saussure, R. de. Ueber genetische Psychologie und Psychoanalyse. *Imago, 20.*
47. Sears, R. R. Survey of objective studies of psychoanalytic concepts. *Soc. Sci. Res. Council Bull.*, 1943, No. 51.
48. Sears, R. R. Experimental analyses of psychoanalytic phenomena. In J. McV. Hunt (Ed.), *Personality and behavior disorders*, Vol. I, New York: Ronald Press, 1944.
49. Spence, K. W. Theoretical interpretations of learning. In F. A. Moss (Ed.), *Comparative psychology*. New York: Prentice-Hall, 1942 (rev. ed.).
50. Spitz, R. Hospitalism. An inquiry into the genesis of psychiatric conditions in early childhood. *Psychoanal. Stud. Child*, 1945, *1*, 53-74.
51. Wälder, R. The problem of the genesis of psychical conflict in earliest infancy. *Int. J. Psychoanal.*, 1937, *18*, 406-473.
52. Wälder, R. Present trends in psychoanalytic theory and practice. *Bulletin of the Menninger Clinic*, 1944, *8*, 9-17.
53. Wolf, Katherine M. Evacuation of children in wartime. A survey of the literature with a bibliography. *Psychoanal. Stud. Child*, 1945, *1*, 389-404.
54. Zeigarnik, Bluma. Ueber das Behalten von erledigten und unerledigten Handlungen. *Psychol. Forsch.*, 1927, *9*, 1-85.

PART C

*

Methods and Problems of the
Social Sciences

JOHN STUART MILL

On the Logic of the Social Sciences *

"*If man can predict with almost complete confidence phenomena whose laws are known to him; if, even when they are not known to him, he can in accord with experience foresee with high probability future events, why should we regard it fanciful to undertake to trace with some likelihood the picture of the future destination of the human species in accordance with the results of its history? The only foundation for belief in the natural sciences is the following idea: the general laws, known or unknown, which govern the phenomena of the universe, are necessary and constant; and is there some reason why this principle should be less true for the development of the intellectual and moral faculties of man than for the other operations of nature? Finally, since opinions formed in accord with experience . . . are the only rule of conduct of the wisest of men, why should we forbid the philosopher to rest his surmises on the same base, provided that he does not attribute to them a certainty higher than what may grow out of the number, constancy, and accuracy of observations?*"—Condorcet.

CHAPTER I

INTRODUCTORY REMARKS

1. *The backward state of the moral sciences can only be remedied by applying to them the methods of physical science, duly extended and generalized.*

Principles of evidence and theories of method are not to be constructed *a priori*. The laws of our rational faculty, like those of every other natural agency, are only learned by seeing the agent at work. The earlier achievements of science were made without the conscious observance of any scientific method, and we should never have known by what process truth is to

* Book VI of Mill's A SYSTEM OF LOGIC: Ratiocinative and Inductive Being a Connected View of the Principles of Evidence and the Methods of Scientific Investigation. Eighth Edition (Abridged), New York, 1881. Reprinted with the courtesy of Hafner Publishing Co., New York, and of Ernest Nagel whose edited version, *John Stuart Mill's Philosophy of Scientific Method* (Hafner Library of Classics, No. 12, New York, 1950), has been excerpted here. Book V On the Logic of the Moral Sciences is Book VI in the eighth edition. The term "Moral Sciences" includes what we should today call "Social Sciences." Mill headed this Book with a quotation in French from Condorcet's *Esquisse d'un Tableau Historique de l'Esprit Humain* (Sketch of a Historical Picture of the Human Mind) which was written by the great French mathematician and liberal philosopher while imprisoned by the more extreme Jacobin regime during the reign of terror of 1793-4. The quotation given by Mill is translated above.

be ascertained if we had not previously ascertained many truths. But it was only the easier problems which could be thus resolved; natural sagacity, when it tried its strength against the more difficult ones, either failed altogether, or, if it succeeded here and there in obtaining a solution, had no sure means of convincing others that its solution was correct. In scientific investigation, as in all other works of human skill, the way of obtaining the end is seen, as it were, instinctively by superior minds in some comparatively simple case and is then, by judicious generalization, adapted to the variety of complex cases. We learn to do a thing in difficult circumstances by attending to the manner in which we have spontaneously done the same thing in easier ones.

This truth is exemplified by the history of the various branches of knowledge which have successively, in the ascending order of their complication, assumed the character of sciences, and will doubtless receive fresh confirmation from those of which the final scientific constitution is yet to come and which are still abandoned to the uncertainties of vague and popular discussion. Although several other sciences have emerged from this state at a comparatively recent date, none now remain in it except those which relate to man himself, the most complex and most difficult subject of study on which the human mind can be engaged.

Concerning the physical nature of man as an organized being—though there is still much uncertainty and much controversy which can only be terminated by the general acknowledgment and employment of stricter rules of induction than are commonly recognized—there is, however, a considerable body of truths which all who have attended to the subject consider to be fully established; nor is there now any radical imperfection in the method observed in the department of science by its most distinguished modern teachers. But the laws of mind and, in even a greater degree, those of society are so far from having attained a similar state of even partial recognition that it is still a controversy whether they are capable of becoming subjects of science in the strict sense of the term, and among those who are agreed on this point there reigns the most irreconcilable diversity on almost every other. Here, therefore, if anywhere, the principles laid down in the preceding Books may be expected to be useful.

If, on matters so much the most important with which human intellect can occupy itself, a more general agreement is ever to exist among thinkers, if what has been pronounced "the proper study of mankind" is not destined to remain the only subject which philosophy cannot succeed in rescuing from empiricism, the same process through which the laws of many simpler phenomena have by general acknowledgment been placed beyond dispute must be consciously and deliberately applied to those more difficult inquiries. If there are some subjects on which the results obtained have finally received the unanimous assent of all who have attended to the proof, and others on which mankind have not yet been equally successful, on which the most sagacious minds have occupied themselves from the earliest date and have never succeeded in establishing any considerable body of truths so as to be beyond denial or doubt, it is by generalizing the methods successfully followed in the former inquiries and adapting them to the latter that we may hope to remove this blot on the face of science. The remaining chapters are an endeavor to facilitate this most desirable object.

CHAPTER II *

THAT THERE IS, OR MAY BE, A SCIENCE OF
HUMAN NATURE

1. There may be sciences which are not exact sciences

It is a common notion, or, at least, it is implied in many common modes of speech, that the thoughts, feelings, and actions of sentient beings are not a subject of science in the same strict sense in which this is true of the objects of outward nature. This notion seems to involve some confusion of ideas which it is necessary to begin by clearing up.

Any facts are fitted, in themselves, to be a subject of science which follow one another according to constant laws, although those laws may not have been discovered nor even be discoverable by our existing resources. Take, for instance, the most familiar class of meteorological phenomena, those of rain and sunshine. Scientific inquiry has not yet succeeded in ascertaining the order of antecedence and consequence among these phenomena, so as to be able, at least in our regions of the earth, to predict them with certainty or even with any high degree of probability. Yet no one doubts that the phenomena depend on laws, and that these must be derivative laws resulting from known ultimate laws, those of heat, electricity, vaporization and elastic fluids. Nor can it be doubted that if we were acquainted with all the antecedent circumstances, we could, even from those more general laws, predict (saving difficulties of calculation) the state of the weather at any future time. Meteorology, therefore, not only has in itself every natural requisite for being, but actually is, a science, though, from the difficulty of observing the facts on which the phenomena depend (a difficulty inherent in the peculiar nature of those phenomena), the science is extremely imperfect, and, were it perfect, might probably be of little avail in practice, since the data requisite for applying its principles to particular instances would rarely be procurable.

A case may be conceived of an intermediate character between the perfection of science and this its extreme imperfection. . . .

. . . No one doubts that tidology (as Dr. Whewell proposes to call it) is really a science. As much of the phenomena as depends on the attraction of the sun and moon is completely understood and may, in any, even unknown, part of the earth's surface, be foretold with certainty, and the far

* [Chapter III of the eighth edition.]

greater part of the phenomena depends on those causes. But circumstances of a local or casual nature, such as the configuration of the bottom of the ocean, the degree of confinement from shores, the direction of the wind, etc., influence, in many or in all places, the height and time of the tide; and, a portion of these circumstances being either not accurately knowable, not precisely measurable, or not capable of being certainly foreseen, the tide in known places commonly varies from the calculated result of general principles by some difference that we cannot explain, and in unknown ones may vary from it by a difference that we are not able to foresee or conjecture. Nevertheless, not only is it certain that these variations depend on causes and follow their causes by laws of unerring uniformity, not only, therefore, is tidology a science, like meteorology, but it is, what hitherto, at least, meteorology is not, a science largely available in practice. General laws may be laid down respecting the tides, predictions may be founded on those laws, and the result will in the main, though often not with complete accuracy, correspond to the predictions.

And this is what is or ought to be meant by those who speak of sciences which are not *exact* sciences. Astronomy was once a science, without being an exact science. It could not become exact until not only the general course of the planetary motions, but the perturbations also, were accounted for and referred to their causes. It has become an exact science because its phenomena have been brought under laws comprehending the whole of the causes by which the phenomena are influenced, whether in a great or only in a trifling degree, whether in all or only in some cases, and assigning to each of those causes the share of effect which really belongs to it. But in the theory of the tides the only laws as yet accurately ascertained are those of the causes which affect the phenomenon in all cases and in a considerable degree, while others which affect it in some cases only, or, if in all, only in a slight degree, have not been sufficiently ascertained and studied to enable us to lay down their laws, still less to deduce the completed law of the phenomenon by compounding the effects of the greater with those of the minor causes. Tidology, therefore, is not yet an exact science, not from any inherent incapacity of being so, but from the difficulty of ascertaining with complete precision the real derivative uniformities. By combining, however, the exact laws of the greater causes and of such of the minor ones as are sufficiently known with such empirical laws or such approximate generalizations respecting the miscellaneous variations as can be obtained by specific observation, we can lay down general propositions which will be true in the main, and on which, with allowance for the degree of their probable inaccuracy, we may safely ground our expectations and our conduct.

2. To what scientific type the science of human nature corresponds

The science of human nature is of this description. It falls far short of the standard of exactness now realized in astronomy, but there is no reason that it should not be as much a science as tidology is, or as astronomy was when its calculations had only mastered the main phenomena but not the perturbations.

The phenomena with which this science is conversant being the thoughts, feelings, and actions of human beings, it would have attained the ideal perfection of a science if it enabled us to foretell how an individual would think, feel, or act throughout life with the same certainty with which astronomy enables us to predict the places and the occultations of the heavenly bodies. It needs scarcely be stated that nothing approaching to this can be done. The actions of individuals could not be predicted with scientific accuracy, were it only because we cannot foresee the whole of the circumstances in which those individuals will be placed. But further, even in any given combination of (present) circumstances, no assertion which is both precise and universally true can be made respecting the manner in which human beings will think, feel, or act. This is not, however, because every person's modes of thinking, feeling, and acting do not depend on causes; nor can we doubt that, if, in the case of any individual, our data could be complete, we even now know enough of the ultimate laws by which mental phenomena are determined to enable us in many cases to predict with tolerable certainty what, in the greater number of supposable combinations of circumstances, his conduct or sentiments would be. But the impressions and actions of human beings are not solely the result of their present circumstances, but the joint result of those circumstances and of the characters of the individuals; and the agencies which determine human character are so numerous and diversified (nothing which has happened to the person throughout life being without its portion of influence) that in the aggregate they are never in any two cases exactly similar. Hence, even if our science of human nature were theoretically perfect, that is, if we could calculate any character as we can calculate the orbit of any planet, *from given data,* still, as the data are never all given nor ever precisely alike in different cases, we could neither make positive predictions nor lay down universal propositions.

Inasmuch, however, as many of those effects which it is of most importance to render amenable to human foresight and control are determined, like the tides, in an incomparably greater degree by general causes than by all partial causes taken together, depending in the main on those circumstances and qualities which are common to all mankind, or, at least, to large bodies of them, and only in a small degree on the idiosyncrasies of organization or the peculiar history of individuals, it is evidently possible with regard to all such effects to make predictions which will *almost* always be verified and general propositions which are almost always true. And whenever it is sufficient to know how the great majority of the human race or of some nation or class of persons will think, feel, and act, these propositions are equivalent to universal ones. For the purposes of political and social science this *is* sufficient. As we formerly remarked,* an approximate generalization is, in social inquiries, for most practical purposes

* [Chapter II of the eighth edition, "Of Liberty and Necessity."]

equivalent to an exact one, that which is only probable when asserted of individual human beings indiscriminately selected being certain when affirmed of the character and collective conduct of masses.

It is no disparagement, therefore, to the science of human nature that those of its general propositions which descend sufficiently into detail to serve as a foundation for predicting phenomena in the concrete are for the most part only approximately true. But, in order to give a genuinely scientific character to the study, it is indispensable that these approximate generalizations, which in themselves would amount only to the lowest kind of empirical laws, should be connected deductively with the laws of nature from which they result, should be resolved into the properties of the causes on which the phenomena depend. In other words, the science of human nature may be said to exist in proportion as the approximate truths which compose a practical knowledge of mankind can be exhibited as corollaries from the universal laws of human nature on which they rest, whereby the proper limits of those approximate truths would be shown, and we should be enabled to deduce others for any new state of circumstances in anticipation of specific experience.

.   .   .   .

CHAPTER V *

OF THE CHEMICAL, OR EXPERIMENTAL METHOD IN THE SOCIAL SCIENCE

1. *Characters of the mode of thinking which deduces political doctrines from specific experience*

The laws of the phenomena of society are and can be nothing but the laws of the actions and passions of human beings united together in the social state. Men, however, in a state of society are still men; their actions and passions are obedient to the laws of individual human nature. Men are not, when brought together, converted into another kind of substance with different properties, as hydrogen and oxygen are different from water, or as hydrogen, oxygen, carbon, and azote are different from nerves, muscles, and tendons. Human beings in society have no properties but those which are derived from, and may be resolved into, the laws of the nature of individual man. In social phenomena the composition of causes is the universal law.

Now, the method of philosophizing which may be termed chemical overlooks this fact and proceeds as if the nature of man as an individual were not concerned at all, or were concerned in a very inferior degree, in the operations of human beings in society. All reasoning in political or social affairs, grounded on principles of human nature, is objected to by

* [Chapter VII of the eighth edition.]

reasoners of this sort under such names as "abstract theory." For the direction of their opinions and conduct, they profess to demand, in all cases without exception, specific experience.

This mode of thinking is not only general with practitioners in politics and with that very numerous class who (on a subject which no one, however ignorant, thinks himself incompetent to discuss) profess to guide themselves by common sense rather than by science, but is often countenanced by persons with greater pretensions to instruction—persons who, having sufficient acquaintance with books and with the current ideas to have heard that Bacon taught mankind to follow experience and to ground their conclusions on facts instead of metaphysical dogmas, think that, by treating political facts in as directly experimental a method as chemical facts, they are showing themselves true Baconians and proving their adversaries to be mere syllogizers and schoolmen. As, however, the notion of the applicability of experimental methods to political philosophy cannot co-exist with any just conception of these methods themselves, the kind of arguments from experience which the chemical theory brings forth as its fruits (and which form the staple, in this country especially, of parliamentary and hustings oratory) are such as, at no time since Bacon, would have been admitted to be valid in chemistry itself or in any other branch of experimental science. They are such as these: that the prohibition of foreign commodities must conduce to national wealth because England has flourished under it, or because countries in general which have adopted it have flourished; that our laws or our internal administration or our constitution are excellent for a similar reason; and the eternal arguments from historical examples, from Athens or Rome, from the fires in Smithfield or the French Revolution.

I will not waste time in contending against modes of argumentation which no person with the smallest practice in estimating evidence could possibly be betrayed into, which draw conclusions of general application from a single unanalyzed instance, or arbitrarily refer an effect to some one among its antecedents, without any process of elimination or comparison of instances. It is a rule both of just and of good sense to grapple not with the absurdest, but with the most reasonable form of a wrong opinion. We shall suppose our inquirer acquainted with the true conditions of experimental investigation and competent in point of acquirements for realizing them, so far as they can be realized. He shall know as much of the facts of history as mere erudition can teach—as much as can be proved by testimony, without the assistance of any theory—and, if those mere facts, properly collated, can fulfill the conditions of a real induction, he shall be qualified for the task.

But that no such attempt can have the smallest chance of success, has been abundantly shown in the tenth chapter of the Third Book. We there examined whether effects which depend on a complication of causes can be made the subject of a true induction by observation and experiment, and concluded, on the most convincing grounds, that they cannot. . . .

CHAPTER VI

OF THE GEOMETRICAL, OR ABSTRACT, METHOD

1. *Characters of this mode of thinking*

The misconception discussed in the preceding chapter is, as we said, chiefly committed by persons not much accustomed to scientific investigation, practitioners in politics who rather employ the commonplaces of philosophy to justify their practice than seek to guide their practice by philosophic principles, or imperfectly educated persons who, in ignorance of the careful selection and elaborate comparison of instances required for the formation of a sound theory, attempt to found one upon a few coincidences which they have casually noticed.

The erroneous method of which we are now to treat is, on the contrary, peculiar to thinking and studious minds. It never could have suggested itself but to persons of some familiarity with the nature of scientific research, who, being aware of the impossibility of establishing, by casual observation or direct experimentation, a true theory of sequences so complex as are those of the social phenomena, have recourse to the simpler laws which are immediately operative in those phenomena and which are no other than the laws of the nature of the human beings therein concerned. These thinkers perceive (what the partisans of the chemical or experimental theory do not) that the science of society must necessarily be deductive. But, from an insufficient consideration of the specific nature of the subject-matter—and often because (their own scientific education having stopped short in too early a stage) geometry stands in their minds as the type of all deductive science—it is to geometry rather than to astronomy and natural philosophy that they unconsciously assimilate the deductive science of society.

Among the differences between geometry (a science of co-existent facts, altogether independent of the laws of the succession of phenomena) and those physical sciences of causation which have been rendered deductive, the following is one of the most conspicuous: that geometry affords no room for what so constantly occurs in mechanics and its applications, the case of conflicting forces, of causes which counteract or modify one another. In mechanics we continually find two or more moving forces producing not motion, but rest, or motion in a different direction from that which would have been produced by either of the generating forces. It is true that the effect of the joint forces is the same when they act simultaneously as if they had acted one after another or by turns, and it is in this that the difference between mechanical and chemical laws consists. But still the effects, whether produced by successive or by simultaneous action, do, wholly or in part, cancel one another; what the one force does the other partly or altogether undoes. There is no similar state of things in

* [Chapter VIII of the eighth edition.]

geometry. The result which follows from one geometrical principle has nothing that conflicts with the result which follows from another. What is proved true from one geometrical theorem, what would be true if no other geometrical principles existed, cannot be altered and made no longer true by reason of some other geometrical principle. What is once proved true is true in all cases, whatever supposition may be made in regard to any other matter.

Now a conception similar to this last would appear to have been formed of the social science in the minds of the earlier of those who have attempted to cultivate it by a deductive method. Mechanics would be a science very similar to geometry if every motion resulted from one force alone and not from a conflict of forces. In the geometrical theory of society, it seems to be supposed that this is really the case with the social phenomena, that each of them results always from only one force, one single property of human nature.

At the point which we have now reached, it cannot be necessary to say anything either in proof or in illustration of the assertion that such is not the true character of the social phenomena. There is not, among these most complex and (for that reason) most modifiable of all phenomena, any one over which innumerable forces do not exercise influence, which does not depend on a conjunction of very many causes. We have not, therefore, to prove the notion in question to be an error, but to prove that the error has been committed, that so mistaken a conception of the mode in which the phenomena of society are produced has actually been ascertained.

2. *The interest-philosophy of the Bentham school*

Passing over less important instances, I shall come at once to the most remarkable example afforded by our own times of the geometrical method in politics, emanating from persons who are well aware of the distinction between science and art, who knew that rules of conduct must follow, not precede, the ascertainment of laws of nature, and that the latter, not the former, is the legitimate field for the application of the deductive method. I allude to the interest-philosophy of the Bentham school.

The profound and original thinkers who are commonly known under this description founded their general theory of government on one comprehensive premise, namely, that men's actions are always determined by their interests. There is an ambiguity in this last expression; for, as the same philosophers, especially Bentham, gave the name of an interest to anything which a person likes, the proposition may be understood to mean only this, that men's actions are always determined by their wishes. In this sense, however, it would not bear out any of the consequences which these writers drew from it, and the word, therefore, in their political reasonings, must be understood to mean (which is also the explanation they themselves, on such occasions, gave of it) what is commonly termed private or worldly interest.

Taking the doctrine, then, in this sense, an objection presents itself *in limine* which might be deemed a fatal one, namely, that so sweeping a proposition is far from being universally true. Human beings are not governed in all their actions by their worldly interests. This, however, is by no means so conclusive an objection as it at first appears, because in politics we are for the most part concerned with the conduct not of individual persons, but either of a series of persons (as a succession of kings), or a body or mass of persons, as a nation, an aristocracy, or a representative assembly. And whatever is true of a large majority of mankind may without much error be taken for true of any succession of persons, considered as a whole, or of any collection of persons in which the act of the majority becomes the act of the whole body. Although therefore, the maxim is sometimes expressed in a manner unnecessarily paradoxical, the consequences drawn from it will hold equally good if the assertion be limited as follows: Any succession of persons, or the majority of any body of persons, will be governed in the bulk of their conduct by their personal interests. We are bound to allow to this school of thinkers the benefit of this more rational statement of their fundamental maxim which is also in strict conformity to the explanations which, when considered to be called for, have been given by themselves.

The theory goes on to infer, quite correctly, that if the actions of mankind are determined in the main by their selfish interests, the only rulers who will govern according to the interest of the governed, are those whose selfish interests are in accordance with it. And to this is added a third proposition, namely, that no rulers have their selfish interest identical with that of the governed unless it be rendered so by accountability, that is, by dependence on the will of the governed. In other words (and as the result of the whole), that the desire of retaining or the fear of losing their power and whatever is thereon consequent is the sole motive which can be relied on for producing on the part of rulers a course of conduct in accordance with the general interest.

We have thus a fundamental theorem of political science, consisting of three syllogisms and depending chiefly on two general premises, in each of which a certain effect is considered as determined only by one cause, not by a concurrence of causes. In the one, it is assumed that the actions of average rulers are determined solely by self-interest; in the other, that the sense of identity of interest with the governed is produced and producible by no other cause than responsibility.

Neither of these propositions is by any means true; the last is extremely wide of the truth.

.   .   .   .

I am not here attempting to establish a theory of government and am not called upon to determine the proportional weight which ought to be given to the circumstances which this school of geometrical politicians left out of their system and those which they took into it. I am only concerned to show that their method was unscientific, not to measure the amount of error which may have affected their practical conclusions.

.   .   .   .

It is not to be imagined possible, nor is it true in point of fact, that these philosophers regarded the few premises of their theory as including all that is required for explaining social phenomena or for determining the choice of forms of government and measures of legislation and administration. They were too highly instructed, of too comprehensive intellect, and some of them of too sober and practical a character for such an error. They would have applied and did apply their principles with innumerable allowances. But it is not allowances that are wanted. There is little chance of making due amends in the superstructure of a theory for the want of sufficient breadth in its foundations. It is unphilosophical to construct a science out of a few of the agencies by which the phenomena are determined and leave the rest to the routine of practice or the sagacity of conjecture. We either ought not to pretend to scientific forms, or we ought to study all the determining agencies equally and endeavor, so far as it can be done, to include all of them within the pale of the science, else we shall infallibly bestow a disproportionate attention upon those which our theory takes into account while we misestimate the rest and probably underrate their importance. That the deductions should be from the whole and not from a part only of the laws of nature that are concerned would be desirable even if those omitted were so insignificant in comparison with the others that they might, for most purposes and on most occasions, be left out of the account. But this is far indeed from being true in the social science. The phenomena of society do not depend, in essentials, on some one agency or law of human nature with only inconsiderable modifications from others. The whole of the qualities of human nature influence those phenomena, and there is not one which influences them in a small degree. There is not one the removal or any great alteration of which would not materially affect the whole aspect of society and change more or less the sequences of social phenomena generally.

.   .   .   .

CHAPTER VII *

Of the Physical, or Concrete Deductive, Method

1. *The direct and inverse deductive methods*

After what has been said to illustrate the nature of the inquiry into social phenomena, the general character of the method proper to that inquiry is sufficiently evident and needs only to be recapitulated, not proved.

* [Chapter IX of the eighth edition.]

However complex the phenomena, all their sequences and co-existences result from the laws of the separate elements. The effect produced, in social phenomena, by any complex set of circumstances amounts precisely to the sum of the effects of the circumstances taken singly, and the complexity does not arise from the number of the laws themselves, which is not remarkably great, but from the extraordinary number and variety of the data or elements—of the agents which, in obedience to that small number of laws, co-operate toward the effect. The social science, therefore (which, by a convenient barbarism, has been termed sociology), is a deductive science, not, indeed, after the model of geometry, but after that of the more complex physical sciences. It infers the law of each effect from the laws of causation on which that effect depends, not, however, from the law merely of one cause, as in the geometrical method, but by considering all the causes which conjunctly influence the effect and compounding their laws with one another. Its method, in short, is the concrete deductive method, that of which astronomy furnishes the most perfect, natural philosophy a somewhat less perfect, example, and the employment of which, with the adaptations and precautions required by the subject, is beginning to regenerate physiology.

Nor does it admit of doubt that similar adaptations and precautions are indispensable in sociology. In applying to that most complex of all studies what is demonstrably the sole method capable of throwing the light of science even upon phenomena of a far inferior degree of complication, we ought to be aware that the same superior complexity which renders the instrument of deduction more necessary renders it also more precarious, and we must be prepared to meet, by appropriate contrivances, this increase of difficulty.

The actions and feelings of human beings in the social state are, no doubt, entirely governed by psychological and ethological laws; whatever influence any cause exercises upon the social phenomena, it exercises through those laws. Supposing, therefore, the laws of human actions and feelings to be sufficiently known, there is no extraordinary difficulty in determining from those laws the nature of the social effects which any given cause tends to produce. But when the question is that of compounding several tendencies together and computing the aggregate result of many co-existent causes, and especially when, by attempting to predict what will actually occur in a given case, we incur the obligation of estimating and compounding the influences of all the causes which happen to exist in that case, we attempt a task to proceed far in which surpasses the compass of the human faculties.

.   .   .   .

But, without dissembling the necessary imperfections of the *a priori* method when applied to such a subject, neither ought we, on the other hand, to exaggerate them. The same objections which apply to the method of deduction in this its most difficult employment apply to it, as we formerly showed, in its easiest, and would even there have been insuperable if there had not existed, as was then fully explained, an appropriate remedy. This remedy consists in the process which, under the name of "verification," we have characterized as the third essential constituent part of the deductive method, that of collating the conclusions of the ratiocination either with the concrete phenomena themselves or, when such are obtainable, with their empirical laws. The ground of confidence in any concrete deductive science is not the *a priori* reasoning itself but the accordance between its results and those of observation *a posteriori*. Either of these processes, apart from the other, diminishes in value as the subject increases in complication, and this is in so rapid a ratio as soon to become entirely worthless, but the reliance to be placed in the concurrence of the two sorts of evidence not only does not diminish in anything like the same proportion but is not necessarily much diminished at all. Nothing more results than a disturbance in the order of precedency of the two processes, sometimes amounting to its actual inversion; insomuch that, instead of deducing our conclusions by reasoning and verifying them by observation, we in some cases begin by obtaining them provisionally from specific experience, and afterward connect them with the principles of human nature by *a priori* reasonings, which reasonings are thus a real verification.

. . . .

We shall begin, then, by looking at the social science as a science of direct deduction and considering what can be accomplished in it, and under what limitations, by that mode of investigation. We shall, then, in a separate chapter, examine and endeavor to characterize the inverse process.

2. *Difficulties of the direct deductive method in the social science*

It is evident, in the first place, that sociology, considered as a system of deductions *a priori*, cannot be a science of positive predictions but only of tendencies. We may be able to conclude, from the laws of human nature applied to the circumstances of a given state of society, that a particular cause will operate in a certain manner unless counteracted, but we can never be assured to what extent or amount it will so operate or affirm with certainty that it will not be counteracted, because we can seldom know, even approximately, all the agencies which may co-exist with it and still less calculate the collective result of so many combined elements. The remark, however, must here be once more repeated that knowledge insufficient for prediction may be most valuable for guidance. It is not necessary for the wise conduct of the affairs of society, no more than of anyone's private concerns, that we should be able to foresee infallibly the results of what we do. We must seek our objects by means which may perhaps be defeated and take precautions against dangers which possibly may never be realized. The aim of practical politics is to surround any given society with the greatest possible number of circumstances of which the tendencies are beneficial and to remove or counteract, as far as practicable, those of which the tendencies are injurious. A knowledge of the tendencies only, though without the power of accurately predicting their conjunct result, gives us to a considerable extent this power.

It would, however, be an error to suppose that even with respect to tendencies we could arrive in this manner at any great number of propositions which will be true in all societies without exception. Such a supposition would be inconsistent with the eminently modifiable nature of the social phenomena and the multitude and variety of the circumstances by which they are modified—circumstances never the same, or even nearly the same, in two different societies or in two different periods of the same society. This would not be so serious an obstacle if, though the causes acting upon society in general are numerous, those which influence any one feature of society were limited in number, for we might then insulate any particular social phenomenon and investigate its laws without disturbance from the rest. But the truth is the very opposite of this. Whatever affects, in an appreciable degree, any one element of the social state affects through it all the other elements. The mode of production of all social phenomena is one great case of intermixture of laws. We can never either understand in theory or command in practice the condition of a society in any one respect without taking into consideration its condition in all other respects. There is no social phenomenon which is not more or less influenced by every other part of the condition of the same society and, therefore, by every cause which is influencing any other of the contemporaneous social phenomena. There is, in short, what physiologists term a *consensus,* similar to that existing among the various organs and functions of the physical frame of man and the more perfect animals, and constituting one of the many analogies which have rendered universal such expressions as the "body politic" and "body natural." It follows from this *consensus* that, unless two societies could be alike in all the circumstances which surround and influence them (which would imply their being alike in their previous history), no portion whatever of the phenomena will, unless by accident, precisely correspond; no one cause will produce exactly the same effects in both. Every cause, as its effect spreads through society, comes somewhere in contact with different sets of agencies and thus has its effects on some of the social phenomena differently modified; and these differences, by their reaction, produce a difference even in those of the effects which would otherwise have been the same. We can never, therefore, affirm with certainty that a cause which has a particular tendency in one people or in one age will have exactly the same tendency in another, without referring back to our premises and performing over again for the second age or nation that analysis of the whole of its influencing circumstances which we had already performed for the first. The deductive science of society will not lay down a theorem asserting in a universal manner the effect of any cause, but will rather teach us how to frame the proper theorem for the circumstances of any given case. It will not give the laws of society in general, but the means of determining the phenomena of any given society from the particular elements or data of that society.

All the general propositions which can be framed by the deductive science are, therefore, in the strictest sense of the word, hypothetical. They are grounded on some suppositious set of circumstances and declare how some given cause would operate in those circumstances, supposing that no others were combined with them. If the set of circumstances supposed have been copied from those of any existing society, the conclusions will be true of that society, provided, and in as far as, the effect of those circumstances shall not be modified by others which have not been taken into the account. If we desire a nearer approach to concrete truth, we can only aim at it by taking, or endeavoring to take, a greater number of individualizing circumstances into the computation.

.   .   .   .

3. To what extent the different branches of sociological speculation can be studied apart. Political economy characterized

Notwithstanding the universal *consensus* of the social phenomena, whereby nothing which takes place in any part of the operations of society is without its share of influence on every other part, and notwithstanding the paramount ascendancy which the general state of civilization and social progress in any given society must hence exercise over all the partial and subordinate phenomena, it is not the less true that different species of social facts are in the main dependent, immediately and in the first resort, on different kinds of causes, and, therefore, not only may with advantage, but must, be studied apart, just as in the natural body we study separately the physiology and pathology of each of the principal organs and tissues, though every one is acted upon by the state of all the others, and though the peculiar constitution and general state of health of the organism co-operates with, and often preponderates over, the local causes in determining the state of any particular organ.

On these considerations is grounded the existence of distinct and separate though not independent branches or departments of sociological speculation.

There is, for example, one large class of social phenomena in which the immediately determining causes are principally those which act through the desire of wealth, and in which the psychological law mainly concerned is the familiar one that a greater gain is preferred to a smaller. I mean, of course, that portion of the phenomena of society which emanate from the industrial or productive operations of mankind, and from those of their acts through which the distribution of the products of those industrial operations takes place, in so far as not effected by force or modified by voluntary gift. By reasoning from that one law of human nature and from the principal outward circumstances (whether universal or confined to particular states of society) which operate upon the human mind through that law, we may be enabled to explain and predict this portion of the phenomena of society, so far as they depend on that class of circumstances only, overlooking the influence of any other of the circumstances of society and, therefore, neither tracing back the circumstances which we do take into account to their possible origin in some other facts in the social state nor making allowance for the manner in which any of those other circumstances may interfere with and counteract or modify the effect of the former. A department of science may thus be constructed which has received the name of political economy.

The motive which suggests the separation of this portion of the social phenomena from the rest, and the creation of a distinct branch of science relating to them is—that they do *mainly* depend, at least in the first resort, on one class of circumstances only, and that, even when other circumstances interfere, the ascertainment of the effect due to the one class of circumstances alone is a sufficiently intricate and difficult business to make it expedient to perform it once for all and then allow for the effect of the modifying circumstances; especially as certain fixed combinations of the former are apt to recur often, in conjunction with ever-varying circumstances of the latter class.

. . . .

4. *The empirical laws of the social science*

We have seen that, in most deductive sciences, and among the rest in ethology itself, which is the immediate foundation of the social science, a preliminary work of preparation is performed on the observed facts to fit them for being rapidly and accurately collated (sometimes even for being collated at all) with the conclusions of theory. This preparatory treatment consists in finding general propositions which express concisely what is common to large classes of observed facts, and these are called the empirical laws of the phenomena. We have, therefore, to inquire whether any similar preparatory process can be performed on the facts of the social science; whether there are any empirical laws in history or statistics.

In statistics, it is evident that empirical laws may sometimes be traced, and the tracing them forms an important part of that system of indirect observation on which we must often rely for the data of the deductive science. The process of the science consists in inferring effects from their causes, but we have often no means of observing the causes except through the medium of their effects. In such cases the deductive science is unable to predict the effects for want of the necessary data; it can determine what causes are capable of producing any given effect, but not with what frequency and in what quantities those causes exist. An instance in point is afforded by a newspaper now lying before me. A statement was furnished by one of the official assignees in bankruptcy showing, among the various bankruptcies which it had been his duty to investigate, in how many cases the losses had been caused by misconduct of different kinds, and in how many by unavoidable misfortunes. The result was, that the number of failures caused by misconduct greatly preponderated over those arising from all other causes whatever. Nothing but specific experience could have given sufficient ground for a conclusion to this purport. To collect, therefore, such empirical laws (which are never more than approximate generalizations) from direct observation is an important part of the process of sociological inquiry.

The experimental process is not here to be regarded as a distinct road to the truth, but as a means (happening accidentally to be the only, or the best, available) for obtaining the necessary data for the deductive science. When the immediate causes of social facts are not open to direct observation, the empirical law of the effects gives us the empirical law (which in that case is all that we can obtain) of the causes likewise. But those immediate causes depend on remote causes, and the empirical law, obtained by this indirect mode of observation, can only be relied on as applicable to unobserved cases so long as there is reason to think that no change has taken place in any of the remote causes on which the immediate causes depend. In making use, therefore, of even the best statistical generalizations for the purpose of inferring (though it be only conjecturally) that the same empirical laws will hold in any new case, it is necessary that we be well acquainted with the remoter causes, in order that we may avoid applying the empirical law to cases which differ in any of the circumstances on which the truth of the law ultimately depends. And thus, even where conclusions derived from specific observation are available for practical inferences in new cases, it is necessary that the deductive science should stand sentinel over the whole process, that it should be constantly referred to, and its sanction obtained to every inference.

The same thing holds true of all generalizations which can be grounded on history. Not only there are such generalizations, but it will presently be shown that the general science of society, which inquires into the laws of succession and co-existence of the great facts constituting the state of society and civilization at any time, can proceed in no other manner than by making such generalizations—afterward to be confirmed by connecting them with the psychological and ethological laws on which they must really depend.

. . . .

5. *The verification of the social science*

But (reserving this question for its proper place) in those more special inquiries which form the subject of the separate branches of the social science, this twofold logical process and reciprocal verification is not possible; specific experience affords nothing amounting to empirical laws. This is particularly the case where the object is to determine the effect of any one social cause among a great number acting simultaneously, the effect, for example, of corn laws, or of a prohibitive commercial system generally. Though it may be perfectly certain, from theory, what *kind* of effects corn laws must produce and in what general direction their influence must tell upon industrial prosperity, their effect is yet of necessity so much disguised by the similar or contrary effects of other influencing agents that specific experience can at most only show that, on the average of some great number of instances, the cases where there were corn laws exhibited the effect in a greater degree than those where there were not. Now the number of instances necessary to exhaust the whole round of combinations of the various influential circumstances and thus afford a fair average never can be obtained. Not only we can never learn with sufficient authenticity the facts of so many instances, but the world itself does not afford them in sufficient numbers, within the limits of the given state of society and civilization which such inquiries always presuppose. Having thus no previous empirical generalizations with which to collate the conclusions of theory, the only mode of direct verification which remains is to compare those conclusions with the result of an individual experiment or instance. But here the difficulty is equally great. For in order to verify a theory by an experiment, the circumstances of the experiment must be exactly the same with those contemplated in the theory. But in social phenomena the circumstances of no two cases are exactly alike. A trial of corn laws in another country or in a former generation would go a very little way toward verifying a conclusion drawn respecting their effect in this generation and in this country. It thus happens, in most cases, that the only individual instance really fitted to verify the predictions of theory is the very instance for which the predictions were made, and the verification comes too late to be of any avail for practical guidance.

Although, however, direct verification is impossible, there is an indirect verification, which is scarcely of less value, and which is always practicable. The conclusion drawn as to the individual case can only be directly verified in that case, but it is verified indirectly, by the verification of other conclusions drawn in other individual cases from the same laws. The experience which comes too late to verify the particular proposition to which it refers is not too late to help toward verifying the general sufficiency of the theory. The test of the degree in which the science affords safe ground for predicting (and consequently for practically dealing with) what has not yet happened is the degree in which it would have enabled us to predict what has actually occurred. Before our theory of the influence of a particular cause, in a given state of circumstances, can be entirely trusted, we must be able to explain and account for the existing state of all that portion of the social phenomena which that cause has a tendency to influence. . . .

To prove, in short, that our science and our knowledge of the particular case render us competent to predict the future, we must show that they would have enabled us to predict the present and the past. If there be anything which we could not have predicted, this constitutes a residual phenomenon, requiring further study for the purpose of explanation, and we must either search among the circumstances of the particular case until we find one which, on the principles of our existing theory, accounts for the unexplained phenomenon, or we must turn back and seek the explanation by an extension and improvement of the theory itself.

CHAPTER VIII *

OF THE INVERSE DEDUCTIVE, OR HISTORICAL METHOD

1. *Distinction between the general science of society and special sociological inquiries*

There are two kinds of sociological inquiry. In the first kind, the question proposed is what effect will follow from a given cause, a certain general condition of social circumstances being presupposed. As, for example, what would be the effect of imposing or of repealing corn laws, of abolishing monarchy or introducing universal suffrage, in the present condition of society and civilization in any European country, or under any other given supposition with regard to the circumstances of society in general, without reference to the changes which might take place, or which may already be in progress, in those circumstances. But there is also a second inquiry, namely, what are the laws which determine those general circumstances themselves. In this last the question is not what will be the effect of a given cause in a certain state of society, but what are the causes which produce and the phenomena which characterize states of society generally. In the solution of this question consists the general science of society, by which the conclusions of the other and more special kind of inquiry must be limited and controlled.

2. *What is meant by a state of society?*

In order to conceive correctly the scope of this general science and distinguish it from the subordinate departments of sociological speculation, it is necessary to fix the ideas attached to the phrase, "A State of Society." What is called a state of society is the simultaneous state of all the greater social facts or phenomena. Such are: the degree of knowledge and of intellectual and moral culture existing in the community and in every class of it; the state of industry, of wealth and its distribution; the habitual occupations of the community; their division into classes and the relations of those classes to one another; the common beliefs which they entertain on all the subjects most important to mankind, and the degree of assurance with which those beliefs are held; their tastes, and the character and degree of their aesthetic development; their form of government, and the more important of their laws and customs. The condition of all these things and of many more which will readily suggest themselves constitute the state of society or the state of civilization at any given time.

* [Chapter X of the eighth edition.]

When states of society and the causes which produce them are spoken of as a subject of science, it is implied that there exists a natural correlation among these different elements, that not every variety of combination of these general social facts is possible, but only certain combinations, that, in short, there exist uniformities of co-existence between the states of the various social phenomena. And such is the truth; as is indeed a necessary consequence of the influence exercised by every one of those phenomena over every other. It is a fact implied in the *consensus* of the various parts of the social body.

States of society are like different constitutions or different ages in the physical frame; they are conditions not of one or a few organs or functions, but of the whole organism. Accordingly, the information which we possess respecting past ages and respecting the various states of society now existing in different regions of the earth does, when duly analyzed, exhibit uniformities. It is found that when one of the features of society is in a particular state, a state of many other features, more or less precisely determinate, always or usually co-exists with it.

But the uniformities of co-existence obtaining among phenomena which are effects of causes must (as we have so often observed) be corollaries from the laws of causation by which these phenomena are really determined. The mutual correlation between the different elements of each state of society is, therefore, a derivative law, resulting from the laws which regulate the succession between one state of society and another, for the proximate cause of every state of society is the state of society immediately preceding it. The fundamental problem, therefore, of the social science is to find the laws according to which any state of society produces the state which succeeds it and takes its place. This opens the great and vexed question of the progressiveness of man and society, an idea involved in every just conception of social phenomena as the subject of a science.

3. *The progressiveness of man and society*

It is one of the characters, not absolutely peculiar to the sciences of human nature and society, but belonging to them in a peculiar degree, to be conversant with a subject matter whose properties are changeable. I do not mean changeable from day to day, but from age to age, so that not only the qualities of individuals vary, but those of the majority are not the same in one age as in another.

The principal cause of this peculiarity is the extensive and constant reaction of the effects upon their causes. The circumstances in which mankind are placed, operating according to their own laws and to the laws of human nature, form the characters of the human beings, but the human beings, in their turn, mold and shape the circumstances for themselves and for those who come after them. From this reciprocal action there must necessarily result either a cycle or a progress. . . .

.   .   .   .

7. *Outlines of the historical method*

In order to obtain better empirical laws, we must not rest satisfied with noting the progressive changes which manifest themselves in the separate elements of society and in which nothing is indicated but the relation of fragments of the effect to corresponding fragments of the cause. It is necessary to combine the statical view of social phenomena with the dynamical, considering not only the progressive changes of the different elements, but the contemporaneous condition of each, and thus obtain empirically the law of correspondence not only between the simultaneous states, but between the simultaneous changes, of those elements. This law of correspondence it is which, duly verified *a priori*, would become the real scientific derivative law of the development of humanity and human affairs.

In the difficult process of observation and comparison which is here required, it would evidently be a great assistance if it should happen to be the fact that some one element in the complex existence of social man is pre-eminent over all others as the prime agent of the social movement. For we could then take the progress of that one element as the central chain, to each successive link of which the corresponding links of all the other progressions being appended, the succession of the facts would by this alone be presented in a kind of spontaneous order, far more nearly approaching to the real order of their filiation than could be obtained by any other merely empirical process.

Now, the evidence of history and that of human nature combine, by a striking instance of consilience, to show that there really is one social element which is thus predominant and almost paramount among the agents of the social progression. This is the state of the speculative faculties of mankind, including the nature of the beliefs which by any means they have arrived at concerning themselves and the world by which they are surrounded.

It would be a great error, and one very little likely to be committed, to assert that speculation, intellectual activity, the pursuit of truth, is among the more powerful propensities of human nature, or holds a predominating place in the lives of any save decidedly exceptional individuals. But, notwithstanding the relative weakness of this principle among other sociological agents, its influence is the main determining cause of the social progress, all the other dispositions of our nature which contribute to that progress being dependent on it for the means of accomplishing their share of the work. Thus (to take the most obvious case first), the impelling force to most of the improvements effected in the arts of life is the desire of increased material comfort; but, as we can only act upon external objects in proportion to our knowledge of them, the state of knowledge at any time is the limit of the industrial improvements possible at that time, and the progress of industry must follow and depend on the progress of knowledge. The same thing may be shown to be true, though it is not quite so obvious, of the progress of the fine arts. Further, as the strongest propensities of uncultivated or half-cultivated human nature (being the purely selfish ones, and those of a sympathetic character which partake most of the nature of selfishness) evidently tend in themselves to disunite mankind, not to unite them—to make them rivals, not confederates—social existence is only possible by a disciplining of those more powerful propensities, which consists in subordinating them to a common system of opinions. The degree of this subordination is the measure of the completeness of the social union, and the nature of the common opinions determines its kind. But in order that mankind should conform their actions to any set of opinions, these opinions must exist, must be believed by them. And thus, the state of the speculative faculties, the character of the propositions assented to by the intellect, essentially determines the moral and political state of the community, as we have already seen that it determines the physical.

These conclusions, deduced from the laws of human nature, are in entire accordance with the general facts of history. Every considerable change historically known to us in the condition of any portion of mankind, when not brought about by external force, has been preceded by a change, of proportional extent, in the state of their knowledge or in their prevalent beliefs. As between any given state of speculation and the correlative state of everything else, it was almost always the former which first showed itself, though the effects, no doubt, reacted potently upon the cause. Every considerable advance in material civilization has been preceded by an advance in knowledge; and when any great social change has come to pass, either in the way of gradual development or of sudden conflict, it has had for its precursor a great change in the opinions and modes of thinking of society. Polytheism, Judaism, Christianity, Protestantism, the critical philosophy of modern Europe, and its positive science —each of these has been a primary agent in making society what it was at each successive period while society was but secondarily instrumental in making *them,* each of them (so far as causes can be assigned for its existence) being mainly an emanation not from the practical life of the period but from the previous state of belief and thought. The weakness of the speculative propensity in mankind generally has not, therefore, prevented the progress of speculation from governing that of society at large; it has only, and too often, prevented progress altogether, where the intellectual progression has come to an early stand for want of sufficiently favorable circumstances.

From this accumulated evidence, we are justified in concluding that the order of human progression in all respects will mainly depend on the order of progression in the intellectual convictions of mankind, that is, on the law of the successive transformations of human opinions. The question remains whether this law can be determined, at first, from history as an empirical law, then, converted into a scientific theorem by deducing it *a priori,* from the principles of human nature. As the progress of knowledge and the changes in the opinions of mankind are very slow and manifest themselves in a well-defined manner only at long intervals, it cannot be expected that the general order of sequence should be discoverable from the examination of less than a very considerable part of the duration of the social progress. It is necessary to take into consideration the whole of past time, from the first recorded condition of the human race to the memorable phenomena of the last and present generations.

CHAPTER IX *

OF THE LOGIC OF PRACTICE, OR ART; INCLUDING MORALITY AND POLICY

1. *Morality not a science but an art*

In the preceding chapters we have endeavored to characterize the present state of those among the branches of knowledge called "moral" which are sciences in the only proper sense of the term, that is, inquiries into the course of nature. It is customary, however, to include under the term moral knowledge and even (though improperly) under that of moral science an inquiry the results of which do not express themselves in the indicative but in the imperative mood, or in periphrases equivalent to it; what is called the knowledge of duties: practical ethics, or morality.

Now, the imperative mood is the characteristic of art, as distinguished from science. Whatever speaks in rules or precepts, not in assertions respecting matters of fact, is art; and ethics, or morality, is properly a portion of the art corresponding to the sciences of human nature and society.[1]

The method, therefore, of ethics can be no other than that of art, or practice, in general; and the portion yet uncompleted of the task which we proposed to ourselves in the concluding Book is to characterize the general method of art, as distinguished from science.

2. *Relation between rules of art and the theorems of the corresponding science*

. . . .

The relation in which rules of art stand to doctrines of science may be thus characterized: The art proposes to itself an end to be attained, defines the end, and hands it over to the science. The science receives it, considers it as a phenomenon or effect to be studied, and, having investigated its causes and conditions, sends it back to art with a theorem of the combination of circumstances by which it could be produced. Art then examines these combinations of circumstances and, according as any of them are or are not in human power, pronounces the end attainable or not. The only one of the premises, therefore, which art supplies is the original major premise, which asserts that the attainment of the given end

* [Chapter XII of the eighth edition.]

is desirable. Science then lends to art the proposition (obtained by a series of inductions or of deductions) that the performance of certain actions will attain the end. From these premises art concludes that the performance of these actions is desirable, and finding it also practicable, converts the theorems into a rule or precept.

3. *Art cannot be deductive*

The error is, therefore, apparent of those who would deduce the line of conduct proper to particular cases from supposed universal practical maxims, overlooking the necessity of constantly referring back to the principles of the speculative science in order to be sure of attaining even the specific end which the rules have in view. How much greater still, then, must the error be of setting up such unbending principles not merely as universal rules for attaining a given end, but as rules of conduct generally, without regard to the possibility not only that some modifying cause may prevent the attainment of the given end by the means which the rule prescribes, but that success itself may conflict with some other end which may possibly chance to be more desirable.

.   .   .   .

4. *Every art consists of truths of science, arranged in the order suitable for some practical use*

The grounds, then, of every rule of art are to be found in the theorems of science. An art or a body of art consists of the rules, together with as much of the speculative propositions as comprises the justification of those rules. The complete art of any matter includes a selection of such a proportion from the science as is necessary to show on what conditions the effects which the art aims at producing depend. And art in general consists of the truths of science, arranged in the most convenient order for practice instead of the order which is the most convenient for thought. Science groups and arranges its truths so as to enable us to take in at one view as much as possible of the general order of the universe. Art, though it must assume the same general laws, follows them only into such of their detailed consequences as have led to the formation of rules of conduct, and brings together from parts of the field on science most remote from one another the truths relating to the production of the different and heterogeneous conditions necessary to each effect which the exigencies of practical life require to be produced.

.   .   .   .

5. *Teleology, or the doctrine of ends*

But though the reasonings which connect the end or purpose of every art with its means belong to the domain of science, the definition of the end itself belongs exclusively to art and forms its peculiar province. Every art has one first principle or general major premise not borrowed from science, that which enunciates the object aimed at and affirms it to be a desirable object. The builder's art assumes that it is desirable to have buildings; architecture, as one of the fine arts, that it is desirable to have them beautiful or imposing. The hygienic and medical arts assume, the one that the preservation of health, the other that the cure of disease, are fitting and desirable ends. These are not propositions of science. Propositions of science assert a matter of fact: an existence, a co-existence, a succession, or a resemblance. The propositions now spoken of do not assert that anything is, but enjoin or recommend that something should be. They are a class by themselves. A proposition of which the predicate is expressed by the words *ought* or *should be* is generically different from one which is expressed by *is* or *will be*. It is true that, in the largest sense of the words, even these propositions assert something as a matter of fact. The fact affirmed in them is that the conduct recommended excites in the speaker's mind the feeling of approbation. This, however, does not go to the bottom of the matter; for the speaker's approbation is no sufficient reason why other people should approve, nor ought it to be a conclusive reason even with himself. For the purpose of practice, everyone must be required to justify his approbation; and for this there is need of general premises determining what are the proper objects of approbation and what the proper order of precedence among those objects.

These general premises, together with the principal conclusions which may be deduced from them, form (or rather might form) a body of doctrine which is properly the art of life, in its three departments, morality, prudence or policy, and aesthetics—the right, the expedient, and the beautiful or noble, in human conduct and works. To this art (which, in the main, is unfortunately still to be created) all other arts are subordinate, since its principles are those which must determine whether the special aim of any particular art is worthy and desirable and what is its place in the scale of desirable things. Every art is thus a joint result of laws of nature disclosed by science and of the general principles of what has been called teleology, or the doctrine of ends,[2] which, borrowing the language of the German metaphysicians, may also be termed, not improperly, the principles of practical reason.

A scientific observer or reasoner, merely as such, is not an adviser for practice. His part is only to show that certain consequences follow from certain causes and that, to obtain certain ends, certain means are the most effectual. Whether the ends themselves are such as ought to be pursued, and if so, in what cases and to how great a length it is no part of his business as a cultivator of science to decide, and science alone will never qualify him for the decision. In purely physical science, there is not much temptation to assume this ulterior office, but those who treat of human nature and society invariably claim it; they always undertake to say not merely what is, but what ought to be. To entitle them to do this, a complete doctrine of teleology is indispensable. A scientific theory, however perfect, of the subject matter considered merely as part of the order of nature, can in no degree serve as a substitute. In this respect the various subordinate arts afford a misleading analogy. In them there is seldom any visible necessity for justifying the end, since in general its desirableness is denied by nobody, and it is only when the question of precedence is to be decided between that end and some other that the general principles of teleology have to be called in; but a writer on morals and politics requires those principles at every step. The most elaborate and well-digested exposition of the laws of succession and co-existence among mental or social phenomena and of their relation to one another as causes and effects will be of no avail toward the art of life or of society, if the ends to be aimed at by that art are left to the vague suggestions of the *intellectus sibi permissus*, or are taken for granted without analysis or questioning.

6. *Necessity of an ultimate standard, or first principle of teleology*

There is, then, a *philosophia prima* peculiar to art as there is one which belongs to science. There are not only first principles of knowledge, but first principles of conduct. There must be some standard by which to determine the goodness or badness, absolute and comparative, of ends or objects of desire. And whatever that standard is, there can be but one; for, if there were several ultimate principles of conduct, the same conduct might be approved by one of those principles and condemned by another, and there would be needed some more general principle as umpire between them.

Accordingly, writers on moral philosophy have mostly felt the necessity not only of referring all rules of conduct and all judgments of praise and blame to principles, but of referring them to some one principle, some rule or standard with which all other rules of conduct were required to be consistent, and from which by ultimate consequence they could all be deduced. Those who have dispensed with the assumption of such a universal standard have only been enabled to do so by supposing that a moral sense or instinct, inherent in our constitution, informs us both what principles of conduct we are bound to observe and also in what order these should be subordinated to one another.

The theory of the foundations of morality is a subject which it would be out of place, in a work like this, to discuss at large, and which could not to any useful purpose be treated incidentally. I shall content myself, therefore, with saying that the doctrine of intuitive moral principles, even if true, would provide only for that portion of the field of conduct which is properly called moral. For the remainder of the practice of life some general principle or standard must still be sought, and if that principle be rightly chosen, it will be found, I apprehend, to serve quite as well for the ultimate principle of morality, as for that of prudence, policy, or taste.

Without attempting in this place to justify my opinion or even to define the kind of justification which it admits of, I merely declare my conviction that the general principle to which all rules of practice ought to conform and the test by which they should be tried is that of conduciveness to the happiness of mankind, or, rather, of all sentient beings; in other words, that the promotion of happiness is the ultimate principle of teleology.†

I do not mean to assert that the promotion of happiness should be itself the end of all actions or even of all rules of action. It is the justification and ought to be the controller of all ends, but it is not itself the sole end. There are many virtuous actions and even virtuous modes of action (though the cases are, I think, less frequent than is often supposed) by which happiness in the particular instance is sacrificed, more pain being produced than pleasure. But conduct of which this can be truly asserted admits of justification only because it can be shown that, on the whole, more happiness will exist in the world if feelings are cultivated which will make people, in certain cases, regardless of happiness. I fully admit that this is true, that the cultivation of an ideal nobleness of will and conduct should be to individual human beings an end to which the specific pursuit either of their own happiness or of that of others (except so far as included in that idea) should, in any case of conflict, give way. But I hold that the very question what constitutes this elevation of character is itself to be decided by a reference to happiness as the standard. The character itself should be, to the individual, a paramount end, simply because the existence of this ideal nobleness of character or of a near approach to it, in any abundance, would go farther than all things else toward making human life happy, both in the comparatively humble sense of pleasure and freedom from pain, and in the higher meaning of rendering life not what it now is almost universally, puerile and insignificant, but such as human beings with highly developed faculties can care to have.

[25]

JOHN DEWEY

Does Human Nature Change? *

I have come to the conclusion that those who give different answers to the question I have asked in the title of this article are talking about different things. This statement in itself, however, is too easy a way out of the problem to be satisfactory. For there is a real problem, and so far as the question is a practical one instead of an academic one, I think the proper answer is that human nature *does* change.

† For an express discussion and vindication of this principle, see the little volume entitled "Utilitarianism." [Reprinted in the "Little Library of Liberal Arts."]

* From *The Rotarian Magazine.* Vol. LII, no. 2, Feb. 1946, pp. 8 ff. By permission of the publisher.

By the practical side of the question, I mean the question whether or not important, almost fundamental, changes in the ways of human belief and action have taken place and are capable of still taking place. But to put this question in its proper perspective, we have first to recognize the sense in which human nature does not change. I do not think it can be shown that the innate needs of men have changed since man became man or that there is any evidence that they will change as long as man is on the earth.

By "needs" I mean the inherent demands that men make because of their constitution. Needs for food and drink and for moving about, for example, are so much a part of our being that we cannot imagine any condition under which they would cease to be. There are other things not so directly physical that seem to me equally engrained in human nature. I would mention as examples the need for some kind of companionship; the need for exhibiting energy, for bringing one's powers to bear upon surrounding conditions; the need for both coöperation with and emulation of one's fellows for mutual aid and combat alike; the need for some sort of aesthetic expression and satisfaction; the need to lead and to follow, etc.

Whether my particular examples are well chosen or not does not matter so much as does recognition of the fact that there are some tendencies so integral a part of human nature that the latter would not be human nature if they changed. These tendencies used to be called instincts. Psychologists are now more chary of using that word than they used to be. But the word by which the tendencies are called does not matter much in comparison to the fact that human nature has its own constitution.

Where we are likely to go wrong, after the fact is recognized that there is something unchangeable in the structure of human nature, is the inference we draw from it. We suppose that the manifestation of these needs is also unalterable. We suppose that the manifestations we have got used to are as natural and as unalterable as are the needs from which they spring.

The need for food is so imperative that we call the persons insane who persistently refuse to take nourishment. But what kinds of food are wanted and used are a matter of acquired habit influenced by both physical environment and social custom. To civilized people today, eating human flesh is an entirely unnatural thing. Yet there have been peoples to whom it seemed natural because it was socially authorized and even highly esteemed. There are well-accredited stories of persons needing support from others who have refused palatable and nourishing foods because they were not accustomed to them; the alien foods were so "unnatural" they preferred to starve rather than eat them.

Aristotle spoke for an entire social order as well as for himself when he said that slavery existed by nature. He would have regarded efforts to abolish slavery from society as an idle and utopian effort to change human nature where it was unchangeable. For according to him it was not simply the desire to be a master that was engrained in human nature. There were persons who were born with such an inherently slavish nature that it did violence to human nature to set them free.

The assertion that human nature cannot be changed is heard when social changes are urged as reforms and improvements of existing conditions. It is always heard when the proposed changes in institutions or conditions stand in sharp opposition to what exists. If the conservative were wiser, he would rest his objections in most cases, not upon the unchangeability of human nature, but upon the inertia of custom; upon the resistance that acquired habits offer to change after they are once acquired. It is hard to teach an old dog new tricks and it is harder yet to teach society to adopt customs which are contrary to those which have long prevailed. Conservatism of this type would be intelligent, and it would compel those wanting change not only to moderate their pace, but also to ask how the changes they desire could be introduced with a minimum of shock and dislocation.

Nevertheless, there are few social changes that can be opposed on the ground that they are contrary to human nature itself. A proposal to have a society get along without food and drink is one of the few that are of this kind. Proposals to form communities in which there is no cohabitation have been made and the communities have endured for a time. But they are so nearly contrary to human nature that they have not endured long. These cases are almost the only ones in which social change can be opposed simply on the ground that human nature cannot be changed.

Take the institution of war, one of the oldest, most socially reputable of all human institutions. Efforts for stable peace are often opposed on the ground that man is by nature a fighting animal and that this phase of his nature is unalterable. The failure of peace movements in the past can be cited in support of this view. In fact, however, war is as much a social pattern as is the domestic slavery which the ancients thought to be an immutable fact.

I have already said that, in my opinion, combativeness is a constituent part of human nature. But I have also said that the manifestations of these native elements are subject to change because they are affected by custom and tradition. War does not exist because man has combative instincts, but because social conditions and forces have led, almost forced, these "instincts" into this channel.

There are a large number of other channels in which the need for combat has been satisfied, and there are other channels not yet discovered or explored into which it could be led with equal satisfaction. There is war against disease, against poverty, against insecurity, against injustice, in which multitudes of persons have found full opportunity for the exercise of their combative tendencies.

The time may be far off when men will cease to fulfill their need for combat by destroying each other and when they will manifest it in common and combined efforts against the forces that are enemies of all men equally. But the difficulties in the way are found in the persistence of certain ac-

quired social customs and not in the unchangeability of the demand for
combat.

Pugnacity and fear are native elements of human nature. But so are
pity and sympathy. We send nurses and physicians to the battlefield and
provide hospital facilities as "naturally" as we change bayonets and discharge machine guns. In early times there was a close connection between
pugnacity and fighting, for the latter was done largely with the fists.
Pugnacity plays a small part in generating wars today. Citizens of one
country do not hate those of another nation by instinct. When they attack
or are attacked, they do not use their fists in close combat, but throw
shells from a great distance at persons whom they have never seen. In
modern wars, anger and hatred come after the war has started; they are
effects of war, not the cause of it.

It is a tough job sustaining a modern war; all the emotional reactions
have to be excited. Propaganda and atrocity stories are enlisted. Aside
from such extreme measures there has to be definite organization, as we
saw in the two World Wars, to keep up the morale of even non-combatants.
And morale is largely a matter of keeping emotions at a certain pitch; and
unfortunately fear, hatred, suspicion, are among the emotions most easily
aroused.

I shall not attempt to dogmatize about the causes of modern wars. But
I do not think that anyone will deny that they are social rather than psychological, though psychological appeal is highly important in working up
a people to the point where they want to fight and in keeping them at it.
I do not think, moreover, that anyone will deny that economic conditions
are powerful among the social causes of war. The main point, however, is
that whatever the sociological causes, they are affairs of tradition, custom,
and institutional organization, and these factors belong among the changeable manifestations of human nature, not among the unchangeable elements.

I have used the case of war as a typical instance of what is changeable
and what is unchangeable in human nature, in their relation to schemes of
social change. I have selected the case because it is an extremely difficult
one in which to effect durable changes, not because it is an easy one. The
point is that the obstacles in the way are put there by social forces which
do change from time to time, not by fixed elements of human nature. This
fact is also illustrated in the failures of pacifists to achieve their ends by
appeal simply to sympathy and pity. For while, as I have said, the kindly
emotions are also a fixed constitutent of human nature, the channel they
take is dependent upon social conditions.

There is always a great outburst of these kindly emotions in time of
war. Fellow feeling and the desire to help those in need are intense during
war, as they are at every period of great disaster that comes home to
observation or imagination. But they are canalized in their expression;
they are confined to those upon our side. They occur simultaneously with
manifestation of rage and fear against the other side, if not always in the

same person, at least in the community generally. Hence the ultimate failure of pacifist appeals to the kindly elements of native human nature when they are separated from intelligent consideration of the social and economic forces at work.

William James made a great contribution in the title of one of his essays, *The Moral Equivalents of War*. The very title conveys the point I am making. Certain basic needs and emotions are permanent. But they are capable of finding expression in ways that are radically different from the ways in which they now currently operate.

An even more burning issue emerges when any fundamental change in economic institutions and relations is proposed. Proposals for such sweeping change are among the commonplaces of our time. On the other hand, the proposals are met by the statement that the changes are impossible because they involve an impossible change in human nature. To this statement, advocates of the desired changes are only too likely to reply that the present system or some phase of it is contrary to human nature. The argument *pro* and *con* then gets put on the wrong ground.

As a matter of fact, economic institutions and relations are among the manifestations of human nature that are most susceptible of change. History is living evidence of the scope of these changes. Aristotle, for example, held that paying interest is unnatural, and the Middle Ages reëchoed the doctrine. All interest was usury, and it was only after economic conditions had so changed that payment of interest was a customary and in that sense a "natural" thing, that usury got its present meaning.

There have been times and places in which land was held in common and in which private ownership of land would have been regarded as the most monstrous of unnatural things. There have been other times and places when all wealth was possessed by an overlord and his subjects held wealth, if any, subject to his pleasure. The entire system of credit so fundamental in contemporary financial and industrial life is a modern invention. The invention of the joint stock company with limited liability of individuals has brought about a great change from earlier facts and conceptions of property. I think the need of owning something is one of the native elements of human nature. But it takes either ignorance or a very lively fancy to suppose that the system of ownership that exists in the United States in 1946, with all its complex relations and its interweaving with legal and political supports, is a necessary and unchangeable product of an inherent tendency to appropriate and possess.

Law is one of the most conservative of human institutions; yet through the cumulative effect of legislation and judicial decisions it changes, sometimes at a slow rate, sometimes rapidly. The changes in human relations that are brought about by changes in industrial and legal institutions then react to modify the ways in which human nature manifests itself, and this brings about still further changes in institutions, and so on indefinitely.

It is for these reasons that I say that those who hold that proposals for social change, even of rather a profound character, are impossible and utopian because of the fixity of human nature confuse the resistance to change that comes from acquired habits with that which comes from original human nature. The savage, living in a primitive society, comes nearer to being a purely "natural" human being than does civilized man. Civilization itself is the product of altered human nature. But even the savage is bound by a mass of tribal customs and transmitted beliefs that modify his original nature, and it is these acquired habits that make it so difficult to transform him into a civilized human being.

The revolutionary radical, on the other hand, overlooks the force of engrained habits. He is right, in my opinion, about the indefinite plasticity of human nature. But he is wrong in thinking that patterns of desire, belief, and purpose do not have a force comparable to the momentum of physical objects once they are set in motion, and comparable to the inertia, the resistance to movement, possessed by these same objects when they are at rest. Habit, not original human nature, keeps things moving most of the time, about as they have moved in the past.

If human nature is unchangeable, then there is no such thing as education and all our efforts to educate are doomed to failure. For the very meaning of education is modification of native human nature in formation of those new ways of thinking, of feeling, of desiring, and of believing that are foreign to raw human nature. If the latter were unalterable, we might have training but not education. For training, as distinct from education, means simply the acquisition of certain skills. Native gifts can be trained to a point of higher efficiency without that development of new attitudes and dispositions which is the goal of education. But the result is mechanical. It is like supposing that while a musician may require by practice greater technical ability, he cannot rise from one plane of musical appreciation and creation to another.

The theory that human nature is unchangeable is thus the most depressing and pessimistic of all possible doctrines. If it were carried out logically, it would mean a doctrine of predestination from birth that would outdo the most rigid of theological doctrines. For according to it, persons are what they are at birth and nothing can be done about it, beyond the kind of training that an acrobat might give to the muscular system with which he is originally endowed. If a person is born with criminal tendencies, a criminal he will become and remain. If a person is born with an excessive amount of greed, he will become a person living by predatory activities at the expense of others; and so on. I do not doubt at all the existence of differences in natural endowment. But what I am questioning is the notion that they doom individuals to a fixed channel of expression. It is difficult indeed to make a silk purse out of a sow's ear. But the particular form which, say, a natural musical endowment will take depends upon the social influences to which he is subjected. Beethoven in a savage tribe would doubtless have been outstanding as a musician, but he would not have been the Beethoven who composed symphonies.

The existence of almost every conceivable kind of social institution at some time and place in the history of the world is evidence of the plasticity of human nature. This fact does not prove that all these different social systems are of equal value, materially, morally, and culturally. The slightest observation shows that such is not the case. But the fact in proving the changeability of human nature indicates the attitude that should be taken toward proposals for social changes. The question is primarily whether they, in special cases, are desirable or not. And the way to answer that question is to try to discover what their consequences would be if they were adopted. Then if the conclusion is that they are desirable, the further question is how they can be accomplished with a minimum of waste, destruction, and needless dislocation.

In finding the answer to this question, we have to take into account the force of existing traditions and customs; of the patterns of action and belief that already exist. We have to find out what forces already at work can be reinforced so that they move toward the desired change and how the conditions that oppose change can be gradually weakened. Such questions as these can be considered on the basis of fact and reason.

The assertion that a proposed change is impossible because of the fixed constitution of human nature diverts attention from the question of whether or not a change is desirable and from the other question of how it shall be brought about. It throws the question into the arena of blind emotion and brute force. In the end, it encourages those who think that great changes can be produced offhand and by the use of sheer violence.

When our sciences of human nature and human relations are anything like as developed as are our sciences of physical nature, their chief concern will be with the problem of how human nature is most effectively modified. The question will not be whether it is capable of change, but of how it is to be changed under given conditions. This problem is ultimately that of education in its widest sense. Consequently, whatever represses and distorts the processes of education that might bring about a change in human dispositions with the minimum of waste puts a premium upon the forces that bring society to a state of deadlock, and thereby encourages the use of violence as a means of social change.

[26a]

OLIVER WENDELL HOLMES, JR.

Life of the Law *

The object of this book is to present a general view of the Common Law. To accomplish the task, other tools are needed besides logic. It is something to show that the consistency of a system requires a particular

* From *The Common Law* (1881), Ch. I, pp. 1-3, 35-37.

result, but it is not all. The life of the law has not been logic; it has been experience. The felt necessities of the time, the prevalent moral and political theories, intuitions of public policy, avowed or unconscious, even the prejudices which judges share with their fellow-men, have had a good deal more to do than the syllogism in determining the rules by which men should be governed. The law embodies the story of a nation's development through many centuries, and it cannot be dealt with as if it contained only the axioms and corollaries of a book of mathematics. In order to know what it is, we must know what it has been, and what it tends to become. We must alternately consult history and existing theories of legislation. But the most difficult labor will be to understand the combination of the two into new products at every stage. The substance of the law at any given time pretty nearly corresponds, so far as it goes, with what is then understood to be convenient; but its form and machinery, and the degree to which it is able to work out desired results, depend very much upon its past.

.   .   .   .

I shall use the history of our law so far as it is necessary to explain a conception or to interpret a rule, but no further. In doing so there are two errors equally to be avoided both by writer and reader. One is that of supposing, because an idea seems very familiar and natural to us, that it has always been so. Many things which we take for granted have had to be laboriously fought out or thought out in past times. The other mistake is the opposite one of asking too much of history. We start with man full grown. It may be assumed that the earliest barbarian whose practices are to be considered, had a good many of the same feelings and passions as ourselves.

.   .   .   .

It is commonly known that the early forms of legal procedure were grounded in vengeance. Modern writers have thought that the Roman law started from the blood feud, and all the authorities agree that the German law began in that way. The feud led to the composition, at first optional, then compulsory, by which the feud was bought off. The gradual encroachment of the composition may be traced in the Anglo-Saxon laws (e.g., Ine, c. 74; Alfred, c. 42; Ethelred, IV. 4, sec. 1), and the feud was pretty well broken up, though not extinguished, by the time of William the Conqueror. The killings and house-burnings of an earlier day became the appeals of mayhem and arson. The appeals *de pace et plagis* and of mayhem became, or rather were in substance, the action of trespass which is still familiar to lawyers (cf. Bracton, fol. 144, 145; Fleta, I. c. 40, 41; Co. Lit. 126 b; Hawkins, P.C., Bk. 2, ch. 23, sec. 15). . . .

.   .   .   .

The foregoing history, apart from the purposes for which it has been given, well illustrates the paradox of form and substance in the development of law. In form its growth is logical. The official theory is that each new decision follows syllogistically from existing precedents. But just as, the clavicle in the cat only tells of the existence of some earlier creature to which a collar-bone was useful, precedents survive in the law long after the use they once served is at an end and the reason for them has been forgotten. The result of following them must often be failure and confusion from the merely logical point of view.

On the other hand, in substance the growth of the law is legislative. And this in a deeper sense than what the courts declare to have always been the law is in fact new. It is legislative in its grounds. The very considerations which judges most rarely mention, and always with an apology, are the secret root from which the law derives all the juices of life. I mean, of course, considerations of what is expedient for the community concerned. Every important principle which is developed by litigation is in fact and at bottom the result of more or less definitely understood views of public policy; most generally, to be sure, under our practice and traditions, the unconscious result of instinctive preferences and inarticulate convictions, but none the less traceable to views of public policy in the last analysis. And as the law is administered by able and experienced men, who know too much to sacrifice good sense to a syllogism, it will be found out that, when ancient rules maintain themselves in the way that has been and will be shown in this book, new reasons more fitted to the time have been found for them, and that they gradually receive a new content, and at last a new form, from the grounds to which they have been transplanted.

But hitherto this process has been largely unconscious. It is important, on that account, to bring to mind what the actual course of events has been. If it were only to insist on a more conscious recognition of the legislative function of the courts, as just explained, it would be useful, as we shall see further on.

What has been said will explain the failure of all theories which consider the law only from its formal side, whether they attempt to deduce the *corpus* from *a priori* postulates, or fall into the humbler error of supposing the science of the law to reside in the *elegantia juris,* or *logical* cohesion of part with part. The truth is, that the law is always approaching, and never reaching consistency. It is forever adopting new principles from life at one end, and it always retains old ones from history at the other, which have not yet been absorbed or sloughed off. It will become entirely consistent only when it ceases to grow.

The study upon which we have been engaged is necessary both for the knowledge and for the revision of the law.

However much we may codify the law into a series of seemingly self-sufficient propositions, those propositions will be but a phase in a continuous growth. To understand their scope fully, to know how they will be dealt with by judges trained in the past which the law embodies, we must ourselves know something of that past. The history of what the law has been is necessary to the knowledge of what the law is.

[26b]

MORRIS RAPHAEL COHEN

The Place of Logic in the Law [1]

It is a curious fact that while critics and reformers of the law used to take their stand on self-evident truths, and eternal principles of justice and reason, their appeal now is predominantly to vital needs, social welfare, the real or practical need of the times, etc. Those who believe law to be not an isolated island *in vacuo* but a province of the life we call civilization, occupying similar soil and subject to the same change of intellectual season as the other provinces, will see in the fact noted above but an indication of the general passing out of fashion of the old rationalism or intellectualism.

The seed of the protest against the over-emphasis of the logical element in the law was planted by Von Jhering and Justice Holmes over a generation ago.[2] But legal science in this country was then so far behind that of Germany that the logical elaboration and systematization of the law embodied in the work of Langdell and Ames proved the more pressing need and obtained the right of way. There are many indications that the forces of anti-intellectualism are now rising in American legal thought, and they are sure to find powerful support in the public impatience with legal technicalities.

Imitators or followers seldom possess the manysided catholicity of the pioneer or master. Thus Jhering and Holmes, while emphasizing other factors, by no means, deny all importance to legal logic. A large part of Jhering's *Geist* is devoted to a logical analysis of the method and general ideas of the law; [3] Justice Holmes is careful to emphasize the function of general ideas in the development of the law (*e.g.*, the idea of identity in succession after death and *inter vivos*), and his book abounds in illustrations of how difficult legal problems can be cleared up by just logical analyses.[4] But the new, more zealous crusaders against legal ideology are less cautious, and are inclined to deny all value to logic and general principles.[5] Now it is a rather simple task to show the inadequacies of the proposed substitutes for the traditional principles of legal science. Sound common sense, the lessons of experience, the unspoiled sense of justice, the teachings of the as-yet-to-be-established science of sociology, or the some-what elusive and perhaps altogether mythical will of the dominant class, cannot, without the aid of a logical legal technique, help us elaborate the laws of gifts, sales, mortgages, or determine the precise liability of a rail-road company to those who use its sleeping-car service. It is also easy enough to refute these new crusaders out of their own mouths and show that they themselves attach great value to a clear and logically consistent elaboration of the law.[6] But such easy refutations, while they may be just, are seldom illuminating, unless we examine the situation with some thoroughness. This may lead us into the supposedly foreign fields of logic and metaphysics. But at the time when the foundations of our legal system are questioned both inside and outside of the legal fraternity, it would be only the wisdom of the ostrich which would counsel us to refrain from entering into these fields because, forsooth, the old tradition says that law is law, and has nothing to do with any other field of human inquiry. It may be reassuring to orthodox legal scholarship to note that the foremost representatives of the exact and natural sciences have now outgrown the childish fear of metaphysics as the intellectual bogey—witness the writings of Russell, Poincaré, Duhem, Ostwald, and Driesch.

I

A suggestive parallel can be drawn between the functions of the law and of natural science. Both facilitate transactions by increasing our reli-ance on the future. We build our modern houses, bridges, and machinery because science makes us more certain that these structures will withstand the variations of pressure, etc. We enter into business because we expect that people will continue to desire certain commodities, and we count on the state to continue to protect us against robbery. We sell on credit not only because we expect that most people will be moved (by habit or con-science) to pay, but also because the law provides us with a machinery for collecting what is due. If our debtors also know that this machinery exists, they will pay more readily and the expense of using this legal machinery will be accordingly reduced. That the law should be readily knowable is, thus, essential to its usefulness. So far is this true that there are many in-conveniences or injustices in the law that men would rather suffer than be paralyzed in their action by uncertainty. Primitive law, i.e., all legal sys-tems uninfluenced by Greek science, try to achieve this certainty by fixed rules or dooms enumerating specific actions and their consequences, just as they store up wisdom in isolated saws or proverbs. Clearly the multi-tudinous and complicated relations of modern life could not possibly be regulated by such a method. Like the classical Romans, we utilize instead that most wonderful discovery, or invention, of the Greeks—the rational deductive system. We try to reduce the law to the smallest number of general principles from which all possible cases can be reached, just as we try to reduce our knowledge of nature to a deductive mathematical system. This rational form also gives the law the appearance of complete freedom from arbitrary will and thus satisfies the modern demand for equality in the enforcement of law.[7]

The law, of course, never succeeds in becoming a completely deductive system. It does not even succeed in becoming completely consistent. But the effort to assume the form of a deductive system underlies all constructive legal scholarship. In our own day, for instance, Thayer's general views on evidence and Wigmore's classical treatise on the subject have transformed a conglomeration of disconnected rules into something like a system. Ames' doctrine of unjust enrichment has brought together a number of artificially tacked-on appendages to the law of contract into the somewhat coherent body of law known as quasi-contract. Forty years ago we had so little of a general theory of torts that if anyone had thought of writing a treatise on the subject he might simply have treated of a number of torts in alphabetic order. Today we have not only a general theory of liability, but also there is a marked tendency to make the law of torts and the law of contracts branches of the law of obligations. This effort at generalization and system has always been the task of the jurist. We use the notions of property, contract, or obligation so often now that we are apt to think that they are "as old as the law itself." But legal history shows clearly enough that the notion of property came as a result of a long process of unification of diverse laws against robbery. A great deal of material had to be eliminated before the abstract idea of property could be extracted. The idea of contract is so late that even as developed a legal system as the Roman had no general law of contract, but merely laws of *stipulatio, depositum, pignus, locatio conductio,* etc. The notion of possession seems to the classical jurists simply one of fact. But the possessory remedies did not originate in the principle of possession but rather in a number of diverse situations.[8]

In thus endeavoring to make the law systematic, jurists are not merely pursuing their own purely theoretic or scientific interest. They are performing a duty to the community by thus transforming the law. A legal system that works with general principles has powerful instruments. Just as the generalized arithmetic which we call advanced mathematics has increased manifold our power of solving physical problems, so a generalized jurisprudence enlarges the law's control over the diversity of legal situations It is like fishing with large nets instead of with single lines.

As nature has other cares besides letting us paint her deductive charm, she constantly reveals aspects that hamper or complicate our beautiful analytic equations. So, also, the affairs of practical life generate situations which mock our well-intentioned efforts to reduce the law to a rational system. In the presence of these, as of other seemingly insurmountable obstacles, human frailty is tempted to blink at the difficulties. So urgent is the need for assured first principles that most people resent the service that the skeptical-minded—the stray dogs of the intellectual world—

render by showing the uninhabitableness of our hastily constructed legal or philosophic kennels. In the legal field, the blinking at the practical diffi-
it is none of our fault if any inconvenience results. *Fiat justitia pereat*
culties is facilitated by the ready assurance that if our principles are just
mundus, is a very edifying excuse for refusing to reexamine our principles
in the light of the harsh results to which they lead.

According to the prevailing popular theory, facts are "out there" in nature and absolutely rigid, while principles are somewhere "in the mind" under our scalps and changeable at will. According to this view scientific theories are made to fit preexisting facts somewhat as clothes are made to fit people. A single inconsistent fact, and the whole theory is abandoned. Actually, however, what we call facts are not so rigid and theories not so flexible; and when the two do not fit, the process of adaptation is a bilateral one. When new facts come up inconsistent with previous theories, we do not give up the latter, but modify both the theory and our view of the facts by the introduction of new distinctions or hypothetical elements. If the facts of radiation do not fit in with the theory of the conservation of energy, an ether is invented and endowed with just as many properties as are necessary to effect a reconciliation, though in the end this results in inordinate complexity. Similarly legal theories, attempting to assimilate new facts by stretching old rules and introducing distinctions and fictions, become so complex and full of arbitrary elements that the very end of legal system is thereby defeated. It is this artificial complexity that caused the abandonment of the Ptolemaic astronomy and is causing the abandonment of the physics of the ether today. The classical system of common-law pleading, based on a few self-evident principles, was just such a system. It fell precisely because, as the forms of actions expanded to comprehend the new industrial order, the system became so choked with artificial distinctions and fictions that a conservative and long-suffering people had to sweep it all away. Similarly has the law of employers' liability, based on a simple principle—no responsibility without fault—grown to such monstrous complexity (witness Labatt's voluminous book)[9] that legislation is sweeping it away.

The foregoing parallel between natural science and legal system should, of course, be corrected by noting the important differences between the two. Legal principles are not so simple or so readily applicable to single cases as are the principles of physics; nor are the facts of the legal order so definite and so rigid as those of the physical order. Crucial experiments are possible in science. Single experiments have sometimes caused such difficulties to reigning theories as to lead to their ultimate abandonment. The facts of physics admit of highly exact description in terms of number and can be indefinitely repeated, whereas the "facts" of the legal order, "practices," or decisions, can almost always be disputed and disregarded as entirely wrong in principle. Nevertheless, enough has been said above to indicate that the rule of deduction is not an accidental incident in law and natural science but is rather an essential part of their life.

II

In modern times the widespread opinion has grown up that deduction is incapable of genuinely extending our knowledge and can serve at best only as an ornament of exposition. It is sometimes thought that the introduction of the "case method" in law teaching marks the entrance of inductive scientific methods in law. The latter view is, however, obviously a misapprehension. Both Langdell and Ames regarded the case method as a sound pedagogical device, but in no way doubted the existence of legal principles according to which cases should be decided. Langdell even asserted that the number of such principles is very small.[10] It is from an entirely different quarter that the whole of traditional legal science has, because of this very belief in principles, been attacked as scholastic and out of harmony with the methods of modern science.[11] Whatever may be these critics' knowledge of modern science, they certainly have a very vague idea of scholasticism, and use the term as a locus for all that is intellectually undesirable, a sort of inferno for all ideas to which they are opposed. Now there is one virtue which no one who has ever read Aquinas or Duns Scotus denies them, and that is clarity and consistency—a virtue which, if not sufficient for admission into the modern juristic heaven, is at least not to be altogether despised. Moreover, every student of the history of thought knows that the contrast between modern science and medieval philosophy is not to be dismissed by the mere shibboleth of induction or deduction. The founders of modern science—Copernicus, Kepler, Galileo, Huygens, Descartes, and Newton—certainly did not despise deduction. The history of science completely belies the dogma as to the fruitlessness of deduction, and shows many important physical discoveries, such as Maxwell's discovery of the electro-magnetic character of light, brought about by deductive or mathematical procedure. The great apostle of induction was Bacon—a good lawyer, trained in the handling of cases in the Inns of Court, but one who made no contribution at all to any natural science.[12] The present apotheosis of induction arose in the middle of the nineteenth century as a result of a violent reaction against the frenzied excesses brought about by the classical German philosophies of Fichte, Hegel, and Schelling. It became a dogma of popular philosophy through the popularity of Mill's *Logic*. Now Mill was not himself a scientist. He was an administrator—an official of the East India Company—and his acquaintance with natural science was gathered from such secondhand sources as Whewell's *History of the Inductive Sciences*. But so strong has become the hold of Mill's simple formulae on popular thought that even men of science have accepted his account of scientific method—which is not surprising if we remember that healthy men or athletes are not necessarily good physiologists or trainers. The actual procedure, however, of natural as well as of legal science involves constant reliance on principles, and is incompatible with Mill's nominalism, *i.e.*, the assumption that only particulars exist in nature.

It may seem a bold and reckless statement to assert that an adequate discussion of cases like *Berry v. Donovan*,[13] *Adair v. United States*[14] or *Commonwealth v. Boston and Maine R.*,[15] involves the whole medieval controversy over the reality of universals. And yet, the confident assertion of "fundamental principles of justice inhere in the very idea of free government"[16] made by the writers of these decisions, and the equally confident assertion of their critics that there are no such principles,[17] show how impossible it is to keep out of metaphysics. Can we dodge the question by saying that while legal principles are unchanging the law is a practical or progressive science?[18] How can a principle or undisputed formula remain the same if all the cases to which it is to be applied are constantly changing? You may decide to enter the realm of metaphysics or not, just as you may decide to go to church or not; but you cannot deny that an intelligent decision in either case demands considerable thought.

The matter is not very difficult if we refuse to be browbeaten by a word like "reality," which often represents nothing definite except a certain emotional afflatus. It ought to be quite clear that abstractions and universals exist in every situation in which individual things can be said to exist, and by the same evidence. If any statement like, "Smith is white and an honest man" is true, whiteness, honesty, and manhood must exist as truly as Smith. Similarly, if it is true that one body is equal to, greater than, or less than another, then the relations of equality, greater than, or less than, exist just as truly as the bodies between which they hold. If the results of logical and mathematical reasoning are observed to hold true of nature, it seems more proper to say that nature is logical and mathematical than to suppose that logical and mathematical principles are just words having no meaning in nature, or that they have a dubious existence "in the mind only" (the "mind" being conceived as outside of nature). The difficulty that most people have in conceiving of the existence of universals is due to the tendency to *reify* all relations, *i.e.*, to think of these relations or universals as if they were themselves additional *things*, instead of what they are defined to be, *viz.*, qualities or relations of things. This shows itself in the naïve question, "*Where* do these universals exist?" as if universals were particular entities occupying space. In brief, it seems that the actual procedure of natural and legal science demands the doctrine that universals do exist, but that they exist as universals, not as additional individual things. Surely a barren if somewhat truistic doctrine, you may say. But the following may show that it offers us a clew whereby to distinguish the use from the abuse of logic in the law.

III

Every science must use logic to test whether certain conclusions do follow from given premises. But that which distinguishes one science from another, *e.g.*, law from physical chemistry, is the subject-matter, the axioms and postulates from which conclusions are drawn. The subject-matter of the law is the regulation of the conduct of individuals living in those more or less permanent relations which we call society. Now, from the point of view of logic the existence of men in society or their desire to regulate their mutual relations is just as brute an empirical fact as that water expands when cooled just above the freezing point. All metaphysical philosophies of law (like Stammler's) which pretend to have no empirical elements at their basis, thus really attempt the logically impossible. You cannot construct a building merely out of the rules of architecture. As a matter of fact, all metaphysical philosophies of law do smuggle in, in more or less disguised form, the main material facts of the social order. In this they are assisted by a fact that empiricists—especially those intoxicated with the doctrine of evolution—do not fully realize, *viz.*, the large fund of common humanity possessed by all peoples whose history we can study. Private law especially deals with those traits of human nature that have changed least in the comparatively short period that is covered by the whole of legal history. Our history "starts with man full grown. It may be assumed that the earliest barbarian whose practices are to be considered had a good many of the same feelings and passions as ourselves." [19] Thus is explained the paradoxical fact that metaphysical philosophers of law, who try to ignore or rise high above the factual order, are frequently more productive of genuine social insight than those who are lost in the multitudinous but unimportant details of historic or ethnologic jurisprudence.

The law, at any given time, is administered and expounded by men who cannot help taking for granted the prevalent ideas and attitudes of the community in which they live. Even if it were logically, it would certainly not be psychically, possible for any man to think out an absolutely new system of jural relations. The law reformer who urges the most radical change, can justify his proposal only by appealing to some actually prevailing idea as to what is desirable; and the history of the law shows how comparatively small is the addition or subtraction to the system of jural concepts and ideas that the most creative judges and jurists have been able to bring about. There are, therefore, first or fundamental principles of the law that may be regarded as practically or *quasi a priori*. But though we cannot avoid relying on principles, the complex and constantly changing subject-matter requires continuous caution and a mind humbly open to the dangers of the eternal tendency of all intellectual effort in the direction of oversimplification.

Among the first principles of the law there are at least two kinds: (1) axioms or fundamental assumptions (*a*) as to fact, *e.g.*, that men desire their economic advantage, and are deterred from actions to which penalties are attached, and (*b*) as to the aim of the law, *e.g.*, that property should be protected, that men should be equal before the law, etc.; and (2) postulates which are really ways of procedure or methods of analysis and construction, *e.g.*, the distinction between rights and duties, or between law and equity, the principle that no man can be his own agent, or that no man can convey more or a greater estate than that which in law he has. The

abuse of first principles of the first class consists in setting up economic
or political maxims of public policy that are at best applicable only to a
given period or historical economic system, as eternal principles for all
times. Examples of this may be found in the use of the principle that the
public interest always demands competition, a free market, and an open
shop, and the maxim that only by the separation of powers, checks and
balances, and judicial control over legislation can liberty be maintained.
The fallacy of regarding these as eternal first principles is readily detected
and has been frequently pointed out in recent times. The fallacy, however,
of setting up what I have called above postulates, as eternal necessities of
all legal systems, is less easily detected. These postulates have the appearance of self-evident truths. But physics has learned to regret accepting
such seemingly self-evident propositions as that a thing cannot act where
it is not, and modern mathematics has learned that such seemingly self-
evident assertions as that the whole is greater than a part, or Euclid's
parallel postulate, are not necessarily true. The theoretical sciences now
select their fundamental propositions not because of their immediate self-
evidence, but because of the system of consequences that follows from
them. A practical science like the law ought not to despise that procedure. . . .

[26c]

JEROME HALL

Science and Reform in Criminal Law*

Foreword

Even a casual glance at legal controls reveals the paramount role of
criminal law. For nothing less than liberty and life are at stake as well as
basic attitudes which determine whether decency and respect for human
beings are realities or mere pretensions. And it may not be superfluous to
note, in view of the insensitivity of leading members of the Bar to the importance of this field, that the criminal law affects all of us, sometimes in
ominous ways that disturb and challenge.

In the international sphere, the prospect of personal penal liability
raises interesting questions, and even more significant are foreign political
movements in which criminal law is recast and used as the principal instrument of domination. If we wish to understand what is happening in the

* From University of Pennsylvania Law Review, Vol. 100, No. 6 (April, 1952), pp.
787–804. Reprinted by permission of the author and publishers. The author is Professor
of Law at Indiana University.

world, we must study the criminal law of those countries. In the settled areas of foreign affairs the uniformity of criminal law has long attracted scholarly attention, although we continue to ignore it. Nor do our current studies of foreign and international law draw upon the resources of specialists in criminal law—so departmentalized has modern scholarship become. Yet, as one probes the problems of local, national, foreign, and international criminal law, it becomes clear that common ideas permeate all of these artificially separated branches of a single discipline.

Accordingly, for the various reasons indicated above, almost any problem of criminal law is worthy of serious study. But there are times and tides in the development of a discipline which bring certain questions into greater relevancy than others. They are not necessarily problems which concern practical matters directly. They are often theoretical issues whose impact may in the long run be far more important than urgent immediate questions. Allowance should be made, also, for individual taste in such matters, and any writer can only hope that his sense of what is relevant will be shared by others. But we are interested primarily in contemporary American criminal law, and that sets some objective bounds to the quest for what is most significant. Thus, the insistence of the need to solve procedural problems has diminished because of the recent provision of the federal rules. Although these problems are, of course, never fully solved, we may in the immediate future concentrate on the substantive criminal law.

System—an Essential Phase of a Science of Criminal Law

In this area the broadest formulation of "significant problem" must be in terms of the dual aspect of any empirical science—its formal or systematic side and its content. So far as actually solving problems is concerned, the formal and the empirical attributes of any science are interdependent—we not only need verified generalizations, we must also be able to find them quickly and to recognize their full implications. Practical utility, itself, depends finally upon available knowledge; and such knowledge in the developed sciences comprises valid generalizations that are systematized. Stated otherwise, the significance of a scientific generalization depends largely on its location in a system of such generalizations. Accordingly, although an analogy drawn from physical science must be employed with due caution, it can be accepted for the present purpose, namely, to indicate that we need not only sound rules of criminal law but also an *organization*, a *system*, of such rules.[1] Whatever one's view of the social disciplines may be, organized knowledge is an ultimate desideratum.

In Europe, organization of the law has long been exhibited in codes, and the French Code Pénal of 1810, the culmination of legal developments in the latter part of the eighteenth century, became the basic system of criminal law in the civilian world. European codification had ancient antecedents which reached a peak in Justinian's Code; besides, the influence of

scholars and their treatises as well as a philosophical tradition made systematization of the law both respectable and expected.

In the Anglo-American legal world, the accepted dogma is that the
common law, being the product of adjudication, is wholly disorganized; in
Austin's blunt phrase, it is "a mess." One must be careful, however, how he
interprets this criticism lest it become a gross exaggeration. In a sense there
is just as much logic in the common law as in the civil law. For example, in
the criminal law it has long been recognized that certain basis notions, e.g.,
"act," "mens rea," "concurrence," and so on run through the entire field of
crimes; they are certainly systematizing constructs.[2] Moreover, in the
common law, treatises have also exerted great influence, as is evident on
any notice of case-law references to Hale, Blackstone, Stephen, Bishop,
Holmes and Wigmore. *Sound treatises are the essential instruments of
systematization of the law and the prerequisite of its codification.*

When codification was much debated in this country about seventy-
five years ago, Bishop opposed Field's proposal on that ground, namely,
that a necessary condition was lacking—scholarly treatises containing
sound analyses of the basic problems.[3] One may believe that we are now
better situated in this regard than was Bishop, and not least because of his
contributions. But it would surely be fatuous to assume that it is possible
to proceed directly to the codification of the criminal law without relying
on or providing treatises, essays, and monographs that perform the essential
job of analysis and systematization. Whatever validity available treatises
may lack, the important thing is recognition of the function of thorough
analysis and systematization and, then, improvement of the extant work.

The writer's efforts in that direction,[4] building on earlier scholarship
in the field, culminated in the classification of the substantive criminal law
into three main divisions: (1) principles—the foundations of criminal law,
(2) rules—specific "material" elements of crimes, and (3) doctrines—
general "material" elements of crimes. Rules and doctrines differ substantively as well as in the degree or level of generalization. Combined,
they express the criminal law. The principles (they may be called premises
or postulates or hypotheses if one prefers)[5] are the ultimate ideas permeating the criminal law. That is, given rules and doctrines combined, the
principles are intended to answer the question, what common ideas are
represented?

Of the three primary divisions of the field, that termed "principles" is
the most important because of its central, ultimate place in the system
and because of the consequences of the acceptance of the principles. Just
as the addition or radical modification of a fundamental law of physics
has great effect upon the entire science,[6] so, too, as regards the principles
of criminal law. Yet, to some persons the word principles is obnoxious—
perhaps their own principles oppose the use of language that suggests objective values. Or they fear that some sort of arbitrary dogma is being
thrust upon them. But this is surely to ignore the structure of any science.
In the writer's opinion, the principles of criminal law—a traditional and

practically universal term among scientists as well as elsewhere [7]—are more than bare postulates. They include meanings to which various degrees of validity (truth-value) are ascribed. One may prefer to minimize their status in order to encourage critical testing, but in any event they are more than mere assumptions, as may be seen if one attempts to substitute their opposites and organize the criminal law accordingly.[8]

LEGALITY, PUNISHMENT, AND HARM

Since the principles of criminal law are not only organizational constructs but are also substantively important, it is possible and necessary to consider them from both viewpoints. Here we can discuss only a few of the important problems involved. Specifically, of the seven suggested principles of criminal law (legality, conduct, mens rea, concurrence, harm, causation, and punishment) we shall briefly discuss certain aspects of legality, punishment, and harm, in the course of which it will become necessary to allude to the principle of conduct and to the doctrine of criminal attempt.

Specifically, the problems to be considered involve difficulties resulting from a pervasive ambiguity in the professional literature due to the failure to consider the standpoint one is taking when he analyzes the criminal law or when he criticizes another scholar's theory of it. What are the chief standpoints? First, one may be interested in studying the existing criminal law and its functions, the elucidation of meanings, the organization of the rules, and so on. Second, one may wish to criticize the existing law for various inconsistencies and imperfections *while accepting the principles of the present criminal law*. For example, if one's study of the criminal law leads him to conclude that the principle of mens rea (understood to include intentionality and recklessness) is sound, he may, for reasons he articulates, criticize adversely certain segments of criminal law where ordinary negligence is held sufficient, consider the implications of the felony-murder rule and of objective and strict liability from that viewpoint, and so on. Third, a scholar may engage in much more drastic criticism of the existing law, challenging basic principles and proposing far-reaching reforms.[9]

The fact that these perspectives shift, sometimes imperceptibly, increases the difficulties in the way of communication. It does not render it less essential to cogent criticism to determine what perspective has guided a scholarly contribution for the most part, and at what points a different perspective was operative. No less important is the scholar's awareness of his own perspectives. Their articulation would permit precise discovery of apparent differences, which would often become greatly narrowed once the issues were precisely formulated. The subject is of such importance and difficulty in criminal law, where deeply rooted attitudes are naturally involved, that it is worth pursuing farther.

For example, if a writer defends the inclusion within the criminal law of harms caused by ordinary negligence, he may mean that that is the present law, that negligence is within the presently accepted meaning of mens rea (without stating what he understands that to be, and why). He may mean that that *ought* to be the law. He may intend to say both. In any case, he should first determine by careful analysis just what the criminal law is regarding negligence and in what crimes, if any, such behavior is penalized. The homicide field, especially criminal homicide by automobile, would be important in such an inquiry. An historical survey reveals trends regarding criminal liability for negligence, hence it is essential to keep a close eye on the dates of the decisions relied upon. Presumably, such a survey of criminal liability should precede proposals for reform. If negligence has been progressively and almost entirely eliminated from the sphere of criminal liability wherever the question has been directly faced, especially during the past two decades, that might influence one's evaluation of the criminal law and restrain the advocacy of punitive treatment of negligent persons. In any event, if it is clear that reform is the perspective involved, it becomes essential to know whether prevailing standards of criminal liability are accepted or not, together with the supporting reasons. Whatever position is taken, much more than the assertion of a preference is required. *E.g.,* there are non-legal, as well as legal, studies relevant to the wisdom of penalizing negligent persons. This literature may be seriously deficient, but an obligation to read it and to provide a thoughtful discussion of the grounds of preference seems axiomatic.

Legality

Let us now consider briefly some of the polemics on the principle of legality, the "rule of law" in the field of crimes. The difficulties encountered here frequently stem from the same failure to distinguish analysis of existing law from sweeping proposals to reform that law, which sometimes imply wholesale rejection of widely accepted standards. The gap between the perspective of criminologists and that of lawyers, including most legal scholars, is noteworthy. The influence of recent developments in authoritarian states seems to have had a greater effect on the latter. Prior to the last war, American academic opinion, greatly influenced by the Italian School, was largely opposed to legal controls, including the strict construction of penal statutes. Confidence in the social sciences, including psychiatry, ran extremely high, and the problem of protecting the political values of a democratic society lay dormant. In effect, the proposed reforms sought the abrogation of legal guarantees and the substitution of the opinions of sociologists and psychiatrists in their place. With regard to strict construction of penal statutes, it was argued that the need for it, obvious in interpreting the harsh law of the eighteenth century, no longer existed. The rise of brutal dictators and powerful governments everywhere would seem to have outmoded such complacency.

If some scholars have not been influenced by recent history, many courts, aided by established principle regarding common law offenses, have insisted on the preservation of legal values, at least in ordinary cases. In Louisiana, *e.g.,* the new code provided for "genuine construction" of criminal statutes. With reference to a case involving the word "immoral," it was argued that this implied abandonment of "strict interpretation," and reliance was placed upon an assumed civil law doctrine, supposedly French, a persuasive kind of argument in Louisiana. Actually, French law accords with ours in requiring strict construction of penal statutes.[10] The Louisiana Supreme Court, without benefit of French law, repudiated the recommendation that it interpret the criminal code liberally.[11]

Undeterred, the current Wisconsin project would abolish strict construction of criminal statutes.[12] The commentary lists a goodly number of states as having abolished the common law principle and as having substituted "liberal construction." But no citation of cases is provided, and there are cases in many, if not all, of the states listed which make it perfectly clear that they have not abandoned the common law principle.[13] Here, again, it would be helpful to know whether the perspective of the Wisconsin project is analysis of existing law or whether far-reaching reform is sought regarding the construction of penal statutes. So, too, it is important to know if strict construction has been repudiated by some courts and, if so, where, as regards which crimes, and to what extent? A precise determination of these questions would stimulate careful differentiation of specific problem-areas and promote sound appraisal of proposed reforms.

A similar confusion is evident in discussions of the Model Youth Correction Authority Act, which assert that *the Model Act* has been adopted in several states. It would be much more accurate, though not adequate, to assert that it has not been adopted in any state. For the provisions which aroused criticism, namely, those that comprise the unique features of the Model Act, sought to narrow greatly or eliminate entirely an important phase of legality, *i.e.*, legal control of treatment. These provisions were not included in any of the statutes enacted by the five states which adopted the so-called "Authority programs." [14] The statutes actually adopted represent progress mostly in the administration of penal institutions,[15] and everybody agrees that improvements there are sorely needed.[16]

It should be superfluous to add that nothing written above is intended to discourage criticism of the criminal law or to suggest that the discovery and advocacy of sound reforms are not important. But it must still be recognized that the advocacy of reform is quite different from disinterested inquiry, including the discovery of needed reforms. That, at least, is the essential postulate of any science. If it is not accepted, the obstacles in the way of communication, not to speak of those barring the construction of a science of criminal law, are practically insuperable.

PUNISHMENT

The persistent observance of the difference between advocacy of reform and scientific inquiry is most difficult in discussions of punishment and treatment. For, added to especially complex linguistic requirements, if precision and clarity are to be attained, are the limitations resulting from deeply rooted attitudes regarding basic issues which inevitably involve a complete philosophy of life. It is therefore a serious, not a rhetorical, question to ask: is it possible to improve considerably the analysis, research, and discussion of punishment? If one answers that affirmatively he should carefully attend to ways and means of doing it.

The "prevention of crime" and the "protection of society" are ends accepted by everyone, hence it should be obvious that their mere affirmation does not solve problems any more than it helps to argue as though some persons reject those ends. And if we are considering the existing criminal law, the institution conveniently dated from the thirteenth century and Bracton's treatise, it will also be generally agreed that, whatever else is included in them, the sanctions contain a punitive element. That is the reason for designating punishment as a principle of criminal law. But the meaning of "punishment" is far from univocal and the linguistic difficulties can be resolved only by sustained efforts. In the present state of the literature, it will be helpful if those who discuss punishment specify: (1) whether they are talking about the existing criminal law; (2) whether they are repudiating its premises and are proposing substitutes for them; and (3) what, concretely, they regard as treatment and punishment by pointing to what actually happens in various situations and institutions. These measures would help, but they would not suffice in the absence of carefully formulated standards, as may be seen when one asks whether suspended sentence and probation are punitive or not. To some extent, linguistic conventions would also be needed. In any event, certain elementary expectations seem reasonable as regards professional writing, *e.g.*, that punishment under civilized laws be not identified with vengeance or other merely emotional reactions or with cruel and inhuman imposition of suffering.

Cogent analysis would be facilitated if it were generally agreed that involuntary incarceration is punishment regardless of the kindliness of the administrators of the institution or the unexceptionable quality of the treatment program. This might also aid the adoption of worthy reforms because if the public need for a punitive element in the criminal law were satisfied by imprisonment, that would enable administrators to individualize treatment in the most humane, enlightened ways known to them, limited only by the fact and the legal limits of confinement. The careful use of an improved terminology and of the other indicated methods of promoting clarity and precision would free the literature of much irrelevant polemic. It would be folly to expect that differences in opinion stemming from deeply rooted attitudes regarding punishment can be wholly eliminated. But it ought to be possible, without the aid of psychoanalysis, to discover rather definitely what the actual disagreements are and what working compromises can be made by scholars holding diverse perspectives, who wish to improve the criminal law.[17]

In addition to the ambiguities of "punishment," the lack of careful articulation of theories, and the unavoidable fact that the problem involves ultimate "can't helps" which have reverberated through the ages, there is another serious difficulty which, however, seems to be more readily soluble; and its solution would greatly improve the present state of the professional literature. This difficulty stems from the advocacy of a particular theory of punishment or objective of criminal law—retribution, *or* deterrence, *or* correction. In the recent past in academic circles, correction was espoused and retribution was damned as a vestige of man's instinctual past, while deterrence was excluded as ineffective, rationalistic, and even as a cause of crime. In legal and official circles, on the other hand, deterrence has been supported as a necessary and potent defense of social values,[18] and rehabilitation has been summarily dismissed, *e.g.*, by Holmes. Surviving also, but hardly noticed until recently except among students of ethics, are theories of retribution,[19] implying a moral attribute of criminal law.[20] Finally, there is the theory, defended by the writer, that all three elements—justice, deterrence, and reformation—are essential.[21] Because the morality of criminal law had been greatly neglected, that factor was emphasized, but it was made clear that deterrence and correction are also important.[22]

It is interesting to observe that criticism of this theory is apt to focus on its inclusion of the moral quality of criminal law.[23] The problem is much too large for adequate discussion here; [24] indeed, it is the major issue of our times and permeates all the social disciplines. But this much may be ventured here: to interpret just punishment narrowly as the mere infliction of suffering for a past harm is only to construct a straw man lacking any resemblance to the relevant realities and meanings. It is but slightly less misleading to ask *only*: "for what end is punishment imposed?" because this automatically excludes the intrinsic value of any moral experience. It is equally unfortunate to neglect thorough investigation of the thesis that just punishment also operates in some, perhaps many, cases to bring about reformation and to deter potential offenders.[25]

Although it is impossible here to discuss in any detail the consequences of particularistic theories of punishment, it is important for the present purpose to indicate the logic of the opposing theories. Let $1 =$ rehabilitation, $2 =$ deterrence, and $3 =$ justice. A affirms only 1; B affirms only 2; C affirms only 3; while D affirms 1 and 2 and 3. It should not be difficult to plot the issues involved in the various combinations, and thus articulate the different positions represented in the literature. Much clarification would result if the implications of such an exercise for discussions of punishment were considered. For example, it would be clear that D, when he adversely criticizes deterrence or correction, cannot be understood to reject those objectives. If he is consistent, he can criticize only exclusive or excessive claims for deterrence or rehabilitation.

To apply the logic of the theories more specifically to the extant literature, it may be noted that: A espouses rehabilitation, but he never inquires whether "corrective treatment" is wholly free of punitive elements. Is it possible to eliminate retribution entirely, while assuming that involuntary incarceration or other control is a necessary condition of correction?[26] Nor does *A* consider the implications of "pure correction" for cases like those of Professor Webster, Whitney, and other numerous "while collar" criminals—men who are often better educated and more intelligent than the penological experts themselves, at least those likely to be members of a treatment board. On the other hand, what does *A* say regarding the many thousands of incorrigible petty offenders? Motivated by humanitarian ideals, is he willing to incarcerate them for life, so that they may never rejoin their friends and families? If *A* could be persuaded to deal carefully with such questions, he might contribute a more precise knowledge of "treatment," help to discover exactly what the areas of actual difference of opinion are, and prepare the way for cooperative concentration on the reforms that are greatly needed.

We may briefly indicate analogous questions to be asked of *B* and *C*. *B*, the advocate of deterrence, would be shocked by the suggestion that insane persons or petty thieves should be executed regardless of any amount of proof that criminal conduct would be thus greatly deterred.[27] The execution of civilian hostages in the last war and harsh repression in dictatorial states seem to have been effective deterrents; certainly we cannot ignore such data on the comfortable assumption that very severe punishment does not deter. But if *B* does not articulate his thinking in relation to that phase of punishment, he will not recognize that an element of "retribution" (*i.e.,* justice) is required in any legal order he can fully approve.

So, finally, *C*, who sees only the intrinsic moral worth of carefully determined public condemnation of intentional or reckless harms, should consider that from the beginning of Western thought deterrence has been approved and education (correction) of the corrigible has been emphasized by many great thinkers who, nevertheless, did not subordinate justice to those ends. The finest teachings of religion emphasize brotherhood and forgiveness,[28] which should temper the administration of criminal law. And, on the other hand, the elementary needs of survival require the deterrence of potential harmdoers. We should not shut our eyes to that and irresponsibly advocate the substitution of *agape* for criminal law no matter how generously we may treat those who have seriously harmed us.[29]

If theories of punishment took adequate account of the various values involved, they would not only increase the knowledge of criminal law; the problems needing research would also be discovered and carefully formulated. The entire outlook so far as scientific research is concerned—and consequently also with reference to administration and reform (though not for judges and administrators who already have an integrative viewpoint)—would be greatly altered. The overall problem would be recognized as one calling for the discriminating integration of the various values and their careful implementation along lines suggested by specific questions, *e.g.,* in what particular offenses, regarding which types of offender, in relation to what prevalent crime rates, and so on, should the peno-correctional treatment be determined and adjusted thus and so in order to preserve the maximum values? [30] This approach would exemplify the truism that the job of theory is to be objective. When compromises are made out of regard for the progress of reform, theory abdicates and reform suffers.

While the above discussion has ranged beyond the purely logical problem of organizing the criminal law, it is also true that improvement in any of the basic principles has far-reaching effects. For the principles, functioning as major organizational constructs, refer ultimately to facts and values. As the principles are improved, they therefore gather around them more valid supporting data, suggestive implications, and other important consequences. In sum, the improved empirico-value significance of the principles is reflected throughout the entire body of legal rules and doctrines.

HARM

The formal function of the next principle of the criminal law which we shall briefly discuss—the principle of harm—is more readily recognized.[31] It can hardly be doubted that a marked advance is gained by using "harm" to resolve the ambiguity of "act." The necessity to deal with the effects of conduct for some purposes and with the conduct, alone, for others makes evident the advantage of having two distinct notions so far as case-analysis is concerned.[32] Superior craftsmanship depends on the availability of sharp, precise tools.

But what of the larger problem of system in the criminal law? How does the notion of harm contribute to that so importantly as to become a principle, a basic organizational construct? One answer to that question is simply a spelling-out of what has just been said regarding case-analysis, *i.e.*, if the idea of harm improves that, there must be good reasons for it, hence we have only to extend the implications throughout the criminal law. But we can approach the problem from more specific directions.

In order to place our major inquiry in a relevant context, we may note that harm serves the following purposes:

1. It is essential in distinguishing criminal law from ethics and a theory of ethics from one of law.[33]

2. It provides a rational basis for the range and differentiation of punishments, *i.e.*, in general proportion to the gravity of the harm.

3. Causation, another principle of criminal law, is meaningful in explanation of the relation between conduct and harm. If harm is excluded, causation becomes meaningless, and the combined result is a great loss in systematization of the criminal law.

4. It is necessary in interpretation of statutes and in solving many other questions, *e.g.*, jurisdictional ones.

5. It is important in corrective treatment if an offender's harm to social values is considered in determining his dangerousness.[34]

6. Finally, and most important, is the function of the principle of harm as a basic organizational construct. It is impossible here to discuss

the above phases of the principle of harm, but we can attend briefly to this one.

If we examine the major crimes, *i.e.*, both the legal prescriptions and the relevant fact-situations, the harms involved are usually recognized without difficulty. Physical harm is the simplest type found among them, *e.g.*, a human being dies, a dwelling-house burns, a human body has been injured, and so on.

But it is equally clear that the proscribed effects of criminal conduct are not confined to physical harms. For example, criminal libel damages an intangible interest, and in rape, physical injury is not the important one involved. That might amount to a minor battery, yet the gravity of the harm to such intangibles as the autonomy of women and the preservation of the family would be no less serious. These instances and other injuries to incorporeal values, which might be noted, are included in ultimate crimes; hence it is clear that harm cannot be restricted to physical injury.

It is against this background that we must interpret the "inchoate" or relational crimes such as the criminal attempts and the conspiracies. Criminal attempt is particularly suggestive with regard to the systematization of criminal law because of its relation to harm; hence, we may profitably consider two or three aspects of it in the present connection.

In studies of criminal attempt published in this country, including those of the present writer, the preponderant judgment of those writers who have expressed an opinion on the question is that criminal attempts include harms.[35] Perhaps the common thought underlying these estimates is that in criminal attempts (and other relational crimes) the harm is a dangerous condition or situation, voluntarily produced, in which the probability of still greater harm is substantially increased. If that is a sound insight it has far-reaching implications because it brings within the orbit of defensible generalization numerous offenses such as possession of burglars' tools or stolen property, and it would also resolve uncertainties regarding burglary, larceny, kidnapping, and so on, *i.e.*, wherever a more serious harm than the one committed may follow.

The necessary interpretation of intangible injuries as harms, as seen above, supports the insight that the relational crimes also include harms. In addition, the ideal of system undoubtedly provides some stimulus to advance tenable generalization to the point where a principle of criminal law is established. On the other hand, if those who simply dismiss harm from the material elements of the "inchoate" and many other offenses remain content with a negative exclusion, the result, involving also the principle of causation, etc., is a serious loss in an essential phase of criminal science, namely, its formal aspect.[36]

Nevertheless, if we are to be realistic regarding divergent viewpoints and if we wish to advance as far as possible toward construction of a science of criminal law, this would seem to present an area for necessary compromise and acceptance of some terms, in part, by convention. Specifically, if "effect" [37] were substituted for "harm" and this were generally accepted, it might go far to preserve the progress made toward systematization of the criminal law. From the perspective of those who hold that the criminal law rests ultimately on a moral foundation, "effect" would not be as acceptable a substitute as "wrong." But it would certainly be preferable to the serious disorganization that prevails when the many crimes involving incorporeal or relatively subtle harms are left outside the range of basic principles.

It is evident that theories of punishment which avowedly or tacitly deny any place to moral considerations in the criminal law are at the root of inadequate analysis of the problem of harm, including the difference between preparation and attempt, as well as that of the wide range of sanctions, etc. Indeed, the consequences are more serious than has been stated, because impairment of any basic principle, no less than its improvement, has systematic effect, *e.g.*, on the principle of causation. And, in some discussions, even conduct is excluded from the scope of criminal law or its importance is depreciated. However defensible such theses may be in relation to penological reform, it is certain that they do not contribute to a science of criminal law.

A theory which takes due account of relevant moral values can provide an explanation of the problems raised in relation to the criminal law. And, as indicated above, the necessary inclusion of deterrent and corrective viewpoints permits adjustment and individualization, but it does not warrant abandonment of the evaluation of the harm done. Many of the current disputes could be thus resolved.

For example, in some criminal attempts the offender may have desisted of his own accord; or his failure to consummate his intention may have resulted from the fact that when he finally faced his victim and the mechanism of identification became operative, he lacked the stomach required to execute his intention successfully. He would thus reveal evidence of being a less dangerous person than offenders who committed the ultimate harms. In these cases retributive punishment would tend to coincide with the requirements of correction. But there are some instances where, in theory at least, it is difficult to effect a harmony. Where, for example, failure was due to accident, correction would proceed as though the ultimate harm had been committed, while a retributive view would insist on distinguishing the respective actual harms. The flexibility of modern criminal law might permit even such theoretically refractory cases to be resolved in practice, *e.g.*, if parole boards discharged at the earliest possible time some offenders who committed ultimate crimes while retaining in custody such attemptors, as the last indicated ones, for the maximum sentence. Yet, it must be granted, there remains an irreducible area of uncertainty where presently conflicting viewpoints lead to opposing solutions. At such points, in light of the limited knowledge available especially regarding borderline cases, both theorists and administrators should take a stand which is consistent with a sound view of the entire criminal law.

If systematic efforts to increase knowledge of the criminal law, including relevant empirical knowledge, are not employed, the problems of paramount importance remain insistently neglected. Everyone agrees that a science of criminal law would be of very great value; but the implications of that estimate are not thoroughly appreciated. For example, if a science of criminal law would be very valuable, that implies systematization of the field—and how is that to be accomplished? What, specifically, are the necessary ideas, principles, doctrines, bases, criteria, and so on; and what illustrations can be offered in support of claims that the job can be done along lines of a particular theory? These questions are asked neither in a spirit of idle challenge nor rhetorically, for the problems facing any serious scholar in the field of criminal law are much too difficult for complacency. They are raised to draw out the implications of various important viewpoints and to encourage experimentation with unexamined perspectives.

POSTSCRIPTS

Social research has long been emphasized in the field of criminal law. Indeed, while legal science in most fields even now remains largely in the realm of hope or is confined to general discussions of methodology, many important contributions to an emerging science of criminal law have been made. One has only to cast a reflective eye over the professional literature of criminal law and criminology which has appeared during the past one hundred years, as compared with that of other fields of law, to appreciate the potentialities of the former with regard to the progress of legal science.

Even in the criminal law, however, we have only studies of relatively narrow problems and, significant as they may be, we have hardly begun the larger task of fitting the specific researches into a pattern of systematic knowledge. Sustained, thoughtful efforts to codify the criminal law might well lead to analysis of the relations between a sound code and a science of criminal law.[38] We should then confront problems which have been neglected because they did not need to be considered when research was confined to segments of the criminal law. It has been the primary purpose of this discussion to raise some pertinent questions about inquiries of that kind.

JOHN HERMAN RANDALL, JR.

History and the Social Sciences*

It is well to start this examination of the relations between history and the social sciences with a confession. I have long been convinced that there is no such thing as "history," and for some time I have been coming to doubt whether there are any social sciences. These unfortunate facts might seem to leave me in the fix of Santayana, who is credibly reported to have asserted: "There is no God, and Mary is his mother." So any reader who hopes to find out from these pages something about the relation between these very dubious entities would be wise to skip them.

But fortunately, I am by profession a "philosopher"—in the technical and very Pickwickian sense. And I should certainly hate to achieve the distinction of being the first philosopher who ever stopped talking about any subject-matter just because that subject-matter does not happen to exist. So I am really in the same boat with the historians and the social scientists—there is no such thing as "philosophy" either. Consequently, we can all begin from scratch, and proceed from there. And just as Santayana, although he is convinced there is no God, can nevertheless be fascinating on the theme of theology without ontology, I want to begin by explaining why there is no such thing as "history," and why the social sciences are not "sciences," before going on to explore the very important relations between these non-existent disciplines.

I remember once long ago asking a friend what he was particularly interested in doing. This was in the morning of life, and we both had our ambitions. "I want to study history," he replied. "The history of what?" I went on to inquire—quite naturally, it seemed to me. To my surprise, my friend was greatly perplexed at this simple question. "Why," he finally managed to come out with, "I'm not interested in the history of anything in particular. What I want to go on and study is just history."

* The substance of this paper was given as a talk at Yale University on March 2, 1949, as the first in a series of Trumbull Lectures.

Reprinted by permission of the author and publishers from *Freedom and Reason, Studies in Philosophy and Jewish Culture in Memory of Morris Raphael Cohen*, ed. Salo Baron, Ernest Nagel, Koppel S. Pinson; Jewish Social Studies, Publications No. 4 (New York: Conference on Jewish Relations, 1951), copyright by The Free Press (Glencoe, Illinois). Pp. 287–308.

Now what this "just history" may be, that so many men seem anxious to study, I have never been able to understand. It is easy to observe that those devoted to it in the past have rarely been agreed on just what it is; no two of the classic "historians" have understood what "history" is in precisely the same way. And it is hard today to avoid rival schools of "historians" vociferously debating just what kinds of material their "history" should include. We have all been taught, I presume, that "history" is not merely or primarily past politics or past battles, but must comprehend a great deal more than those very minor matters. Many tell us "history" must include primarily facts about the economic institutions under which men have lived. Others bid us study the great ideas that have meant so much to those capable of appreciating their significance, the ideas of science and philosophy. For some, it is the religion that has organized and expressed the life of entire cultures that seems of fundamental "historical" importance. Art and literature, those consummate expressions of what the past has been and has felt, have their devoted followers. Still others insist that the true "history" is of the beliefs and institutionalized habits of men, the beliefs which the masses have actually entertained, and which have determined the course of all men's social relations.

Now I can understand sympathetically a genuine interest in all these things. I can indeed understand and share in an interest in everything that men have done and thought and felt and made during their long sojourn upon the earth. I can even understand what used to be called "natural history"—though I find that today what nature has done is not regarded as the province of the "historian," and enters therein, if at all, only if it has done something to his "history"—usually in the first chapter. But I must confess I cannot understand even the meaning of the questions, which of these many different interests should "history" include, and which should it emphasize and make central? Nor, if "history" is to include all of them, and is to be a complete record of everything that man has achieved on this planet, can I see how "history" differs from the entire sum of human knowledge. For everything that is has an historical aspect, and can hence be the appropriate subject-matter of historical investigation. Even mathematics, though it may deal with an order that is timeless and eternal, as a human enterprise is essentially progressive and historical in character.

For these reasons, we are told, "history" must inevitably be selective. I am inclined to agree, at least to the extent that I have always found it necessary to make a selection. But I have never understood why "history" has to. I am unable to see why a detailed study of Hannibal's campaigns is not perfectly valid "history," although I too know all the reasons why such study should not be inflicted upon the young. I have been amused to find that the historians of Columbia University, committed to the insignificance of military history, nevertheless imported an historian of military strategy as soon as it became apparent that military problems were about to become central. What should be taught to the young in the

schools is a perfectly legitimate question, which demands its own answers;
but this pedagogical question hardly delimits "history." I am not unacquainted with the familiar observation: "That used to be what history
was considered, of course; but now it is only the history of military
strategy." I am perfectly aware that "history" has itself enjoyed a history;
and I flatter myself that I can with the best of them explain why different
historians have been and still are interested in the histories of different
things. But I must say that I can see no reason in the most complete
understanding of why "history" has become what in practice it is today,
for answering in one way rather than in another the question, "What
should 'history' be and include?"

When pressed, historians will tell us that "history" selects from the
record of the past that which gives us "understanding." I am perfectly
willing to admit that that is just what historians actually do. To be sure,
I have never yet found an historian who did not dwell lovingly on an
immense amount of detail, not because it had any discoverable connection
with the "understanding" of anything else, but simply because he was
fascinated by it. I have never yet found any historian so puritanical as to
be really bound by this pragmatic theory; nor do I ever expect to. But,
granted the historian is trying to help us understand something else, it is
still terribly difficult to find any plausible theory as to why what he selects
does enable us to "understand."

One school of historians much in vogue today is very insistent that
"history" should aim to explain why we are acting the way we are, and
how we got into the mess we are in. The history of that mess does seem
to me to be very important, and to illuminate what we should do about it.
But I really cannot see why the history of our present mess is to be
identified with "just history" in general. If it is, then the history of
ancient Egypt, for example, will hardly be "history," for it seems to have
made only a minor contribution to our troubles. This is a view I cannot
accept, for I find Egyptian history fascinating. I cannot even regard it as
the proper aim of "history" to account for how the Egyptians got into
their messes; for their history seems to be about other things than messes,
and is in fact largely irrelevant to them. And the same holds of the history
of Greece. Despite the efforts of very able historians today, I am still not
clear that the most important thing about the Greeks was their failures,
though I hope I can point a moral as well as the next man. And though
like their gods the Greeks were very human, I find that what interests
me about them is not the way they resemble us, but the things they did
that we cannot do. In any event, moreover, if "history" is really to explain
why we are acting the way we are, I should think it would have to explain
why we paint the kind of pictures we do, and compose the kind of music
we write, and why we are puzzling our heads over the general theory of
relativity. But that, I shall at once be told, is not "history"; that is the
history of art or of music or of physics.

Ah! says another school, "history" helps us to understand where we are because it explains why things have been as they have. It makes clear the "pattern of the historical process." This seems a promising answer, until we reflect that it means that what "history" explains to us is "history" itself. And this is very puzzling and odd—*pace* Spengler, Toynbee, Sorokin, and other extremely speculative "positivists" who, in searching for a "pattern of history," for an "historical morphology," piously hope that they are being very "scientific" indeed—which is an act of faith rather than of knowledge. For it is clearly not history that enables us to understand history, but science—anthropology, psychology, economics, and the rest. This wisdom as to the relation of the social sciences to history has been common knowledge for several generations. And the basic question remains: even if "history" could miraculously explain history, we should still have no light thrown on why we select the particular things we do to label "history."

There is of course a simple answer much in fashion today: "history" is really economic history. It is through the history of men's economic activities and relations that we can alone gain a genuine understanding of "history." But I observe that those who say this proceed to use economic history primarily to explain political history. What they are interested in understanding seems to be political struggles and fights; and they all point to further political battles in the future. I am inclined to agree that this is an excellent way to understand political goings on; and it certainly sheds a good deal of light on many other things as well. But I am still in the dark as to why it should be politics alone that "history" is trying to explain; and with the best will in the world I cannot see that economic history throws much light on many other things I want to understand—why, for instance, British thinkers have persisted down to Bertrand Russell in making the same initial assumptions as William of Ockham, despite the absurd consequences it has been shown in every generation those assumptions entail; or why and how the theory of quantum mechanics has transformed Newtonian science. The histories of such things seem intelligible without much reference to how men have made a living—to what a fashionable jargon calls the "relations of production." But perhaps "history" in general is merely what economics *does* enable us to explain. If that be true, it would at least simplify matters.

As a result of perplexing questions like these, I have been driven to ask whether there is any such thing as "history" in general. At present, I am convinced there is no such "thing." Nor do I know of any good reason why there should be men set apart as "Professors of History," or why there should be special "Departments of History" in our colleges and universities—except that I greatly enjoy and profit by what these men tell me, and am convinced that they ought to be supported in some way or other.

In any strictly rational organization of academic teaching, there would clearly be no place for any separate and independent "Departments of History." Rather, each department of knowledge concerned with a separate subject-matter would include members with a major intellectual interest in the history of that subject-matter, and of the intellectual efforts to grasp it. Of course, I am really not trying to be invidious. I believe there is equally no strictly rational reason for the existence of any separate and independent "Departments of Philosophy" in academic teaching. Every department should include members with philosophic imagination and horizons, and capable of philosophic analysis.

To be sure, however justified it might be rationally, I am not myself so addicted to the vice of pure reason as to have any immediate intention of starting such a purge. I am trying rather to emphasize certain fundamental facts about the nature of history. Everything in our world has *a* history, and the man who wants to understand any particular thing or field is well advised to inquire into *its* history. Everything that is, is historical in character, and has an existence that can be measured in time. And this historical aspect which any particular thing has and possesses is an essential part of what it is. But "just history" in general seems to have no meaning, unless it be taken as synonymous with knowledge as a whole. History is not a "thing" at all; it is not a noun, a "substance." It is rather a character, an adjective, a predicate. Or, put in somewhat more formal terms, "history" is not a distinctive subject-matter to be inquired into. It is rather at once a trait of all subject-matters, something to be discovered and understood about each of them; and a distinctive way of inquiring into any subject-matter—though by no means the only way.

And therefore I find no meaning in the questions: What should "history" include? What should "the historian" emphasize? There is no such thing as "history" in general, nor are there any men who are just "historians." Every history is *the* history *of* something, and every historian is trying to trace *the* past *of* something. In terms of that "something," it is not hard to discover what *its* history must include. The various strands so viewed fall into their proper perspective, once we have decided just what it is, the historical aspect of which we are interested in. The history of our science will then be one thing, and the history of our present mess a somewhat different one; although in investigating either we shall often find ourselves concerned with the same factors that are in a different way involved in the other. There is no "process of history" in general; but every historian of anything will find himself discovering *the* "historical processes" by which that particular thing came about.

Actually, of course, there does seem to be a need for "history" in the academic curriculum, and for "historians"—just as there is need for philosophy. Each interest in its own way can contribute powerfully to the unification of intellectual perspectives. But this need is pedagogical rather than strictly rational, and it is probably best satisfied when neither historians nor philosophers remain isolated in separate "departments" of their own, but co-operate with teachers whose interests are focused in other disciplines. But then—of what academic "department" can this not be said?

On the basis of these facts about the nature of history, we can now proceed to state certain fundamental relations between history and the so-called social "sciences."

(1) For any understanding of the histories that things posses, the social sciences are essential. The processes of change by which anything human has come about are the proper subject-matter of the social sciences, which distinguish those processes, and analyze their structure, and how they co-operate with and interact with other processes as they are found operating in the present. Every history is full of "processes" at work: it exhibits a complex co-operation of processes interacting with each other. A particular history, to be sure, is not itself as a whole a "process." "Process" has meaning only if it exhibits an invariant structure—only if that same process can be repeated in various instances. A process, in other words, is always an instance of a way of acting; and its structure is a way of acting, a "law" or "universal." In contrast, "the history of" anything is always a particular—it is always, as a whole, something unique and unrepeatable, something that is never an instance of any repeated pattern. When we can say justly, "History is repeating itself," we mean we have found a "process" at work—a process whose structure has been exemplified before.

The particular historical changes that have brought about the state of anything whose history we are considering are to be "explained" by drawing on the best available science of human behavior at our disposal—those sciences of cultural change in which certain patterns or constant ways of operating of human behavior have been arrived at through the experimental analysis of observed human behavior. The record of the past of course furnishes materials to these "sciences of cultural change," in the form of instances of the patterns of behavior that can be observed also in the present; and without this temporal dimension our knowledge of the way human nature functions would be exceedingly thin and provincial. But it remains inescapable that it is in terms of our present sciences of human behavior, such as they are—in terms of our anthropology, our psychology, our political science, our economics, our sociology, and the rest—that we must ultimately understand past human behavior, if we are to understand it at all.

"The history of" anything is always a particular, with a unique set of materials of its own, a unique set of human actors, and a unique pattern or structure of the action brought to bear on those materials. The sciences of the processes at work in histories will clearly not explain the presence of these particular materials in a history—institutions, ideas, and men—which are there in it to interact and change, within the unique limits set by those materials in each case. To explain the presence in a history of these particular materials, we have to turn not to the sciences of cultural change, but to tracing the histories of these materials back to those points where they were worked out and formed in their past.

A particular history is thus understood both in terms of the "origins" of its unique materials—"origins" which are themselves always unique histories—and in terms of the operations of human thought and action upon those materials—operations which are illustrations of the sciences of human operations, the social sciences. A history is understood, that is, in terms both of the "continuities" and of the "changes" it exhibits.

For these reasons, it is clear that historical inquiry is not strictly a "science." It includes and makes central this concern with unique materials—institutions, ideas, men, actions. Historical inquiry is thus an "art" or *techne* in the Aristotelian sense—it deals with particulars, but in terms of universals. This means, however, not that historical inquiry is less than a science, but that it is more—it is, as Morris Cohen clearly sees, an "applied science." [1] There is a sense, of course, in which every science in the fullest extent of its functioning is an "applied science." On this view, a body of formalized theoretical principles and conclusions is not itself so much a "science" as it is one of the instruments in the functioning of a science.[2] In such a conception, which has everything to recommend it, history like medicine would be more rather than less scientific than mathematics or theoretical physics, just because it is an art to be practiced.

As an art, or an "applied science," history draws on all the social sciences—they are its essential instruments for dealing with the processes at work in histories. The theoretical "science" history employs, it is well to emphasize, is the subject-matter and the conclusions of the social sciences. Despite repeated attempts, men have never been able to discover any verifiable "scientific laws" of history itself.[3]

There exists a considerable body of evidence to support the position that there are discoverable patterns or "laws" of social change. In this complex field, we have not as yet arrived at any very precise or any very well-established conclusions. But there seems no reason to conclude that the inquiry after such laws should be ruled out as misdirected. There do seem to be patterns discoverable in such change. Naturally, since he has observed so many more instances than any of the other social scientists, it is the anthropoligist who has carried this inquiry furthest, and investigated the complex processes of diffusion and invention and their consequences. Other social sciences have likewise discovered specific patterns of change—like the business cycle of the economists.

But these "laws" of social change belong to the dynamic aspects of the various social sciences, not to history itself. Such a "social dynamics," or "dynamic sociology," is clearly not the same thing as historical inquiry —though the latter eagerly uses and applies all that can be learned from it. The "science of social change" has different problems and procedures from historical inquiry. We may sum up the present state of the evidence, not despite the heroic attempts of Vico, Spengler, Toynbee, Sorokin, and the rest, but rather as a result of the recognized if not acknowledged failure of these attempts, that while there are discoverable patterns of the processes at work in histories, there is no shred of evidence for any "pattern of history" in general.

The results of this analysis indicate that evangelists like James Harvey Robinson and Harry Elmer Barnes are right—in principle. If he is really going to try to write the "history" of everything, "the historian" ought to know all the social sciences, and all the natural sciences and the cultural sciences as well. Very fortunately, there is no such thing as the "history of everything," and no such animal as "the historian," committed to such omniscience. The actual historical profession can more modestly select an historical subject for which it does possess something of the appropriate equipment. Any historian, obviously, should know the sciences of the particular subject-matter whose history he is undertaking to investigate. Not "the historian," but only "the philosopher," is really committed to the obligation to know everything. But then, the last man to be justly called "the philosopher" was Aristotle, who did.

Having made clear how, for any understanding of the histories that things possess, the social sciences are essential, we can now proceed to examine the second fundamental relation between history and the social sciences.

(2) For inquiry in the social sciences, a knowledge of history is essential. This is true because the social sciences are fundamentally historical in character, in at least three basic ways: (a) their subject-matter is fundamentally historical; (b) many of the institutions they deal with have an essentially temporal and historical structure: they are human ways of acting that become unified only in the light of historically generated problems; (c) they necessarily employ methods of historical analysis—though by no means exclusively. I wish now to elucidate these three points.

(a) The subject-matter of the social sciences is fundamentally historical in character. That subject-matter is *human culture,* in the widest sense, as the anthropologist views it. The different social scientists select different aspects of human culture—aspects which are cut out from a common matrix. They are all exploring different perspectives on the same institutionalized behavior of men. This is true even of psychology, which is often considered to deal with "human nature." But "human nature" is nothing other than culture individualized and personalized. In reality, all the social sciences are merely different branches of a common "science of culture." The present division of labor among investigators is largely accidental, historically conditioned, and intelligible only in historical terms. Why, for example, are there "Departments of Sociology" in our institutions of higher learning? And where do they fit in with the other social sciences? Only the intellectual history of the last half of the nineteenth century could possibly give a rationale for a situation that is so rationally unintelligible.

Now human culture, the subject-matter of all the social sciences, is basically historical in character. Not only is it changing in time, and not immutable and eternal like the subject-matters of physics or chemistry, which seem to have remained unchanged during recorded history. Not only is culture historically conditioned, in that it always requires dating in time and location in place. Fundamentally, human culture is progressive and cumulative—it is a series of reworkings of materials inherited from the past, reworkings effected in the light of historically generated tensions.

This historical character of the subject-matter of the social sciences is the major difference between them and the natural sciences. There are, to be sure, natural sciences that are likewise historical in character—such as historical geology, paleontology, etc. The difference between the social and the natural sciences is consequently not the sharp opposition it was made in the German reflection on history and the *Geisteswissenschaften* during the last generation. This opposition, in Dilthey, Windelband, Simmel, Rickert, and others, has made their thought, despite its wealth of incidental insights, pretty confused and sterile. Rather, the social sciences and history have to consider an additional trait in their subject-matter—the trait of being "historical" in character, and of demanding in consequence historical treatment. The more abstract natural sciences, like physics and chemistry, can disregard this pervasive historical trait of the world, with its demand for historical knowledge. The social sciences simply cannot so disregard the historical character of all existence.[4]

Now every society or culture displays a number of distinguishable sets of complex social habits, of "structures" or "patterns" of institutionalized organization of habitual human behavior, institutionalized methods or ways of doing things. These sets include: (1) a technological organization—a set of habitual ways of turning natural materials to human use; (2) an economic organization—a set of habitual ways of controlling the technology of that society, and its fruits; (3) a political organization—a set of institutionalized methods for adjusting conflicts; (4) an intellectual organization—a set of habitual ways of believing about various objects of its experience; we commonly call this the folklore of that society, or, when it is systematically organized in terms of recognized standards, that society's science; (5) a religious organization—a set of institutionalized ways of acting, feeling, and even believing, holding that society together and expressing its common experience, by celebrating, consecrating, and clarifying its accepted values.

These sets of institutionalized social habits are channels or limits within which what men do in that society is carried on and human activities take place. They are not "forces"—they themselves *do* nothing. They are rather ways in which things are done. When for any reason men are led to act differently, then these ways of acting change—they are historically conditioned, we say. Like all habits, however, they have a very considerable inertia, and are changed only with great difficulty.

These "organizations" of socially institutionalized habitual behavior are sets of concrete ways of doing things, viewed *functionally*. They are selected from the total culture in terms of various distinguishable social ends. They are different ways of organizing men's habits to perform various kinds of function. Hence the same concrete activities of men will figure in several or even in all such types of organization—going out on strike, for instance, or leaving money to a church. Each such organization is really a perspective on all the activities of that society from the viewpoint of its distinctive social function. In part, each organization selects certain human activities as having a special bearing on that function. In part, it selects certain consequences of all, or nearly all, human activities.

Now, it is these functional organizations of human behavior that are the distinctive subject-matters of the different social sciences. And it is clear that as subject-matters they are all *historical* in character. They are temporally changing. They are historically conditioned. They are progressive and cumulative. They are "relative" and "limited to" a particular historical situation. And they all demand historical analysis.

This is true also of the subject-matter of psychology, "human nature." Human nature not only exhibits different powers in different cultures. It actually possesses a different constitution in different cultures. For "human nature" is not in any significant sense the wealth of possibility of response inherent in the human organism at birth, in the human "frame." It is rather the organization of the responses the human frame makes possible, the particular set of organized habits generated by the social institutions that are its primary environment. It is the organism, the human frame, that is constant and "original," not human nature, which is fundamentally historical, like the more specifically functional organizations of habits already indicated. Human nature is an "historical nature."

The human frame is extraordinarily plastic, before its organization into "human nature"—into a particular set of institutionalized group habits. It often seems that anthropologists have discovered every conceivable form of organization of human nature, in some culture or other. And human nature when so organized is extraordinarily tough and refractory. The toughness explains the fact of persistence, continuity, and tradition, where change has not been forced on human nature. The plasticity explains the novel behavior, when new ways of acting have been imposed—as by technology in our own culture, for example. This double fact makes plain, for instance, why the Russians are today still behaving in many ways as they always have, with their long tradition of Byzantine organization, despite the most drastic social revolution of all time. It also makes clear why no limits are set on the ways they will eventually display, by the ways in which we find, say, Americans now acting.

This illustration suggests that the powers of human nature—that is, of social institutions or group behavior—are revealed only in their operation under varied conditions. They are manifested only in history. But how those powers have operated in the past sets no limits on how they will operate in the future, with changed conditions in any one of the determining organizations, technological, economic, political, intellectual, religious, etc. History thus reveals much but teaches nothing about human nature. It explains why human nature is today what it is. It points to the factors and events that have organized it in the way we now find it functioning— and also to the factors and events that are changing that way and that organization. But history does not and cannot reveal what human nature will be.

(b) The social sciences are fundamentally historical in character, secondly, because many of the institutions they deal with have a structure that is itself essentially temporal and historical.

The simplest illustration of an "historical nature," that is, of something whose nature *is identical* with its history, and is definable only in historical terms, is a biological organism, like a seed we plant and watch unfold the pattern of its growth. The seed *is* its career in time; the structure of that career is temporal and cumulative, *time* enters into its very substance. Such a "career" in time can be traced from its very beginning; we can follow the development of what eventuates as a whole, of what emerges at the harvest. Similarly, the life of a man is just such a temporal "career."

Of such "careers" or historical natures we can tell the story. They lend themselves to the art of story-telling, of historical narrative. This art naturally selects its own appropriate materials. And past historians, having been great story-tellers, have chosen such "careers" as their subject-matter —episodes with some degree of dramatic unity, like the biographies of men, dramatic episodes such as wars, political campaigns and struggles, strikes, such dramatic themes as the rise of Rome or the conquest of Peru.

But the social scientist is usually concerned with more complex temporal structures or "historical natures," with societies, cultures, and institutions. These historical natures are likewise fundamentally historical in essence or structure, but they have no "career" as a whole, like the seed, that can be traced from its beginnings; for they are not wholes. A society or a social institution is not an "organism," despite the many attempts so to view them, especially in the heyday of evolutionary biological ideas in the last century. And all attempts to conceive an organism as a "society," like those of Leibniz, Diderot's "swarm of bees," Whitehead's generalization, have broken down in the face of the problem of accounting for that factor in a living organism which a "society" obviously does not possess— a unified "life" or "soul." A seed possesses what Aristotle called a "vegetative life," and an animal has a behavior as a whole. But a society has no "life," "mind," "soul," or *"Geist"*—it has no behavior as a whole. For it is not a "whole," a "totality." A society is not like a unified organism, but is more like a biological "religion"—like the lake Peattie describes in Oak Grove, Illinois, or like what the biologist means when he writes on "the natural history of the Plains region." A society, that is, is like a biological region, a group of interacting careers and histories, constituted by certain geographic and climatic limits.

Negatively, this means that there is no "career" of a society, with a single unified temporal pattern, like the career of the seed. Nor is there any unified "career" of a particular social institution—for such institutions are likewise not unities or wholes. Thus, there is no single "science" that has enjoyed a career in Western culture, like the career of the seed. If we ask, what was the career of "science" during the Middle Ages? we have to go on to ask, which "science" would it be? The symbolic science worked out by the Victorines? Or the Aristotelian science that gained a foothold in the universities in the thirteenth century? Or "our own" science? But "our" science did not as yet exist—though its "history" certainly takes us back to the Middle Ages.

Likewise, there is no discoverable "career" of medieval culture. For there were no "Middle Ages" until self-conscious "moderns" arose to criticize and fight and escape from them. There is also no career of "feudalism." For "feudalism" did not make its appearance—that is, men's action and thought were not taken as illustrating any unified political institution of "feudalism"—until the seventeenth- and eighteenth-century lawyers began to want to escape from certain features of their institutionalized political behavior, and proceeded to analyze those particular features of their "political organization" whose elimination formed their practical problem.[5]

Nor is there any discoverable "career" of "capitalism"; for "capitalism" did not exist—in the welter of confused and contradictory ways in which men have always acted economically—until men appeared who wanted to escape from certain of those ways, and proceeded to formulate a "capitalistic system" in the light of those features. It is notorious that the term "capitalism" was invented by the Socialists; and it is only in the last twenty-five years that it has been accepted as the name of something to be defended, in conscious reaction against socialistic attacks. The term "capitalism" was first used in English in 1854.[6] And Werner Sombart writes: "The concept of capitalism and even more clearly the term itself may be traced primarily to the writings of *socialist* theoreticians. It has in fact remained one of the key concepts of socialism down to the present time. Nevertheless, it cannot be said that a clear cut definition has ever been attempted. Even Karl Marx, who virtually discovered the phenomenon, defined only certain aspects of capitalism as the occasion required." [7]

Positively, these institutions which are so fundamental to social science are one complex type of "historical nature"; they are ways of acting that have become historically unified in the light of historically generated problems. We may hence call them, in distinction from other types of historical nature, like the unities that possess a "career," "historical unifications." They all possess a "history," when we look backward from the focus of the problems they have generated. We can then trace factors in them back into the past, find the "sources" and "genesis" of different elements, antecedents that have led up to what has eventuated. We can trace the genesis of the problems in terms of which they have now become historically unified institutions. But there is no "career" of them, in the sense of beginning at the "beginning," or at any "beginning," or at any given point, and following the development of what eventuated as a whole. What has eventuated is not a whole, but a plurality of ways of behaving, interacting and generating unifying problems.

Societies and social institutions possess a complex, pluralistic structure of interacting habit patterns. They are not unified "wholes" or "organisms" with an organic structure. Rather, to borrow a current jargon, they are "an interpenetration of opposites." What belongs to that institution, and what "interpenetrates" it, is not known until the latter has become an "opposite"—that is, until it has generated a tension and a problem. Such institutions are "historical unifications" of behavior, selected by their historical development as structures and patterns with which the social sciences must deal. They do not merely possess an historical and temporal structure, like the seed, or the life of a man, or whatever exhibits a career. They are actually *created* as structures, as institutions, by historical processes. And they are intelligible only to the light of that history, through historical analysis, which singles out that historical structure from the complex facts and unifies it.

When so selected and unified, such historically generated institutions stand out against the confused facts. Consider the contrast between the infinitely complex mass of arrangements that succeeded each other during the Middle Ages, and the neat theory of the "feudalism" the eighteenth-century *philosophes* wanted to abolish completely. Or take the contrast between the welter of conflicting philosophical doctrines of the nineteenth century, and the philosophic naturalism we now see to have been emerging, and support. Or mark the contrast between the confused and contradictory ways of acting our culture displays today—its actual complex functioning, as the institutional economist would describe it—and the unified "capitalistic system" we can formulate in the light of the problems those ways generate.

Such historical unifications are intelligible only by means of an historical analysis. How much and what part of our present economic activities constitute "capitalism"? How much and what part of our present religious activities constitute "Christianity"? These activities are so manifold and confused, they exhibit so much "interpenetration," that no strictly contemporary analysis could avoid being arbitrary. Analysis of such institutions can become objective only by becoming historical. What is "essential" to capitalism or to Christianity is revealed only in the histories of our economic or our religious problems; it is clarified only when we see what has happened to saddle us with those problems.

In these problems, they have become genuine historical unifications, which have histories; and it is precisely these histories which made the unifications objective. No "earlier stages" are clearly distinguishable until problems have emerged. But those problems and their elements are then understood only in the light of "earlier stages" *of* those elements—stages which are quite objectively relative to the present form. Take "private property," for example. Only an historical analysis can determine what is "private property" today, and why. What private property, for instance, is represented by a share of non-voting common stock in a holding company for a bankrupt railroad mortgaged to the R. F. C.? It took an historian—Charles A. Beard—to find out who "owns" what in our railroads today.

(c) This is an illustration of the fact that, since their subject-matter is basically historical, and since many of the institutions they deal with are "historical unifications" created by history, the social sciences necessarily employ methods of historical analysis—though not exclusively so.

There is, in the first place, no such thing as *the* historical method," or *the* method of historical analysis." There are rather many different types of historical analysis, appropriate to different kinds of problems in different social sciences. These various types need careful analysis and distinguishing; but this is hardly the place to undertake it. It would require a year's course, or an entire volume, to deal even cursorily with all the problems involved.

Secondly, historical analysis is not of itself sufficient to deal with any problem in the social sciences. It must always be used in connection with other types of analysis—formal or structural analysis, and functional analysis. The latter is primary, and involves the others; though the reasons why are hardly pertinent to the present theme.

Here, I can only illustrate something of the relation between historical and functional analysis in the case of the very difficult problem of evaluation. Tracing the continuous history of a way of acting or believing—that is, of any institution—will disclose the specific function performed by that way or institution in the past. And it will reveal how well that way did its job. Such tracing of a history will not reveal the present functioning of that way, or its adequacy today. But it will illuminate the difference between past and present conditions, in which the institution has functioned and is functioning. And it will illuminate the consequent decline in adequacy of functioning—or even the changes in the very function performed.

This is why history is always relevant to an evaluation in the present, although it can never in itself furnish such an evaluation. To believe that it can and does is the "genetic fallacy," so justly condemned in our generation, in atonement for the intellectual sins of our evolutionary fathers. Since the genetic fallacy was so strongly castigated by Morris Cohen, a few general remarks may be in order on the sense in which the genesis of any belief is relevant to its validity, and the sense in which to appeal to origins is fallacious.

Beliefs are in fact, in the actual procedure of the scientist, judged to be scientifically "warranted," "verified," or proved to be "true," when they give a satisfactory solution to the specific problem to which they have been proposed as an answer. They are validated only when they have succeeded in doing what they were instituted to do. Beliefs, in scientific inquiry, are always designed to perform some determinate function. The objective criterion of their validity is the success of their functioning in the specific way in which they were designed to function. The question always is: Do they actually solve the specific and determinate problem they were designed to solve? This functional test is decisive. Whatever their origin, beliefs are ultimately validated by the way they function, not by the way they were generated.[8] To maintain that genetic considerations can of themselves validate or invalidate a belief, that the origin of knowledge is the test of its extent and certainty, is to commit the "genetic fallacy"— and it is a logical fallacy.

But in determining whether beliefs are functioning adequately so as to solve the specific problem they were worked out to solve, reference *to* that problem is obviously involved. In this sense, the standard of the adequate functioning of beliefs *does* involve the problematic situation from which they take their start. This genesis or origin can therefore be said to determine the specific problem the belief must satisfy in order to be warranted. It determines the context and the conditions in which the belief must function, and the nature of the function it must perform.

Thus any functional test of the validity and value of a belief does involve knowledge of the genesis of that belief, of its history. The functional method must include as a part of its procedure just such a "genetic analysis." Stated more fully, the functional method of verifying or warranting beliefs is a "genetic-functional" method. And as a matter of fact, every scientist, in reporting his conclusions or discoveries, does give a detailed account of just what he did to arrive at that outcome—his problem, his reasoning, his experiments, his findings, his interpretation. These genetic considerations are clearly relevant to the question of whether his conclusions are validated or warranted. To deny the relevance of this specification of the problem and context in which the beliefs were formulated, is to commit the "formalistic" or "structuralist" fallacy—and it is a logical fallacy. It is one which I am afraid Morris Cohen often committed, in theory at least. He failed to give due weight to genetic considerations, just because he was not enough of a functionalist in his thinking. His own method remains largely "intuitionist-structuralist," not "genetic-functional." [9]

In general, then, genetic considerations are always relevant to questions of validity and value, and are usually necessary. But the determination of the problem, what a belief must do, and the context in which it must do it, though a necessary condition of discovering whether the belief is valid, is unfortunately not a sufficient condition. Beliefs cannot be validated in terms of their origins alone, though they cannot be validated without reference to the problem in which they originated. Nothing can be judged in terms of its history alone, though nothing can be judged without reference to the function for which it originated.

This logical analysis of the procedure of validation and evaluation can be illustrated in the process of the evaluation of social institutions. For example, a famous remark of the late President Roosevelt ran: "The Constitution was devised for the horse-and-buggy age." This is an undoubted historical fact—though it raises questions in detail as to the history of transportation. Actually, the Constitution is more "old-fashioned" than the buggy, and was invented several generations earlier. This historical fact, however, does not indicate whether or not a "horse-and-buggy" Constitution is adequate for our own steamlined era—though it does suggest the inquiry. Rather, when we today find that the checks and balances of the Constitution, its decentralization, etc., are not wholly adequate to our own political needs, and when we are hence forced to face the practical problems generated, the history of the Constitution makes clear why we are facing those problems. It focuses attention on the changed function we now require of our constitutional instrument. It reveals how well the Constitution performed in the past the functions which a functional analysis of our present situation may well indicate we can no longer afford to let it continue to perform.

The history of an institution is thus not in itself an evaluation. Nothing is good or bad merely because it has been—though familiarity is certainly a positive value. But history can make clear that a fresh evaluation is called for. And history provides many—though not all—of the factors necessary for that evaluation.

What has just been illustrated in connection with judging and evaluating is true of understanding in general. Nothing in the social sciences can be understood in terms of its history alone, though nothing can be understood without reference to that history. In general, we may state the conclusion of this analysis of the relation between history and the social sciences as follows: History cannot do its job without the social sciences, and the social sciences cannot do theirs without history. Each needs the other, but neither is to be confused with the other, or absorbed in or reduced to the other. Here are all the makings of a perfect marriage. What God hath joined together, let no man put asunder.

[28a]

MAX WEBER

"Objectivity" in Social Science *

There is no absolutely "objective" scientific analysis of culture—or put perhaps more narrowly but certainly not essentially differently for our purposes—of "social phenomena" independent of special and "one-sided" viewpoints according to which—expressly or tacitly, consciously or unconsciously—they are selected, analyzed and organized for expository purposes. The reasons for this lie in the character of the cognitive goal of all research in social science which seeks to transcend the purely *formal* treatment of the legal or conventional norms regulating social life.

* Reprinted from Max Weber, *On the Methodology of the Social Sciences*. Translated and edited by Edward A. Shils and Henry A. Finch. The Free Press of Glencoe, Illinois, 1949. Copyright, 1949, by The Free Press. Pp. 72–90. By permission of The Free Press.

The type of social science in which we are interested is an *empirical science* of concrete *reality* (*Wirklichkeitswissenschaft*). Our aim is the understanding of the characteristic uniqueness of the reality in which we move. We wish to understand on the one hand the relationships and the cultural significance of individual events in their contemporary manifestations and on the other the causes of their being historically *so* and not *otherwise*. Now, as soon as we attempt to reflect about the way in which life confronts us in immediate concrete situations, it presents an infinite multiplicity of successively and coexistently emerging and disappearing events, both "within" and "outside" ourselves. The absolute infinitude of this multiplicity is seen to remain undiminished even when our attention is focused on a single "object," for instance, a concrete act of exchange, as soon as we seriously attempt an exhaustive description of *all* the individual components of this "individual phenomena," to say nothing of explaining it causally. All the analysis of infinite reality which the finite human mind can conduct rests on the tacit assumption that only a finite portion of this reality constitutes the object of scientific investigation, and that only it is "important" in the sense of being "worthy of being known." But what are the criteria by which this segment is selected? It has often been thought that the decisive criterion in the cultural sciences, too, was in the last analysis, the "regular" recurrence of certain causal relationships. The "laws" which we are able to perceive in the infinitely manifold stream of events must—according to this conception—contain the scientifically "essential" aspect of reality. As soon as we have shown some causal relationship to be a "law," i.e., if we have shown it to be universally valid by means of comprehensive historical induction or have made it immediately and tangibly plausible according to our subjective experience, a great number of similar cases order themselves under the formula thus attained. Those elements in each individual event which are left unaccounted for by the selection of their elements subsumable under the "law" are considered as scientifically unintegrated residues which will be taken care of in the further perfection of the system of "laws." Alternatively they will be viewed as "accidental" and therefore scientifically unimportant *because* they do not fit into the structure of the "law"; in other words, they are not typical of the event and hence can only be the objects of "idle curiosity." Accordingly, even among the followers of the Historical School we continually find the attitude which declares that the ideal which all the sciences, including the cultural sciences, serve and towards which they should strive even in the remote future is a system of propositions from which reality can be "deduced." As is well known, a leading natural scientist believed that he could designate the (factually unattainable) ideal goal of such a treatment of cultural reality as a sort of *"astronomical"* knowledge.

Let us not, for our part, spare ourselves the trouble of examining these matters more closely—however often they have already been discussed. The first thing that impresses one is that the "astronomical" knowledge which was referred to is not a system of laws at all. On the contrary, the laws which it presupposes have been taken from other disciplines like mechanics. But it too concerns itself with the question of the *individual* consequence which the working of these laws in an unique *configuration* produces, since it is these individual configurations which are *significant* for us. Every individual constellation which it "explains" or predicts is causally explicable only as the consequence of another equally individual constellation which has preceded it. As far back as we may go into the grey mist of the far-off past, the reality to which the laws apply always remains equally *individual,* equally *undeducible* from laws. A cosmic "primeval state" which had no individual character or less individual character than the cosmic reality of the present would naturally be a meaningless notion. But is there not some trace of similar ideas in our field in those propositions sometimes derived from natural law and sometimes verified by the observation of "primitives," concerning an economic-social "primeval state" free from historical "accidents," and characterized by phenomena such as "primitive agrarian communism," sexual "promiscuity," etc., from which individual historical development emerges by a sort of fall from grace into concreteness?

The social-scientific interest has its point of departure, of course, in the *real,* i.e., concrete, individually-structured configuration of our cultural life in its universal relationships which are themselves no less individually-structured, and in its development out of other social cultural conditions, which themselves are obviously likewise individually structured. It is clear here that the situation which we illustrated by reference to astronomy as a limiting case (which is regularly drawn on by logicians for the same purpose) appears in a more accentuated form. Whereas in astronomy, the heavenly bodies are of interest to us only in their *quantitative* and exact aspects, the *qualitative* aspect of phenomena concerns us in the social sciences. To this should be added that in the social sciences we are concerned with psychological and intellectual (*geistig*) phenomena the emphatic understanding of which is naturally a problem of a specifically different type from those which the schemes of the exact natural sciences in general can or seem to solve. Despite that, this distinction in itself is not a distinction in principle, as it seems at first glance. Aside from pure mechanics, even the exact natural sciences do not proceed without qualitative categories. Furthermore, in our own field we encounter the idea (which is obviously distorted) that at least the phenomena characteristic of a money-economy—which are basic to our culture—are quantifiable and on that account subject to formulation as "laws." Finally it depends on the breadth or narrowness of one's definition of "law" as to whether one will also include regularities which because they are not quantifiable are not subject to numerical analysis. Especially insofar as the influence of psychological and intellectual (*geistige*) factors is concerned, it does not in any case exclude the establishment of *rules* governing rational conduct. Above all, the point of view still persists which claims that the task of psychology is to play a role comparable to mathematics for the *Geistes-*

wissenschaften in the sense that it analyzes the complicated phenomena of social life into their psychic conditions and effects, reduces them to their most elementary possible psychic factors and then analyzes their functional interdependences. Thereby, a sort of "chemistry" if not "mechanics" of the psychic foundations of social life would be created. Whether such investigations can produce valuable and—what is something else—useful results for the cultural sciences, we cannot decide here. But this would be irrelevant to the question as to whether the aim of social-economic knowledge in our sense, i.e., knowledge of *reality* with respect to its cultural *significance* and its causal relationships can be attained through the quest for recurrent sequences. Let us assume that we have succeeded by means of psychology or otherwise in analyzing all the observed and imaginable relationships of social phenomena into some ultimate elementary "factors," that we have made an exhaustive analysis and classification of them and then formulated rigorously exact laws covering their behavior.—What would be the significance of these results for our knowledge of the *historically* given culture or any individual phase thereof, such as capitalism, in its development and cultural significance? As an analytical tool, it would be as useful as a textbook of organic chemical combinations would be for our knowledge of the biogenetic aspect of the animal and plant world. In each case, certainly an important and useful preliminary step would have been taken. In neither case can concrete reality be deduced from "laws" and "factors." This is not because some higher mysterious powers reside in living phenomena (such as "dominants," "entelechies," or whatever they might be called). This, however, is a problem in its own right. The real reason is that the analysis of reality is concerned with the *configuration* into which those (hypothetical!) "factors" are arranged to form a cultural phenomenon which is historically significant to us. Furthermore, if we wish to "explain" this individual configuration "causally" we must invoke other equally individual configurations on the basis of which we will explain it with the aid of those (hypothetical!) "laws."

The determination of those (hypothetical) "laws" and "factors" would in any case only be the first of the many operations which would lead us to the desired type of knowledge. The analysis of the historically given individual configuration of those "factors" and their *significant* concrete interaction, conditioned by their historical context and especially the *rendering intelligible* of the basis and type of this significance would be the next task to be achieved. This task must be achieved, it is true, by the utilization of the preliminary analysis but it is nonetheless an entirely new and *distinct* task. The tracing as far into the past as possible of the individual features of these historically evolved configurations which are *contemporaneously* significant, and their historical explanation by antecedent and equally individual configurations would be the third task. Finally the prediction of possible future constellations would be a conceivable fourth task.

For all these purposes, clear concepts and the knowledge of those (hypothetical) "laws" are obviously of great value as heuristic means—but only as such. Indeed they are quite indispensable for this purpose. But even in this function their limitations become evident at a decisive point. In stating this, we arrive at the decisive feature of the method of the cultural sciences. We have designated as "cultural sciences" those disciplines which analyze the phenomena of life in terms of their cultural significance. The *significance* of a configuration of cultural phenomena and the basis of this significance cannot however be derived and rendered intelligible by a system of analytical laws (*Gesetzesbegriffen*), however perfect it may be, since the significance of cultural events presupposes a *value-orientation* towards these events. The concept of culture is a *value-concept*. Empirical reality becomes "culture" to us because and insofar as we relate it to value ideas. It includes those segments and only those segments of reality which have become significant to us because of this value-relevance. Only a small portion of existing concrete reality is colored by our value-conditioned interest and it alone is significant to us. It is significant because it reveals relationships which are important to us due to their connection with our values. Only because and to the extent that this is the case is it worthwhile for us to know it in its individual features. We cannot discover, however, what is meaningful to us by means of a "presuppositionless" investigation of empirical data. Rather perception of its meaningfulness to us is the presupposition of its becoming an *object* of investigation. Meaningfulness naturally does not coincide with laws as such, and the more general the law the less the coincidence. For the specific meaning which a phenomenon has for us is naturally *not* to be found in those relationships which it shares with many other phenomena.

The focus of attention on reality under the guidance of values which lend it significance and the selection and ordering of the phenomena which are thus affected in the light of their cultural significance is entirely different from the analysis of reality in terms of laws and general concepts. Neither of these two types of the analysis of reality has any necessary logical relationship with the other. They can coincide in individual instances but it would be most disastrous if their occasional coincidence caused us to think that they were not distinct *in principle*. The *cultural significance* of a phenomenon, e.g., the significance of exchange in a money economy, can be the fact that it exists on a mass scale as a fundamental component of modern culture. But the historical fact that it plays this role must be causally explained in order to render its cultural significance understandable. The analysis of the *general* aspects of exchange and the technique of the market is a—highly important and indispensable—*preliminary task*. For not only does this type of analysis leave unanswered the question as to how exchange historically acquired its fundamental significance in the modern world; but above all else, the fact with which we are primarily concerned, namely, the *cultural significance* of the money-economy, for the sake of which we are interested in the description of exchange technique and for the sake of which alone a science exists which deals with that technique—is not derivable from any "law." The *generic features* of exchange, purchase, etc., interest the jurist—but we are concerned with the analysis of the *cultural significance* of the concrete *historical* fact that today exchange exists on a mass scale. When we require an explanation, when we wish to understand what distinguishes the social-economic aspects of our culture for instance from that of antiquity in which exchange showed precisely the same generic traits as it does today and when we raise the question as to where the significance of "money economy" lies, logical principles of quite heterogeneous derivation enter into the investigation. We will apply those concepts with which we are provided by the investigation of the general features of economic mass phenomena—indeed, insofar as they are relevant to the meaningful aspects of our culture, we shall use them as *means* of exposition. The *goal* of our investigation is not reached through the exposition of those laws and concepts, precise as it may be. The question as to what should be the object of universal conceptualization cannot be decided "presuppositionlessly" but only with reference to the *significance* which certain segments of that infinite multiplicity which we call "commerce" have for culture. We seek knowledge of an historical phenomenon, meaning by historical: significant in its individuality (*Eigenart*). And the decisive element in this is that only through the presupposition that a finite part alone of the infinite variety of phenomena is significant, does the knowledge of an individual phenomenon become logically meaningful. Even with the widest imaginable knowledge of "laws," we are helpless in the face of the question: how is the *causal explanation* of an *individual* fact possible—since a *description* of even the smallest slice of reality can never be exhaustive? The number and type of causes which have influenced any given event are always infinite and there is nothing in the things themselves to set some of them apart as alone meriting attention. A chaos of "existential judgments" about countless individual events would be the only result of a serious attempt to analyze reality "without presuppositions." And even this result is only seemingly possible, since every single perception discloses on closer examination an infinite number of constituent perceptions which can never be exhaustively expressed in a judgement. Order is brought into this chaos only on the condition that in every case only a *part* of concrete reality is interesting and *significant* to us, because only it is related to the *cultural values* with which we approach reality. Only certain sides of the infinitely complex concrete phenomenon, namely those to which we attribute a general *cultural significance*—are therefore worthwhile knowing. They alone are objects of causal explanation. And even this causal explanation evinces the same character; an *exhaustive* causal investigation of any concrete phenomena in its full reality is not only practically impossible—it is simply nonsense. We select only those causes to which are to be imputed in the individual case, the "essential" feature of an event. Where the *individuality* of a phenomenon is concerned, the question of causality is not a question of *laws* but of concrete causal *relationships*; it is not a question of the subsumption of the event under some general rubric as a representative case but of its imputation as a consequence of some constellation. It is in brief a *question of imputation*. Wherever the causal explanation of a "cultural phenomenon"—an "historical individual" is under consideration, the knowledge of causal *laws* is not the *end* of the investigation but only a *means*. It facilitates and renders possible the causal imputation to their concrete causes of those components of a phenomenon the individuality of which is culturally significant. So far and only so far as it achieves this, is it valuable for our knowledge of concrete relationships. And the more "general," i.e., the more abstract the laws, the less they can contribute to the causal imputation of *individual* phenomena and, more indirectly, to the understanding of the significance of cultural events.

What is the consequence of all this?

Naturally, it does not imply that the knowledge of *universal* propositions, the construction of abstract concepts, the knowledge of regularities and the attempt to formulate *"laws"* have no scientific justification in the cultural sciences. Quite the contrary, if the causal knowledge of the historians consists of the imputation of concrete effects to concrete causes, a *valid* imputation of any individual effect without the application of *"nomological" knowledge*—i.e., the knowledge of recurrent causal sequences—would in general be impossible. Whether a single individual component of a relationship is, in a concrete case, to be assigned causal responsibility for an effect, the causal explanation of which is at issue, can in doubtful cases be determined only by estimating the effects which we *generally* expect from it and from the other components of the same complex which are relevant to the explanation. In other words, the *"adequate"* effects of the causal elements involved must be considered in arriving at any such conclusion. The extent to which the historian (in the widest sense of the word) can perform this imputation in a reasonably certain manner with his imagination sharpened by personal experience and trained in analytic methods and the extent to which he must have recourse to the aid of special disciplines which make it possible, varies with the individual case. Everywhere, however, and hence also in the sphere of complicated economic processes, the more certain and the more comprehensive our general knowledge the greater is the *certainty* of imputation. This proposition is not in the least affected by the fact that even in the case of all so-called "economic laws" without exception, we are concerned here not with "laws" in the narrower exact natural science sense, but with *adequate* causal relationships expressed in rules and with the application of the category of "objective possibility." The establishment of such regularities is not the *end* but rather the *means* of knowledge. It is entirely a question of expediency, to be settled separately for each individual case, whether a regularly recurrent causal relationship of everyday experience should be formulated into a "law." Laws are important and valuable in the exact natural sciences, in the measure that those sciences are *universally valid*. For the knowledge of historical phenomena in their concreteness, the most general laws, because they are most devoid of content are also the least valuable. The more comprehensive the validity,—or scope—of a term, the more it leads us away from the richness of reality since in order to include the common elements of the largest possible number of phenomena, it must necessarily be as abstract as possible and hence *devoid* of content. In the cultural sciences, the knowledge of the universal or general is never valuable in itself.

The conclusion which follows from the above is that an "objective" analysis of cultural events, which proceeds according to the thesis that the ideal of science is the reduction of empirical reality to "laws," is meaningless. It is not meaningless, as is often maintained, because cultural or psychic events for instance are "objectively" less governed by laws. It is meaningless for a number of other reasons. Firstly, because the knowledge of social laws is not knowledge of social reality but is rather one of the various aids used by our minds for attaining this end; secondly, because knowledge of *cultural* events is inconceivable except on a basis of the significance which the concrete constellations of reality have for us in certain *individual* concrete situations. In *which* sense and in *which* situations this is the case is not revealed to us by any law; it is decided according to the *value-ideas* in the light of which we view "culture" in each individual case. "Culture" is a finite segment of the meaningless infinity of the world process, a segment on which *human beings* confer meaning and significance. This is true even for the human being who views a *particular* culture as a mortal enemy and who seeks to "return to nature." He can attain this point of view only after viewing the culture in which he lives from the standpoint of his values, and finding it "too soft." This is the purely logical-formal fact which is involved when we speak of the logically necessary rootedness of all historical entities (*historische Individuen*) in "evaluative ideas." The transcendental presupposition of every *cultural science* lies not in our finding a certain culture or any "culture" in general to be *valuable* but rather in the fact that we are *cultural beings*, endowed with the capacity and the will to take a deliberate attitude towards the world and to lend it *significance*. Whatever this significance may be, it will lead us to judge certain phenomena of human existence in its light and to respond to them as being (positively or negatively) meaningful. Whatever may be the content of this attitude—these phenomena have cultural significance for us and on this significance alone rests its scientific interest. Thus when we speak here of the conditioning of cultural knowledge through *evaluative* ideas (*Wertideen*) (following the terminology of modern logic), it is done in the hope that we will not be subject to crude misunderstandings such as the opinion that cultural significance should be attributed only to *valuable* phenomena. Prostitution is a *cultural* phenomenon just as much as religion or money. All three are cultural phenomena *only* because and *only* insofar as their existence and the form which they historically assume touch directly or indirectly on our cultural *interests* and arouse our striving for knowledge concerning problems brought into focus by the

evaluative ideas which give *significance* to the fragment of reality analyzed
by those concepts.

All knowledge of cultural reality, as may be seen, is always knowledge
from *particular points of view*. When we require from the historian and
social research worker as an elementary presupposition that they distinguish the important from the trivial and that he should have the necessary
"point of view" for this distinction, we mean that they must understand
how to relate the events of the real world consciously or unconsciously to
universal "cultural values" and to select out those relationships which are
significant for us. If the notion that those standpoints can be derived from
the "facts themselves" continually recurs, it is due to the naive self-deception of the specialist who is unaware that it is due to the evaluative ideas
with which he unconsciously approaches his subject matter, that he has
selected from an absolute infinity a tiny portion with the study of which
he *concerns* himself. In connection with this selection of individual special
"aspects" of the event which always and everywhere occurs, consciously
or unconsciously, there also occurs that element of cultural-scientific work
which is referred to by the often-heard assertion that the "personal" element of a scientific work is what is really valuable in it, and that personality must be expressed in every work if its existence is to be justified. To be
sure, without the investigator's evaluative ideas, there would be no principle of selection of subject-matter and no meaningful knowledge of the
concrete reality. Just as without the investigator's conviction regarding the
significance of particular cultural facts, every attempt to analyze concrete
reality is absolutely meaningless, so the direction of his personal belief, the
refraction of values in the prism of his mind, gives direction to his work.
And the values to which the scientific genius relates the object of his
inquiry may determine, i.e., decide the "conception" of a whole epoch, not
only concerning what is regarded as "valuable" but also concerning what
is significant or insignificant, "important" or "unimportant" in the phenomena.

Accordingly, cultural science in our sense involves "subjective" presuppositions insofar as it concerns itself only with those components of
reality which have some relationship, however indirect, to events to which
we attach cultural *significance*. Nonetheless, it is entirely *causal* knowledge
exactly in the same sense as the knowledge of significant concrete (*indi-
vidueller*) natural events which have a qualitative character. Among the
many confusions which the over-reaching tendency of a formal-juristic
outlook has brought about in the cultural sciences, there has recently appeared the attempt to "refute" the "materialistic conception of history" by
a series of clever but fallacious arguments which state that since all economic life must take place in legally or conventionally *regulated forms*, all
economic "development" must take the form of striving for the creation of
new *legal* forms. Hence, it is said to be intelligible only through ethical
maxims and is on this account essentially different from every type of
"natural" development. Accordingly the knowledge of economic develop-

ment is said to be "teleological" in character. Without wishing to discuss the meaning of the ambiguous term "development," or the logically no less ambiguous term "teleology" in the social sciences, it should be stated that such knowledge need not be "teleological" in the sense assumed by this point of view. The cultural significance of normatively regulated legal *relations* and even norms themselves can undergo fundamental revolutionary changes even under conditions of the formal identity of the prevailing legal norms. Indeed, if one wishes to lose one's self for a moment in phantasies about the future, one might theoretically imagine, let us say, the "socialization of the means of production" unaccompanied by any conscious "striving" towards this result, and without even the disappearance or addition of a single paragraph of our legal code; the statistical frequency of certain legally regulated relationships might be changed fundamentally, and in many cases, even disappear entirely; a great number of legal norms might become *practically* meaningless and their whole cultural significance changed beyond identification. *De lege ferenda* discussions may be justifiably disregarded by the "materialistic conception of history" since its central proposition is the indeed inevitable change in the *significance* of legal institutions. Those who view the painstaking labor of causally understanding historical reality as of secondary importance can disregard it, but it is impossible to supplant it by any type of "teleology." From our viewpoint, "purpose" is the conception of an *effect* which becomes a *cause* of an action. Since we take into account every cause which produces or can produce a significant effect, we also consider this one. Its specific significance consists only in the fact that we not only *observe* human conduct but can and desire to understand it.

Undoubtedly, all evaluative ideas are "subjective." Between the "historical" interest in a family chronicle and that in the development of the greatest conceivable cultural phenomena which were and are common to a nation or to mankind over long epochs, there exists an infinite gradation of "significance" arranged into an order which differs for each of us. And they are, naturally, historically variable in accordance with the character of the culture and the ideas which rule men's minds. But it obviously does not follow from this that research in the cultural sciences can only have results which are "subjective" in the sense that they are *valid* for one person and not for others. Only the degree to which they interest different persons varies. In other words, the choice of the object of investigation and the extent or depth to which this investigation attempts to penetrate into the infinite causal web, are determined by the evaluative ideas which dominate the investigator and his age. In the *method* of investigation, the guiding "point of view" is of great importance for the *construction* of the conceptual scheme which will be used in the investigation. In the mode of their *use*, however, the investigator is obviously bound by the norms of our thought just as much here as elsewhere. For scientific truth is precisely what is *valid* for all who *seek* the truth.

However, there emerges from this the meaninglessness of the idea

which prevails occasionally even among historians, namely, that the goal
of the cultural sciences, however far it may be from realization, is to construct a closed system of concepts, in which reality is synthesized in some
sort of *permanently* and *universally* valid classification and from which it
can again be deduced. The stream of immeasurable events flows unendingly
towards eternity. The cultural problems which move men from themselves
ever anew and in different colors, and the boundaries of that area in the
infinite stream of concrete events which acquires meaning and significance
for us, i.e., which becomes an "historical individual," are constantly subject
to change. The intellectual contexts from which it is viewed and scientifically analyzed shift. The points of departure of the cultural sciences remain changeable throughout the limitless future as long as a Chinese
ossification of intellectual life does not render mankind incapable of setting
new questions to the externally inexhaustible flow of life. A systematic
science of culture, even only in the sense of a definitive, objectively valid,
systematic fixation of the problems which it should treat, would be senseless in itself. Such an attempt could only produce a collection of numerous,
specifically particularized, heterogeneous and disparate viewpoints in the
light of which reality becomes "culture" through being significant in its
unique character.

Having now completed this lengthy discussion, we can finally turn
to the question which is *methodologically* relevant in the consideration of
the "objectivity" of cultural knowledge. The question is: what is the
logical function and structure of the *concepts* which our science, like all
others, uses? Restated with special reference to the decisive problem, the
question is: what is the significance of *theory* and theoretical conceptualization (*theoretische Begriffsbildung*) for our knowledge of cultural
reality?

Economics was originally—as we have already seen—a "technique,"
at least in the central focus of its attention. By this we mean that it viewed
reality from an at least ostensibly unambiguous and stable practical evaluative standpoint: namely, the increase of the "wealth" of the population. It
was on the other hand, from the very beginning, more than a "technique"
since it was integrated into the great scheme of the natural law and rationalistic *Weltanschauung* of the eighteenth century. The nature of that
Weltanschauung with its optimistic faith in the theoretical and practical
rationalizability of reality had an important consequence insofar as it
obstructed the discovery of the *problematic* character of that standpoint
which had been assumed as self-evident. As the rational analysis of society
arose in close connection with the modern development of natural science,
so it remained related to it in its whole method of approach. In the natural
sciences, the practical evaluative attitude toward what was immediately
and technically useful was closely associated from the very first with the
hope, taken over as a heritage of antiquity and further elaborated, of
attaining a purely "objective" (i.e., independent of all individual con-
tingencies) monistic knowledge of the totality of reality in a *conceptual*

system of metaphysical *validity* and mathematical *form*. It was thought that this hope could be realized by the method of generalizing abstraction and the formulation of laws based on empirical analysis. The natural sciences which were bound to evaluative standpoints, such as clinical medicine and even more what is conventionally called "technology" became purely practical "arts." The values for which they strove, e.g., the health of the patient, the technical perfection of a concrete productive process, etc., were fixed for the time being for all of them. The methods which they used could only consist in the application of the laws formulated by the theoretical disciplines. Every theoretical advance in the construction of these laws was or could also be an advance for the practical disciplines. With the end given, the progressive reduction of concrete practical questions (e.g., a case of illness, a technical problem, etc.) to special cases of generally valid laws, meant that extension of theoretical knowledge was closely associated and identical with the extension of technical-practical possibilities.

When modern biology subsumed those aspects of reality which interest us *historically,* i.e., in all their concreteness, under a universally valid evolutionary principle, which at least had the appearance—but not the actuality—of embracing everything essential about the subject in a scheme of universally valid laws, this seemed to be the final twilight of all evaluative standpoints in all the sciences. For since the so-called historical event was a segment of the totality of reality, since the principle of causality which was the presupposition of all scientific work, seemed to require the analysis of all events into generally valid "laws," and in view of the overwhelming success of the natural sciences which took this idea seriously, it appeared as if there was in general no conceivable meaning of scientific work other than the discovery of the *laws* of events. Only those aspects of phenomena which were involved in the "laws" could be essential from the scientific point of view, and concrete "individual" events could be considered only as "types," i.e., as representative illustrations of laws. An interest in such events in themselves did not seem to be a "scientific" interest.

It is impossible to trace here the important repercussions of this will-to-believe of naturalistic monism in economics. When socialist criticism and the work of the historians were beginning to transform the original evaluative standpoints, the vigorous development of zoological research on one hand and the influence of Hegelian panlogism on the other prevented economics from attaining a clear and full understanding of the relationship between concept and reality. The result, to the extent that we are interested in it, is that despite the powerful resistance to the infiltration of naturalistic dogma due to German idealism since Fichte and the achievement of the German Historical School in law and economics and partly because of the very work of the Historical School, the naturalistic viewpoint in certain decisive problems has not yet been overcome. Among these problems we find the relationship between "theory" and "history," which is still problematic in our discipline.

The "abstract"-theoretical method even today shows unmediated and ostensibly irreconcilable cleavage from empirical-historical research. The proponents of this method recognize in a thoroughly correct way the methodological impossibility of supplanting the historical knowledge of reality by the formulation of laws or, vice versa, of constructing "laws" in the rigorous sense through the mere juxtaposition of historical observations. Now in order to arrive at these laws—for they are certain that science should be directed towards these as its highest goal—they take it to be a fact that we always have a direct awareness of the structure of human actions in all their reality. Hence—so they think—science can make human behavior directly intelligible with axiomatic evidentness and accordingly reveal its laws. The only exact form of knowledge—the formulation of immediately and intuitively *evident* laws—is however at the same time the only one which offers access to events which have not been directly observed. Hence, at least as regards the fundamental phenomena of economic life, the construction of a system of abstract and therefore purely formal propositions analogous to those of the exact natural sciences, is the only means of analyzing and intellectually mastering the complexity of social life. In spite of the fundamental methodological distinction between historical knowledge and the knowledge of "laws" which the creator of the theory drew as the *first* and *only* one, he now claims empirical *validity*, in the sense of the *deducibility* of reality from "laws," for the propositions of abstract theory. It is true that this is not meant in the sense of empirical validity of the abstract economic laws as such, but in the sense that when equally "exact" theories have been constructed for all the other relevant factors, all these abstract theories together must contain the true reality of the object—i.e., whatever is worthwhile knowing about it. Exact economic theory deals with the operation of *one* psychic motive, the other theories have as their task the formulation of the behavior of all the other motives into similar sorts of propositions enjoying hypothetical validity. Accordingly, the fantastic claim has occasionally been made for economic theories—e.g., the abstract theories of price, interest, rent, etc.,—that they can, by ostensibly following the analogy of physical science propositions, be validly applied to the derivation of quantitatively stated conclusions from given real premises, since given the ends, economic behavior with respect to means is unambiguously "determined." This claim fails to observe that in order to be able to reach this result even in the simplest case, the totality of existing historical reality including every one of its causal relationships must be assumed as "given" and presupposed as known. But if *this* type of knowledge were accessible to the finite mind of man, abstract theory would have no cognitive value whatsoever. The naturalistic prejudice that every concept in the cultural sciences should be similar to those in the exact natural sciences has led in consequence to the misunderstanding of the meaning of this theoretical construction (*theoretische Gedankengebilde*). It has been believed that it is a matter of the psychological isolation of a specific "impulse," the acquisitive impulse, or of the isolated study of a specific maxim of human conduct, the so-called economic principle. Abstract theory purported to be based on psychological *axioms* and as a result historians have called for an *empirical* psychology in order to show the invalidity of those axioms and to derive the course of economic events from psychological principles. We do not wish at this point to enter into a detailed criticism of the belief in the significance of a—still to be created—systematic science of "social psychology" as the future foundation of the cultural sciences, and particularly of social economics. Indeed, the partly brilliant attempts which have been made hitherto to interpret economic phenomena psychologically, show in any case that the procedure does not begin with the analysis of psychological qualities, moving then to the analysis of social institutions, but that, on the contrary, insight into the psychological preconditions and consequences of institutions presupposes a precise knowledge of the latter and the scientific analysis of their structure. In concrete cases, psychological analysis can contribute then an extremely valuable deepening of the knowledge of the historical cultural *conditioning* and cultural *significance* of institutions. The interesting aspect of the psychic attitude of a person in a social situation is specifically particularized in each case, according to the special cultural significance of the situation in question. It is a question of an extremely heterogeneous and highly concrete structure of psychic motives and influences. Social-psychological research involves the study of various very disparate *individual* types of cultural elements with reference to their interpretability by our emphatic understanding. Through social-psychological research, with the knowledge of individual institutions as a point of departure, we will learn increasingly how to understand institutions in a psychological way. We will not however deduce the institutions from psychological laws or explain them by elementary psychological phenomena.

Thus, the far-flung polemic, which centered on the question of the psychological justification of abstract theoretical propositions, on the scope of the "acquisitive impulse" and the "economic principle," etc., turns out to have been fruitless.

In the establishment of the propositions of abstract theory, it is only apparently a matter of "deductions" from fundamental psychological motives. Actually, the former are a special case of a kind of concept-construction which is peculiar and to a certain extent, indispensable, to the cultural sciences. It is worthwhile at this point to describe it in further detail since we can thereby approach more closely the fundamental question of the significance of theory in the social sciences. Therewith we leave undiscussed, once and for all, whether *the* particular analytical concepts which we cite or to which we allude as illustrations, correspond to the purposes they are to serve, i.e., whether in fact they are well-adapted. The question as to how far, for example, contemporary "abstract theory" should be further elaborated, is ultimately also a question of the strategy of science, which must, however concern itself with other problems as well. Even the "theory of marginal utility" is subsumable under a "law of marginal utility."

We have in abstract economic theory an illustration of those synthetic constructs which have been designated as *"ideas"* of historical phenomena. It offers us an ideal picture of events on the commodity-market under conditions of a society organized on the principles of an exchange economy, free competition and rigorously rational conduct. This conceptual pattern brings together certain relationships and events of historical life into a complex, which is conceived as an internally consistent system. Substantively, this construct in itself is like a *utopia* which has been arrived at by the analytical accentuation of certain elements of reality. Its relationship to the empirical data consists solely in the fact that where market-conditioned relationships of the type referred to by the abstract construct are discovered or suspected to exist in reality to some extent, we can make the *characteristic* features of this relationship pragmatically *clear* and *understandable* by reference to an *ideal-type*. This procedure can be indispensable for heuristic as well as expository purposes. The ideal typical concept will help to develop our skill in imputation in *research*: it *is* no "hypothesis" but it offers guidance to the construction of hypotheses. It is not a *description* of reality but it aims to give unambiguous means of expression to such a description. It is thus the "idea" of the *historically* given modern society, based on an exchange economy, which is developed for us by quite the same logical principles as are used in constructing the idea of the medieval "city economy" as a "genetic" concept. When we do this, we construct the concept "city economy" not as an average of the economic structures actually existing in all the cities observed but as an *ideal-type*. An ideal type is formed by the one-sided *accentuation* of one or more points of view and by the synthesis of a great many diffuse, discrete, more or less present and occasionally absent *concrete individual phenomena*, which are arranged according to those one-sidedly emphasized viewpoints into a unified *analytical* construct (*Gedankenbild*). In its conceptual purity, this mental construct (*Gedankenbild*) cannot be found empirically anywhere in reality. It is a *utopia*. Historical research faces the task of determining in each individual case, the extent to which this ideal-construct approximates to or diverges from reality, to what extent for example, the economic structure of a certain city is to be classified as a "city-economy." When carefully applied, those concepts are particularly useful in research and exposition. . . .

[28b]

WERNER STARK [1]

Capitalism, Calvinism and the Rise of Modern Science *

In the first years of the present century a great German sociologist, Max Weber by name, published a series of articles which shed a flood of new light on the origins of our modern civilisation. What he suggested was that at least one of the main roots of the capitalist system of society reaches back to the great spiritual revolution which we call the reformation, and in particular to the Calvinist religion and morality in which the protestant movement had its highest and most striking expression. Capitalism is above all a dynamic society: it is full of economic progress, it goes all out for higher profits, for higher standards of living, and for an ever higher degree of domination over the productive forces of nature, which it is pressing into the service of the human race. None of its characteristic achievements would have been possible in the Middle Ages because under Catholicism people felt no drive towards an active—I mean economically active—life. The best Catholic leaves the world and retires to the cloister, and there he leads a life of contemplation of which the ultimate aim is the vision of God, a vision which stills all human desires and gives the profoundest peace and contentment and thus is the very antithesis of a dynamical existence. Quietism is the keynote of such a religiousness, not activity. Protestantism was different. It condemned what Milton called the "fugitive and cloistered virtue" of the monk and demanded that the Christian should remain inside the world and do the work of his Master there, amid all the temptations and concupiscences of our fallen state. For thinkers such as Calvin and Knox, the purpose of man was not to be, or to become, a mirror or a vessel of God, but God's tool, the hammer of God as it were which He can use to shape his purposes. There was a definite shift in moral valuation: whereas in the thirteenth century a life of contemplation was more highly estimated than a life in some secular calling, the parts were reversed in the sixteenth century and a life in some secular calling was put, by the Calvinists at any rate, above a life of mere contem-

* From *The Sociological Review* XLIII, 5 (1951), pp. 95–104. By permission of the author and publisher.

plation. In this way a mighty stream of energy was released which, in due time, was to give the world the steam engine, the rail-road, the wireless, and atomic fission.

But it was not only this de-valuation of the contemplative ideal which helped to prepare the ground for the capitalist order, it was still more the emergence and the spread of the doctrine of predestination, one of the most significant features of the Calvinist outlook. According to the medieval system of theology, every human being could secure his own eternal salvation by co-operating with the grace of God, that is to say, by doing good and shunning evil and undergoing penance for any sin he may have committed. Calvin rejected this theory. He taught that God had divided the Elect and the Reprobate long before they were ever born, indeed, before the foundations of the world were laid, and he insisted that nothing a man can do will change his ultimate fate, because man is so vile, so totally perverted, that even his good deeds are no more than wickedness in the sight of Almighty God. Weber shows how deeply this stern doctrine influenced the Calvinist of the seventeenth century. His whole existence was dominated by the one awful question: has God called me to be one of His saints, or has He passed me over and fore-ordained me to eternal damnation? As God's will is inscrutable, there can be no clear answer to such a query, and all the believer could do was to turn away from it and seek to forget it. Now, nothing can help us better to forget our worries than hard and unrelenting work. If we immerse ourselves into our daily duties, if we wear ourselves out in doing them, we simply have no time to rack our brains over problems to which there is no solution, and we are as happy as our circumstances will ever allow us to be. That is the reason why the early Calvinist, whether he was rich or poor, a capitalist or a workman, threw himself head first into his task and his toil, and it was again the economic system which profited by his feverish and fanatical activity. Later on the doctrine of the inscrutability of God's eternal decree was tuned down, as it were, but characteristically again in a manner which was sure to boost the development of capitalism. The new idea was that God would, surely, prosper His chosen children, not only in the world to come, but even in this world, that He would show them His favour by increasing their wealth as He had increased the flocks of Abraham, of Isaak, and of Jacob. In this way, getting rich became a test of salvation, and it is clear that every true Calvinist did all he could to become rich, even though he was convinced that his success was, in the last resort, due to Him who has planned the world and who keeps its wheels turning.

It seems to me that this theory of Weber's is substantially correct. It has been criticised in this country by R. H. Tawney in a very fine book —RELIGION AND THE RISE OF CAPITALISM—but the counter-arguments put forward there are not really convincing. Tawney says that Catholic cities such as Venice and Florence were great commercial centres long before Calvin appeared upon the scene, and that vast fortunes were made there, in spite of the medieval morality that was preached from every pulpit.

True; but the point is that capitalism and commercialism are not the same thing: capitalism, in the sense of Max Weber, is above all a system of production, an organisation of industrial work, and that organisation of industrial work was developed in Holland and in England, not in Italy or in France. The fortunes of trade come and go: they cannot be the basis of a stable order of society; factories last, and they can. It was not long before Venice and Florence had lost the leadership in economic life which they had possessed for a little while. Tawney ascribes this relative decline to the development of Atlantic trade, which deflected commerce to the west, but this fact is hardly important in our connection. The discovery of America benefited Lisbon as much as it did Bristol, but in Portugal the boom was short-lived while in England it produced one of the most power-ful economic systems the world has ever known. The contrast between the two countries proves clearly that the really decisive feature was the difference in the prevailing attitude to economic enterprise which, in turn, reflected the difference in religious outlook—the core and stiffening of any national character.

Another argument which has been brought to bear against Weber is the contention that the relation between capitalism and Calvinism which he seeks to establish, is not so simple as he tries to make out. Granted that Calvinism had something to do with the rise of capitalism, is it not just as true to say that capitalism had something to do with the rise of Calvinism —in other words, that incipient capitalism created for itself in Calvinism an appropriate ideology, a system of thoughts and feelings within which it could fully unfold and flourish? This is, in itself, a very sound line to take, but Weber would have had no objection whatever against it. He knew as much as anybody else that in social life everything is a cause and an effect at the same time—indeed, that the attempt to distinguish pure causes and effects is more than problematic in sociology. The question who was there first, the hen or the egg, is insoluble, not to say nonsensical. Still, the argument is worth following up, and if it is rightly handled it will lead to a confirmation, not to a reversal, of Weber's thesis. The so-called capitalism which sprang up in places like Florence and Venice during the Renaissance period was socially destructive: the wealth which it created led to extreme luxury and riotous living and to a progressive demoralisa-tion. Acton was hardly exaggerating when, in his Inaugural Lecture, he spoke of a "headlong decline and impending dissolution of society" in the sixteenth century. If that decline was arrested, if that dissolution was averted, this was due to the powerful re-moralisation of life which was brought about, first by the Calvinist movement, and later, in the Catholic countries, by the Jesuit reformation which adapted the old faith to the new conditions. The point is that in this evolution the religious and spiritual change played a decisive part. Without it, the wealth of the great trading centres would have melted away as quickly as it was amassed: it was not for nothing that economy was the key-word of the new morality and of the new social discipline which spread over Europe after 1600.

What the reforming movement did was to turn a kind of capitalism that was speculative and predatory into a kind of capitalism that was industrial—industrial and hence constructive and creative. But this is precisely what Max Weber is trying to say. Calvinism may be called the child of an older capitalism—though it would be better to describe it as a reaction against it—but that does not take away from the fact that it became the father of the newer capitalism, the capitalism of modern times, we are justified in regarding as capitalism *par excellence*.

The purpose of the present paper is to show that there is still more—very much more—in Weber's suggestion than meets the eye at a first glance. It explains not only the origin of the capitalist "spirit" with which Weber himself was particularly concerned, but also the rise and the development of modern science, and especially modern physics and technology. Weber's investigation must, in my opinion, be extended to this further field because only if it is so extended can it explain what it sets out to explain, nineteenth-century capitalism. Capitalism, as the great Marx himself emphasised, is not only characterised by the constant pursuit of profit but also—and that is its main historical achievement—by the progressive subjection of the forces of nature to the will of mankind, by the ever more successful utilisation of the elements for the purposes of industrial production and human welfare.

Now, if I try to establish a connection between the Protestant reformation and modern science, I do not mean to revive the old contention that in the Middle Ages science could not flourish because the Church tried to keep the laity in ignorance, and that the later advances in physics and astronomy were the direct result of the breaking of that obscurantism. There is no truth at all in this widespread prejudice. Prof. Butterfield, in his admirable book, THE ORIGINS OF MODERN SCIENCE, has shown that Newton had his forerunners in the Catholic universities of Paris and Padua, and that Copernicus always remained on terms of peace and amity with Rome and the Pope, while, on the other hand, Luther and Melanchthon both condemned the Copernican system and Kepler had at one time to hide among the Jesuits to escape the wrath of the Protestant University at Tübingen. Neither Lutherans nor Calvinists were at first one whit more generous in their treatment of science than the Papists, and that is easily explained. Rome had always favoured a free and imaginative interpretation of the Scriptures; consequently difficulties could be argued away as they cropped up. But Wittenberg and Geneva adamantly insisted on a literal reading of the Bible, and so any discrepancy between theology and science had to develop into a head-on clash. We must not look for the influence of Calvinism on science at the surface: it is a subtle and subterranean connection which we have to uncover. The reformed divines—unbeknown to themselves—developed certain mental attitudes, certain habits of thought, under which mathematics and mechanics could unfold much more easily than under the old Aristotelian philosophy of the Schools, and thus they created the climate of opinion in which the tender plant of science could wax and grow strong until it was ultimately very much stronger than its parent ideologies.

In order to appreciate the truly Copernican revolution which Calvinism in this way helped to usher in, we must compare for a moment the modern scientific attitude with the still primitive modes of thought which it has come to replace. To the scientist of today nature is a system of inter-connected, inter-locking laws : to the thinker of the past it was a battlefield of friendly and hostile wills. Whatever the right interpretation of "pre-logical" thought may be, one thing is certain, namely that the savage sees in every stone and in every star something alive, some effective presence, some rudimentary personality comparable to his own. And this interpreta-tion of the universe is by no means so stupid as it seems to the superficial rationalist. After all, there is nothing we understand so well as our own motives and actions : in fact, one could go further and say without exaggera-tion that we understand nothing at all *bar* motives and actions akin to our own: of all other things we may acquire an outside knowledge but never that internal apprehension which we have when we deal with human affairs. It is very characteristic that even the modern biologist habitually per-sonifies nature, at any rate when he tries to explain her workings: he will say that she "decided" to create species and for that reason split the lines of evolution, or that she "was anxious" that the species which she had made should survive in the given environment, and more in the same style, as if nature were a lady that could make decisions and perform operations, or be anxious about things. It is no good assuring us that all this is only a convenient mode of expression, a manner of talking. Of course it is no more. But it is clear that the simile involved, the appeal to human experience, helps us to understand what is going on in nature, and it also helps us to understand what is going on in the primitive's mind when he tries to get to grips with natural phenomena. He cannot explain the mysteries he beholds unless he interprets them in human terms. The matter has been splendidly elucidated by Hans Kelsen in his SOCIETY AND NATURE, and before him by Henri Bergson in his TWO SOURCES OF MORALITY AND RELIGION. Now, it goes without saying that such a philosophy of nature will lead, not to science, but to magic—not to an investigation of the powers around us but to the attempt to make them friendly to our purposes, to win them over to our side. When the Tarahumare Indians of Mexico perform their ceremonial rain-dance, what they do is to put forward a suggestion to the clouds which they feel are ready to take in such a suggestion, or perhaps to impose their wills, their combined and concentrated wills, on the clouds which have not so far done their duty, and whose reluctance to comply may conceivably be broken by a stronger determination.

Now, the Aristotelian system which lasted down to the dawn of the Newtonian age, was still a natural philosophy of this kind. It still saw the universe as an interaction of wills, and not as an inter-connection of laws. It still saw things instinct with personality, drenched as it were in a human fluid. Two examples will prove how true this is. Aristotle realised that falling bodies move at an accelerating speed. But he did not reduce this observation to its underlying law. He suggested that the stone is moving more quickly because it wants to be at home—the earth being the natural home of all stones, their mother as it were—in the same way in which horses will run more briskly when they feel the stable is near and the hay is waiting. In a similar vein it was suggested that the stars were moved across the sky by spirits or intelligences—spirits and intelligences which formed a hierarchy comparable to the hierarchy in the medieval church or the medieval state. Wherever there was movement, there was to be a mover; wherever there was action, there was to be an actor; the concept of impersonal forces was alien both to primitive and to medieval man.

In saying this I do not want to assert that there was no progress between, say, 1500 B.C. and 1500 A.D. On the contrary, a very important change was taking place which, in its measure, prepared the coming of science, but it belongs still to the pre-history of the scientific world-view, and not yet to the first chapter of its history. What happened was that men's fear of the demonic was broken by the Christian religion. The savage properly so called—the heathen—had lived in terror of the forces of nature: he had regarded many of them as hostile and horrific. The teaching that came forth from Galilee dispelled these ideas: it convinced the world that the universe has only One Master, and that this Master is good, and that His handiwork is good, even if the power of the Devil is something of a reality at the same time. Without this liberation of the human spirit from the terrors of demonism and darkness, man would never have dared to approach nature as he has done, and to pry into her secrets and reduce her to submission. Far from being, in the last analysis, anti-scientific, Christianity was one of the indispensable path-breakers and road-makers of science.

But the conquest of the demons, though it weakened the old interpretation of nature, did not do away with it. Natural philosophy continued to think in terms of wills and not of laws. Though there was no longer a quasi-human presence in every tree and in every well, there was still at any rate One Will which regulated and sustained the whole of creation—the will of God. And that Supreme Will was supremely active. He was not the God of Leibniz who had made the universal mechanism and then set it going and turned away from it, but the God of St. Francis who will never turn away from His creatures but always remain lovingly in their midst. That God, it is true, has given laws to His creation—to His lower, physical creation at any rate—and usually its wheels run smoothly according to these laws: but, then, these laws can at any moment be suspended in a miracle if God sees fit to make one, and He will not hesitate to make one whenever it serves His loving purpose. Clearly, this medieval type of mind was not yet ready to conceive the world as a set of impersonal laws: the miracle was too centrally situated in its world-view. And—I should like to emphasise that very specially—this attitude was not at all irrational. If there is a supreme law-giver, surely He can suspend His laws if and when

He sees good reason for doing so: it is much more unreasonable to believe with Leibniz in a legislator who resigns as soon as he has done his work and never looks at it again.

But to return to our argument. The decisive importance of Calvinism for the rise of modern science in general, and for the rise of modern physics in particular, consists in this that its theology made the God of St. Francis into the God of Leibniz—that it excluded the Divine Will from the day-to-day working of the universe, and shifted its action back to the origin of things, to the period (if I may so express it) before the beginning of concrete time, when the world was as yet an idea taking shape in the Divine Mind. We see here another of the tremendous effects of the doctrine of predestination which played such an important part in Weber's essays. This doctrine, it will be recalled, maintained that God had not only foreseen but even foreordained all that was to befall the human race in the course of its history,[2] and that nothing that could possibly happen after the sixth day, would change one jot or one tittle in the eternal decree of Almighty Inexorable Providence. But if the ways of men are thus fixed from all eternity, even though they *seem* to be endowed with freedom, how can there be *any* indetermination in the realm of nature which is so obviously subject to compelling regularities? Of course, Calvin did not suggest that God *could* not interfere with the goings-on in the world—that would have been blasphemous—but he held very strongly that He *would* not do so: his God was a consistent God who could not be turned away from His original design and purpose. It is clear that such a theology made an ideal background for a deterministic science. A Divine Will which has, once and for all, expressed itself in the pattern and principles of an unchanging universe, *is* no longer a personal will which need be taken into account,—it is much rather an impersonal law from which the element of volition has finally and irrevocably departed. It has congealed as it were into an objective order which—because of its essential stability—is amendable to systematic study and objective analysis. I am quite certain that we must see in this set of convictions one of the roots from which the modern scientific world-view has gradually grown.

The effect of this Calvinist theology on scientific thought was very powerful indeed, and it is easy to trace it in the history of science during the reformation century. Copernicus, who was born in 1473 and remained all his life a good Catholic, still believed in the animation of the universe. In Kepler, who came into the world roughly a hundred years later, in 1571, after the religious revolution had run its course, and who was himself a Protestant, we find a radically different attitude. For him, the universe is already a piece of mechanism, composed of dead matter and subject to inexorable regularities. If later thinkers, such as Boyle, still speak now and then of aspirations, dispositions, and repulsions as residing in or coming from things, they no longer mean what they say—they are clearly using metaphors and not trying to depict reality. It is supremely characteristic of the new spirit that was abroad that Newton's theories were at first received with some suspicion because he used words such as attraction—words which savoured of the old animism of Aristotle and the Schools, as if he believed that the stars could feel a sympathy for each other such as humans do now and then. Of course, he meant no such thing. The days of the humanisation of the universe were irrevocably over.

But I have not told the whole story yet. Calvinism not only created the mental atmosphere within which science could unfold unhampered by any uncongenial metaphysics, it also provided a new and powerful incentive to study the laws and the workings of the physical universe. The Calvinist's mind, as we have seen, was always turned towards action: it was, in consequence, his natural conviction that a man's character could be inferred, not only from his words, but still more from his behaviour. Now, the same idea could easily be applied to Almighty God: granted that He can partially be discovered in His word, that is, in the Bible, is it not clear that His character can also be studied, and still more effectively, in His handiwork, that is to say, in material creation? There was a definite religious aspiration behind the scientific investigations of such pioneers as Kepler and Leibniz, a desire to know nature, not for its own sake, but for the sake of Him who speaks in and through it, and that aspiration helped to drive science forward from success to success and from triumph to triumph, until different and less creditable motives came in and took over from religious sentiment. Without the original religious sentiment, science would not have developed so quickly as it did. Science for science's sake is all very well: electrons, mesons and protons are no doubt rather interesting in themselves, but their study can never be so mind-arresting and so soul-filling as the search for the countenance of Almighty God in which—if we could only behold it—we would read in the twinkling of an eye the answer to all the riddles of the universe.

I have now told the whole of my story, but I should like to add a short postscript. It is obvious, and nobody will deny, that the old Aristotelian and animist world-view was seriously unbalanced. It did not grant the physical sciences that spiritual independence which they need if they are to flourish: it pressed on them, very foolishly, the forms of thought which are only applicable to the human sphere. But today we are in a similar situation, only that the shoe is on the other foot. For three hundred years the methods which have led astronomy and mechanics to power and glory have been encroaching more and more upon the territory of the biological and the sociological branches of learning, and they have created considerable havoc there. When Descartes said that an animal is a mechanism, and that the yell of agony which is heard when we tread on its paws is only the creaking of a machine, he gave an excellent example of the absurdities and inanities which are bound to arise if the living is treated as if it were dead. And that tendency to treat the living as if it were dead is universal today: it has done immeasurable harm already and threatens to ruin sociology altogether: it is every bit as objectionable and disastrous as the corresponding opposite stupidity, the stupidity of treating the dead as if it were alive.

The prestige of mathematics and mechanics has become oppressive. If we are not to sink into the bottomless pit of a new scholasticism more inhuman than the old, we must begin to realise that we need a dualistic outlook as desperately as we need the daily bread. Only the equal cooperation and the mutual independence of the physical sciences and the social can give us a truly balanced system of ideas and, beyond it, a saner world.

[29a]

KARL MANNHEIM

The Sociology of Knowledge*

I. PRELIMINARY APPROACH TO THE PROBLEM

1. THE SOCIOLOGICAL CONCEPT OF THOUGHT

This book is concerned with the problem of how men actually think. The aim of these studies is to investigate not how thinking appears in textbooks on logic, but how it really functions in public life and in politics as an instrument of collective action.

Philosophers have too long concerned themselves with their own thinking. When they wrote of thought, they had in mind primarily their own history, the history of philosophy, or quite special fields of knowledge such as mathematics or physics. This type of thinking is applicable only under quite special circumstances, and what can be learned by analysing it is not directly transferable to other spheres of life. Even when it is applicable, it refers only to a specific dimension of existence which does not suffice for living human beings who are seeking to comprehend and to mould their world.

Meanwhile, acting men have, for better or for worse, proceeded to develop a variety of methods for the experiential and intellectual penetration of the world in which they live, which have never been analysed with the same precision as the so-called exact modes of knowing. When, however, any human activity continues over a long period without being subjected to intellectual control or criticism, it tends to get out of hand.

Hence it is to be regarded as one of the anomalies of our time that those methods of thought by means of which we arrive at our most crucial decisions, and through which we seek to diagnose and guide our political

* From *Ideology and Utopia: An Introduction to the Sociology of Knowledge.* By Karl Mannheim. Translated from the German by Louis Wirth and Edward Shils. New York: Harcourt, Brace and Co.; London: Kegan Paul, Trench, Trubner & Co., 1936. Pp. 1–11. By permission of the publishers.

and social destiny, have remained unrecognized and therefore inaccessible to intellectual control and self-criticism. This anomaly becomes all the more monstrous when we call to mind that in modern times much more depends on the correct thinking through of a situation than was the case in earlier societies. The significance of social knowledge grows proportionately with the increasing necessity of regulatory intervention in the social process. This so-called pre-scientific inexact mode of thought, however (which, paradoxically, the logicians and philosophers also use when they have to make practical decisions), is not to be understood solely by the use of logical analysis. It constitutes a complex which cannot be readily detached either from the psychological roots of the emotional and vital impulses which underlie it or from the situation in which it arises and which it seeks to solve.

It is the most essential task of this book to work out a suitable method for the description and analysis of this type of thought and its changes, and to formulate those problems connected with it which will both do justice to its unique character and prepare the way for its critical understanding. The method which we will seek to present is that of the sociology of knowledge.

The principal thesis of the sociology of knowledge is that these are modes of thought which cannot be adequately understood as long as their social origins are obscured. It is indeed true that only the individual is capable of thinking. There is no such metaphysical entity as a group mind which thinks over and above the head of individuals, or whose ideas the individual merely reproduces. Nevertheless it would be false to deduce from this that all the ideas and sentiments which motivate an individual have their origin in him alone, and can be adequately explained solely on the basis of his own life-experience.

Just as it would be incorrect to attempt to derive a language merely from observing a single individual, who speaks not a language of his own but rather that of his contemporaries and predecessors who have prepared the path for him, so it is incorrect to explain the totality of an outlook only with reference to its genesis in the mind of the individual. Only in a quite limited sense does the single individual create out of himself the mode of speech and of thought we attribute to him. He speaks the language of his group; he thinks in the manner in which his group thinks. He finds at his disposal only certain words and their meanings. These not only determine to a large extent the avenues of approach to the surrounding world, but they also show at the same time from which angle and in which context of activity objects have hitherto been perceptible and accessible to the group or the individual.

The first point which we now have to emphasize is that the approach of sociology of knowledge intentionally does not start with the single individual and his thinking in order than to proceed directly in the manner of the philosopher to the abstract heights of "thought as such." Rather, the sociology of knowledge seeks to comprehend thought in the concrete setting of an historical-social situation out of which individually differentiated thought only very gradually emerges. Thus, it is not men in general who think, or even isolated individuals who do the thinking, but men in certain groups who have developed a particular style of thought in an endless series of responses to certain typical situations characterizing their common position.

Strictly speaking it is incorrect to say that the single individual thinks. Rather it is more correct to insist that he participates in thinking further what other men have thought before him. He finds himself in an inherited situation with patterns of thought which are appropriate to this situation and attempts to elaborate further the inherited modes of response or to substitute others from them in order to deal more adequately with the new challenges which have arisen out of the shifts and changes in his situation. Every individual is therefore in a two-fold sense predetermined by the fact of growing up in a society : on the one hand he finds a ready-made situation and on the other he finds in that situation preformed patterns of thought and of conduct.

The second feature characterizing the method of the sociology of knowledge is that it does not sever the concretely existing modes of thought from the context of collective action through which we first discover the world in an intellectual sense. Men living in groups do not confront the objects of the world from the abstract levels of a contemplating mind as such, nor do they do so exclusively as solitary beings. On the contrary they act with and against one another in diversely organised groups, and while doing so they think with and against one another. These persons, bound together into groups, strive in accordance with the character and position of the groups to which they belong to change the surrounding world of nature and society or attempt to maintain it in a given condition. It is the direction of this will to change or to maintain, of this collective activity, which produces the guiding thread for the emergence of their problems, their concepts, and their forms of thought. In accord with the particular context of collective activity in which they participate, men always tend to see the world which surrounds them differently. Just as pure logical analysis has severed individual thought from its group situation, so it also separated thought from action. It did this on the tacit assumption that those inherent connections which always exist in reality between thought on the one hand, and group and activity on the other, are either insignificant for "correct" thinking or can be detached from these foundations without any resultant difficulties. But the fact that one ignores something by no means puts an end to its existence. Nor can anyone who has not first given himself wholeheartedly to the exact observation of the wealth of forms in which men really think decide a priori whether this severance from the social situation and context of activity is always realizable. Nor indeed can it be determined offhand that such a complete dichotomy is fully desirable precisely in the interest of objective factual knowledge.

It may be that, in certain spheres of knowledge, it is the impulse to

act which first makes the objects of the world accessible to the acting subject, and it may be further that it is this factor which determines the selection of those elements of reality which enter into thought. And it is not
inconceivable that if this volitional factor were entirely excluded (in so far
as such a thing is possible), the concrete content would disappear from the
concepts, and the organizing principle which first makes possible an intelligent statement of the problem would be lost.

But this is not to say that in those domains where attachment to the
groups and orientation towards action seem to be an essential element in
the situation, every possibility of intellectual, critical self-control is futile.
Perhaps it is precisely when the hitherto concealed dependence of thought
on group existence and its rootedness in action becomes visible that it
really becomes possible for the first time, through becoming aware of them,
to attain a new mode of control over previously uncontrolled factors in
thought.

This brings us to the central problem of the book. These remarks
would make it clear that a preoccupation with these problems and their
solution will furnish a foundation for the social sciences and answer the
question as to the possibility of the scientific guidance of political life. It
is, of course, true that in the social sciences, as elsewhere, the ultimate
criterion of truth or falsity is to be found in the investigation of the object,
and the sociology of knowledge is no substitute for this. But the examination of the object is not an isolated act; it takes place in a context which
is coloured by values and collective-unconscious, volitional impulses. In
the social sciences it is this intellectual interest, oriented in a matrix of
collective activity, which provides not only the general questions, but the
concrete hypotheses for research and the thought-models for the ordering
of experience. Only as we succeed in bringing into the area of conscious
and explicit observation the various points of departure and of approach
to the facts which are current in scientific as well as popular discussion,
can we hope, in the course of time, to control the unconscious motivations
and presuppositions which, in the last analysis, have brought these modes
of thought into existence. A new type of objectivity in the social sciences is
attainable not through the exclusion of evaluations but through the critical
awareness and control of them.

2. The Contemporary Predicament of Thought

It is by no means an accident that the problem of the social and activ-
istic roots of thinking has emerged in our generation. Nor is it accidental
that the unconscious, which has hitherto motivated our thought and activity, has been gradually raised to the level of awareness and thereby made
accessible to control. It would be a failure to recognize its relevance to our
own plight if we did not see that it is a special social situation which has
impelled us to reflect about the social roots of our knowledge. It is one of
the fundamental insights of the sociology of knowledge that the process by

which collective-unconscious motives become conscious cannot operate in every epoch, but only in a quite specific situation. This situation is sociologically determinable. One can point out with relative precision the factors which are inevitably forcing more and more persons to reflect not merely about the things of the world, but about thinking itself and even here not so much about truth in itself, as about the alarming fact that the same world can appear differently to different observers.

It is clear that such problems can become general only in an age in which disagreement is more conspicuous than agreement. One turns from the direct observation of things to the consideration of ways of thinking only when the possibility of direct and continuous elaboration of concepts concerning things and situations has collapsed in the face of a multiplicity of fundamentally divergent definitions. Now we are enabled to designate more precisely than a general and formal analysis makes possible, exactly in which social and intellectual situation such a shift of attention from things to divergent opinions and from there to the unconscious motives of thought must necessarily occur. In what follows we wish to point out only a few of the most significant social factors which are operating in this direction.

Above all, the multiplicity of ways of thinking cannot become a problem in periods when social stability underlies and guarantees the internal unity of a world-view. As long as the same meanings of words, the same ways of deducing ideas, are inculcated from childhood on into every member of the group, divergent thought-processes cannot exist in that society. Even a gradual modification in ways of thinking (where it should happen to arise), does not become perceptible to the members of a group who live in a stable situation as long as the tempo in the adaptations of ways of thinking to new problems is so slow that it extends over several generations. In such a case, one and the same generation in the course of its own life span can scarcely become aware that a change is taking place.

But in addition to the general dynamics of the historical process, factors of quite another sort must enter before the multiplicity of the ways of thinking will become noticeable and emerge as a theme for reflection. Thus it is primarily the intensification of social mobility which destroys the earlier illusion, prevalent in a static society, that all things can change, but thought remains eternally the same. And what is more, the two forms of social mobility, horizontal and vertical, operate in different ways to reveal this multiplicity of styles of thought. Horizontal mobility (movement from one position to another or from one country to another without changing social status) shows us that different peoples think differently. As long, however, as the traditions of one's national and local group remain unbroken, one remains so attached to its customary ways of thinking that the ways of thinking which are perceived in other groups are regarded as curiosities, errors, ambiguities, or heresies. At this stage one does not doubt either the correctness of one's own traditions of thought or the unity and uniformity of thought in general.

Only when horizontal mobility is accompanied by intensive vertical mobility, i.e., rapid movement between strata in the sense of social ascent and descent, is the belief in the general and eternal validity of one's own thought-forms shaken. Vertical mobility is the decisive factor in making persons uncertain and sceptical of their traditional view of the world. It is, of course, true that even in static societies with very slight vertical mobility, different strata within the same society have had different ways of experiencing the world. It is the merit of Max Weber [1] to have clearly shown in his sociology of religion how often the same religion is variously experienced by peasants, artisans, merchants, nobles, and intellectuals. In a society organized along the lines of closed castes or ranks the comparative absence of vertical mobility served either to isolate from each other the divergent world-views or if, for example, they experienced a common religion, according to their different contexts of life, they interpreted it in a different way. This accounts for the fact that the diversity of modes of thought of different castes did not converge in one and the same mind and hence could not become a problem. From a sociological point of view, the decisive change takes place when that stage of historical development is reached in which the previously isolated strata begin to communicate with one another and a certain social circulation sets in. The most significant stage of this communication is reached when the forms of thought and experience, which had hitherto developed independently, enter into one and the same consciousness impelling the mind to discover the irreconcilability of the conflicting conceptions of the world.

In a well stabilized society the mere infiltration of the modes of thought of the lower strata into the higher would not mean very much since the bare perception by the dominant group of possible variations in thinking would not result in their being intellectually shaken. As long as society is stabilized on the basis of authority, and social prestige is accorded only to the achievements of the upper stratum, this class has little cause to call into question its own social existence and the value of its achievements. Apart from a considerable social ascent, it is not until we have a general democratization that the rise of the lower strata allows their thinking to acquire public significance. [2] This process of democratization first makes it possible for the ways of thinking of the lower strata, which formerly had no public validity, to acquire validity and prestige. When the stage of democratization has been reached, the techniques of thinking and the ideas of the lower strata are for the first time in a position to confront the ideas of the dominant strata on the same level of validity. And now, too, for the first time these ideas and modes of thought are capable of impelling the person who thinks within their framework to subject the objects of his world to a fundamental questioning. It is with this clashing of modes of thought, each of which has the same claims to representational validity, that for the first time there is rendered possible the emergence of the question which is so fateful, but also so fundamental in the history of thought, namely, how it is possible that identical human thought-processes con-

cerned with the same world produce divergent conceptions of that world.
And from this point it is only a step further to ask: Is it not possible that
the thought-processes which are involved here are not at all identical? May
it not be found, when one has examined all the possibilities of human
thought, that there are numerous alternative paths which can be followed?

Was it not this process of social ascent which in the Athenian democracy called forth the first great surge of scepticism in the history of Occi-
dental thought? Were not the Sophists of the Greek Enlightenment the expression of an attitude of doubt which arose essentially out of the fact
that in their thinking about every object, two modes of explanation
collided? On the one hand was the mythology which was the way of thinking of a dominant nobility already doomed to decline. On the other hand
was the more analytical habit of thought of an urban artisan lower stratum,
which was in the process of moving upwards. Inasmuch as these two forms
of interpreting the world converged in the thought of the Sophists, and
since for every moral decision there were available at least two standards,
and for every cosmic and social happening at least two explanations, it is
no wonder that they had a sceptical notion of the value of human thought.
It is therefore pointless to censure them in schoolmaster fashion for having
been sceptics in their epistemological efforts. They simply had the courage
to express what every person who was really characteristic of the epoch felt,
namely, that the previous unambiguity of norms and interpretations had
been shattered, and that a satisfactory solution was to be found only in a
thoroughgoing questioning and thinking through of the contradictions. This
general uncertainty was by no means a symptom of a world doomed to
general decay, but it was rather the beginning of a wholesome process
which marked a crisis leading to recovery.

Was it not, furthermore, the great virtue of Socrates that he had the
courage to descend into the abyss of this scepticism? Was he not originally
also a Sophist who took up the technique of raising questions and then
raising further questions, and made it his own? And did he not overcome
the crisis by questioning even more radically than the Sophists and thus
arrive at an intellectual resting-point which, at least for the mentality of
that epoch, showed itself to be a reliable foundation? It is interesting to
observe that thereby the world of norms and of being came to occupy the
central place in his inquiry. Furthermore, he was at least as intensively
concerned with the question as to how individuals are able to think of and
judge the same facts in different ways as he was with the facts themselves.
Even at this stage in the history of thought it becomes apparent that in
various periods the problems of thinking can be solved not solely by preoccupation with the object but rather only through discovering why
opinions concerning them really differ.

In addition to those social factors which account for the early unity
and subsequent multiplicity in the dominant forms of thought, another important factor should be mentioned. In every society there are social
groups whose special task it is to provide an interpretation of the world

for that society. We call these the "intelligentsia." The more static a society is, the more likely is it that this stratum will acquire a well-defined status or the position of a caste in that society. Thus the magicians, the Brahmins, the medieval clergy are to be regarded as intellectual strata, each of which in its society enjoyed a monopolistic control over the moulding of that society's world-view, and over either the reconstruction or the reconciliation of the differences in the naively formed world-views of the other strata. The sermon, the confession, the lesson, are in this sense, means by which reconciliation of the different conceptions of the world takes place at less sophisticated levels of social development.

This intellectual stratum, organized as a caste and monopolizing the right to preach, teach, and interpret the world is conditioned by the force of two social factors. The more it makes itself the exponent of a thoroughly organized collectivity (e.g., the Church), the more its thinking tends towards "scholasticism." It must give a dogmatically binding force to modes of thought which formerly were valid only for a sect and thereby sanction the ontology and epistemology implicit in this mode of thought. The necessity of having to present a unified front to outsiders compels this transition. The same result may also be brought about by the possibility that the concentration of power within the social structure will be so pronounced that uniformity of thought and experience can be imposed upon the members of at least one's own caste with greater success than heretofore.

The second characteristic of this monopolistic type of thought is its relative remoteness from the open conflicts of everyday life; hence it is also "scholastic" in this sense, i.e., academic and lifeless. This type of thought does not arise primarily from the struggle with concrete problems of life nor from trial and error, nor from experiences in mastering nature and society, but rather much more from its own need for systematization, which always refers the facts which emerge in the religious as well as in other spheres of life back to given traditional and intellectually uncontrolled premises. The antagonisms which emerge in these discussions do not embody the conflict of various modes of experience so much as various positions of power within the same social structure, which have at the time identified themselves with the different possible interpretations of the dogmatized traditional "truth." The dogmatic content of the premises with which these divergent groups start and which this thought then seeks in different ways to justify turns out for the most part to be a matter of accident, if judged by the criteria of factual evidence. It is completely arbitrary in so far as it depends upon which sect happens to be successful, in accordance with historical-political destiny, in making its own intellectual and experiential traditions of the entire clerical caste of the church.

From a sociological point of view the decisive fact of modern times, in contrast with the situation during the Middle Ages, is that this monopoly of the ecclesiastical interpretation of the world which was held by the priestly caste is broken, and in the place of a closed and thoroughly organized stratum of intellectuals, a free intelligentsia has arisen. Its chief characteristic is that it is increasingly recruited from constantly varying social strata and life-situations, and that its mode of thought is no longer subject to regulation by a caste-like organization. Due to the absence of a social organization of their own, the intellectuals have allowed those ways of thinking and experiencing to get a hearing which openly competed with one another in the larger world of the other strata. When one considers further that with the renunciation of the monopolistic privileges of a caste type of existence, free competition began to dominate the modes of intellectual production, one understands why, to the extent that they were in competition, the intellectuals adopted in an ever more pronounced fashion the most various modes of thought and experience available in society and played them off against one another. They did this inasmuch as they had to compete for the favour of a public which, unlike the public of the clergy, was no longer accessible to them without their own efforts. This competition for the favour of various public groups was accentuated because the distinctive modes of experiencing and thinking of each attained increasing public expression and validity.

In this process the intellectual's illusion that there is only one way of thinking disappears. The intellectual is now no longer, as formerly, a member of a caste or rank whose scholastic manner of thought represents for him thought as such. In this relatively simple process is to be sought the explanation for the fact that the fundamental questioning of thought in modern times does not begin until the collapse of the intellectual monopoly of the clergy. The almost unanimously accepted world-view which had been artificially maintained fell apart the moment the socially monopolistic position of its producers was destroyed. With the liberation of the intellectuals from the rigorous organization of the church, other ways of interpreting the world were increasingly recognized.

The disruption of the intellectual monopoly of the church brought about a sudden flowering of an unexampled intellectual richness. But at the same time we must attribute to the organizational disintegration of the unitary church the fact that the belief in the unity and eternal nature of thought, which had persisted since classical antiquity, was again shaken. The origins of the profound disquietude of the present day reach back to this period, even though in most recent times additional causes of a quite different nature have entered into the process. Out of this first upsurge of the profound disquietude of modern man there emerged those fundamentally new modes of thought and investigation, the epistemological, the psychological, and the sociological, without which to-day we could not even formulate our problem. . . .

KARL R. POPPER

The Sociology of Knowledge *

Rationality, in the sense of an appeal to a universal and impersonal standard of truth, is of supreme importance . . . , not only in ages in which it easily prevails, but also, and even more, in those less fortunate times in which it is despised and rejected as the vain dream of men who lack the virility to kill where they cannot agree.

BERTRAND RUSSELL

It can hardly be doubted that Hegel's and Marx's historicist philosophies are characteristic products of their time—a time of social change. Like the philosophies of Heraclitus and Plato, and like those of Comte and Mill, Lamarck and Darwin, they are philosophies of change, and they witness to the tremendous and undoubtedly somewhat terrifying impression made by a changing social environment on the minds of those who live in this environment. Plato reacted to this situation by attempting to arrest all change. The more modern social philosophers appear to react very differently, since they accept, and even welcome, change; yet this love of change seems to me a little ambivalent. For even though they have given up any hope of arresting change, as historicists they try to predict it, and thus to bring it under rational control; and this certainly looks like an attempt to tame it. Thus it seems that to the historicist, change has not entirely lost its terrors.

In our own time of still more rapid change, we even find the desire not only to predict change, but to control it by centralized large-scale planning. These holistic views (which I have criticized in *The Poverty of Historicism* †) represent a compromise, as it were, between Platonic and Marxian theories. Plato's will to arrest change, combined with Marx's doctrine of its inevitability, yields, as a kind of Hegelian 'synthesis,' the demand that since it cannot be entirely arrested, change should at least be 'planned,' and controlled by the state whose power is to be vastly extended.

An attitude like this may seem, at first sight, to be a kind of rationalism; it is closely related to Marx's dream of the 'realm of freedom' in

* Reprinted from *The Open Society and Its Enemies* by Karl R. Popper. Princeton University Press, 1950. Copyright, 1950, by Karl R. Popper. Ch. 23, pp. 398–409, and notes pp. 705–7, by permission of the author and publisher.
† *Economica* (1944). See Note 1.

which man is for the first time master of his own fate. But as a matter of fact, it occurs in closest alliance with a doctrine which is definitely opposed to rationalism (and especially to the doctrine of the rational unity of mankind; see chapter 24 *), one which is well in keeping with the irrationalist and mystical tendencies of our time. I have in mind the Marxist doctrine that our opinions, including our moral and scientific opinions, are determined by class interest, and more generally by the social and historical situation of our time. Under the name of 'sociology of knowledge' or 'sociologism,' this doctrine has been developed recently (especially by M. Scheler and K. Mannheim [1]) as a theory of the social determination of scientific knowledge.

The sociology of knowledge argues that scientific thought, and especially thought on social and political matters, does not proceed in a vacuum, but in a socially conditioned atmosphere. It is influenced largely by unconscious or subconscious elements. These elements remain hidden from the thinker's observing eye because they form, as it were, the very place which he inhabits, his *social habitat*. The social habitat of the thinker determines a whole system of opinions and theories which appear to him as unquestionably true or self-evident. They appear to him as if they were logically and trivially true, such as, for example, the sentence 'all tables are tables.' This is why he is not even aware of having made any assumptions at all. But that he has made assumptions can be seen if we compare him with a thinker who lives in a very different social habitat; for he too will proceed from a system of apparently unquestionable assumptions, but from a very different one; and it may be so different that no intellectual bridge may exist and no compromise be possible between these two systems. Each of these different socially determined systems of assumptions is called by the sociologists of knowledge a *total ideology*.

The sociology of knowledge can be considered as a Hegelian version of Kant's theory of knowledge. For it continues on the lines of Kant's criticism of what we may term the 'passivist' theory of knowledge. I mean by this the theory of the empiricists down to and including Hume, a theory which may be described, roughly, as holding that knowledge streams into us through our senses, and that error is due to our interference with the sense-given material, or to the associations which have developed within it; the best way of avoiding error is to remain entirely passive and receptive. Against this receptacle theory of knowledge (I usually call it the 'bucket theory of the mind'), Kant [2] argued that knowledge is not a collection of gifts received by our senses and stored in the mind as if it were a museum, but that it is very largely the result of our own mental activity; that we must most actively engage ourselves in searching, comparing, unifying, generalizing, if we wish to attain knowledge. We may call this theory the 'activist' theory of knowledge. In connection with it, Kant gave up the untenable ideal of a science which is free from any kind of presuppositions. (That this ideal is even self-contradictory will be shown in

* In the author's book.

the next chapter.*) He made it quite clear that we cannot start from nothing, and that we have to approach our task equipped with a system of presuppositions which we hold without having tested them by the empirical methods of science; such a system may be called a 'categorial apparatus.' [3] Kant believed that it was possible to discover the one true and unchanging categorial apparatus, which represents as it were the necessarily unchanging framework of our intellectual outfit, i.e. human 'reason.' This part of Kant's theory was given up by Hegel, who, as opposed to Kant, did not believe in the unity of mankind. He taught that man's intellectual outfit was constantly changing, and that it was part of his social heritage; accordingly the development of man's reason must coincide with the historical development of his society, i.e. of the nation to which he belongs. This theory of Hegel's, and especially his doctrine that all knowledge and all truth is 'relative' in the sense of being determined by history, is sometimes called 'historism' (in contradistinction to 'historicism,' as mentioned in the last chapter). The sociology of knowledge or 'sociologism' is obviously very closely related to or nearly identical with it, the only difference being that, under the influence of Marx, it emphasizes that the historical development does not produce one uniform 'national spirit,' as Hegel held, but rather several and sometimes opposed 'total ideologies' within one nation, according to the class, the social stratum, or the social habitat, of those who hold them.

But the likeness to Hegel goes further. I have said above that according to the sociology of knowledge, no intellectual bridge or compromise between different total ideologies is possible. But this radical scepticism is not really meant quite as seriously as it sounds. There is a way out of it, and the way is analogous to the Hegelian method of superseding the conflicts which preceded him in the history of philosophy. Hegel, a spirit freely poised above the whirlpool of the dissenting philosophies, reduced them all to mere components of the highest of syntheses, of his own system. Similarly, the sociologists of knowledge hold that the 'freely poised intelligence' of an intelligentsia which is only loosely anchored in social traditions may be able to avoid the pitfalls of the total ideologies; that it may even be able to see through, and to unveil, the various total ideologies and the hidden motives and other determinants which inspire them. Thus the sociology of knowledge believes that the highest degree of objectivity can be reached by the freely poised intelligence analyzing the various hidden ideologies and their anchorage in the unconscious. The way to true knowledge appears to be the unveiling of unconscious assumptions, a kind of psychotherapy, as it were, or if I may say so, a *sociotherapy*. Only he who has been socioanalyzed or who has socioanalyzed himself, and who is freed from this social complex, i.e. from his social ideology, can attain to the highest synthesis of objective knowledge.

In a previous chapter, when dealing with 'Vulgar Marxism,' I mentioned a tendency which can be observed in a group of modern philosophies,

* In the author's book.

the tendency to unveil the hidden motives behind our actions. The sociology of knowledge belongs to this group, together with psychoanalysis and certain philosophies which unveil the 'meaninglessness' of the tenets of their opponents.[4] The popularity of these views lies, I believes, in the ease with which they can be applied, and in the satisfaction which they confer on those who see through things, and through the follies of the unenlightened. This pleasure would be harmless, were it not that all these ideas are liable to destroy the intellectual basis of any discussion, by establishing what I have called [5] a 'reinforced dogmatism.' (Indeed, this is something rather similar to a 'total ideology.') Hegelianism does it by declaring the admissibility and even fertility of contradictions. But if contradictions need not be avoided, then any criticism and any discussion becomes impossible since criticism always consists in pointing out contradictions, either within the theory to be criticized, or between it and some facts of experience. The situation with psychoanalysis is similar: the psychoanalyst can always explain away any objections by showing that they are due to the repressions of the critic. And the philosophers of meaning, again, need only point out that what their opponents hold is meaningless, which will always be true, since 'meaninglessness' can be so defined that any discussion about it is by definition without meaning.[6] Marxists, in a like manner, are accustomed to explain the disagreement of an opponent by his class bias, and the sociologists of knowledge by his total ideology. Such methods are both easy to handle and good fun for those who handle them. But they clearly destroy the basis of rational discussion, and they must lead, ultimately, to antirationalism and mysticism.

In spite of these dangers, I do not see why I should entirely forgo the fun of handling these methods. For just like the psychoanalysts, the people to whom psychoanalysis applies best,[7] the socioanalysts with almost irresistible hospitality invite the application of their own methods to themselves. For is not their description of an intelligentsia which is only loosely anchored in tradition a very neat description of their own social group? And is it not also clear that, assuming the theory of total ideologies to be correct, it would be part of every total ideology to believe that one's own group was free from bias, and was indeed that body of the elect which alone was capable of objectivity? Is it not, therefore, to be expected, always assuming the truth of this theory, that those who hold it will unconsciously deceive themselves by producing an amendment to the theory in order to establish the objectivity of their own views? Can we, then, take seriously their claim that by their sociological self-analysis they have reached a higher degree of objectivity; and their claim that socioanalysis can cast out a total ideology? But we could even ask whether the whole theory is not simply the expression of the class interest of this particular group; of an intelligentsia only loosely anchored in tradition, though just firmly enough to speak Hegelian as their mother tongue.

How little the sociologists of knowledge have succeeded in sociotherapy, that is to say, in eradicating their own total ideology, will be particularly obvious if we consider their relation to Hegel. For they have no idea that they are just repeating him; on the contrary, they believe not only that they have outgrown him, but also that they have successfully seen through him, socioanalyzed him; and that they can now look at him, not from any particular social habitat, but objectively, from a superior elevation. This palpable failure in self-analysis tells us enough.

But, all joking apart, there are more serious objections. The sociology of knowledge is not only self-destructive, not only a rather gratifying object of socioanalysis, it also shows an astounding failure to understand precisely its main object, the *social aspects of knowledge,* or rather, of scientific method. It looks upon science or knowledge as a process in the mind or 'consciousness' of the individual scientist, or perhaps as the product of such a process. If considered in this way, what we call scientific objectivity must indeed become completely ununderstandable, or even impossible; and not only in the social or political sciences, where class interests and similar hidden motives may play a part, but just as much in the natural sciences. Everyone who has an inkling of the history of the natural sciences is aware of the passionate tenacity which characterizes many of its quarrels. No amount of political partiality can influence political theories more strongly than the partiality shown by some natural scientists in favor of their intellectual offspring. If scientific objectivity were founded, as the sociologistic theory of knowledge naïvely assumes, upon the individual scientist's impartiality or objectivity, then we should have to say good-by to it. Indeed, we must be in a way more radically sceptical than the sociology of knowledge; for there is no doubt that we are all suffering under our own system of prejudices (or 'total ideologies,' if this term is preferred); that we all take many things as self-evident, that we accept them uncritically and even with the naïve and cocksure belief that criticism is quite unnecessary; and scientists are no exception to this rule, even though they may have superficially purged themselves from some of their prejudices in their particular field. But they have not purged themselves by socioanalysis or any similar method; they have not attempted to climb to a higher plane from which they can understand, socioanalyze, and expurgate their ideological follies. For by making their minds more 'objective' they could not possibly attain to what we call 'scientific objectivity.' No, what we usually mean by this term rests on different grounds.[8] It is a matter of scientific method. And, ironically enough, objectivity is closely bound up with the *social aspect of scientific method,* with the fact that science and scientific objectivity do not (and cannot) result from the attempts of an individual scientist to be 'objective,' but from the cooperation of many scientists. Scientific objectivity can be described as the intersubjectivity of scientific method. But this social aspect of science is almost entirely neglected by those who call themselves sociologists of knowledge.

Two aspects of the method of the natural sciences are of importance in this connection. Together they constitute what I may term the 'public character of scientific method.' First, there is something approaching free criticism. A scientist may offer his theory with the full conviction that it is unassailable. But this does not necessarily impress his fellow scientists; rather it challenges them. For they know that the scientific attitude means criticizing everything, and they are little deterred even by authorities. Secondly, scientists try to avoid talking at cross-purposes. (I may remind the reader that I am speaking of the natural sciences, but a part of modern economics may be included.) They try very seriously to speak one and the same language, even if they use different mother tongues. In the natural sciences this is achieved by recognizing experience as the impartial arbiter of their controversies. When speaking of 'experience' I have in mind experience of a 'public' character, like observations, and experiments, as opposed to experience in the sense of more 'private' æsthetic or religious experience; and an experience is 'public' if everybody who takes the trouble can repeat it. In order to avoid speaking at cross-purposes, scientists try to express their theories in such a form that they can be tested, i.e. refuted (or otherwise confirmed) by such experience.

This is what constitutes scientific objectivity. Everyone who has learned the technique of understanding and testing scientific theories can repeat the experiment and judge for himself. In spite of this, there will always be some who come to judgments which are partial, or even cranky. This cannot be helped, and it does not seriously disturb the working of the various *social institutions* which have been designed to further scientific objectivity and impartiality; for instance the laboratories, the scientific periodicals, the congresses. This aspect of scientific method shows what can be achieved by institutions designed to make public control possible, and by the open expression of public opinion, even if this is limited to a circle of specialists. Only political power, when it is used to suppress free criticism, or when it fails to protect it, can impair the functioning of these institutions, on which all progress, scientific, technological, and political, ultimately depends.

In order to elucidate further still this sadly neglected aspect of scientific method, we may consider the idea that it is advisable to characterize science by its methods rather than by its results.

Let us first assume that a clairvoyant produces a book by dreaming it, or perhaps by automatic writing. Let us assume, further, that years later as a result of recent and revolutionary scientific discoveries, a great scientist (who has never seen that book) produces one precisely the same. Or to put it differently, we assume that the clairvoyant 'saw' a scientific book which could not then have been produced by a scientist owing to the fact that many relevant discoveries were still unknown at that date. We now ask: is it advisable to say that the clairvoyant produced a scientific book? We may assume that, if submitted at the time to the judgment of competent scientists, it would have been described as partly ununderstandable, and partly fantastic; thus we shall have to say that the clairvoyant's book was not when written a scientific work, since it was not the result of scientific method. I shall call such a result, which, though in agreement with some scientific results, is not the product of scientific method, a piece of 'revealed science.'

In order to apply these considerations to the problem of the publicity of scientific method, let us assume that Robinson Crusoe succeeded in building on his island physical and chemical laboratories, astronomical observatories, etc., and in writing a great number of papers, based throughout on observation and experiment. Let us even assume that he had unlimited time at his disposal, and that he succeeded in constructing and in describing scientific systems which actually coincide with the results accepted at present by our own scientists. Considering the character of this Crusonian science, some people will be inclined, at first sight, to assert that it is real science and not 'revealed science.' And, no doubt, it is very much more like science than the scientific book which was revealed to the clairvoyant, for Robinson Crusoe applied a good deal of scientific method. And yet, I assert that this Crusonian science is still of the 'revealed' kind; that there is an element of scientific method missing, and consequently, that the fact that Crusoe arrived at our results is nearly as accidental and miraculous as it was in the case of the clairvoyant. For there is nobody but himself to check his results; nobody but himself to correct those prejudices which are the unavoidable consequence of his peculiar mental history; nobody to help him to get rid of that strange blindness concerning the inherent possibilities of our own results which is a consequence of the fact that most of them are reached through comparatively irrelevant approaches. And concerning his scientific papers, it is only in attempts to explain his work to *somebody who has not done it* that he can acquire the discipline of clear and reasoned communication which, too, is part of scientific method. In one point—a comparatively unimportant one—is the 'revealed' character of the Crusonian science particularly obvious; I mean Crusoe's discovery of his 'personal equation' (for we must assume that he made this discovery), of the characteristic personal reaction-time affecting his astronomical observations. Of course it is conceivable that he discovered, say, changes in his reaction-time, and that he was led, in this way, to make allowances for it. But if we compare this way of finding out about reaction-time, with the way in which it was discovered in 'public' science—through the contradiction between the results of various observers—then the 'revealed' character of Robinson Crusoe's science becomes manifest.

To sum up these considerations, it may be said that what we call 'scientific objectivity' is not a product of the individual scientist's impartiality, but a product of the social or public character of scientific method; and the individual scientist's impartiality is, so far as it exists, not the source but rather the results of this socially or institutionally organized objectivity of science.

Both [9] Kantians and Hegelians make the same mistake of assuming that our presuppositions (since they are, to start with, undoubtedly indispensable instruments which we need in our active 'making' of experiences) can neither be changed by decision nor refuted by experience; that they are above and beyond the scientific methods of testing theories, constituting as they do the basic presuppositions of all thought. But this is an exaggeration, based on a misunderstanding of the relations between theory and experience in science. It was one of the greatest achievements of our time when Einstein showed that, in the light of experience, we may question and revise our presuppositions regarding even space and time, ideas which had been held to be necessary presuppositions of all science, and to belong to its 'categorial apparatus.' Thus the sceptical attack upon science launched by the sociology of knowledge breaks down in the light of scientific method. The empirical method has proved to be quite capable of taking care of itself.

But it does so not by eradicating our prejudices all at once; it can eliminate them only one by one. The classical case in point is again Einstein's discovery of our prejudices regarding time. Einstein did not set out to discover prejudices; he did not even set out to criticize our conceptions of space and time. His problem was a concrete problem of physics, the redrafting of a theory that had broken down because of various experiments which in the light of the theory seemed to contradict one another. Einstein together with most physicists realized that this meant that the theory was false. And he found that if we alter it in a point which had so far been held by everybody to be self-evident and which had therefore escaped notice, then the difficulty could be removed. In other words, he just applied the methods of scientific criticism and of the invention and elimination of theories, of trial and error. But this method does not lead to the abandonment of all our prejudices; rather, we can discover the fact that we had a prejudice only after having got rid of it.

But it certainly has to be admitted that, at any given moment, our scientific theories will depend not only on the experiments, etc., made up to that moment, but also upon prejudices which are taken for granted, so that we have not become aware of them (although the application of certain logical methods may help us to detect them). At any rate, we can say in regard to this incrustation that science is capable of learning, of breaking down some of its crusts. The process may never be perfected, but there is no fixed barrier before which it must stop short. Any assumption can, in principle, be criticized. And that anybody may do so constitutes scientific objectivity.

Scientific results are 'relative' (if this term is to be used at all) only in so far as they are the results of a certain stage of scientific development and liable to be superseded in the course of scientific progress. But this does not mean that *truth* is 'relative.' If an assertion is true, it is true forever.[10] It only means that most scientific results have the character of hypotheses, i.e. sentences for which the evidence is inconclusive, and which are therefore liable to revision at any time. These considerations (with which I have dealt more fully elsewhere),[11] though not necessary for a criticism of the sociologists, may perhaps help to further the understanding of their theories. They also throw some light, to come back to my main criticism, on the important role which cooperation, intersubjectivity, and the publicity of method plays in scientific criticism and scientific progress.

It is true that the social sciences have not yet fully attained this publicity of method. This is due partly to the intelligence-destroying influence of Aristotle and Hegel, partly perhaps also to their failure to make use of the social instruments of scientific objectivity. Thus they are really 'total ideologies'; or putting it differently, some social scientists are unable, and even unwilling, to speak a common language. But the reason is not class interest, and the cure is not a Hegelian dialectical synthesis, nor self-analysis. The only course open to the social sciences is to forget all about the verbal fireworks and to tackle the practical problems of our time with the help of the theoretical methods which are fundamentally the same in *all* sciences. I mean the methods of trial and error, of inventing hypotheses which can be practically tested, and of submitting them to practical tests. *A social technology is needed whose results can be tested by piecemeal social engineering.*

The cure here suggested for the social sciences is diametrically opposed to the one suggested by the sociology of knowledge. Sociologism believes that it is not their unpractical character, but rather the fact that practical and theoretical problems are too much intertwined in the field of social and political knowledge that creates the methodological difficulties of these sciences. Thus we can read in a leading work on the sociology of knowledge: 'The peculiarity of political knowledge, as opposed to "exact" knowledge, lies in the fact that knowledge and will or the rational element and the range of the irrational, are inseparably and essentially intertwined.' [K. Mannheim, *Ideology and Utopia* (German ed., p. 167).] To this we can reply that 'knowledge' and 'will' are, in a certain sense, always inseparable; and that this fact need not lead to any dangerous entanglement. No scientist can know without making an effort, without taking an interest; and in his effort there is usually even a certain amount of self-interest involved. The engineer studies things mainly from a practical point of view. So does the farmer. Practice is not the enemy of theoretical knowledge but the most valuable incentive to it. Though a certain amount of aloofness may be becoming to the scientist, there are many examples to show that it is not always important for a scientist to be thus disinterested. But it *is* important for him to remain in touch with reality, with practice, for those who overlook it have to pay by lapsing into scholasticism. Practical application of our findings is thus the means by which we may eliminate irrationalism from social science, and not any attempt to separate knowledge from 'will.'

As opposed to this, the sociology of knowledge hopes to reform the social sciences by making the social scientists aware of the social forces and ideologies which unconsciously beset them. But the main trouble about prejudices is that there is no such direct way to get rid of them. For how shall we ever know that we have made any progress, in our attempt to

rid ourselves from prejudice? Is it not a common experience that those who
are most convinced of having got rid of their prejudices are most prej-
udiced? The idea that a sociological or a psychological or an anthropological or any other study of prejudices may help us to rid ourselves of them
is quite mistaken; for many who pursue these studies are full of prejudice;
and not only does self-analysis not help us to overcome the unconscious
determination of our views, it often leads to even more subtle self-deception. Thus we can read in the same work on the sociology of knowledge
the following references to its own activities: 'There is an increasing
tendency towards making conscious the factors by which we have so far
been unconsciously ruled (*op. cit.*, 167). . . . Those who fear that our
increasing knowledge of determining factors may paralyze our decisions
and threaten "freedom" should put their minds at rest. For only he is
truly determined who does not know the most essential determining factors
but acts immediately under the pressure of determinants unknown to
him (*op. cit.*, 166).' Now this is clearly just a repetition of a pet idea of
Hegel's which Engels naïvely repeated when he said: [12] 'Freedom is the
appreciation of necessity.' And it is a reactionary prejudice. For are those
who act under the pressure of well-known determinants, for example, of a
political tyranny, made free by their knowledge? Only Hegel could tell
us such tales. But that the sociology of knowledge preserves this particular
prejudice shows clearly enough that there is no possible short-cut to rid
us of our ideologies. (Once a Hegelian, always a Hegelian.) Self-analysis
is no substitute for those practical actions which are necessary for establishing the democratic institutions which alone can guarantee the freedom
of critical thought, and the progress of science.

[30]

SIDNEY HOOK

*Dialectic and Nature** *

The social importance of a philosophy is measured by the number of
people who hold it, the practices it is used to justify, and the habits of
thought and valuation it leaves in its wake. From this point of view the
philosophy of dialectical materialism is easily one of the most important
social doctrines of our times. Sometimes the scope of this philosophy is
restricted to the realm of social and cultural phenomena; sometimes it is
identified with a systematic elaboration of the principles of scientific

* Reprinted in part from *Reason, Social Myths, and Democracy*. Copyright, 1940,
by Sidney Hook; reprinted 1950 by The Humanities Press, New York. Pages 183–209,
222–224 from Chapter Nine are reprinted by permission of the author.

method; but most often its adherents interpret it as a set of doctrines which describes the fundamental characters of existence in the large as well as in the small, enabling us to formulate laws that operate in nature as well as in human and social activity. An examination, however, of the writings of those who profess to be dialectical materialists in this last sense shows that they are unified more by a community of allegiance than by a community of meaning. This becomes apparent when one seeks a clear answer from them to the questions: "What is dialectic? How is it related to scientific method? What does it mean to say that dialectic is found in nature?"

Aside from the fancied political implications of the doctrine, the sweeping theoretical claims made for it, the insistence that the dialectic is universal, that it is not merely a method of proof but an instrument for winning new truths in the sciences,[1] that it transcends the limitations of formal logic and opens new horizons of research—all warrant the closest analysis. For if these claims are true, then the neglect of this philosophy by natural scientists is nothing short of reprehensible.

The chief sources of the views we are to consider are Engels' *Herrn Eugen Dührings Umwälzung der Wissenschaft*,[1a] better known as *Anti-Dühring*, and his *Dialektik und Natur* published posthumously in the *Marx-Engels Archiv*, Bd. II. The philosophical writings of Plekhanov, Kautsky, Lenin, Trotsky, and Mehring and the minor figures in the orthodox tradition contain little on these themes not already to be found in Engels.

What I propose to do is (i) to distinguish the various senses of the term "dialectic" in the major writings of Engels; (ii) to determine whether they are mutually compatible; (iii) to analyze the so-called universal laws of dialectic and the illustrations offered of each; and (iv) to investigate whether there is any sense in which the dialectic can serve as a corrective, supplement, or substitute for scientific method.

1. *Seven Meanings of Dialectic*

I. DIALECTIC AS UNIVERSAL AND OBJECTIVE

For Engels, as for Hegel, the laws of dialectic are both objective and universal. Every field of knowledge, the objects known as well as the processes by which they are known, is subject to their sway. What, indeed, can be more comprehensive than Engels' statement that "the dialectic is nothing more than the science of the general laws of motion and development of nature, human society and thought"? (p. 144.) The illustrations offered are drawn from mathematics, physics, chemistry, biology, geology, history, and philosophy.

Engels does not assert that the knowledge of these laws by itself is sufficient to give mastery over things, for these laws are "unconsciously operative in nature and history" and their discovery in specific situations presupposes the possession of specific knowledge. But whenever man thinks correctly, he thinks dialectically, and whenever he controls things, he does so only by adapting himself to the dialectic processes implicit within them. The failure, however, to take explicit note of these laws probably—and an open disregard of them, necessarily—will lead to error. Like the laws of grammar and correct usage they operate as restrictive conditions. People may speak correctly without a knowledge of the rules of syntax; but for difficult constructions they are a help, and when deliberately flouted, soon re-establish their necessity in facilitating communication or make way for new rules. In passing, it should be noticed that the admission that there is undialectical thinking, even as a psychological fact, invalidates the claim made for the universality of dialectic. But we shall return to this later. It is clear, then, that one important sense of the term dialectic makes it *a constitutive principle in everything*, a pervasive ontological character of anything that is or may be conceived. Therefore, once we have acquired genuine knowledge of any situation, we can show that it conforms to the laws of dialectic. But at this point we are confronted by a difficulty. Engels emphatically maintains in defending Marx against Dühring that the former "does not dream of attempting to prove" the historical necessity of capitalist accumulation and decline by the laws of dialectic. "On the contrary: after he has historically proved that in fact the process has already in part occurred and in part must occur, he characterizes it in addition as a process which develops according to a definite dialectical law" (*op. cit.*, p. 136). In other words, the process of proof need not be dialectical. At best, the dialectic is *one* of a number of modes of proof even when the subject matter under investigation is historical. It cannot be true, then, that all thinking—even all valid thinking—is dialectical any more than the fact that I can translate all languages into English establishes the latter as *the* universal language. Nor can it be argued that the universal, constitutive character of dialectic is demonstrated by the fact that knowledge of anything can be acquired only by employing the dialectic method, for there are at least some things which can be known non-dialectically. The question remains whether, and to what extent, the dialectic as a method of proof and as a method of discovery is different from non-dialectical methods, and in what situations its application leads to greater truth than other available methods.

II. DIALECTIC AS THE LOGIC OF TRANSITION

The most relevant suggestion bearing on this question to be found in Engels' writings is that the dialectic method applies to situations where no hard and fast lines can be drawn, where areas of indetermination, critical phases and twilight zones are present. He contrasts the dialectic here with what he calls metaphysical thinking which postulates the unconditional validity of the principle of excluded middle. But metaphysical thinking, according to Engels, cannot give an accurate analysis of even the simplest forms of motion and is conspicuously incompatible with the evolutionary hypothesis. Two of many passages express this meaning of dialectic with forthright clarity. In *Dialektik und Natur*, speaking of transitions in nature, he writes:

"For those stages in natural science, where all oppositions are bridged by intermediate steps, the old metaphysical method of thought no longer suffices. The dialectic which recognizes no hard and fast lines, no unconditionally valid either-or!, which transforms fixed metaphysical differences into each other, mediates opposites and puts at the correct place besides the either-or! the this-as-well-as-that!, (*Sowohl dies—wie jenes!*), is the only method of thought eminently suited to such situations. For daily use, for scientific retail, the metaphysical categories retain their validity." (*Op. cit.*, p. 189.)

In the *Anti-Dühring,* Engels generalizes his criticism and calls the whole of modern science to the bar of dialectic to hear an indictment of its metaphysical character:

"It is, however, precisely the polar oppositions that are set forth as irreconcilable and insoluble, the arbitrarily imposed fixed lines of distinction and differences between classes which have given modern theoretical natural science its limited metaphysical character. The knowledge that these oppositions and differences are indeed present in nature but only with relative validity and that their conceived rigidity and absolute validity is introduced into nature only by our reflective activity—this knowledge is the kernel of the dialectical conception of nature." (p. xix.)

Here again certain crucial difficulties emerge. Either the whole of nature and experience is in a fluid state or the dialectic is not universal. If nothing that exists is *in any respect* sharply demarcated from something else, then the abstractions employed in scientific analysis, which presuppose some such demarcation, must be regarded merely as convenient fictions. In that case, the fruitfulness of one set of fictions rather than another would be a mystery. But if all thought, as Engels continually asserts, is a mirror or image of reality, the recognition of the existence and operative efficacy of fictions necessitates a modification of his theory of knowledge.

More important still, the ontological assumption behind the claim that every *entweder-oder* must be modified by a *sowohl dies—wie jenes* entails the belief that in any situation where a disjunction is employed, a third real or grounded possibility is *always* to be found. Empirically there is no warrant for such a sweeping generalization, and in fact it is flatly inconsistent with the Marxist theory of history according to which at certain historic periods society is confronted by only two possible alternatives. Time and again Engels denied that there was a genuine third alternative in modern times to socialism and capitalism. Those of his followers for whom the slogans socialism or barbarism, democracy or fascism, are not mere rhetoric, cannot square a reasoned defense of the antitheses drawn with an acceptance of the *universal relevance* of the logic of *sowohl dies— wie jenes.*[2] But of course all things are possible by a systematic abuse of definitions.

III. DIALECTIC AS THE LOGIC OF DISJUNCTION

Interestingly enough, Engels' own political experience, combined with his stress upon the facts of polarity, leads him on occasion to speak of dialectical situations as if they were pre-eminently characterized by the logic of exclusive and exhaustive disjunction. (The identification of polar opposition and dialectic we shall discuss below.) In a passage which begins by stating that "the so-called objective dialectic" obtains for the whole of nature, and that "the so-called subjective dialectic" is merely the reflection of the "movement of opposites" everywhere valid in nature, Engels writes:

"It is in history that the movement of opposites really comes to the fore in all the critical epochs of the leading nations. At such moments a nation has a choice only between two horns of a dilemma: either—or. And indeed the question is always posed quite differently from the way in which the political philistindom of all times wishes to pose it. Even the liberal German philistines of 1848 found themselves in 1849 suddenly and unexpectedly and against their own will faced by the question: either a return to the old reaction in intensified form or progress of the revolution to a republic. . . . Likewise the French bourgeoisie stood before the certainly unexpected dilemma: either caricature of imperial rule, Praetorianism and the exploitation of France by a pack of scoundrels (*Lumpenbande*) or a social-democratic republic." (*Dialektik und Natur, loc. cit.,* p. 190.)

It is clear that it is precisely in such situations that the liberals, of whose undialectical approach Engels speaks so scornfully, seek for third alternatives, intermediate paths, and formulae which attempt to reconcile the irreconcilable. Such a quest, according to the present sense of dialectic, is branded undialectical, even though it invokes the logic of continuity and inveighs against hard and fast lines. But what, now, shall we say of nature in which Engels has assured us no hard and fast lines occur? It is certainly not dialectical in the present sense. In an attempt to escape this obvious difficulty it is sometimes held that the dialectic expresses *both* the logic of continuity (*sowohl dies—wie jenes*) and that of discontinuity (*entweder—oder*). Nature and history provide situations in which the two approaches are legitimate. Granted. But even so, they are not both applicable at the same time, in the same respect, and from the same point of view. Since both cannot be universally applicable, when is the *either-or* aspect of the dialectic to be employed and when *the-this-as-well-as that?*

No matter what answer is made, it will entail the recognition that recourse must be had to other methodological considerations in order to determine when it is legitimate to apply the narrow form of the principle of excluded middle and when it is not. These considerations, of course, are derived from the logic of scientific inquiry whose task it is to determine whether the material under investigation is such that various formal rules may be significantly applied. Later on we shall see that there is a sense of dialectic which makes it equivalent to scientific method but we shall also see that it is highly dubious whether any science can achieve significant results by denying the principle of excluded middle.

Some dialectical materialists are under the strange delusion that a trichotomy such as "either *a* or *b* or *both*" represents a violation of the law of excluded middle. This would be the case only if *b* were the formal contradictory of *a,* in which case it is simply nonsense to say that they are both true. Sometimes we find ourselves in a position in which we seem to be saying that neither *a* nor its contradictory is true, as e.g., "the soul weighs more than a gram" and "the soul does not weigh more than a gram," but all such statements are pseudo-propositions. They involve a confusion of categories and are meaningless.

IV. DIALECTIC AS POLAR OPPOSITION

Another sense of the term dialectic gives it the meaning of *polarity* and *polar opposition.* For Engels the sources of this conception are to be found in Hegel's doctrine of Essence. Physical phenomena are cited as the most striking illustration of polarity and provide the basic analogy in this respect for all other fields. "Just as electricity and magnetism polarize themselves, move in opposites, so do thoughts." (*Ibid.*, p. 156.) In other passages, he traces its presence in chemistry, biology, and psychology. Nowhere is an analysis given of the logical structure of polarity, so that it is difficult to tell whether Engels is using the concept of polarity metaphorically or whether he actually believes that thoughts, for example, polarize themselves like magnets, which is comparable to saying that the concept of weight itself has weight.

The clearest meaning that can be given to the statement that polarity is universal in nature and history derives from some linguistic principle of significant assertion. Every term which enters significantly into discourse must have an intelligible opposite. This is not an arbitrary rule of language but flows from the fact, recognized both by Hegel and Engels, that everything can be surveyed from at least two different aspects and that the existence of anything involves the existence of at least some one *other* thing. But even so, this by no means justifies the deduction that the other, from which an aspect or thing is distinguished, is *polar* in character, that it necessitates, and is necessitated by, the existence of its opposite. The "poles" of a magnet are such not because the two ends are merely *different* from each other. The two ends still remain different even when demagnetization has taken place. But the polarity is gone. Materially interpreted, either polar opposition means no more than that there are differences in nature, which is true but trivial since it is the kind, quality and degree of difference that are scientifically important; or polar opposition is not at all a universal phenomenon but must be empirically established, once its structure is clearly defined, in various fields and situations.

It must be further indicated that the structure of the polar opposition in magnetism is quite different from the structure of the polar opposition between male and female, arithmetical plus and minus, heredity and environment (the illustrations are Engels'), and bourgeoisie and proletariat. The expression is systematically ambiguous and is of no help in any concrete inquiry which seeks to discover how various elements within a situation are functionally related to each other.

v. "subjective" dialectic

A more special sense of the term dialectic in Engels makes it relevant primarily to the development of concepts. This converts the dialectic into a constitutive principle not of everything but of a determinate realm of existence—the realm of mind. The growth of knowledge, individual and social, is often cited as an illustration of the dialectic process in this sense. Sometimes such statements are accompanied by the remark that the growth of knowledge actually reflects or mirrors the changes and evolution in the subject matter known, from which it would follow that the order of the development of knowledge is the same as the order of the objective development of things. The later proposition, already explicitly drawn by Hegel, is palpably false and is compatible only with some form of philosophical idealism.

When Engels refers to dialectic as the structure of the thought process, it is to contrast it with other modes of thinking. Man shares with the animals, he tells us, all the activities of the understanding—induction, deduction, abstraction, analysis, synthesis, and experimentation.[3] In these respects, there is no essential difference between man and the animals except in degree. "On the other hand dialectical thinking is possible only for man just because it has as its presupposition the investigation of the nature of concepts themselves" (*op. cit.*, p. 187). It seems, then, that the nature of concepts is the privileged subject matter of dialectic, and further, that all the activities of the understanding enumerated above, which constitute far and away the larger portion of thought, can be carried on without an "investigation of the nature of concepts"—an interesting doctrine if true.

This clearly seems to restrict dialectic to a method of analyzing concepts, although previously it had been characterized as a method of proof and a method of discovery—activities which, according to Engels, man shares with animals incapable of dialectic thought. And even as a method of analysis, Engels does not hesitate to contrast it with mathematical thought. He prefaces some remarks on work as the measure of motion with the observation that "perhaps it will be seen that when it is a question of handling ideas, dialectical thinking at the very least carries one just as far as mathematical calculation" (*op. cit.*, p. 307). The "perhaps," of course, turns out to be purely rhetorical.

Now conceptual thought may be "analyzed" from at least three different points of view. (i) Inquiry may be made into the natural history of ideas, the structure and function of the thought processes out of which they arise—all of which is roughly classified under psychology. Or (ii) the formal relationships between ideas may be investigated so as to disclose whether the systematic pattern of meanings (propositions, statements) involved is consistent—formal and symbolic logic. Or (iii) the relationships between things, symbols, and human behavior may be analyzed in order to show how normative principles of thought arise and operate in inquiry. It is difficult to determine whether Engels' statement that formal logic and dialectic is "the science of thought and its laws" refers to any one of these aspects of thought or to all three.[4] If the dialectic is a description of the ways in which human beings actually think, then all thinking, good, bad, or indifferent, is dialectical, and as pure descriptive psychology, it has little bearing upon the laws of *valid* proof or discovery. If dialectic is not concerned with psychology and sets itself up as a theory of consistent and valid thinking in all fields, then since it has been granted that some people think undialectically and yet not always incorrectly, then the dialectic is universal neither as fact nor norm. The third possible approach to thinking, so far as I know, has not been identified with the dialectic by any canonic interpreter nor has any theory of the nature of signs and symbols been developed.

VI. DIALECTIC AS ORGANIC INTERRELATION

Another meaning attached to the term dialectic in the writings of Engels is asserted to have great heuristic value. The dialectic approach to nature and history recognizes that all things are organically interrelated in one great totality. No object, therefore, can be exhaustively explained in its own specific categories. The totality is such that all of its elements are in continuous interaction with each other so that cause and effect are abstracted, partial phases of an interlocking, developing whole. What is often called "dialectical" interrelation between part and part, and whole and part, is universal and necessary. Many passages can be cited from Engels' writings which imply this view:

"We also find upon closer examination that the both poles of an opposition, like positive and negative, are as inseparable from each other as they are opposed, and that despite their opposition interpenetrate each other. In the same way, cause and effect are ideas that have validity only when applied to the particular case as such, but just as soon as we consider the individual event in its universal connection with the world as a whole are dissolved in the conception of a universal, reciprocal interaction (*Wechselwirkung*) in which causes and effects continually change places, and what now or here is effect becomes there or then cause and *vice versa*." (*Anti-Dühring*, pp. 7–8.) [5]

Now the statement "all things are interrelated" is, as such, ambiguous, unless it is indicated *how* they are interrelated, or at the very best, what *kind* of interrelation is meant. To say that things are "dialectically" interrelated introduces the conceptions of necessity and systematic connection but still leaves open the question whether they are physically interrelated or logically interrelated. On Engels' view, however, since logical relations are reflections of relations which exist in the natural world, there is no essential difference between causal determination and logical determination. As in Hegel, where a distinction is recognized, it turns out to be merely epistemic.

This conception of universal dialectical interrelation is the fountainhead of Engels' monism and is defended by a number of logical and empirical considerations scattered throughout Engels' writings. The logical arguments are all variants of the Hegelian theory of internal relations. The ascription of any property or relation to a term presupposes the existence of another term. Every term is a congeries of an infinite set of relations all of which are necessary to its nature. Strictly speaking, then, it is impossible to deny that a term has any of its determinate properties without lapsing into self-contradiction. As a matter of fact, however, it is possible meaningfully to deny that a term is characterized by any of its properties or relations except when the latter are part of the *definition* of the term. But if all the relationships into which a thing can possibly enter are already involved in its definition, it would follow that all propositions of fact are analytic, which is clearly false. The influence of the notion of universal, "dialectical interrelation" is also revealed in the curious reluctance on the part of orthodox Hegelians and dialectical materialists to admit that "hypotheticals contrary to fact," i.e., judgments which take the form "*if* a thing or event had been different from what it was," are meaningful assumptions in science or history.

The empirical argument for the dialectical interrelatedness of everything is buttressed by the citation of many instances in which the growth of knowledge has led to the modification of earlier views held, to the redefinition of concepts, and to the discovery of unifying principles between apparently disparate fields. But it is or should be obvious that the empirical evidence in the nature of the case has to be piecemeal and cannot serve as the premise for a deduction that any new piece of knowledge must *necessarily* lead to the abandonment or modification of the old.

VII. DIALECTIC AS SCIENTIFIC METHOD

There remains, finally, the conception of dialectic which makes it equivalent to scientific method. Although there is little direct statement of this interpretation, suggestions and intimations abound in Engels' discussions. On occasions the critical role of hypotheses is recognized, admission is made of the existence of relatively isolated systems, and the methodological inadequacy of physical and biological "reductionism" is very forcibly stated. In many passages stress is placed upon the relative (and relational), historical and contextual character of judgment, including scientific propositions, and some of Engels' formulations, despite his crude theory of abstraction, would give comfort even to contemporary positivism.[6] When Engels criticizes the excesses of empiricists, it is in order to

call attention either to their neglect of hypotheses or their failure to introduce the proper controls in experiment without which observations have no
evidential value.[7] A typical passage of this strain in Engels' thought is
the following:

"The form of development of natural science insofar as it is reflective is
the *hypothesis*. A new fact is observed which makes the customary mode of
explanation for facts of the same class impossible. From this moment on, there
is a need for new modes of explanation which at first rest upon a limited
number of facts and observations. Further observation purifies these hypotheses, eliminates some, corrects others until the law is established in pure
form. Were one to wait until the materials out of which the law is derived
appear in *pure* form, that would mean to suspend reflective inquiry indefinitely,
and already for that reason alone the law would never be established." (*Dialektik und Natur, op. cit.*, p. 155.)

Engels very properly adds that the fact that hypotheses succeed each
other, so that none can claim to be absolutely true, does not justify the
belief that the essence of things is unknowable or that a legitimate scientific distinction can be drawn between appearance and reality.

We are all the more warranted in emphasizing this interpretation in
virtue of Engels' claims that the dialectic is a method by which new truths
are discovered, for whatever else scientific method may be disclosed to be,
it is primarily the organized procedure of inference, prediction, and control
by which man extends the boundaries of knowledge.

In this section we have distinguished in the major works of Engels
seven distinct meanings of the term dialectic insofar as it bears upon
natural phenomena. They are: (1) dialectic as a constitutive principle of
all things—a universal form of behavior to which there are no actual or
conceivable exceptions; (2) dialectic as the logical pattern of transition
and continuity; (3) dialectic as the logic of disjunction in situations where
two alternatives are exclusive and exhaustive; (4) dialectic as the principle of polar opposition; (5) dialectic as a special constitutive principle
whose existential locus is the development of *concepts*; (6) dialectic as
the constitutive and heuristic principle that all things are systematically
interrelated, and (7) dialectic as a grouping, first approximation to the
logic of scientific method. Other meanings may be found but with the
exception of conceptions of dialectic that apply only to history and sociology (which are not included in the scope of this chapter) none will be
discovered to play a significant role in the corpus of Engels' writings.

It remains to ask now: to what extent are these seven conceptions
compatible with each other? And if they are incompatible, which concep-
tion(s) of dialectic does Engels regard as most basic to his own thinking?

2. *The Ambiguities and Inconsistencies of Dialectic*

A first glance at the seven different meanings of dialectic in Engels
will show that they fall within three groups: (a) dialectic as a universal
constitutive principle, justifying the logic of organic totality (1 and 6 of

the enumeration above); (b) in which the constitutive reference of the dialectic is limited to a restricted field, or to a particular aspect of all fields (2, 3, 4 and 5); (c) in which it is synonymous with scientific method.

Are (a) and (b) compatible with each other? Yes, if (b) were subject to *special* laws of dialectic applicable to special fields without impugning the validity of the laws of (a). But there are no dialectical laws asserted to hold for (b) which are not restatements of, or deductions from, the dialectical laws asserted to hold for (a). However, we have seen that the point of the enumeration of special fields of (b) in which dialectic structure is found is to distinguish them from other fields of existence *not* characterized by dialectical structure. Or in other words, what (b) asserts is not "some, perhaps all, fields of existence are characterized by dialectic," but "some fields are so characterized and some are not." It follows therefore that (a) and (b) are related to each other as A and O propositions in the traditional logic, i.e., they are formal contradictories.

Are (a) and (c) compatible with each other? This depends on what we understand by scientific method. Now there is at least one proposition which every theory of scientific method must accept in some form or other if it desires to do justice to the actual procedures of scientific inquiry, viz., that it is possible to discover the functional relationships between a limited number of variables without taking into account the rest of the universe. Without this presupposition—whose fruitfulness proves that it is not arbitrary—scientific experimentation would be impossible. In fact, to say that all things are interrelated is to utter a formula devoid even of heuristic value. When it is invoked as an *obiter dictum,* it will be found that what is meant is that *some* things are related in certain *specific* ways to some other things. It is simply not the case that each additional piece of knowledge leads to a modification of every other piece of knowledge. Nothing can be discovered except on the assumption that the particular situation investigated is determined by a finite number of *relevant* factors. The infinity of universes and the possible infinity of their interrelations, if they have any significance for science at all, mean not that knowledge *must* be inaccurate but merely that there is always something more to be known. At times Engels himself recognizes this, as when he writes: "The extremest limit of our natural science is until now *our* universe and we do not need the infinite number of universes which exist out there in order to have knowledge of nature" (*op. cit.,* p. 159).

Another characteristic property of scientific method is that its techniques involve a transformation of materials, an intervention into natural processes, an introduction of *redirective activities* upon what is given to hand in order to achieve the tested knowledge necessary for prediction and control. Were everything in the world interrelated in one complex network of objective dialectic, then science as a human and cultural phenomenon would be *theoretically* inferrible from the existence of that which is to be known. The world would have to be declared such that it could not *both* be true that (i) it has the structure it is actually discovered to have and (ii) science itself not have emerged. This is to assert, for example, that a star cluster in the heavens or the adrenal glands in man could not possibly exist unless they were discovered. Or, more generally, that it is theoretically possible by an organic logic to prove that a *necessary* connection exists between what is and what is known. This is the open gateway to idealism. Berkeley and Hegel stand on either side of the tortuous path beckoning unwary dialectical materialists who believe this to come closer.

A still more important implication is involved in the view that the historic development of science is subject to the immanent necessities of the one dialectical whole of which it is a part. For science as a phase of human culture is controlled by values, interests and needs which are revealed most clearly in the direction of scientific research and the variety of its applications. Human values, then, on the above view of organic determinism, must have not only a cosmic support but must be constitutively involved in the very nature of things. Like all other things, nature and society must be "dialectically" and, therefore, necessarily interrelated. But for Marxism, as for every other non-Platonic philosophy, there are no values where there is no consciousness, or at least some form of sentience. To make values constitutive elements in the dialectic totality, therefore, is to make consciousness an integral element of all existence, is to endow the scheme of things with some pervasive purpose or system of purposes which is gradually being fulfilled. What this leads to was pointed out by Engels himself when he taxed Dühring with surreptitiously introducing conscious activity into natural processes and relapsing into theology.[8]

A final root incompatibility between (a) and (c) is to be discovered in their respective notions of necessity as applied to existence. In (a) necessity is logical, systematic, and circular. In (c) necessity is conditional and justifies only probability judgments. From the point of view of a philosophy which regards the world as a dialectic totality, the "necessities" expressed by scientific laws are abstract and contingent. Abstract, because they are asserted to hold for all situations which conform to certain initial definitions irrespective of what *other* properties may be present; contingent, because the relationships discovered to hold between the various elements of a situation are not derived from the "systematic dynamic nature" (Hegel) or "the self-moving nature" (Engels) of the objects investigated. For the ordinary scientist, however, there is no such thing as *the* nature of anything with inherent qualities of self-movement which constitute its so-called set of essential attributes. All attributes, properties, and relations possess the same degree of essentiality or inherence except where, in the course of inquiry, he isolates certain characteristics for purposes of identification and uses them as defining traits in subsequent investigation. His mode of analysis is thoroughly relational and when he speaks of the *normal* or *natural* properties of anything he is employing these terms in a statistical sense.

The difference between the concepts of necessity in (a) and (c) may be illustrated by an example from Engels which is all the more to the point because it indicates what meaning the term "dialectic" normally has for Engels himself. In critically discussing "mathematical materialism" which explains the phases of a developed mental process step by step in terms of the functional relationships existing between the elements in any given region of space and time, Engels quotes with approval Hegel's doctrine of *der innere Zweck* (internal purpose). According to this doctrine, the nature of an organism (and for Hegel, as for Whitehead, all things may be characterized as organisms) determines the specific type of relationship which exists at any time between its constituent elements. It is denied that the nature of anything can be explained as the resultant structure of cumulative, empirically observable relationships between its elements and the complex of environmental conditions. At most, the absence of environmental conditions may prevent the nature of a thing from realizing itself, but once the conditions are present (and something guarantees that sooner or later they will be), then the essential properties of a thing can be explained only in terms of its antecedently defined self-moving nature.

"The point is," writes Engels, "that mechanism (also the materialism of the eighteenth century) never frees itself from abstract necessity and therefore from contingency. That matter has developed out of itself a thinking human brain is for it a purely contingent fact, although every step in its occurrence is necessarily conditioned. In truth, however, it is the nature of matter to progress to the development of thinking creatures and this occurs, therefore, always of necessity when the conditions for it (not necessarily everywhere and always the same) are present." (*Dialektik und Natur, loc. cit.*, p. 292.)

This asserts two things which can never be established by scientific methods. One, that somewhere and sometimes the conditions *must* appear which are necessary for the nature of matter to realize itself in the form of a thinking brain, for if the conditions of emergence *never* appeared, wherein would the *necessity* of the emergence lie except in an arbitrary definition of matter? Second, that the emergence of a thinking brain is not univocally determined by a definite set of conditions, so that the necessity of the emergence of the brain cannot be attributed to the interacting complex of determinate conditions at a given time but to the nature of matter as such —a matter which, Engels tells us elsewhere, is "a pure creation of thought, an abstraction." [9]

That Engels is in earnest with his contention that the nature of matter is such that it must *necessarily* develop into a thinking brain, a striking passage from the same work testifies. "We have the certainty," he says, "that matter in all its transformations remains eternally the same, that none of its attributes can ever be lost, and that therefore with the same iron necessity with which, on earth, it exterminates its highest product, the thinking spirit, it must some day somewhere else create it again" (p. 255).

This is a certainty that dialectic (I had almost said religion) may give—science never.

In the light of the foregoing, I think we are justified in maintaining that the class of meanings of dialectic in group (a) is incompatible with dialectic conceived as scientific method, group (c).

Are (b) and (c) compatible with each other? Here we must briefly compare the members of class (b) and (c).

(b)2 and (c). (b)2 is the logic of transition and continuity. It is obvious that scientific method takes note of continuities. In fact it is only in virtue of the application of scientific method that continuities have been uncovered and adequately described. But Engels interprets (b)2 as if it entailed the denial of the laws of identity and contradiction. "Abstract identity, $a = a$, and negatively, a cannot be equal and unequal to a at the same time—are also inapplicable to organic nature" (*ibid.*, p. 157). Were this so, the work of science would come to a dead stop. As we shall see below, where science seems to violate the law of contradiction, it is in virtue of incompatible descriptions and statements, an incompatibility which is a spur either to further qualification of the descriptions or to re-definition—both designed to eliminate contradiction. Engels' interpretation of (b)2 must be declared incompatible with (c).

(b)3 and (c). (b)3 is the logic of disjunction where alternatives are mutually exclusive and exhaustive. This is compatible with (c). In fact, it is a special case of the method of residues. Scientific method, however, never *guarantees* that all the known alternatives are exhaustive unless we are dealing with a proposition and its logical contradictory. And even here it may rule out both on the ground that their meaning content is irrelevant to the specific inquiry. Scientific conclusions, therefore, even when the purely deductive form of the method of residues is employed, cannot give us more than probabilities.

(b)4 and (c). (b)4 is the principle of polar opposition. If the metaphor of polarity is taken seriously, it is the purest mythology to extend it to everything. In this form, (b)4 is a vestige of the Romantic *Natur-philosophie* and is inconsistent with any non-mystical conception of scientific method. If the principle of polarity states that every scientific category must have an intelligible opposite, then it is "true" and enjoys the status of a syntactical rule of significant assertion. The successful application of this rule in the construction of a scientific system justifies the inference that no situation in nature can be found which is resolvable into one element or possesses only one aspect. Attempts have sometimes been made to interpret the principle of polarity as if it meant that in every situation forces will be found which are moving in opposite directions. But Engels scorns this interpretation as the sheerest commonplace devoid of any possibility of application (*Anti-Dühring*, p. 122).

(b)5 and (c). (b)5 is dialectic conceived as the structural form of the natural history of concepts. If concepts do have this form, (c) is the only valid method by which that fact can be discovered. (c) and (b)5, therefore, are compatible, and related to each other as method and specific conclusion.

There remains the question of the relationships which the different conceptions of dialectic in class (b) bear to each other. To save space we shall state only the conclusions of the analysis.

(b)2 and (b)3, strictly interpreted, are incompatible, especially if both are regarded as having universal import.

(b)2 and (b)4 are incompatible.

(b)2 and (b)3 are related as (b)2 and (c), depending upon how (b)2 is taken.

(b)3 and (b)4 are compatible.

(b)3 and (b)5 are compatible.

(b)4 and (b)5 are related as (b)4 and (c).

We have already answered the first question we set ourselves in Section II. The various meanings of dialectic in Engels are incompatible with each other. The second question is: which meaning does Engels regard as primary in his own thought? Sufficient documentation has been given to indicate that the answer is (1)—dialectic as a universal constitutive principle operating everywhere and in everything. That Engels regards this as the primary meaning of dialectic is apparent also in the fact that the major part of his discussion of dialectic in the *Anti-Dühring* consists of an attempt to state the objective and universal *laws* of dialectic. In short, the laws of dialectic are laws of *ontology*. In Section 3 we shall critically examine these laws from the point of view of logic and scientific method.

3. *The "Laws" of Dialectic*

We have already seen that according to Engels dialectic is the science of extremely general, comprehensive, and, therefore, important laws of development in nature, history, and thought. The basic laws of dialectic are three in number. Running reference is made to them throughout all of Engels' writings. The formulation of these laws varies and the only extended discussion of them in the *Anti-Dühring* concerns itself in the main with the citation of illustrations.

The chief laws of dialectic are:

(I) "The identity of contradictories." Sometimes alternate phrasings are found, such as "the identity of opposites." On occasions the term "unity" is substituted for "identity." All four of the following expressions are used interchangeably in the works of most dialectical materialists: (a) the identity of contradictions, (b) the unity of contradictions, (c) the identity of opposites, (d) the unity of opposites.

(II) The law of "the negation of the negation." Sometimes this is called "the law of the transformation of contradictions (opposites) into each other."

(III) "The transition of quantity to quality and vice versa."

I. CONTRADICTION

The fundamental presupposition of all the laws of dialectic is the belief that contradiction "is objectively present in things and processes." To say the very least, this is a strange use of the term "contradiction," for since the time of Aristotle it has been a commonplace of logical theory that *propositions* or *judgments* or *statements* are contradictory, not things or events. Engels is perfectly aware of the traditional usage but argues against Dühring that the refusal to make the concept of contradiction applicable to things is precisely what reveals the limitations of commonsense and formal logic. Indeed, not only does Engels maintain that contradiction is objectively present in nature, he insists that it is "an actual force as well." [10] Literally construed, this would make a physical relation out of a logical category, so that the whole of mathematics and logic would be nothing more than a branch of physics. The difficulties in such a view are enormous. In addition to being flatly irreconcilable with basic principles of scientific inquiry, it cannot even be consistently stated.

If all existence is self-contradictory and, as Engels holds, all correct thinking is an image or reflection of things, then consistency would be an unfailing sign of falsity. The sciences, which regard consistency as at least a necessary condition of truth, could not take a step. If all existence is self-contradictory, then Engels is hardly entitled to say that thought which is a product of nature must "correspond" with it instead of contradicting it.[11] If logic is part of physics, then logical propositions could not possess the qualities of universality and necessity which Engels attributes to them also. And further, if propositions of logic have the same existential character as propositions of physics, then Engels is owing an explanation of why it is that denials of propositions of the first class always lead to statements that are self-contradictory while denials of propositions of the second class never do.

Engels does not concern himself with an answer to these difficulties. Instead, he offers illustrations of the alleged fact that contradiction is objectively present in things and processes. The illustrations are: 1. The existence of motion. 2. The nature of life. 3. The form of the knowledge process. 4. The basic notions of mathematics.

1. *Motion.* The only argument which Engels advances for his contention that motion is contradictory is a variant of one of the general considerations adduced as long ago as Zeno. But whereas Zeno employed it to prove the unreality of motion, Engels uses it to establish the objective reality of contradiction:

"Motion is itself a contradiction: even simple mechanical change of place (*Ortsbewegung*) can only occur by a body at one and the same moment of time being both in one place and in another place, in one and the same place and not in it. And the continuous occurrence (*Setzung*) and the simultaneous solution of this contradiction is just what motion is." (*Anti-Dühring*, p. 120.)

Now there is an important leap in this argument. For all that Engels could have established by considerations like the above is that certain *descriptions* or *statements* of motion violate the law of contradiction. Before he can conclude that motion itself is contradictory, he must first show that it is impossible to find, and operate with, any other *description* or statement of motion without falling into inconsistency. Not only does he fail to do this; it was already clear in 1894 when Engels wrote the preface to the third edition of *Anti-Dühring* that motion could be described in perfectly consistent fashion. The motion of any particle can be described by an expression indicating that its position in space at any moment is a continuous function of time. And the concept of a continuous function has been made clear without assuming the existence of infinitesimal intervals of space and time which Engels believes to be involved in motion and fundamental to the theory of the differential and integral calculus.

Further, it might be pointed out that, strictly interpreted, Engels' *description* of motion reveals no formal contradiction at all. To say that a body occupies two different places at one and the same time is perfectly legitimate if we recognize that the body has different parts; and there is no difficulty in admitting that a body can be and not be in the same place if we distinguish between different times. And still more, since in *rerum natura* there are no points without extension or moments without duration, Engels' formulation applies just as much to bodies at rest as to bodies in motion. He would thus be proving too much, for not only would motion be contradictory but its opposite, rest, would also be contradictory. And since everything in the world to which we may significantly apply spatio-temporal co-ordinates is either in motion or at rest, and this not absolutely but always relatively to something else, the term contradiction has no differential meaning. When not actually obfuscating, it is useless. The confusion is confounded when Engels speaks of contradiction as being the driving force of all movement and development, transforming logical notions into *demiurgoi* in a fashion which even the logical idealism of Hegel does not justify.

2. *Life.* In citing organic phenomena as illustrations of the objectivity of contradiction, Engels equates contradiction to *struggle*,[12] and seems to suggest that wherever two terms are so related that they may be characterized as contradictory there is an actual struggle, conscious or unconscious, going on between them. There is no doubt that *struggle* is an appropriate term to apply to the relationship which exists between social classes, and in the Darwinian sense, to the relationship between biological species, and to a lesser degree even to some of the relationships between individuals within the same species. But since struggles are only found where *living* creatures are found, Engels must have been speaking metaphorically when he suggests that it is a universal and objective trait of existence. Unless, of course, he is to be classified with the Romantic *Natur-philosophen* for whom all nature is animate and who were wont to speak of *things* strug-

gling with each other. We are probably closest to Engels' meaning if we take him to mean that life is contradictory for the same general reason that motion is, *viz.*, that it violates the law of contradiction. In fact, Engels sometimes employs the same formulation in both cases:

"We saw above that life consists before all just in this that a living creature is at each moment itself and yet something else. Life is therefore also a contradiction present in things and processes, continually occurring and solving itself; and as soon as the contradiction ceases life also ceases and death steps in." (*Op. cit.*, p. 121.)

Of course Engels should have added that as soon as the contradiction ceases a new one steps in, for on his own premises only the forms of contradiction change. But there is nothing contradictory about this description of life; it merely suffers from vagueness. Once we introduce the proper distinctions and qualifications, we can get a consistent enough account of the phenomenon of life. Life is distinguished from non-living things in that it is a self-conserving process, with a physico-chemical structure which regulates the ingestion, digestion, and excretion of food and makes possible selective activity, growth and reproduction. At any definite time, its behavior is a function of a complex of environmental stimuli, and of its own physico-chemical state in relation to which only certain phases of the environment can serve as stimuli. That an organism can keep going only in virtue of the dissolution and assimilation of certain organic compounds from without—"living is a process of dying"—is not a contradiction; nor is it a fact which compels us to utter contradictory statements in describing it except where we are licensed by poetic usage. An animal, for example, can keep on living only if plants (or *other* animals) keep on dying. An animal can keep on living only if it keeps on eliminating its dead cells. But the fact that we distinguish between living and dead cells in any body makes it impossible to say that *in the same respect* and *at the same time* any cell of the body (as well as the body as a whole) is both living and dead. Nor is there any mystery in the fact that we speak of the *same* body although the materials of the body are completely renewed every seven years or so, if we bear in mind that identity, when it is employed as an explanatory category, depends upon some defining perspective. Identity of personality, for example, depends more upon social, legal and psychological considerations than upon physical or biological states.

3. *Knowledge.* One of the most interesting passages in *Anti-Dühring* consists of an attempt to trace the way in which any doctrine that affirms the existence of final, ultimate and eternal truths slips by degrees into ethical and social apologetics. For Engels, eternal truths are either tautologies or trivialities. Absolute Truth is conceived as the limit of the knowledge process carried on by an endless number of generations. As far as the individual thinker is concerned, the knowledge he acquires always contains more elements that can be improved upon than elements that cannot (p. 80). Here undoubtedly Engels has justification in the history of science and the nature of scientific procedure for his stress upon the ap-

proximate character of knowledge. But he professes to find in the self-corrective processes of knowledge a contradiction—a contradiction between thought which is sovereign and absolute considered from the point of view of its ideal *possibility* and *aim,* and thought which is limited and relative in its actual exemplifications. Science strives for absolute knowledge but at any definite moment of time falls short of it; but the contradiction is solved, says Engels, by the infinite progression of the knowledge-getting activities of man:

> "We likewise saw how even in the domain of thought we cannot escape contradictions, and how, e.g., the contradiction between man's intrinsically unlimited faculty of thought and its actual existence in men so completely limited by their external conditions as well as in their knowledge, is solved, in what is, at least for us, practically an endless succession of generations, in infinite progress." (*Anti-Dühring*, p. 121.)

Strictly speaking, only problems, puzzles and difficulties are solved, not contradictions. And solutions always involve the elimination of contradictions, not from things, but from our analysis of them. Even, however, if we grant that Engels has described the aim and procedure of scientific knowledge correctly, there is no contradiction involved in positing an ideal, and failing to realize it, any more than there is a contradiction in aspiring towards perfect health and failing to achieve it in some respect. There are two questionable assumptions, however, concealed in Engels' account of the alleged "contradiction" in the knowledge process. The first is that the ideal of scientific knowledge is absolutely valid knowledge, and second that, assuming this is the ideal of scientific knowledge, there must be absolutely certain truths which enable us to order series of truths which are not absolutely certain. For Engels, these absolute truths are limits of unending series of relative truths which approach closer and closer to their limits with the passage of time and the accumulation of knowledge. Modern science, however, is primarily interested in knowledge which is *sufficiently fruitful* and *reliable* to enable us to solve problems of inquiry. Where it employs the term "truth," the reference is to the degree to which a proposition coheres with a set of other propositions and ultimately to its relative adequacy in enabling us to make verifiable predictions. At no point in his procedure is the scientist compelled to assume that there are absolutely certain truths about matters of fact.[13]

Secondly, insofar as science operates with a definition of truth, the definition serves as a *rule* to guide scientific procedure in ordering the reliability of a series of propositions: it does not serve as a warrant for inferring that absolute truth exists as a limit of an infinite series of relative truths. In this it functions analogously to other definitions. A definition of hardness, for example, enables us to order various substances in a series of increasing or decreasing hardness, but it does not at all follow that therefore an absolutely hard substance exists which is the limit of an infinite series of substances of varying hardnesses. Engels' remarks exhibit a confusion between an ordering principle according to which a series is organized and a limit towards which a series converges.

4. $\sqrt{-1}$. Although, as we have seen in Part I, Engels often refers to mathematics as the realm in which undialectical yet valid thinking proceeds on the basis of the abstract laws of identity and non-contradiction, he just as often couples this assertion with the claim that many fields of mathematics are still subject to the higher laws of dialectic where contradiction is king. The chief illustration is drawn from the calculus but is unfortunately vitiated by the antiquated theory of infinitesimals already abandoned by mathematicians in Engels' own day. But even elementary mathematics, according to Engels, teems (*wimmelt*) with contradictions. And the most striking of these is

"The contradiction that a negative quantity should be the square of anything, for every negative magnitude multiplied by itself gives a positive square. The square root of minus one, therefore, is not only a contradiction but even an absurd contradiction, actual nonsense (*wirklicher Widersinn*). And yet the $\sqrt{-1}$ is in many cases a necessary result of correct mathematical operations. (*Op. cit.*, pp. 121-122.)

It would follow that since all thought, particularly when applied successfully to nature, is a "reflection" of natural procecces, nature must not only be contradictory but "in many cases" positively absurd. And were Engels to qualify the fidelity and universality of the "reflex" character of thought, it would still remain hard to understand how, by operating with absurd contradictions and actual nonsense, we could so successfully predict, construct and explain things. The absurdity, however, must not be laid to the door of the $\sqrt{-1}$ but to Engels' own characterization of it. The rule that the square of a negative number must be positive holds only for integers, rational, and irrational numbers, but not for the imaginaries, and this only in virtue of our definitions. It is true that according to some historic definitions of number the $\sqrt{-1}$ could not be regarded as a number, just as, according to a still earlier conception of number, the $\sqrt{2}$ was an illegitimate notion. But all this only led to a *redefinition* of number in which every shadow of contradiction disappeared. Engels' failure to appreciate the logic by which the structure of mathematics has developed is so profound that it leads him to assert that there is a contradiction even in the fact that a root of a ($\sqrt{a}$) should be a power of a ($a^{1/2}$) whereas both symbolic expressions are merely different ways of stating the same relation.

In none of the illustrations considered has Engels demonstrated the presence of contradiction. In all of them, the appearance of contradiction is due to inaccuracy of phrasing or disregard of context.

.   .   .   .

If the dialectic method, properly understood, is nothing but scientific method, then the dialectic, as it applies to the realm of history and sociology, is a name for the operation of scientific method in that specific field. It was in the name of scientific method that Engels protested against the attempt to reduce history and psychology to physics. "We are certain some day experimentally to reduce thinking to molecular and chemical movements in the brain; but is the essence of thinking therewith exhausted?" (*Ibid.*, p. 167.) Not that thinking is possible without the presence of molecular motion of some sort, but this motion it shares with non-thinking organisms as well as inorganic things. Consequently it cannot serve as a clue to its distinctive quality or nature. Again, it was in the name of scientific method that Engels protested against reducing history to biology. The "struggle for existence," made an all-inclusive explanatory principle after Darwin, is dubious enough, even as a purely biological category, for there is more in nature than struggles, but when applied to history, Engels maintains, it overlooks the fact that men are distinguished from other animals in that they produce, and do not merely collect, the means of life. The differences are subject to other laws and descriptions. "The carrying over of biological laws of animal societies to human societies without further qualification is therewith made impossible" (p. 191).

It is sometimes maintained that the dialectic method is the method which corrects the errors scientists fall into when they wander into fields outside their special interests. But it is obvious that the errors so made result from a violation of scientific method and can be corrected without invoking any other method. The errors of those who believe that the dialectic method is something different from scientific method are no less egregious than are those of spiritualistic minded scientists, and less entertaining.

We conclude, then, that the dialectic method can claim to have meaning and validity only when it is understood to be synonymous with scientific method; that since in its traditional formulation it is burdened with many misleading and mistaken conceptions, it would be more conducive to clear thinking if the phrase were dropped; that its retention engenders a mythical philosophy of nature, prepares the way for a doctrine of "two truths," one ordinary, scientific and profane, the other, esoteric, "dialectical" and "higher"; and, finally, that it encourages an attitude which easily leads to censorship, dictation, and persecution of scientists.[14]

In identifying the only intelligent meaning that can be given to the dialectic method with scientific method, it is not implied that the nature of scientific method is so clearly defined that universal agreement exists concerning all of its principles. On certain problems, especially those involving induction and probability, not to speak of meaning and verification, there is considerable divergence of opinion. It may even be that every systematic theory of scientific method is committed to some "metaphysical" presuppositions, whatever these are. But scientific philosophy as distinct from traditional dialectics not only arises out of reflection upon the procedures of the sciences, it receives its test in the fruitfulness of its bearings upon those procedures. In order to justify its claims that it adds to knowledge and understanding, it must offer a coherent account of these procedures, or call attention to and eliminate inconsistencies in the statements made in the communication of scientific findings, and interpret science as a human enterprise in relation to other aspects of social life and experience. Short of this, the very least it can do is to avoid infecting scientific minds with the errors that have been permanently embalmed in spiritualistic metaphysics. Historically and analytically, the belief in a *Naturdialektik* has been a central doctrine of every system of metaphysical idealism from Plotinus to Hegel. Almost every variety of dialectical materialism current today is a bastard offspring, fathered by a politically-motivated metaphysical idealism upon the body of modern science.

·   ·   ·   ·   ·   ·   ·   ·   ·   ·

[31]

BRONISLAW MALINOWSKI

A Scientific Theory of Culture *

I. CULTURE AS THE SUBJECT OF SCIENTIFIC INVESTIGATION

The "Study of Man" is certainly a somewhat presumptuous, not to say preposterous, label when applied to academic anthropology as it now stands. A variety of disciplines, old and recent, venerable and new, deal also with inquiries into human nature, human handiwork, and into the relations between human beings. These can claim, one and all, to be regarded as branches of the legitimate Study of Man. The oldest, of course, are the contributions to moral philosophy, to theology, to more-or-less legendary history, and to the interpretations of old law and custom. Such contributions can be traced back to cultures still perpetuating the Stone Age; they certainly have flourished in the old civilizations of China and India, of Western Asia and Egypt. Economics and jurisprudence, political science and aesthetics, linguistics, archaeology, and the comparative study of religions, constitute a more recent addition to humanism. Some two centuries ago psychology, the study of the mind, and later on, sociology, an inquiry into human relations, were added to the list of official academic studies.

Anthropology, as the science of man at large, as the most comprehensive discipline in humanism without portfolio, was the last to come. It

* Reprinted from *A Scientific Theory of Culture and other Essays* by Bronislaw Malinowski. Chapel Hill: University of North Carolina Press, 1944. Copyright, 1944, by the University of North Carolina Press. Pp. 3–14. By permission of the publishers.

had to peg out its claims as to scope, subject matter, and method as best it could. It absorbed what was left over, and even had to encroach on some older preserves. It consists now of such studies as prehistory, folklore, physical anthropology, and cultural anthropology. These come dangerously near other legitimate fields of social and natural sciences: psychology, history, archaeology, sociology and anatomy.

The new science was born under the star of enthusiastic evolutionism, of anthropometric methods, and of revelatory discoveries in prehistory. No wonder that its original interests centered round the reconstruction of human beginnings, the search for the "missing link," and inquiries into parallels between prehistoric finds and ethnographic data. Looking back at the achievements of the last century, we could at worst see in them little more than an assemblage of antiquarian odds and ends, embracing ethnographic erudition, the measuring and counting of skulls and bones, and a collection of sensational data about our semi-human ancestors. This estimate, however, would certainly miss the best contributions of such pioneering students in comparative human cultures as Herbert Spencer and Adolf Bastian, E. B. Tylor and L. H. Morgan, General Pitt-Rivers and Frederick Ratzel, W. G. Sumner and R. S. Steinmetz, É. Durkheim and A. G. Keller. All these thinkers, as well as some of their successors, have been gradually working towards a scientific theory of human behavior, towards a better understanding of human nature, human society, and human culture.

Thus, in writing about the scientific approach to the Study of Man, an anthropologist has a task which, though perhaps not easy, is of some importance. It is his duty to define in what relation to one another the various branches of anthropology really stand. He has to determine the place which anthropology ought to occupy in the wider fraternity of humanistic studies. He has also to reopen the old question, in what sense humanism can be scientific.

In this essay I shall attempt to show that the real meeting-ground of all branches of anthropology is the scientific study of culture. As soon as the physical anthropologist recognizes that "race is as race does," he will also admit that no measurements, classifications, or descriptions of physical type have any relevancy unless and until we can correlate physical type with the cultural creativeness of a race. The task of the prehistorian and archaeologist is to reconstruct the full living reality of a past culture from partial evidence confined to material remnants. The ethnologist, again, who uses the evidence of present-day primitive and more advanced cultures in order to reconstruct human history in terms of either evolution or diffusion, can base his arguments on sound scientific data only if he understands what culture really is. Finally, the ethnographic field-worker cannot observe unless he knows what is relevant and essential, and is thus able to discard adventitious and fortuitous happenings. Thus, the scientific quota in all anthropological work consists in the theory of culture, with reference to the method of observation in the field and to the meaning of culture as process and product.

In the second place, I think that if anthropology can contribute towards a more scientific outlook on its legitimate subject matter, that is, culture, it will render an indispensable service to other humanities. Culture, as the widest context of human behavior, is as important to the psychologist as to the social student, to the historian as to the linguist. I submit that the linguistics of the future, especially as regards the science of meaning, will become the study of language in the context of culture. Again, economics as an inquiry into wealth and welfare, as means of exchange and production, may find it useful in the future not to consider economic man completely detached from other pursuits and considerations, but to base its principles and arguments on the study of man as he really is, moving in the complex, many-dimensional medium of cultural interests. Indeed, most of the modern tendencies in economics, whether labelled "institutional," "psychological," or "historical," are supplementing the old, purely economic theories by placing economic man within the context of his multiple drives, interests and habits, that is, man as he is molded by his complex, partly rational, partly emotional cultural setting.

Jurisprudence, again, is gradually tending to regard law not as a self-contained universe of discourse, but as one of the several systems of social control in which concepts of purpose, value, moral constraint, and customary force have to be considered, besides the purely formal apparatus of code, court, and constabulary. Thus, not merely anthropology, but the Study of Man in general, comprising all the social sciences, all the new psychologically or sociologically oriented disciplines, may and must coöperate in the building of a common scientific basis, which perforce will have to be identical for all the diverse pursuits of humanism.

II. A Minimum Definition of Science for the Humanist

It remains now to define more specifically why and in what manner anthropology, of all social studies, can claim to be a direct contributor towards making the Study of Man more scientific. I would like to state first that the scientific approach is obviously not the only interest or inspiration in the domain of humanism. Moral or philosophical points of view; aesthetic, humanitarian, or theological zeal or inspiration; the desire to know what the past was because the past appeals to our sentiments in a manner which need not be vindicated but cannot be gainsaid—all these are legitimate motivations in all humanities. Science, however, as a tool at least, as a means to an end, is indispensable.

As I shall try to point out, a genuine scientific method has been inherent in all historic work, in all chronicling, in every argument used in jurisprudence, economics, and linguistics. There is no such thing as description completely devoid of theory. Whether you reconstruct historic scenes, carry out a field investigation in a savage tribe or a civilized community, analyze statistics, or make inferences from an archaeological monument or a prehistoric find—every statement and every argument has to be made in words, that is, in concepts. Each concept, in turn, is the result of a theory which declares that some facts are relevant and others adventitious, that some factors determine the course of events and others are merely accidental byplay; that things happen as they do because personalities, masses, and material agencies of the environment produced them. The hackneyed distinction between nomothetic and ideographic disciplines is a philosophical red herring which a simple consideration of what it means to observe, to reconstruct or to state an historic fact ought to have annihilated long ago. The cause of all the trouble consists in the fact that most principles, generalizations, and theories were implicit in the historian's reconstruction, and were intuitive rather than systematic in nature. The typical historian and many anthropologists spend most of their theoretical energy and epistemological leisure hours in refuting the concept of scientific law in cultural process, in erecting watertight compartments for humanism as against science, and in claiming that the historian or anthropologist can conjure up the past by some specific insight, some intuition or revelation, in short, that he can rely on the grace of God instead of on a methodical system of conscientious work.

However we may define the word *science* in some philosophical or epistemological system, it is clear that it begins with the use of previous observation for the prediction of the future. In this sense the spirit as well as the performance of science must have existed in the reasonable behavior of man, even as he was embarking on his career of creating, constructing, and developing culture. Take any primitive art or craft, one of those with which culture probably started, which is developed and remolded, and has ever since remained at its very foundations: the art of making fire, of constructing implements out of wood or stone, of building rudimentary shelters, or of using caves for living. What assumptions have we to make concerning man's reasonable behavior, the permanent incorporation of such reasonable behavior in tradition, and the fidelity of each generation to the traditional knowledge inherited from their ancestors?

One of the simplest and most fundamental primitive crafts is that of fire-making. In this, over and above the manual ability of the craftsman, we find a definite scientific theory embodied in each performance, and in the tribal tradition thereof. Such a tradition had to define in a general, that is, abstract manner, the material and form of the two types of wood used. The tradition also had to define the principles of performance, the type of muscular movement, its speed, the capture of the spark, and the nourishment of the flame. The tradition was kept alive not in books nor yet in explicit physical theories. But it implied two pedagogical and theoretical elements. First and foremost, it was embodied in the manual skills of each generation, which, by example and precept, were handed over to the new growing members. Secondly, whether primitive symbolism was accomplished by verbal statement, by significant gesture, or by substantial performance, such as instructions where to find and how to store the materials and produce the forms, such symbolism must have been at work, even as

I myself have seen it at work in my field research. That this is so we have to infer, because the final performance, that is, the production of fire, would never be possible unless general distinctions as to material, activity, and coördination were kept within the conditions necessary and sufficient for a successful pragmatic performance.

I would like to add here at once that primitive knowledge has yet another factor. When we study present-day savages who still produce fire by friction, make stone implements, and build rudimentary shelters, we can observe that their reasonable behavior, their fidelity to the theoretical principles on which they work, and their technical accuracy are determined by the desired end of their activity. This end is a value in their culture. It is something they appreciate because it satisfies one of their vital require-ments. It is a prerequisite of their very existence. This sense of value, how-ever, also pervades and becomes permanently attached to both manual ability and theoretical knowledge. The scientific attitude, embodied in all primitive technology and also in the organization of primitive economic enterprises and social organization, that reliance on past experience with the view to future performance, is an integral factor which must be assumed as having been at work from the very beginning of mankind, ever since the species started on its careers as *homo faber,* as *homo sapiens,* and as *homo politicus.* Were the scientific attitude and the valuation of it to become extinct even for one generation in a primitive community, such a com-munity would either lapse into an animal status or, more likely, become extinct.

Thus, out of an inchoate body of environmental factors, random adaptations, and experiences, primitive man in his scientific approach had to isolate the relevant factors and to embody them into systems of relations and determining factors. The final motive or drive in all this was primarily biological survival. The flame of the fire was necessary for warmth and cooking, for safety and for light. Stone implements, shaped and constructed wood, matting and vessels, also had to be produced in order for men to live. All such productive technological activities were based on a theory in which relevant factors were isolated, in which the value of theoretical accuracy was appreciated, in which forethought in achievement was based on care-fully formulated experiences from the past.

The main point I am attempting to make here is not so much that primitive man has his science, but first, rather, that the scientific attitude is as old as culture, and second, that the minimum definition of science is derived from any pragmatic performance. Were we to check these conclu-sions as to the nature of science, drawn from our analysis of the discoveries, inventions, and theories of primitive man, by the advance of modern physics since Copernicus, Galileo, Newton, or Faraday, we would find the same differential factors which distinguish the scientific from other modes of human thought and behavior. Everywhere we find, first and foremost, the isolation of the real and relevant factors in a given process. The reality and relevancy of these factors are discovered by observation or experiment, which establishes their permanent recurrence. Constant empirical verification, as well as the original founding of scientific theory and experience, is obviously of the very essence of science. A theory which fails must be amended by discovering why it has failed. Incessant cross-fertilization of experience and principles is, therefore, indispensable. Science really begins when general principles have to be put to the test of fact, and when practical problems and theoretical relations of relevant factors are used to manipulate reality in human action. The minimum definition of science, therefore, implies invariably the existence of general laws, a field for experiment or observation, and last, but not least, a control of academic discourse by practical application.

It is at this point that the claims of anthropology might be pegged out. This study, for various reasons, has had to converge on the central subject matter in the widest context of all humanistic pursuits, that is, culture. Again, anthropology, especially in its modern developments, has to its credit the fact that most of its votaries have to do ethnographic field-work, that is, an empirical type of research. Anthropology was perhaps the first of all social sciences to establish its laboratory, side by side with its theoretical workshop. The ethnologist studies the realities of culture under the greatest variety of conditions, environmental, racial and psychological. He must be at the same time skilled in the art of observation, that is, in ethnological field-work, and an expert in the theory of culture. In this field-work and in his comparative analysis of culture, he has learned that neither of these two pursuits has any value unless they are carried out conjointly. To observe means to select, to classify, to isolate on the basis of theory. To construct a theory is to sum up the relevancy of past observation and to anticipate empirical confirmation or rebuttal of theoretical problems posed.

Thus, in terms of historical studies, the anthropologist has had to function simultaneously as his own chronicler and as the manipulator of his self-produced sources. In terms of modern sociology, the ethnologist, through his very much simpler task, is able to envisage cultures as a whole and to observe them integrally through personal contact. He has thus provided much of the inspiration towards the really scientific tendencies in modern sociology, the analysis of modern cultural phenomena and direct observation, rather than intuitive, apodeictic armchair revelations. In terms of jurisprudence, economics, politics or the theory of religion, the anthropologist develops the widest inductive evidence for comparison and discrimination.

Thus, it is not as futile, jejune, and presumptuous as it might first appear to discuss the scientific approach to the Study of Man as the real contribution of modern and future anthropology to humanism as a whole. We need a theory of culture, of its processes and products, of its specific determinism, of its relation to basic facts of human psychology and the organic happenings within the human body, and of the dependence of society upon the environment. Such a theory is by no means the monopoly of the anthropologist. He has, however, a special contribution to make, and this may provoke corresponding efforts on the part of the empirically-minded historians, sociologists, psychologists and students of specific type-activities, legal, economic, or educational.

This somewhat pedantic discussion of the scientific quota in social studies needs no apology. There is no doubt that in the present crisis of our civilization we have risen to vertiginous heights in the mechanical and chemical sciences, pure and applied, and in materialistic theory and mechanical engineering. But we have neither faith in, nor respect for, the conclusions of humanistic arguments, nor yet in the validity of social theories. Today we very much need to establish the balance between the hypertrophied influence of natural science and its applications on the one hand, and the backwardness of social science, with the constant impotence of social engineering, on the other. The easy-going flippancy of many a humanist and historian concerning the scientific nature of his pursuits is not merely epistemologically despicable, but in a way immoral, in the pragmatic sense. History and sociology, as well as economics and jurisprudence, must lay their foundations carefully, consciously and deliberately, on the bedrock of scientific method. Social science also must develop into the power of mind used for the control of mechanical power. Humanism will never cease to have its artistic, sentimental and moral elements. But the very essence of ethical principles demands its cogency, and this can only be attained if the principle is as true to fact as it is indispensable to sentiment.

Another reason why I have dwelt so explicitly on the minimum definition of science is because, in an entirely new field of inquiry such as culture, one of the most dangerous procedures is to borrow the methods of one of the older and better established disciplines. Organic similes and mechanical metaphors, the belief that counting and measuring define the line of distinction between science and loose talk—all this and many other tricks of borrowing and leaning upon another discipline have done more harm than good to sociology. Our minimum definition implies that the first task of each science is to recognize its legitimate subject matter. It has to proceed to methods of true identification, or isolation of the relevant factors of its process. This is nothing else than the establishment of general laws, and of concepts which embody such laws. This, of course, implies that every theoretical principle must always be translatable into a method of observation, and again, that in observation we follow carefully the lines of our conceptual analysis. Finally, in all this the inspiration derived from practical problems—such as colonial policy, missionary work, the difficulties of culture contact, and transculturation—problems that legitimately belong to anthropology, is an invariable corrective of general theories.

[32]

ABRAHAM KAPLAN

Sociology Learns the Language of Mathematics *

Some Recent Studies Analyzed

A troubling question for those of us committed to the widest application of intelligence in the study and solution of the problems of men is
whether a general understanding of the social sciences will be possible much
longer. Many significant areas of these disciplines have already been removed by the advances of the past two decades beyond the reach of anyone who does not know mathematics; and the man of letters is increasingly
finding, to his dismay, that the study of mankind proper is passing from
his hands to those of technicians and specialists. The aesthetic effect is
admittedly bad: we have given up the belletristic "essay on man" for the
barbarisms of a technical vocabulary, or at best the forbidding elegance of
mathematical syntax. What have we gained in exchange?

To answer this question we must be able to get at the content of the
new science. But when it is conveyed in mathematical formulas, most of us
are in the position of the medieval layman confronted by clerical Latin—
with this difference: mathematical language cannot be forced to give way
to a vernacular. Mathematics, if it has a function at all in the sciences, has
an indispensable one; and now that so much of man's relation to man has
come to be treated in mathematical terms, it is impossible to ignore or
escape the new language any longer. There is no completely satisfactory
way out of this dilemma. All this article can do is to grasp either horn,
sometimes oversimplifying, sometimes taking the reader out of his depth;
but hoping in the end to suggest to him the significance of the growing use
of mathematical language in social science.

To complicate matters even further, the language has several dialects.
"Mathematics" is a plural noun in substance as well as form. Geometry,
algebra, statistics, and topology use distinct concepts and methods, and
are applicable to characteristically different sorts of problems. The role of
mathematics in the new social science cannot be discussed in a general way:
as we shall see, everything depends on the kind of mathematics being used.

* From *Commentary*, published and copyright, 1952, by the American Jewish Committee. Vol. 14, no. 3, Sept., 1952, pp. 274–284. Reprinted by permission of the author,
editors, and publishers.

I

The earliest and historically most influential of the mathematical sciences is geometry. Euclid's systematization of the results of Babylonian astronomy and Egyptian surveying set up a model for scientific theory that remained effective for two thousand years. Plato found in Euclid's geometry the guide to the logical analysis of all knowledge, and it was the Renaissance's "rediscovery" of Plato's insistence on the fundamentally geometric structure of reality that insured the triumph of the modern world view inaugurated by Copernicus. Scientists like Kepler accepted the Copernican hypothesis because it made the cosmos more mathematically elegant than Ptolemy's cumbersome epicycles had been able to do.

The study of man—to say nothing of God!—enthusiastically availed itself of mathematical method: witness Spinoza's *Ethics*, which claimed that it "demonstrated according to the geometrical manner." But Spinoza's *Ethics* failed, as demonstrative science, because the 17th century did not clearly understand the geometry it was applying with such enthusiasm. The discovery of non-Euclidean geometries two hundred years later revealed that the so-called axioms of geometry are not *necessary* truths, as Spinoza and his fellow rationalists had always supposed, but merely postulates: propositions put forward for the sake of subsequent inquiry. It is only by deducing their consequences and comparing these with the perceived facts that we can decide whether or not the postulates are true. Geometry is a fully developed example of a set of undefined terms, prescribed operations, and the resulting postulates and theorems which make up a *postulational system*; it is in this form that it is influential in some of the recent developments in the social sciences.

Perhaps the most elaborate postulational system for dealing with the data of social and psychological science was constructed in 1940 by Clark Hull and associates of the Yale Institute of Human Relations (C. L. Hull et al., *Mathematico-Deductive Theory of Rote Learning*, Yale University Press, 1940). "Rote learning" is a very specialized branch of psychology that studies the learning of series of nonsense syllables; presumably, this tells us something about the act of learning in its "purest" form, with no admixture of influence from the thing learned.

The problems of the field revolve around ways of explaining the patterns of learning that are in fact discovered; why the first syllables in any series are learned first, the last soon after, and why the syllables a little past the middle of the given series take longest to memorize, and so on. There is a vast number of observations of this sort to be made, and Hull's ideal was to set up a postulational system which would allow observed patterns of learning to be logically deduced from relatively few postulates.

The system consists of 16 undefined terms, 86 definitions, and 18 postulates. From these, 54 theorems are deduced. The deductions can, in principle, be checked against the results of direct observation, in experimental situations or elsewhere. In many cases, as the book points out, existing evidence is as yet inadequate to determine whether the theorems hold true; in the great majority of cases, experimental evidence is in agreement with logically deduced theorems; in others, there is undoubted disagreement between deduced expectation and observed fact. Such disagreements point to basic defects in the postulate system, which, however, can be progressively improved.

The authors consider their book to be principally important as an example of the proper scientific method to be used in the study of behavior. And certainly, as a formal demonstration of the handling of definitions, postulates, and theorems, the book is unexceptionable. However, science prides itself on its proper method because of the fruitfulness of its results; and it is to the fruitfulness of this effort that we must address ourselves.

One example of the method may suggest better than general criticism the problem raised. Hull proves in one of his theorems that the greater the "inhibitory potential" at a given point in the learning of a rote series, the greater will be the time elapsing between the stimulus (the presentation of one nonsense syllable in the list) and the reaction (the pronouncing of the next memorized nonsense syllable). "Inhibitory potential" is one of the undefined terms of the system; it denotes the inability of the subject, before his involvement in the learning process, to pronounce the appropriate syllable on the presentation of the appropriate stimulus. (It may be pictured as a force that wanes as the stimuli are repeated and the syllable to be uttered is learned.)

Now this theorem certainly follows logically from three postulates of the system (they involve too many special terms to be enlightening if quoted). However, on examining these postulates, the theorem is seen to be so directly implied by them that one wonders what additional knowledge has been added by formally deducing it. A certain amount must have been known about rote learning to justify the selection of those postulates in the first place. To deduce this theorem from them has added very little—if anything—to what was already known. In short: the geometric method used by Hull, correct as it is formally, does not, for this reader, extend significantly what we already knew about rote learning from his and others' work.

In the course of Hull's book "qualitative postulates," by which is meant the "unquantified" ideas of thinkers like Freud and Darwin, are condemned because they have "so little deductive fertility"—because so few theorems may be deduced from them. In the narrowest logical sense of the phrase, this may be true. But fertility in the sense of yielding precisely determinable logical consequences is one thing; in the sense of yielding further insights into the subject matter—whether or not these can be presented as strict consequences of a system of postulates—it is quite another. The ideas of Darwin and Freud can hardly be condemned as lacking in fertility, even though they leave much to be desired from the standpoint of logical systematization.

This is not to deny that the postulational method can play a valuable role in science. But it is a question of the scientific context in which the method is applied. Newton and Euclid both had available to them a considerable body of fairly well-established knowledge which they could systematize, and in the process derive other results not apparent in the disconnected materials. Hull recognizes this condition, but supposes it to be already fulfilled in the area of learning theory. The results of the particular system he has constructed raise serious doubts that his supposition is true.

Science, basically, does not proceed by the trial-and-error method to which Hull, as a student of animal learning, is so much attached. It employs insight, itself subject to logical analysis, but too subtle to be caught in the coarse net of any present-day system of postulates. The geometric method in the new social science can be expected to increase in value as knowledge derived from other methods grows. But for the present, it is an elegantly written check drawn against insufficient funds.

II

If the 17th century was the age of geometry, the 18th was that of algebra. The essential idea of algebra is to provide a symbolism in which relations between quantities can be expressed *without a specification of the magnitudes of the quantities*. An equation simply formulates the equality between two quantities in a way that shows how the magnitude of one depends on the magnitude of certain constituents of the other.

The characterization of mathematics as a language is nowhere more appropriate than in algebra; the notation is everything. The power of algebra consists in that it allows the symbolism to think for us. Thought enters into the formulation of the equations and the establishing of the rules of manipulation by which they are to be solved, but the rest is mechanical—so much so that more and more the manipulation is being done, literally, by machines. The postulational method characteristic of classical geometry no longer plays as important a part here. Derivation is replaced by calculation; we proceed, not from postulates of uncertain truth, but from arithmetical propositions whose truth is a matter of logic following necessarily from the definitions of the symbols occurring in them. The equations that express relations between real quantities are, of course, empirical hypotheses; but *if* the equations correctly formulate the function relating two quantities, then certain numerical values for one necessarily imply certain numerical values for the other. Again, as in geometry, the facts are the final test.

In this spirit, the mathematicians of the 18th century replaced Newton's geometrizing by the methods of algebra, and the culmination was Laplace's system of celestial mechanics. Laplace's famous superman, given the position and momentum of every particle in the universe, could compute, it was thought, the entire course of world history, past and future. The development of quantum mechanics made this program unrealizable even in principle, just as the non-Euclidean geometries were fatal to the

aspirations of the 17th-century rationalists. Nevertheless, this scientific
ideal, so nearly realized in physics, has exerted enormous influence on the
study of man, and much of the new social science is motivated by the
attempt to take advantage of the powerful resources of algebra.

Among the most ambitious, but also most misguided, of such attempts
is a 900-page treatise by the sociologist Stuart C. Dodd, *Dimensions of
Society* (Macmillan, 1942). The author's ambition, declared in the subtitle,
is to provide "a quantitative systematics for the social sciences." What is
misguided is the failure to realize that a system is not provided by a symbolism alone : it is necessary also to have something to say in the symbolism
that is rich enough to give point to the symbolic manipulation. Dodd presents a dozen symbols of what he regards as basic sociological concepts,
together with four others for arithmetical operations. They stand for such
ideas as space, time, population, and characteristics (the abstract idea
"characteristics," and not the specific characteristics to be employed in
sociological theory). In addition to these sixteen basic symbols, there are
sixteen auxiliary symbols, compounds or special cases of the basic symbols,
or supplements to them—for instance, the question mark, described as one
of four "new operators," used to denote a hypothesis, or a questioned
assertion. With this notation, every situation studied by sociologists is to be
defined by an expression of the form:

$$S = \; {}^{s}_{s} (T \, ; \, I \, ; \, L \, ; \, P) \; {}^{s}_{s}$$

The capital "S" stands for the *situation*, and the letters within the parentheses for *time*, indicators of the *characteristics* specified, *length* or *spatial
regions*, and *populations, persons*, or *groups*. The semicolon stands for an
unstated form of mathematical combination, and the small "s" for various
ways of particularizing the four major kinds of characterizations. Thus
"T^0" stands for a *date*, "T^1" for a *rate of change*, both of these being different sorts of time specifications. Instructions for the use of the notation require one hundred distinct rules for their formulation.

But this whole notational apparatus is, as Dodd recognizes, "a systematic way of expressing societal data, and not, directly, a system of the
functionings of societal phenomena." "Facts," however, are data only *for*
hypotheses ; without the latter, they are of no scientific significance. Certainly a notational system can hardly be called a "theory," as Dodd constantly designates it, unless it contains some statements *about* the facts.
But *Dimensions of Society* contains only one social generalization : "This
theory . . . generalizes societal phenomena in the statement : 'People, Environments, and Their Characteristics May Change.' This obvious generalization becomes even more obvious if the time period in which the change
is observed is prolonged." The last sentence may save Dodd, but not his
"theory," from hopeless naivety.

Dodd's hope that his system of "quantic classification" will "come to play a role for the social sciences comparable to the classification of the chemical atoms in Mendelyeev's periodic table" is groundless. The periodic table, after all, told us something about the elements; more, it suggested that new elements that we knew nothing of existed, and told us what their characteristics would be when discovered. The fundamental point is that we have, in the case of Dodd, only a *notation*; when he speaks of the "verification" of his "theory," he means only that it is possible to formulate societal data with his notation.

Dodd's basic error is his failure to realize that after "Let x equal such-and-such," the important statement is still to come. The question is how to put *that* statement into mathematical form.

An answer to this question is provided in two books of a very different sort from Dodd's, both by the biophysicist N. Rashevsky: *Mathematical Theory of Human Relations* (The Principia Press, 1947) and *Mathematical Biology of Social Behavior* (University of Chicago Press, 1951). In these two books the author does not merely talk *about* mathematics; he actually *uses* it. In the earlier one, the methods of mathematical biology are applied to certain social phenomena on the basis of formal postulates— more simply, assumptions—about these phenomena. In the later book, these assumptions are interpreted in terms of neurobiophysical theory, and are derived as first approximations from that theory. The results, according to Rashevsky, are "numerous suggestions as to how biological measurements, made on large groups of individuals, may lead to the prediction of some social phenomena."

As a natural scientist, Rashevsky is not seduced, like so many aspirants to a social science, by the blandishments of physics. Scientific method is the same everywhere: it is the method of logical inference from data provided and tested by experience. But the specific techniques of science are different everywhere, not only as between science and science but even as between problem and problem in the same field. The confusion of method and technique, and the resultant identification of scientific method with the techniques of physics (and primarily 19th-century physics at that) has hindered the advance of the social sciences not a little. For the problems of sociology *are* different from those of physics. There are no concepts in social phenomena comparable in simplicity and fruitfulness to the space, time, and mass of classical mechanics; experiments are difficult to perform, and even harder to control; measurement in sociological situations presents special problems from which physics is relatively free. Yet none of these differences, as Rashevsky points out, prevents a scientific study of man. That social phenomena are complex means only that techniques must be developed of corresponding complexity: today's schoolboy can solve mathematical problems beyond the reach of Euclid or Archimedes. Difficulties in the way of experimentation have not prevented astronomy from attaining full maturity as a science. And the allegedly "qualitative" character of social facts is, after all, only an allegation; such facts have their quantitative aspects too. And what is perhaps more to the point, mathematics can also deal with qualitative characteristics, as we shall see.

Rashevsky addresses himself to specific social subject matters: the formation of closed social classes, the interaction of military and economic factors in international relations, "individualistic" and "collectivistic" tendencies, patterns of social influence, and many others. But though the problems are concrete and complex, he deals with them in a deliberately abstract and oversimplified way. The problems are real enough, but their formulation is idealized, and the equations solved on the basis of quite imaginary cases. Both books constantly repeat that the treatment is intended to "illustrate" how mathematics is applicable "in principle" to social science: for actual solutions, the theory is admitted to be for the most part too crude and the data too scarce.

What this means is that Rashevsky's results cannot be interpreted as actual accounts of social phenomena. They are, rather, ingenious elaborations of what *would* be the case if certain unrealistic assumptions were granted. Yet this is not in itself objectionable. As he points out in his own defense, physics made great strides by considering molecules as rigid spheres, in complete neglect of the complexity of their electronic and nuclear internal structures. But the critical question is whether Rashevsky's simplifications are, as he claims, "a temporary expedient." An idealization is useful only if an assumption that is approximately true yields a solution that is approximately correct; or at any rate, if we can point out the ways in which the solution must be modified to compensate for the errors in the assumptions.

It is in this respect that Rashevsky's work is most questionable. Whatever the merits of his idealizations from the standpoint of "illustrating," as he says, the potentialities of mathematics, from the standpoint of the study of man they are so idealized is almost to lack all purchase on reality.

Rashevsky's treatment of individual freedom, for example, considers it in two aspects: economic freedom and freedom of choice. The former is defined mathematically as the fraction obtained when the amount of work a man must actually do is subtracted from the maximum amount of work of which he is capable, and this sum is divided by the original maximum. A person's economic freedom is 0 when he is engaged in hard labor to the point of daily exhaustion; it is 1 when he does not need to work at all. This definition equates increase in economic freedom with shortening of the hours of work; and an unemployed worker, provided he is kept alive on a dole, enjoys complete economic freedom. Such critical elements of economic freedom as real wages, choice of job, and differences in level of aspiration are all ignored.

Freedom of choice, the other aspect of individual freedom, is analyzed as the proportion borne by the amount of time an individual is not in contact with others who might interfere with his choices, to the time he spends alone plus time that is spent in the company of others with the same preferences. This makes freedom of choice decrease with increasing population, so that by this definition one is freer in a small village than a large city. Nothing is said about prying neighbors, or the presence or absence of a secret police, a most important determinant of "freedom of choice." The whole matter of the "introjection" of other persons' standards, as discussed for instance in Erich Fromm's *Escape from Freedom*, is ignored, as are such fundamental considerations as knowledge of the choices available, or the opportunity to cultivate skills and tastes.

On current social issues Rashevsky betrays that he suffers from the same confusions and rationalizations as afflict students without the advantages of a mathematical training. To explain the Lysenko case, for example, he suggests that it is possible that the facts of genetics "may be *interpreted* from two different points of view," thus naively substituting a scientific question (if there be one) for the real issue, which is the political control of science. His assumptions encourage him to attempt the conclusion, "even at the present state of our knowledge," that after World War II peace will be most strongly desired by the Soviet Union, least by the United States, with England and Germany in between. And he confesses that he finds it "difficult to understand why the Soviet Union insists on repatriating individuals who left the Soviet Union during World War II and do not desire to return." Mathematics is not yet capable of coping with the naivety of the mathematician himself.

III

The 19th century saw the rise of mathematical statistics. From its origins in the treatment of games of chance, it was expanded to cope with the new problems posed by the development of insurance, and finally came to be recognized as fundamental to every science dealing with repetitive phenomena. This means the whole of science, for knowledge everywhere rests on the cumulation of data drawn from sequences of situations on whose basis predictions can be made as to the recurrence of similar situations. Mathematical statistics is the theory of the treatment of repeated— or multiple—observations in order to obtain all and only those conclusions for which such observations are evidence. This, and not merely the handling of facts stated in numerical terms, is what distinguishes statistics from other branches of quantitative mathematics.

The application of statistics to social phenomena far exceeds, in fruitfulness as well as extent, the use of mathematics of a fundamentally geometrical—i.e. postulational—or algebraic character in the social sciences. Social scientists themselves have made important contributions to mathematical statistics—which is a good indication of its usefulness to them in their work. Only two of the most recent contributions in the application of statistics to social phenomena can be dealt with here.

The first is a rather remarkable book by a Harvard linguist, G. K. Zipf, *Human Behavior and the Principle of Least Effort* (Addison-Wesley

Press, 1949). Its basic conception is that man is fundamentally a user of tools confronted with a variety of jobs to do. Culture can be regarded as constituting a set of tools, and human behavior can be analyzed as the use of such tools in accord with the principle of minimizing the probable rate of work which must be done to perform the jobs that arise. It is this principle that Zipf calls "the law of least effort." As a consequence of it, he claims, an enormous variety of social phenomena exhibit certain regularities of distribution, in accordance with the principle that the tools nearest to hand, easiest to manipulate, and adapted to the widest variety of purposes are those which tend to be used most frequently. These regularities often take the form, according to Zipf, of a constant rank-frequency relationship, according to which the tenth most frequently used word, for instance, is used one-tenth as often as the most frequently used one of all. This is the case, for example, with James Joyce's *Ulysses* as well as with clippings from American newspapers.

A large part of Zipf's book deals with linguistic phenomena, since he is most at home in this field, and it is there that his results seem most fully established. But an enormous range of other subjects is also treated: evolution, sex, schizophrenia, dreams, art, population, war, income, fads, and many others. Many of these topics are dealt with statistically, as likewise conforming to the law of least effort; and all are discussed with originality and insight. For example, the cities in any country, according to Zipf, tend to show the same regularity—the tenth most populous city will have one-tenth as many people as the most populous, the one-hundredth most populous city will have one-hundredth as many. Where this pattern does not prevail, we have an indication of serious potential conflict. It seems that starting about 1820 the growing divisions between Northern and Southern economies in the United States could be seen by a break in this pattern, which reached a peak of severity around 1840, and disappeared after the Civil War!

But while this breadth of topic endows the book with a distinctive fascination, it also makes the reader skeptical of the validity of the theory it puts forward. In the human sciences, the scope of a generalization is usually inversely proportional to its precision and usefulness—at any rate, in the present state of our knowledge. Zipf's law, or something like it, is well known in physics as Maupertuis' principle of least action. But Zipf applies it to a much wider field of phenomena than physical flows of energy. It is understandable that action will follow some sort of least-action pattern *if* economy enters into its motivation and *if* the action is sufficiently rational. But that the law of least effort should be manifested everywhere in human conduct, as Zipf holds—indeed, "in all living process" —is difficult to believe.

That a theory is incredible is, of course, no logical objection whatever. And Zipf does not merely speculate; he presents an enormous mass of empirical evidence. The question is what it proves. It does not show, as he claims, the existence of "natural social laws," but, at best, only certain regularities. Brute empiricism is not yet science. Unless observed regularities can be brought into logical relation with other regularities previously observed, we remain at the level of description rather than explanation; and without explanation, we cannot attach much predictive weight to description. As a collection of data that deserve the careful attention of the social scientist, Zipf's work will have interest for some time to come. But something more precise and less universal than his principle of least effort will be required to transform that data into a body of scientific knowledge.

The importance of clear conceptualization in giving scientific significance to observed fact is admirably expounded in the recently published fourth volume of the monumental *American Soldier* series (S. A. Stouffer, L. Guttman, et al., *Measurement and Prediction: Studies in Social Psychology in World War II,* Vol. IV, Princeton University Press, 1950). *Measurement and Prediction* deals with the study of attitudes. It is concerned with the development of methodological rather than substantive theory. It deals with the way in which attitudes—any attitudes—should be studied and understood, but says little about attitudes themselves. However, methodology here is not an excuse for irresponsibility in substantive assumptions, or for confusion as to the ultimate importance of a substantive theory of attitudes.

The major problem taken up is this: how can we tell whether a given set of characteristics is to be regarded as variations of some single underlying quality? Concretely, when do the responses to a questionaire constitute expressions of a single attitude, and when do they express a number of attitudes? If there is such a single quality, how can we measure how much of it is embodied in each of the characteristics? If all the items on a questionaire *do* deal with only one attitude, can we measure, in any meaningful sense, how favorable or unfavorable that attitude is, and how intensely it is held by the particular respondent?

This problem arises directly out of the practical—as well as the theoretical—side of opinion study. Consider the case of a poll designed to test the extent and intensity of anti-Semitism. Various questions are included: "Do you think the Jews have too much power?" "Do you think we should allow Jews to come into the country?" "Do you approve of what Hitler did to the Jews?" Some people give anti-Semitic answers to all the questions, some to a few, some to none. Is this because they possess varying amounts of a single quality that we may call "anti-Semitism"? Or is there really a mixture of two or more very different attitudes in the individual, present in varying proportions? If a person is against Jewish immigration, is this because he is against immigration or against Jews, and to what extent? And if there is a single quality such as anti-Semitism, what questions will best bring it out for study? It is problems such as these that the research reported on in *Measurement and Prediction* permits us to solve.

The approach taken stems from the work done in the past few decades by L. L. Thurstone and C. Spearman. Their problems were similar, but arose in a different field, the study of intelligence and other psychological characteristics. Their question was: do our intelligence tests determine a single quality called intelligence? Or do they actually tap a variety of factors, which though combining to produce the total intelligence score, are really quite different from each other? Thurstone and Spearman developed mathematical methods that in effect determined which items in a questionnaire were interdependent—that is, if a person answered *a*, he would tend to answer *b*, but not *c*. On the basis of such patterns, various factors of intelligence were discovered.

In opinion study, one inquires whether items of a questionnaire "hang together"—or, to use the technical term, whether they *scale*. A complex of attitudes is said to be *scalable* if it is possible to arrange the items in it in such a way that every person who answers "yes" to any item also answers "yes" to every item coming after it in the arrangement. In the case of anti-Semitism, we would consider the complex of anti-Semitism scalable—and therefore referring to a single factor in a person's attitudes, rather than including a few distinct attitudes—if we could order the questions in such a way that if someone answered any question in the list "anti-Semitically," he would answer all those following it "anti-Semitically." Attitudes on anti-Semitism would then have the same cumulative character as a series of questions on height—if a person answers "yes" to "Are you more than six feet tall?" we know he will answer "yes" to the question "Are you more than five and a half feet tall?" and all others down the list. This type of reduction of an apparently complex field of attitudes to the simple scheme of a series of cumulative questions is of great value. In *Measurement and Prediction* Louis Guttman describes how to determine whether a group of attitudes does "scale"—that is, does measure a single underlying reality.

Guttman developed, for example, such a scale for manifestations of fear in battle—vomiting, trembling, etc.: soldiers who vomit when faced with combat also report trembling, and so on down the scale; while those who report trembling do not necessarily report vomiting too. On the other hand, it turned out, when he studied paratroopers, various *kinds* of fear of very different types had to be distinguished, for the paratroopers' symptoms were not scalable in terms of a single variable.

One of the most direct applications of scaling methods is in the detection of spurious "causal" connections. We may find, for instance, that the attitude to the continuation of OPS by the government correlates closely with the attitude to farm subsidies. Scale analysis now makes it possible for us to provide an explanation for this fact by testing whether these two items do not in fact express a single attitude—say, the attitude to governmental controls.

Scale analysis permits us to handle another important problem. Suppose we find that 80 per cent of a group of soldiers tested agreed that "the British are doing as good a job as possible of fighting the war, everything considered," while only 48 per cent disagree with the statement that "the British always try to get other countries to do their fighting for them." How many soldiers are "favorable" toward the British? It is clear that we can get different percentages in answer to this question, depending on how we word our question. Scale analysis provides a method which yields what is called an "objective zero point": a division between the numbers of those "favorable" and those "unfavorable" that remains constant no matter what questions we ask about the British. The method demands that, besides asking a few questions testing the attitude, we also get a measure of the "intensity" with which the respondent holds his opinion—we ask for example, whether the respondent feels strongly, not so strongly, or is relatively indifferent about the matter. With this method, it turns out that if we asked a group of entirely different questions about the British, the application of the procedure for measuring the "objective zero point" would show the same result. This limited area of attitude comes to have the same objectivity as the temperature scale, which shows the same result whether we use an alcohol or a mercury thermometer.

Measurement and Prediction also presents, for the first time, a full description of Lazarsfeld's "latent structure" analysis. This is in effect a mathematical generalization of the scaling method of Guttman, which permits us to extend the type of inquiry that scale analysis makes possible into other areas. Scale analysis and latent structure analysis together form an important contribution to the development of more reliable methods of subjecting attitudes—and similar "qualities"—to precise and meaningful measurement.

The prediction part of *Measurement and Prediction* does not contain any comparable theoretical developments. For the most part, prediction in the social sciences today is not above the level of "enlightened common sense," as the authors recognize.

IV

The distinctive development in mathematics in the last one hundred years is the rise of a discipline whose central concept is neither number nor quantity, but *structure*. The mathematics of structure might be said to focus on qualitative differences. *Topology,* as the new discipline is called, is occupied with those properties of figures—conceived as sets of points— that are independent of mere differences of quantity. Squares, circles, and rectangles, of whatever size, are topologically indistinguishable from one another, or from any simple closed figure, however irregular. On the other hand, if a "hole" is inscribed in any of these figures, it thereby becomes qualitatively different from the rest.

Topology, more than most sectors of higher mathematics, deals with questions that have direct intuitive meaning. But intuition often misleads us as to the answers, when it does not fail us altogether. For instance, how many different colors are required to color *any* map so that no two adjoining countries have the same color? It is known, from topological analyses, that five colors are quite enough; but no one has been able to produce a map that needs more than four, or even to prove whether there could or could not be such a map.

It is paradoxical that the field of mathematics which deals with the most familiar subject matter is the least familiar to the non-mathematician. A smattering of geometry, algebra, and statistics is very widespread; topology is virtually unknown, even among social scientists sympathetic to mathematics. To be sure, the late Kurt Lewin's "topological psychology" has given the name much currency. But topology, for Lewin, provided only a notation. The rich content of his work bears no *logical* relation to the topological framework in which it is presented, as is clear from the posthumously published collection of his more important papers, *Field Theory in Social Science* (Harper, 1951). In these papers, talk about the "life space," and "paths," "barriers," and "regions" in it, are elaborately sustained metaphors. Such figures of speech are extraordinarily suggestive, but do not in themselves constitute a strict mathematical treatment of the "life space" in a topological geometry. The actual application of topology to psychology remained for Lewin a program and a hope.

One further development must be mentioned as playing an important role in the new approaches: the rise of symbolic logic. As in the case of topology, this discipline can be traced back to the 17th century, to Leibniz's ideas for a universal language; but not till the late 19th century did it undergo any extensive and precise development. Boolean algebra provided a mechanical method for the determination of the consequences of a given set of propositions (in another form, this is called the "calculus of propositions"). A few years later, De Morgan, Schroeder, and the founder of Pragmatism, Charles Peirce, investigated the formal properties of relations, leading to an elaborately abstract theory of relations. These results, together with work on the foundations of mathematics (like Peano's formulation of five postulates sufficing for the whole of arithmetic), were extended and systematized shortly after the turn of the century in Russell and Whitehead's monumental *Principia Mathematica*.

The word *cybernetics* (N. Wiener, *Cybernetics*, Wiley, 1948) is from the Greek for "steersman," from the same root as the word "governor." It is Wiener's coinage for the new science of "control and communication in the animal and the machine." The element of control is that exemplified in the mechanical device known as a governor, operating on the fundamental principle of the *feed-back*: the working of the machine at a given time is itself a stimulus for the modification of the future course of its working. Communication enters into cybernetics by way of an unorthodox and ingeniously precise concept of "information" as the degree to which the impulses entering a machine reduce the uncertainty among the set of alternatives available to it. Thus if a machine contains a relay which has two possible positions, an impulse which puts the relay into one of these two has conveyed to the machine exactly one "bit" of information. All communication can be regarded as made up of such bits, as is suggested by the dots and dashes of the Morse code, for example. Modern machines actually use a binary arithmetic, i.e., a notation in which all numbers are expressed in terms of powers of 2 (rather than 10), and are therefore formulable as strings of the cyphers for "zero" and "one." One bit of information is conveyed by each choice of either a zero or a one, the word "bit" being an abbreviation for "binary digit."

Working with these concepts of communication and control, cybernetics becomes relevant to the study of man because human behavior is paralleled in many respects by the communication machines. This parallel is no mere metaphor, but consists in a similarity of structure between the machine processes and those of human behavior. The Darwinian continuity between man and the rest of nature has now been carried to completion: man's rationality marks only a difference of degree from other animals, and fundamentally, no difference at all from the machine. For modern computers are essentially logical machines: they are designed to confront propositions and to draw from them their logical conclusions. With communication and control as the key, a similarity of structure can also be traced between an individual (whether human or mechanical) and a society (again, whether human or machines in a well-designed factory). The metaphors of Plato and Hobbes can now be given a literalist interpretation.

Thus cybernetics bears on the study of human behavior in a variety of ways: most directly, by way of neurology and physiological psychology; and by simple extension, to an improved understanding of functional mental disorders, which Wiener finds to be primarily diseases of memory, thus arriving at Freudian conclusions by a totally different route. Of particular interest are the implications, definitely present though not explicitly drawn, for such classical philosophical puzzles as those concerning free will and the mind-body relation. The analysis of mind and individual personality as a structure of certain information processes renders obsolete not only the "mind substance" of the idealist, but mechanistic materialism as well. Mind is a patterning of information and not spirit, matter, or energy.

In a more recent book (*The Human Use of Human Beings*, Houghton Mifflin, 1950) Wiener considers the relationship between cybernetics and the study of man at quite a different level. The sorts of control mechanisms with which cybernetics is concerned are creating, Wiener argues, a fundamental social transformation which he calls the "cybernetic revolution." This is the age of such mechanisms, he says, as the 18th century was of the clock and the 19th of the steam engine. It is now possible to construct machines for almost any degree of elaborateness of performance —chess-playing machines, for example, are no longer the hoaxes of Edgar Allan Poe's day. It is even possible to arrange machines so that they can communicate with one another, and in no merely figurative sense. And in addition to electronic brains, machines can be equipped with sensory receptors and efferent channels.

The social problems posed by the "cybernetic revolution" are basically those of the industrial one, but on an enlarged scale: whether the new technology is to be organized so as to produce leisure or unemployment, the ennoblement or degradation of man. *The Human Use of Human Beings* consists mainly in a forceful statement of this problem. The Industrial Revolution at least allowed for the localization of human dignity in man's reason, which still played an indispensable rôle in the operation of the technology, even though his muscle could be increasingly dispensed with. This last line of defense is in process of being undermined. Wiener accordingly devotes his book to a vigorous protest against "any use of a human being in which less is demanded of him and less is attributed to him than his full status." In the concrete, this inhuman use of man he finds in the increasing control over the individual in social organization, particularly in the control over information, as in scientific research under military sponsorship. But cybernetics itself only allows us to understand something of the technological developments that have posed this social problem; it does not contain, nor does it pretend to contain, any scientific theory—mathematical or otherwise—of how the problem can be resolved.

Among the recent applications to the study of man of this whole general body of ideas, one is especially celebrated; the theory of games presented by J. von Neumann and O. Morgenstern in *Theory of Games and Economic Behavior* (Princeton University Press, 1947). Here the focus is confined to problems of economics, but it is hoped that it will be extended to the whole range of man's social relations.

It may seem, superficially, that von Neumann and Morgenstern, in selecting games as a way of approaching the study of social organization, fall into the trap of oversimplification. But unlike Rashevsky, von Neumann and Morgenstern do not so much introduce simplifying assumptions in order to deal artificially with the whole complex social order as *select* relatively simple aspects of that order for analysis. Only after a theory adequate to the simple problems has been developed can the more complicated problems be attacked fruitfully. To be sure, the decision-maker cannot suspend action to satisfy the scruples of a scientific conscience; but neither can the scientist pretend to an advisory competence that he does not have, in order to satisfy practical demands.

While the theory of games does not deal with the social process in its full complexity, it is not merely a peripheral aspect of that process which it studies, but its very core. The aim is "to find the mathematically complete principles which define 'rational behavior' for the participants in a social economy, and to derive from them the general characteristics of that behavior." Games are analyzed because the pattern of rational behavior that they exhibit is the same as that manifested in social action, insofar as the latter does in fact involve rationality.

The theory is concerned with the question of what choice of strategy is rational when all the relevant probabilities are known and the outcome is not determined by one's choice alone. It is in the answer to this question that the new mathematics enters. And with this kind of mathematics, the social sciences finally abandon the imitation of natural science that has dogged so much of their history.

The authors first present a method of applying a numerical scale other than the price system to a set of human preferences. A man might prefer a concert to the theater, and either to staying at home. If we assign a utility of "1" to the last alternative, we know that going to the theater must be assigned a higher number, and the concert a higher one still. But how much higher? Suppose the decision were to be made by tossing two coins, the first to settle whether to go to the theater or not, the second (if necessary) to decide between the remaining alternatives. If the utility of the theater were very little different from that of staying at home, most of the time (three-fourths, to be exact) the outcome would be an unhappy one; similarly, if the theater and concert had comparable utilities, the outcome would be usually favorable. Just how the utilities compare, therefore, could be measured by allowing the second coin to be a loaded one. When it is a matter of indifference to the individual whether he goes to the theater or else tosses the loaded coin to decide whether he hears the concert or stays home, the loading of the coin provides a numerical measure of the utilities involved.

Once utility can be measured in a way that does not necessarily correspond to monetary units, a theory of rational behavior can be developed which takes account of other values than monetary ones. A game can be regarded as being played, not move by move, but on the basis of an over-all *strategy* that specifies beforehand what move is to be made in every situation that could possibly arise in the game. Then, for every pair of strategies selected—one by each player in the game—the rules of the game determine a *value* for the game: namely, what utility it would then have for each player. An optimal strategy is one guaranteeing a certain value for the game even with best possible play on the part of the opponent. Rational behavior, that is to say, is characterized as the selection of the strategy which minimizes the maximum loss each player can sustain.

If a game has only two players and is "zero-sum"—whatever is won by one player being lost by the other, and vice versa—then, if each player has "perfect information" about all the previous moves in the game, there always exists such an optimal strategy for each player. The outcome of a rationally played game can therefore be computed in advance; in principle, chess is as predictable as ticktacktoe.

Not every game, however, is as completely open as chess. In bridge and poker, for example, we do not know what cards are in the other players' hands; and this is ordinarily the situation in the strategic interplay of management and labor, or in the relations among sovereign states. In such cases rationality consists in playing several strategies, each with a mathematically determined probability. Consider a type of matching pennies in which each player is permitted to place his coin as he chooses. If we were to select heads always, we should be quickly found out; even if we favored heads somewhat, our opponent (assuming it is he who wins when the coins match) could always select heads and thereby win more than half the time. But if we select heads half the time—not in strict alternation, to be sure, but at random—then, no matter what our opponent does, we cannot lose more than half the time. Rational play consists in what is actually done in the game: we toss the coin each time to determine, as it were, whether we select heads or tails. Of course, in more complex games our strategies are not always to be "mixed" in equal proportions. The fundamental theorem of the theory of games is that for every two-person zero-sum game, no matter how complex the rules or how great the range of possible strategies open to each player, there always exists some specific pattern of probabilities of strategies which constitutes rational play. It minimizes the maximum loss that each player can sustain, not in every play of the game, but in the long run. And there is a mathematical solution that tells us what this strategy is.

Unfortunately, many games are not "zero-sum": in the game between management and labor, utilities are created in the process of play; in war they are destroyed. It is simply not true in such cases that what one side loses the other gains, or vice versa. In such cases, the mathematics of the "zero-sum" game will not apply. Moreover, many games have more than two-players: a number of manufacturers may be competing for a single market. Here the mathematics of a two-person game will not hold. The first difficulty, however, can be absorbed into the second. A non-"zero-sum" two-person game can be regarded as a three-person game, where the third person wins or loses whatever is lost or won by the other two together.

But how are we to solve games of more than two persons? Only if coalitions are formed, in effect making the game a two-person one. This is not an unrealistic assumption, since, obviously, if two players can co-ordinate their strategies against a third, they will enjoy a special advantage: odd-man-out is the simple but fundamental principle in such situations. For such games, however, the theory does not provide a detailed solution, for it cannot determine what is a rational division of the spoils between the members of a coalition in the way it can determine what is a rational strategy for the coalition as a whole. And here, of course, is the great difficulty in politics. The United States and Russia may be conceived of, in this theory, as playing a two-person non-"zero-sum" game with nature as the third player: only nature wins from atomic destruction, only nature loses if resources need not be diverted to military purposes. But the coalition of men against nature still leaves open how the utilities acquired in the game are to be divided between the participants. And here conflicting interests stand in the way of the joint interests that would make rational a coalition strategy.

From our present standpoint, the important outcome of the theory is to show that there exists a rigorously mathematical approach to precisely those aspects of the study of man that have seemed in the past to be least amenable to mathematical treatment—questions of conflicting or parallel interest, perfect or imperfect information, rational decision or chance effect. Mathematics is of importance for the social sciences not merely in the study of those aspects in which man is assimilable to inanimate nature, but precisely in his most human ones. On this question the theory of games leaves no room for doubt.

But a mathematical theory of games is one thing, and a mathematical theory of society another. Von Neumann and Morgenstern, it must be said, never confuse the two. Many fundamental difficulties remain, even within the limitations of the games framework. The theory of games involving many players is in a very unsatisfactory state; there is no way at present of comparing the utilities of different persons; and the whole theory is so far a static one, unable to take account of the essential learning process which (it may be hoped) takes place in the course of the selection of real-life strategies. Yet the theory has already provided enormous stimulation to mathematical and substantive research, and much more can be expected from it. Above all, it has shown that the resources of the human mind for the exact understanding of man himself are by no means already catalogued in the existing techniques of the natural sciences.

Thus the application of mathematics to the study of man is no longer a programmatic hope, but an accomplished fact. The books we have surveyed are by no means the only mathematical approaches to problems of social science published even within the past few years. For instance, K. Arrow's *Social Choice and Individual Values* (Wiley, 1951) is a penetrating application of postulational method and the logical theory of relations to the problem of combining, in accord with democratic principles, individual preferences into a representative set of preferences for the group as a whole. Harold Lasswell and his associates report in *The Language of Politics* (G. W. Stewart, 1949) on the procedures and results of the application of the now widely familiar content-analysis techniques to political discourse, in order to objectify and quantify the role of ideologies and utopias in politics. Shannon and Weaver's *Mathematical Theory of Communication* (University of Illinois Press, 1950) reprints the classic papers in which Claude Shannon first developed the precise theory of information now being applied in cybernetics, linguistics, and elsewhere. There are a number of other books; and dozens of papers have appeared in the professional journals of a wide variety of disciplines, including such preeminently "qualitative" fields as social organization, psychiatry, and even literary history.

But if the new language is widely spoken, there are also wide local differences in dialects, and many individual peculiarities of usage. Yet on the scientific scene, this is in itself scarcely objectionable. New problems call for new methods, and if for a time these remain *ad hoc*, it is only from such a rich variety of approaches that systematic and general theories can emerge. No such theories of society or even of part of the social process have yet been developed, though, as we have seen, there have been some premature attempts. But the situation is promising. If the mathematics employed is not merely notational, if it is not merely an "illustration" of an abstract methodology, if it does not outstrip the availability of data and especially of ideas, there is reason to hope that it will eventually contribute as much to the study of man as it already has to the understanding of the rest of nature.

[33]

HERMAN J. MULLER

Will Science Continue? *

One day, early in the nineteenth century, a boy about sixteen years old was picked up on the street, in a dazed and decrepit condition, in the town of Nuremberg, Germany. According to the story which this boy, known as Kaspar Hauser, later gave out—but which may not have been a true one—he had been kept a prisoner in a dark cellar, without room to stand up, since infancy. Food had been thrust in at him, but he had been given no opportunity to learn to speak, to write, or even to walk, until a few months before his release. Finally the man who owned the house, after giving him some simple instructions in speaking and writing, moved away, leaving the door of the cellar unlocked. As Kaspar had not even known that an outside world existed he was bewildered when it burst upon his view. Not being feeble minded, however, he quickly learned the uses of objects and the ways of people. But the strain of it all gradually proved too much for him, his maladjustments led to quarrels, and after a few years he met a violent death. Whether this was by murder or suicide has never been definitely established.

The situation described by Kaspar Hauser in his story of himself is in a way paralleled by that of the whole of humanity in the past few centuries, although it is to be hoped that the ending will not be similar. For ages we human beings have remained cooped up within blank walls of ignorance and superstition, knowing of nothing beyond our immediate view and imagining at most another cell or two much like our own, on the other side of the wall. However, surprisingly enough, we have managed to creep through crevices in this dungeon and have at last gained a view,

* From *Bulletin of Atomic Research Scientists* (Dec., 1952). By permission of the author and of the editor of the *Bulletin*.

for the first time in all history, of the brilliant world of reality outside. It stretches far beyond our immediate reach, yet it is ours to roam, and in considerable measure to master for our own benefit, if we only would set ourselves to it.

For us humans, suddenly confronted by the immensities of the stars and galaxies with their dazzling multitude of worlds so unknown to our ancestors, the universe has expanded explosively almost overnight. But, in addition, there has been a kind of *im*plosion of the whole of nature, of comparable significance. That is, there has opened to our view a marvellous extension of matter inwards, and we have discovered microcosms, one world within another, in the interiors of all parts of all things. These worlds too are bringing to view unlimited vistas for exploration and conquest, and unsuspected avenues of power. Finally, the cosmos has opened tremendously in still another dimension, that is, backwards and forwards in time, and also inwards in time, just as in space. The interpretation of ordinary events in terms of complicated series of operations occupying fractions of microseconds remains an unknown book to many laymen. Moreover, they are hardly yet beginning to take seriously the enormous reaches of time behind us and before us, as compared with our primitive conceptions, and the amazing transformations which all matter, but especially living things, have imperceptibly undergone and will undergo during these stupendous ages. And they still regard with mystification the elusive, underground operations which secretly and slowly bring about these great changes, yet which, when brought to light, become more and more subject to human control, both as to speed and as to direction.

Man, in the sense of an erect, ground-dwelling animal, who makes fires, shapes tools, speaks, and practices other techniques and social customs handed down from his ancestors, is known to have existed for hundreds of thousands of years, and man of our own species, not to be distinguished anatomically from present men, and probably about as able mentally, has existed for at least several tens of thousands of years. Why then is it only in our time, broadly speaking, that man has become aware of the kind of world he is living in? It is instructive to look for the reasons why science did not get on its feet earlier.

Before men could attain this kind of second sight high technologies had to be developed, which relieved men of some material cares and enabled them, in this leisure time, to make reliable observations, measurements and deductions. At the same time, they had to have good means of communicating and recording their findings, for the work is so great that it must be a joint one. And there had to be a mental atmosphere which stimulated such activities and encouraged the expression of new ideas and the development of new methods, instead of stifling them. These techniques and this atmosphere took an enormous time to develop to the high level where real science emerged, with a systematic, consistent body of fundamental principles for interpreting nature. The delay in the emergence of science itself was caused not only by the fact that so many physical and mental tools were prerequisite for it, but also by the fact that these technological developments happened only in relatively short spurts. That is, there were long intervals in between, of virtual stagnation or even retrogression.

The path of progress has been an exceeding long and intermittent one. Some 10,000 years ago, after the hundreds of thousands of years during which men lived as savages, an important spurt occurred, when some men rather suddenly developed agriculture and more or less settled living. There was another spurt 6000 years ago when in the Middle and Near East intensive farming, aided by metals, gave the surpluses that made possible city life, with organized states and many specialized artisans. But this remarkable burst of progress of about 4000 B.C. soon bogged down. Its winnings became increasingly drawn off by the rulers of the top-heavy autocracies and theocracies of that day, to support them in a sterility that became ever more grandiose, wasteful, and given to war. The only knowledge which then remained respectable was the so-called "higher learning", dealing mainly with such things as astrological forecasts, mathematical mysticisms, sacrificial rites, and medical charms and incantations. Only this kind of learning was considered worth writing down. Any skills and knowledge that involved work with the hands was left to miserable slaves and craftsmen. These despised wretches had little energy left for discovering or trying out improved methods. Nor had they adequate incentives to make these improvements, for they could seldom better their own lot by this means; in fact, even to propose modifications in small matters of method was often a risky heresy. Neither could the craftsmen effectively pass along to others any improvements which they might succeed in making. Under these circumstances routine ways of doing things became thoroughly fixed and prescribed, and routine ways of thinking even more so. In short, authoritarianism and obedience became the unquestioned order of life. Such civilizations inevitably faltered and after a time most of them became disrupted by barbarians who had meanwhile learned much of the physical techniques.

In the ensuing dark ages, however, the core of these techniques survived. Finally, a new era of progress set in, often among the former barbarians, because these peoples were less hampered by the heavy weight of perverted tradition. And when this happened the advances in civilization could start from a higher level, and then reach to a higher peak than the previous wave of progress had been able to do. Yet time and again, after such a promising renewal, stagnation, decay and dark ages set in once more. The archeological record, interpreted in the light of observations of human motivation and of the workings of societies, appears to support the inference that the reasons for such declines of highly organized societies were always fundamentally the same—the throttling of progress from above. And the times of substantial advance were on each occasion limited to a few hundred years, while thousands of years usually intervened between the spurts.*

The last period of considerable progress before that of our own time culminated in the classical Greek world of several hundred years B.C. Not until then had the advances in technique become great enough, widely enough diffused among the common people, and coupled with enough healthy disrespect for authority, to allow a few men to begin to search for new insights into nature. But again knowledge tended to become a "higher learning", a caste system developed, society became more autocratic and it finally fell under the deadening hand of Imperial Rome. We all know of the stagnation and disintegration and then the long ages of darkness and superstition which ensued that time.

When finally, in the later Middle Ages, masses of people in Europe found themselves again in a position to better their own lot, they had, to start with, a higher general level of technique, diffused over a wider area, than ever before. In addition, they were provided with certain major innovations, most of which had originated outside of Europe but the uses of which were greatly developed by Europeans. Among these was gunpowder from China, which helped to make knighthood with its oppression of the common people obsolete and thus to give them new freedom of action and thought. Then there was the compass, also from China, which enabled man to travel far and wide, getting new ideas, knowledge and techniques, unsettling ancient misconceptions, and through commerce and colonization deriving material advantages which increased their well-being and leisure. Important too were paper and printing, once more from China, that enormously multiplied the transmission and recording of ideas. Our modern so-called Arabic number system, derived from India via the Arabs, was a necessary basis for the computations so essential to modern commerce, industry and science. The establishment of universities, which seem first to have taken solid root in India and which later had been set up in the Moslem world, was copied in Europe and helped much to disseminate and increase knowledge.

There was also a ferment of ideas caused in Europe as the ancient Greek writings became known again and, not long after them, the achievements in arithmetic and algebra, and the valuable observations and data concerning the human body, concerning many kinds of substances, and concerning the sky, which were being contributed by the Persians, Arabs, Moors and Jews of Moslem countries. With the betterment of communication and transportation, the decline of banditry and petty warfare, the improvement of agriculture and the rise in living standards and (though not excessively) in population, all these currents and others met and mingled in Europe, with increasing productiveness.

* Good accounts of these alternate waves of advance and stagnation are given, for example, in the books by the distinguished British archeologist Gordon Childe, *Man Makes Himself*, and *What Happened in History*, obtainable in thirty-five and sixty-five cent editions of the Mentor Book and Pelican Book pocket-editions, respectively.

One reason why, in Europe, these acquisitions of technique and knowledge were utilized productively, and in such a way as to give rise to still further advances, was that there were certain elements favorable for this in its mental background. One of these was a persistent spirit of enterprise, partly barbarian in source, which all the load of medieval oppression had not been able to quell completely. Another was the fact that the basic principles taught by Jesus, and long since adopted by Europe from the Near East, stressed the potential worth and the dignity of the ordinary human being everywhere, and at the same time inspired in him a spirit of fellow feeling, cooperation, and pride in good works for others. The gradual strengthening of the rights of people of humble birth, achieved by hundreds of years of effort on their part in Europe, was undoubtedly helped along by this way of thinking. As a result, people had more opportunity and incentive to improve their condition, their welfare was advanced, and human potentialities were enhanced in many ways. All this was very important in providing conditions favorable for the betterment of techniques, and the rise of science. It is true, however, that there were also powerful influences opposed to progress exerted by authorities of the Middle Ages in the *name* of Christianity, such as fanatical dogmatism, and the withdrawal of attention from the righting of present evils by promises of postmortem rewards.

But in spite of the reactionary pressure exerted by those whose interests lay in maintaining things as they were, the current of progress proved the stronger one, and became self-increasing. With it, for the first time in history, sound theoretical science was able to raise its head effectively. Our present industrial civilization is mainly a by-product of that science. We ourselves are still in the upswing of this wave, although the forces of autocracy throughout much of the world, feeding on the very successes of science, are also growing more menacing. Whether our new material and social techniques and our deeper understanding of the whole situation will this time manage to subdue the parasitic growth of autocracy is a question that still hangs in the balance. Let us examine some of the conditions on which the decision depends.

A few great minds did concern themselves with scientific questions among the ancient Greeks, but if science is to develop actively it needs more support than a few great minds. It needs the very broad human base which only highly developed techniques, coupled with generally high living standards, popular education, and considerable freedom of expression can provide. It thrives best where people have ample opportunities to better their physical welfare, and where at the same time they have incentives for using their own minds and hands to devise new or improved methods, to discover new facts and interpretations, and to criticize or modify old ones. This presupposes considerable freedom from oppression, physical or mental, and a social system of an essentially democratic kind where the individual can develop his own peculiar potentialities for good, even where this means the challenging of established opinions. That is, one must even have *the right to be honestly wrong.*

This broad human base is necessary not only to furnish the physical surplus required for scientific research, and the refined tools which science needs, but, just as important, to provide a great educated public for encouraging and supporting science, both theoretical and applied, and for generating a sizeable scientific personnel. For the progress of modern science, in fact, the public at large should be educated to understand and sympathize with the methods which science uses, with its major accomplishments in all directions, and with its attitudes of mind and its aims. A public ignorant of these things is much more likely to receive the findings of science with hostility, to withhold the large-scale physical and moral support required by present-day scientific work, and to refuse to grant it the wide freedoms which it needs in choosing its directives. Moreover, unless the public as a whole is educated in this way, many of those who would have found their most useful work in scientific and technological fields will be shunted off into other, less productive and less satisfying activities.

One reason why, for the advancement of science, a large number of people engaged in scientific and technological activities of varied kinds is necessary, and not simply a few prominent scientists, is because so much labor is required for gathering all the information needed, for laying bare difficulties and problems, and for improving methods to the point where important discoveries are possible at all. Another reason is that in countries where many people are drawn into such work the chances are far higher that, included among them, will be those persons who are capable of making the greatest discoveries. By way of contrast, in countries where such work is confined to a few, the chances will be far smaller that any of the numerous persons who could have made great contributions to science and technology will ever have the opportunity to develop this capability and put it to use. Large numbers of scientific and technological workers are also needed because, after any important discovery has been made, new fields are opened up by it, and many men are then required for developing these fields, subjecting them to criticism and refinements, coordinating them with other fields, and bringing out their numerous practical and theoretical applications.

Those of the large corps of technicians and scientists who do not achieve much individual recognition by the public need not have the feeling that they have been at fault. Often it is mere accident that one of them and not another is in the position where he can make the spectacular find or invention. Be he never so original, he must always build upon a great amount of work that went before him (whether he cites it or not!) and an equally great amount of work after him is often necessary for its full fruition. Thus all who work in science or in the technological fields which are necessary to support, supply and apply science can feel a pride of accomplishment whenever any member of their brotherhood makes a strike. Moreover, the public at large, once it has become generally educated in things scientific, and realizes the important part which it, the public, plays in scientific development, will itself feel a justified thrill in the victories of its scientists. This will lead to the acquirement, by all humanity, of a new, invigorating sense of the richness and hopefulness of life.

In considering what types of scientific and technological work are most worth while, it should be recognized that there are few cut and dried categories in science. The scientific work of one field shades off into another and combines with it, and theoretical work shades into practical. A medical man, an engineer or an agriculturist, although an applied scientist, can often hit upon facts or devise instruments or methods which are invaluable in theoretical researches. On the other hand, it is also important to realize that those discoveries which turn out to be of most revolutionary utility in the long run, and of widest applicability too, are often not the ones which were attained by striving for some definite practical end. They are the ones which were found in following up the quest for truth in its own right, with the aim of gaining deeper insights into the basic operations of nature.

No one could foresee, for example, that the "highbrow" conclusion that the earth is round, based on observations in pure astronomy, combined with far-flung theorizing, would result in the discovery of America and Australia and the complete reorganization of world economy. Only Soddy in the first decade of this century foresaw and stated publicly that the discovery of radioactivity and isotopes marked the beginning of a revolutionary road to the control of atomic energy. The laboratory finding of radio waves by Hertz in the 19th century was not at the time realized to be the fundamental discovery on which would be based radio and radar and television. Pasteur was nearly failed in medical school because he wasted his time—so it was thought—on those speculations concerning the asymetrical combining property of the carbon atom which are basic to the achievements of modern organic chemistry, with its growing myriads of compounds and processes so indispensable to us today. The pursuit of seemingly impractical studies on the laws of Mendelian heredity made possible the development of hybrid corn and poultry, worth hundreds of millions of dollars a year to American farmers. And so we could go on and on.

It is said that when, about a century ago in England, Faraday—who by the way had been the son of a blacksmith—was explaining at a lecture the fundamental discovery he had just made of the connection between electricity and magetism, a lady in the audience interrupted him to ask: "But, Mr. Faraday, what is the use of this knowledge?" Faraday was taken aback for a moment and hesitated. Then he came back with a counter-question: "Madam, of what use is a baby?" As we all know today, this baby of Faraday's later developed into dynamos and power lines, electric motors, telegraphs, telephones, electric typewriters, washing machines, and all the innumerable devices by which electric power is utilized to perform work for man. At the same time, the principle that had been disclosed served as one of the necessary bases for those great advances in physics and chemistry centering around the electromagnetic nature of light and other radiation, the properties of atoms, electrons and atom nuclei, and all the practical applications of these fields of knowledge. This is an instructive illustration of the way in which so-called pure science, the discovery of seemingly impractical fundamental truth, primarily for the sake of knowing what kind of a world we live in, so opens man's eyes as to enable him to guide his hands and feet to the conquest of new worlds. This is one reason why such an institution as our National Science Foundation, having the objective of giving support to basic theoretical studies regardless of whether or not they seem practical, should be regarded as representing the payment by society, of but a tiny part of its debt to theoretical and "impractical" science.

It should be realized that although few discoveries can be as important as the theoretical ones just mentioned, nevertheless each contribution fills its indispensable place in the great organism of modern science. For only by the interactions of its many parts, fittingly coordinated, is this organism able to function properly, both in interpreting the operations of nature and in controlling them. Much of this work is bound to be toil and drudgery, as well as the following up of false leads, just as most of the work even of an explorer is a grueling grind. In both cases, however, this routine is ennobled by the fact that the spirit of the great adventure as a whole suffuses into each part of it. In the case of science that adventure is an enterprise on which all humanity is embarked. And it is leading us to ever wider freedoms.

The view of the situation for science which has just been sketched is founded on the assumption that science will continue to advance, and to be used for human betterment. Yet we all know that the ogre of worldwide catastrophe is raising its head and that this monster will itself make use of weapons provided by science. Have we then reached the peak of our present wave of progress?

If we may judge from such knowledge as exists concerning all the previous occasions on which civilization has been seriously set back, the fundamental reason, as we saw in the earlier part of this discussion, has in each case been that the advantages accruing from the higher techniques, which had developed among the people in general, became more and more appropriated by a ruling group. These groups were not themselves well acquainted with these more advanced skills and knowledge, nor with the methods and conditions whereby they became further developed. The techniques, at the behest of these ruling groups, were then misused to swell their autocratic power still further, and with the aid of these powers to freeze into rigid form their own system of ideas, while the bulk of people, divorced from their rulers, became increasingly subject to their dictation and oppression, both physically and in their thoughts.

We see then that the fruits of cultural progress have repeatedly served to feed a parasitic cultural growth which, by its increase, has ultimately reacted to hinder further progress. This process curiously resembles the way in which organisms of a parasitic or predatory kind increase at the expense of the organisms which serve as their food. Eventually this causes so much depletion of the supporting organisms as to result in poorer conditions for the parasitic or predatory group, relatively to the other group, and the latter starts increasing again. In the biological case, the mathematics of the resulting swing of the two types back and forth, in a series of waves, have been calculated by Poincaré, Gauss and others. The formulae which were worked out to express the shape of this continually wavering curve were then checked by observations on living material, and found to conform with them. It is tempting to infer (and I offer the hypothesis for what it may be worth) that the waves of human progress represent the operation of essentially similar principles, applying to cultural and economic rather than to purely biological elements. It is true that, in the human case, the waves are far less regular and are incapable of calculation, because the cultural elements are subject to such enormous qualitative variations and are bound in such a complex organization. This situation prevents any true repetition of previous states when cultural changes occur. However, the essential conditions which in the biological cases give rise to the wave form—the existence of two self-multiplying groups, one of which draws its sustenance from the other—appear to be present likewise in the cultural examples.

The process of concentration of unlimited social power into the hands of a relatively small group, unrepresentative of the people in general, has already taken place in considerable measure, even in the lifetime of the youngest of the readers of this article, in the countries behind the Iron Curtain. Because of the efficiency of modern techniques, it has occurred with a swiftness, to a degree, and on a scale, surpassing any previously known. Tragically enough, these developments took place in consequence of the people's attempt to achieve exactly the opposite result. The mistake they made was to put into power a complete dictatorship, uncontrolled by them, which became ever more ruthless in running the whole of society in its own interests primarily. At present the countries involved in it are nevertheless increasing their physical strength tremendously, and they may be counted on for many decades yet to make important scientific and technological advances in those directions which their rulers regard as serviceable for their own ends. However, the springs of free inquiry in theoretical science, from which the progress of the more distant future must eventually flow, have been seriously vitiated in those countries. For authoritarianism is in the long run incompatible with progress. And the brutality, stupidity and sweeping character of the interference which some important branches of theoretical science, including fundamental biology, chemistry, physics and psychology, have already suffered at the hands of this new authoritarianism, have demonstrated the hollowness of its claim that it, unlike the dictatorships of the past, is scientific in its spirit and methods.

In the meantime, the poverty stricken, ignorant millions in those vast regions of the world still outside the Iron Curtain which are without adequate modern machinery and techniques, have been greatly impressed by the growth in physical strength of the huge Soviet empire, and by the false promises that the social methods used there will better their own conditions of life. At the same time these people have been much embittered by the selfish colonial policies to which they were—till recently, at any rate—subjected by Europeans. And in their eyes Americans have now taken the place of Europeans. These just awakening peoples are therefore feeling more and more inclined to jump, as the Chinese have done, from the frying pan into the fire. We have had a shocking experience, in Korea, of what a powerful force against us they may then become, when supplied with equipment and instruction from the heartland of totalitarianism.

We cannot afford to sit complacently back while this happens on a still larger scale, engulfing one country after another either by force or by hook and crook. Even if we were so selfish that the fate of the rest of the world meant nothing to us, the risk to our own freedoms would then be too great. On the other hand, a major war between the two halves of the world would entail such universal destruction as to make that risk to civilization also a most awful one. It is therefore necessary for us now to understand the situation of these peoples from their own point of view, to sympathize with them, and to use all means we can to show them that their interests and ours are in harmony. For it is the misery of this whole underdeveloped section of the world, the great majority of mankind, and not just the aggressiveness of Russia, which presents the most grievous social problem of today and tomorrow. And even if Russia were defeated this problem of the "have-nots" would rise again to confront our children and grandchildren.

We must demonstrate to these suffering millions that we are on their side, that we believe in freedom and well-being for all, including themselves, and that we will help them to achieve it. More than this, we must realize that their advancement will be to our own material advantage in the end too, just as we have learned that, within our own country, high wages and a high standard of living on the part of the ordinary citizen are actually good business. They tend to keep the wheels of industry, agriculture and commerce turning at a high rate and thus mean more prosperity for all in the end. For a considerable time to come, however, this policy with the outer world will mean additional heavy sacrifices on our part, besides those needed for direct defense. For mere words are not enough for starving people. We must put real effectiveness into the so-called four-point plan, and try in no grudging or condescending spirit to

help these peoples to the attainment of more modern techniques, that will
have a really noticeable effect upon their living standards. This means
giving them the benefit of our knowledge and experience concerning agri-
cultural, industrial and medical methods, and at the same time according
them a significant amount of material support in the setting up of their
factories, mines, waterworks, transportation systems, reforestation and
drainage programs, and so on. There is an enormous need here for the
work of applied scientists and technologists.

Aid in material techniques and goods is in many places likely to fail
of its objective, however, unless the peoples receiving it can at the same
time be encouraged to adopt more enlightened social and economic measures than they now have. For the persistence of parasitic landlordism,
usury, and feudalism in general, which are so prevalent in the technolog-
ically backward portions of the world, tends to drain off the advantages of
higher techniques so as chiefly to serve luxurious living by a few and to
increase the power of the ruling autocracies. This is after all the ancient
pattern which everywhere has resulted in the choking off of progress, and
its existence among these peoples, in the form of domination both by
foreign powers and by their own feudal or semi-feudal overlords, is the
primary cause of their having advanced so little in recent centuries.

The necessary policy must therefore include, among other things, the
encouragement of such changes in practice and in point of view as would
lead to the increase of material and mental freedom among the ordinary
people of those countries. This means the distribution of land among the
people, as occurred on such a grand scale under the direction of our occupation in Japan, the establishment of democratic procedures in general,
of the right to organize effective labor unions, and the setting up of adequate public schools and popular education at all levels. Along with this
goes also the task of assisting in the entrance of modern scientific ideas
concerning the universe and man. On the other hand, this does not imply
that these peoples should be urged to adopt our particular economic,
political or ideological forms but rather that they be given a chance, themselves, to readapt their own cultures in enlightened ways, harmonious so
far as possible with their own traditions—even as India is now so valiantly
engaged in doing. We may rest assured that this will ultimately, without
so much opposition as otherwise, mean the absorption into their own traditions of the elements of good in ours. At the same time, reciprocally, ours
should be able to benefit much from theirs.

One of the most important scientific ideas the recognition of which is
essential if progress is to be made in these great areas of the world is that
an uncontrolled increase in population is incompatible with a permanent
rise in well-being. For if science saves lives only to make this rate of
increase greater, as it has done in these countries in the past several decades
and is doing at an increasing rate today, the end result can only mean
greater misery, and defeat for all their hopes of progress. But if all peoples
learn to control their rate of increase, as Americans and Western Euro-

peans have done in some degree, and to keep it well behind their increase in material productivity, then there is indeed great hope for their futures and much progress can be made by them within a short time. It has suited the purposes of the Russian autocrats to deny this need of birth control, for they wish the masses to grow bigger, more wretched and more credulous, the better to be able to use them for their own purposes and against us.

In all our dealings we must bear in mind that we have no valid grounds to assume that we are intrinsically superior to any of these other peoples. A few of the more important contributions of Oriental peoples were mentioned above. It may also be recalled that Central Africa was one of the first, if not the first, to begin the working of iron, one of the major achievements in the progress of civilization. We of European antecedents just happen to be on the upswing of our greatest wave, while these other peoples have been caught, till recently, in one of those much longer periods of comparative standstill. Thus it is up to us to help them, in all sincerity, to take their place along with us in the worldwide community of free and enlightened citizens. The time is woefully short for us to convince them of this, in view of their desperate plight and the rapidly growing influence which the totalitarians are exerting on all these peoples.

It will be an enormous aid in this great task of aiding world reconstruction if at the same time we continue actively in our job of getting our own house in better order. We must not overlook the existence, right here among ourselves, of those forces of reaction which are ever seeking to limit feedoms in all directions, to narrow the distribution of the fruits of progress, to control thought and expression, and to strengthen further, relatively to the rest, the power of those who already have great power. Discrimination against minorities is a part of this same tendency, and we must continue actively with our job of eliminating it. Moreover, it is especially necessary to eliminate it if we would convince the peoples of Asia and Africa, most of whom are dark skinned, that we are sincere in our show of friendship and brotherhood with them. All citizens, including those engaged in scientific and technological work, must become aware of these dangers and join actively in the efforts to put our own freedoms and our own prosperity on an ever broader basis, and to make them more secure. For it is true, as has so often been said, that "eternal vigilance is the price of freedom."

But if these principles are recognized by citizens in general, including scientists, then the age-old process which time and again has caused the standstill and decline of civilizations may hereafter be stopped in its tracks. For despite all our imperfections, there has never before among all the civilizations of mankind been such an extension of democracy and education, or so much economic and social strength on the part of the people in general, as there is in our own country today. Moreover, the eyes and tools of physical, biological and social science, placed at the disposal of our unprecedentedly democratic social system, have introduced an en-

tirely new element into the picture of human progress. For the first time
we have become aware of the fact of evolutionary change, we can weigh
to some extent the effects of scientific techniques and social processes, and
our people can be given the knowledge and strength to influence these very
processes in their own favor.

In the meantime however another duty of all citizens, and of scientists and technologists especially, is to help build up in ourselves and our
allies strength against physical attack from without. It is true that if war
should come *both* sides may then be defeated more grievously than any
nations were ever defeated before in history. However, we have to take
the long chance here and to do our best in this situation. For if we should
fail to build up our physical strength in this crisis, then indeed we are
practically bound to lose, whether with or without a major war. This is in
fact the wind-up which the totalitarians are hoping for. We know their
manner of thinking well enough to be sure they would take advantage of
our weakness. If allowed their way, they will of course do it gradually,
by a process not of outright official war, but of intrigue, erosion and wear-
ing away, directed first at the less developed countries. But our own
greatest hope is that, if we do build up our defense strength, and if at the
same time we demonstrate our good will and sincere helpfulness to the
destitute peoples of the undecided countries, the crisis may remain stalled
so long that totalitarianism will begin to lose its appeal for them, and even
to lose strength in its own homeland. There is still a great, repressed but
in fact increasing yearning for freedom in the long-suffering population of
the U.S.S.R. itself, and this may finally be directed by these people against
their own autocracy, so as to cause its moderation. In that case too there
need be no war. This is a question which, with good luck, may be settled
even in our own generation.

If at last, as we must hope, the ideal of a world community of free,
well-educated and prosperous citizens prevails, then the outlook for science
and for further progress based upon science will be auspicious as never
before. The long vistas still ahead stretch out far beyond our own horizon.
It is only lack of knowledge and of imagination that still causes some men
to think the we are nearing the end of the road either in the physical or
biological sciences or in their applications.

Man is a minute mote in the vastness of nature. He has only just
begun, through science, to see the world for what it is, and to find large-
scale ways of controlling it in his long-term interests. If only he will settle
the sorry, shameful conflicts between groups of his own kind, he may then
proceed to contests with nature which are really worthy of him. In
these contests it is first necessary to know, and after that to take
action.

The fields open for the scientists and technologists of the future are
such as to challenge the most daring imagination. The mysteries of the
ocean and of the earth's interior have only been glimpsed. On other levels,

our paths of progress lead into the inner recesses of the atom nucleus and into the structure and dynamics of all-pervading space itself. There will be those who find new modes of combination of atoms, molecules and higher categories, who invent and fashion fantastic new substances with marvellous properties. Energy in its varied forms must be grappled with, tamed, converted, and stored, and the sun's rays themselves must be artificially trapped and harnessed. Undoubtedly too men will succeed in leaving the earth and setting foot on other planets, and will establish outposts in interplanetary space. Yet even these conquests would only be the beginning of man's expansion in the cosmos.

Whether man would be worthy of all this is a most important question, one which requires its own kinds of attack. In this connection we must not forget the biological and psychological sides in scientific progress. There are intricate worlds of coordinated members, one within another, right within our own bodies and within those of all other living things. These must be explored and their ways discovered in detail. With knowledge comes the possibility of control, and the conquest over living matter must be pushed as vigorously as that over lifeless matter. In some ways, living things present the most fascinating and multitudinous opportunities of all for exploration and exploitation. There are swarming populations both on land and in the water to learn about, and to remake into new Gardens of Eden. It is for example very likely that algae and other plankton will furnish our most valuable basis of food in the future, and that bacteria and other microorganisms can be "trained" for many useful ends besides those which they already fulfill.

Finally, we must face the problems of human nature itself, for these present us with the greatest tasks of all. We shall then find that the transfiguration of man, by man himself, into a being ever nobler not merely in body but, more important, in spirit, is a direction of progress which will require our utmost resourcefulness and wisdom, and which is never-ending in its possibilities.

Those young people who are to be scientists or technologists, or who are to have anything to do with the teaching, dissemination or utilization of science—and what truly educated man does not have some function of this kind today?—those young persons with this fresh knowledge and skill, to whom this article is mainly addressed, are in a privileged position. By virtue of your education, and of the democratic society in which you live, you provide the eyes of the world, the hands of the world, and the hope of the world. Freed of age-old misconceptions, you, like a glorified but more wholesome Kaspar Hauser, are in the process of escaping, not into a realm of fable but, at long last, into the marvellous world of reality itself! It is you who, more than all others, may soon hold the more distant world-destinies in your hands. You can make us all become the ancestors of increasingly god-like beings. You and those who follow you may some day even be able to throw back an answer to the eight-hundred-year-old verse of the disillusioned, cynical Persian mathematician and poet, Omar Khayyam, in which he complained so bitterly:

> "Would I could take this sorry scheme of things entire
> And mold it nearer to the heart's desire!"

Little did old Omar imagine, despite his own great contributions to science, that the time might come when you and your fellowmen would in fact be taking things into your hands, and bringing this miracle to pass. Your goals, not static but ever advancing ones, are literally no less than the stars, and yet not even the stars alone. They are the expanding universes both of inanimate nature and also of the living body. And paramount in the progression of the living body is that of the spirit which forms an inseparable part of it. It is with the improvement and ennoblement of this spirit that the greatest future exploits of science must deal.

[34]

J. ROBERT OPPENHEIMER

The Scientific Foundations for World Order *

Some years ago Bertrand Russell was lecturing in this country. He went to Harvard to talk on the Quantum Theory—the new theory of the atom. His friend, Professor Whitehead, urged him to take care that his audience really learned something from this lecture. After it was all over, Whitehead was quite grateful and enthusiastic. He thanked Dr. Russell and said it was a fine speech and that he admired him "not least for leaving the vast darkness of the subject unobscured." I shall do my best to live up to that injunction.

First of all, let me say a little more specifically what our problem is. We are not going to discuss world order in the abstract sense; we are not going to talk about the kind of world order that appealed to Genghis Khan, or that appealed to the Nazis. On the other hand, we shall try to deal with science, not just atomic science. I am not going to confine myself just to the atom. I intend first to restrict my discussion to the natural sciences; at the end I should like to indicate in what way other forms of human activity—other forms of reason—may allow a parallel with science, and how that may come to bear on the problem of world order.

As we stand today we are deeply worried about a problem which is

* From *Foundations for World Order* (Second of seven addresses before the Social Science Foundation at the University of Denver, 1946–7, by seven lecturers). Copyright, 1949, by The University of Denver Press. Pp. 37–51 reprinted by permission of the author and publisher.

quite specific. That problem, as I see it, is not as simple as the avoidance of war; but it *is* summarized by the statement, "There should be peace." Many of us have lived through two world wars. I think all of us agree that the next world war is unlikely to leave the United States as unscathed—as relatively unscathed—as we are today. I think all of us are aware of the danger of the destruction of this country; I think all of us are aware of the depths of moral degradation which a war waged in the future is likely to bring with it. I do not know how much the American people took to heart the kind of thing our government did in order to win this war—and had to do, in my opinion. I do not know how much we took to heart the fact that we sent incendiaries against the Japanese cities and demolition bombs against the German cities; that we waged a total war as effectively as we knew how in retaliation against the total war waged by the enemy. But this kind of thing cannot go on if men are to have any sanity—if men are ever to be whole men again. And the first thing we all want is some method by which peace, if not insured, can be made somewhat more likely.

Now I will assume—I will not argue—that the probabilities are rather against the achievement of peace without some order in the world—without a law among nations, and without that community of experience, community of understanding, that fraternity among the peoples of the world, that is the necessary foundation for such law. I am the last person to say that by calling a constitutional convention and fixing up a lot of red tape and a lot of paper work you can unify the world. But certainly one of the elements for unity is a law which is respected everywhere, and a law in which force is available to back it up, not merely to break it.

It would be enough to think of this problem without the specific troubles of the contemporary world. This is certainly a most disordered world. Not only is there no law among nations, but in many parts of the world there is no law within nations. Look, for example, at the state of affairs in China, and to a very large extent in Western Europe, and in Southern and Eastern Asia, and in India, and in the Indies to see how far we are from world order. And there is another point. It is an important one. We add certain concrete conditions to our concept of "world order"—we are not willing to accept just any kind of an arrangement. I can illustrate this by two extreme examples. I do not think that the people of the United States, peace-loving as they are, would accept peace if it meant adopting the beliefs, the religion, the way of life, the economic misery, and the general squalor which prevail in India. Thus, we couple with our desire for world order certain minimum conditions about how the United States should continue its own tradition and continue to work out its own destiny as it has in the past. And above all, I think, there stands the great conflict with Soviet communism. There may be people who believe that this doctrine originated in a desire to provide for the well-being of the people of Russia—for their standard of living, for their health. But whatever its origin, it has given rise to political forms which are deeply abhorrent to us and which we not only would repudiate for ourselves but which we are reluctant to see spread into the many areas of the world where there is great instability, as there still is in Europe and in Asia.

Thus we set up what is by no means a simple order. We would like to see steps taken to insure peace in the world. We would like not to be attacked. We would like to be able to put away our armies and our weapons and turn to the works of peace. But we want this not at the cost of radical changes in the way of life to which this country is dedicated. It is only reasonable to suppose that comparable views may exist elsewhere. When we see that, we see the magnitude of the problem. In my opinion no single simple step will solve this problem. It is a job for work, for effort. And to those who think that world government and world unity are inevitable I will quote Justice Holmes. "The mode by which the inevitable comes to pass is effort," said Justice Holmes. In this effort science has a role to play which is important and which I would like to explore. But I should only be misleading if I pretended that by science alone one could go very far in the solution of this problem. Only if the limitations of what science can contribute are understood will it be able to contribute at all.

When one looks at the world and where we want it to be and where it is, one is always reminded of the story about the stranger who was driving through the Tennessee Valley and asked the way to Jonesville from an old farmer. The farmer tried to tell him, but he got confused. He started over again and tried to tell him, but he still didn't get it straight. Then he turned to him in desperation and said: "Mister, if I wanted to go to Jonesville I wouldn't start from here." That is eminently the problem of today. We have never had a world in which the prospects and possibilities of achieving anything which we could honestly call world order looked grimmer or more difficult.

I want then to say a few simple things. The first is that not science, but the technology which is so closely related to it, has given a very strong argument for trying to get rid of war by any means at all. The second is that the technology which derives from science has fulfilled some of the conditions—not all, but some of the conditions—which are necessary for unifying the world. The third is that in science itself we have a limited but magnificent example of a real international fraternity. The fourth is to tell a little of how these themes have been woven together in a part—and to my way of thinking, a very vital part—of the United States proposals for the international control of atomic energy. And the last thing I shall do is to make some very general and speculative remarks about the relation between reason and our human life.

To begin with, we shall find it useful, I think, to make sharp a distinction which in the actual world is not sharp. By science I do not mean things like the atom bomb, things like the great dam of the Colorado River, things like the jeep. These I would like to call technology. They are impossible without science, and science in turn would be difficult and slow and impossible without technology. They are mutually fructifying. But they differ very much in their motivation, because surely the motive of any scientist, if he is an honest man, is that he wants to understand the world. And the motive of the engineer or the technologist is that he wants to change something about it and make it better. The one is aimed at understanding; the other at control. You cannot have one without the other, but they are not quite the same thing. So I must include technology in my subject. Otherwise I will have very little indeed to write about.

On the first point, then, I need only say that it is technology, and not any innate depravity of man, which has reconverted war from a specialized business of soldiers to the totality which it had with the most primitive of men. It is clear that the reliance of present-day armies on the industrial apparatus of their countries has made the distinction between the soldier and the civilian, between the combatant and the noncombatant, far less sharp, and has made it appear to be fair game to murder as many people in the enemy country as possible. We have a slightly uneasy feeling that the murdering may not all be one way the next time. Of this state of affairs the atomic bomb is a kind of symbol. It certainly has increased the ferocity of warfare vastly. It has made us all aware that it is not a question of the survival of individuals, but of the culture, the civilization in which we all live; we do not have to kill everybody to wipe that out. You cannot demolish city after city, you cannot destroy the knots that tie civilization together, you cannot make humanity and humaneness impossible, without making civilized life impossible. I do not want to belabor this point—it has been belabored too much. But let us not forget this: The incentive to peace has never been greater, and if this has been symbolized by the development of the atomic bomb I think we must be grateful. It was General Eisenhower who said, "Maybe this will at last blackmail mankind into peace." I think perhaps he was right; but we must not leave it to chance if we can help it. I think also that there are many in Europe who believe that there would not be peace such as it is on the earth today if it were not for the atomic bomb. This is not to say that the existence of the bomb has prevented a clash of armies on such and such a front. It is merely that with this thing in the world, people are a bit nervous about going to war. Our first point is then this: The advance of technology has altered the character of war and has made its elimination a pressing need, and has thus raised, far before the time when the world was politically ripe for it, the question of world order.

The positive side of technological progress can be approached in this way. People have often said: Wouldn't it be possible for the United States to monopolize this thing—this atomic bomb? Then we would never do any harm with it, and no other country would need develop it, and we would all be safe. Apart from its not sounding very acceptable abroad, this is a very foolish notion. Our atomic monopoly is like a cake of ice standing in the sun and melting every hour. The things that make it possible for a nation to develop the atomic bomb are things which all people rightly want —namely, a thriving, effective technology, a high degree of industralization—and they want them not only to make atomic bombs; they want them to raise their standard of living, to make it possible to work less, to live a more pleasant and agreeable life, to eat better, to starve less often, to have better medical care—that is, to have a greater choice in what they do with their lives and a greater sense of freedom from the evils of the natural world.

These positive elements, of course, mean that, even if there were no military use for a thing like atomic energy, it would be developed and it would be developed independently, if need be, by all countries that are in any way forward-looking. But the very fact that a desire for technological progress is a universal, or almost universal, characteristic of people everywhere is very important. For all people want to improve their standard of living, they want to have jeeps—and I think that the jeep is a proper symbol of American industry all over the world today. It provides one of the tools for making world unity. That is, of course, the meaning of the very far-reaching program which this country has initiated for economic collaboration throughout the world—namely, you cannot go to people of another country who believe in things differently than you do, who may have a different religion and a different view of what human life is about—and say, "Look! You're wrong. You must do the way we do." But you can go to them and say, "We both agree that it would be a very good thing if we had more housing. It would be a very good thing if we had more automobiles. It would be a very good thing if we didn't have to work more than eight hours a day. And we can help you do it. Let's get together on that and see whether our differences of view may not in time yield to our knowing each other better—to our understanding each other better."

These are, of course, just minor examples of a very important fact, that because of technology there is a great deal more interdependence of one part of the world on another than there used to be. There is a sort of co-determined prosperity. This is not absolutely true, and measures have been taken—I believe they are called autarchical—in an attempt to arrange the economy of a nation so that it is impervious to changes in other countries. But I think these will not succeed and that by and large prosperity, like peace and many other things, *is* indivisible.

This, then, is the second point: Not only has technology made war unendurable; it has provided a generally agreed basis as to what men want. It is a small thing—that men want to work less and live better—it is surely not the whole of human life. Its importance derives from its far-reaching universality.

The fraternity of scientists has been both very well and very badly understood, it seems to me, by the people of this country. Let me give some examples. One of the first things that happened after the atomic bombing of Japan was that we had messages from our colleagues who are physicists there congratulating us and saying what a fine job it was. Now you may say that was partly because they wanted the war to end, and I am sure that is true; but it went beyond this to a genuine professional greeting under circumstances which one might think would have precluded it. And even when our policy with regard to science in Japan, as in the destruction of cyclotrons, seemed so very nearsighted, the scientists in that country never believed that this was done on the advice of, or with the consent of, the scientists of this country. Every working scientist has had innumerable experiences of how really international science is. A few years ago two colleagues of mine in Berkeley published a paper. It was about the theory of cosmic ray showers. During the war, while they were busy working on bombsights and other such·nastiness, two Indians wrote a series of papers saying that their work was no good, that this original work was completely unreliable and tricky. And when my colleagues got back and started to try to answer the Indians, they found that two Russians had written a paper saying that the two students in Berkeley were right after all and that it was the Indians who were tricky. This is not an uncommon experience. Any worker in science will know of hundreds of examples like it.

Yet there are things that make one worry. Before the war some scientists who were quite tolerant of the Nazi regime came to this country, and we found then that it was very easy to talk with them about physics, and a great pleasure. But when it came to things which were not in our own bailiwick, when it came to the evaluation of political situations, a strange, cold tension developed between us, as it would have between almost any American and almost any German. I recently met with scientists in the United Nations Atomic Energy Commission in New York, who were there to advise their governments' representatives on the control of atomic energy. Quite universally it was possible to enjoy each other's science— each other's physics for the most part. We got to be friends with one another. But this has not enabled us to talk freely about the matters of political difference between our countries.

Of course this fraternity of scientists is based on a lot of fortunate breaks. In science one takes almost everything for granted; one talks only about the few new things which are to be evaluated against a great mass of accepted knowledge. And in science (in physical science, surely) one has a way of minimizing the effects of different cultures, different environments, and basing one's procedures on the elements of common sense. One says, "Take a knife," "Take a wire," "Go to a table"—one talks about things which exist in almost every civilization and which are controversial in practically none. And by taking these elementary ways of acting one is able to define the realities of the physical world—even such recondite and wonderful things as the miracles of the atomic world—in such a way that any two groups of people following the same lead will see the same world and will know what they are talking about. It is no wonder that under such circumstances one can achieve universality.

In the right context the fraternity of men of science is a great asset. But if it is used as a way for overcoming deep political differences—and there was a certain tendency to do this in the early pronouncements of the governments of the United States, Canada and Britain on the subjects of atomic energy—then it will fail, because though we are men of science and we have a loyalty to each other everywhere, we also have a loyalty to our homes and our countries against which we will not work.

I would like to say a few words more about an aspect of the United States' proposals for the control of atomic energy, which are based precisely on the three things that I have mentioned—namely, on the unendurability of war, on the common international basis of technology, and on the fraternity of science—and which, perhaps, deserve more attention than they have received. These are the proposals for establishing the control of atomic energy by an international co-operative development in the field. Each one of these words is a sixty-four-dollar word—"international," "co-operative," "development"—and they must not be forgotten. But they comprise only a small part of the United States' proposals and cover only a small part of the problem. It is clear that they do not tell you what to do if you have set up a system and somebody sabotages it. The whole question of sanctions is extraordinarily difficult because it involves the relation between an authority which has no force, and the force which you do not wish to use, namely that of the sovereign states. This question involves the whole legal complex of issues concerned with the relation of the international development authority to the several states and to the organs of the United Nations, such as the Security Council, and even more with the extraordinary difficulties inherent in trying to get from the monopolistic position which the United States enjoys today (and which it is rightly very cautious not to lose indiscreetly) to the kind of pure internationalism which is the only basis of international control. These are difficult matters which have been covered in part, not in very great detail, in the United States' proposals to the United Nations, and in a series of supplementary memoranda. But they are not what I am going to discuss here. What I want to examine is this notion of the use of co-operative development to provide security against atomic warfare.

The basic point is that in the field of atomic energy one happens to have all of the paradoxes of technology, and in an extreme form. It is, on the one hand, the most dangerous and the most troublesome of weapons; on the other, no one can doubt that it will bring an enormous enrichment to human life. I do not want to make unduly optimistic auguries, but if a country really wanted it, as I believe the British do, I think it could be deriving great benefits from atomic energy in ten years—really great benefits, of such magnitude that the whole trouble about the coal mines in Britain would appear in a very different light. I think it will be only a few years before we shall be able to say whether I am talking sense or nonsense. But these are very big stakes and at present we can foresee only a very small part of the story.

Another point is that the achievements of technology may be used for either peace or war. This was particularly true in the case of atomic energy where the job of developing it was independent of motive throughout most of its course. Thus, if we leave these developments in national hands, we are essentially leaving atomic armament in national hands. It seemed to us in this work that here was a magnificent opportunity to exploit such scientific foundations for world order as do appear to exist—on the one hand a common need all over the world for technical advance, and on the other, the established fraternity of scientists, engineers, planners and administrators, to set up an organization in which each man is primarily working with his colleagues in the field of his specialty, and which therefore could provide that human basis for internationalization without which no law could prevail. In other words, we could get people working together for an organization which was not responsive, in the first instance, to the national will of the sovereign states, but to the mandate which had been given to it as an international body.

In making these proposals we not only wanted to start down the path of genuine internationalization, of which the ultimate goal, I suppose, is world government; we wanted also to minimize things which we were sure would in and of themselves not work: the purely negative, repressive measures toward atomic energy which had been so much talked about—measures like inspection and prohibition, and so on. We examined the problem enough to know that we could never get an effective inspectorate; that we could never use the threat of punishment to deter a state which was in fact competing with other states; and that the only way to solve the problem was to take the whole thing out of national hands and put it in a domain where the incentives to warfare and to rivalry no longer obtained.

The President * said recently in a report to Congress that it will take much effort and long and difficult negotiations for us to reach agreement. That is most certainly true, and my own feeling is that this is an optimistic statement. If it should fail, I do not know that there will ever again be an opportunity to bring to bear those elements of science which make for world order. If it succeeds, we must remember that it is only the merest beginning—a sort of bridgehead toward world order—which cannot be held unless it is expanded. We cannot hope that internationalization in the field of atomic energy will survive unrestrained national rivalry in all other fields. We cannot hope that internationalization in this field will survive if year after year national armaments are more powerful than international ones, or if international law is not built up into an active and effective body of law. Internationalization is a way of getting people together, working together in a cause which, perhaps, is as urgent as any in the world. And it is a way based on the habits of the scientific age. It is the best example I know of a scientific foundation for world order.

I should like to conclude by some remarks of a little more general nature. Fundamentally, science is reason. And we all know that the notion of order, the notion of law, implies reason—implies the ability of men by discussion and thought to come to agreement where there had not been agreement before. This raises the question of the extent to which one may

* Harry S. Truman.

expect to have reason to apply the great differences which now divide the
world, and the extent to which one may apply scientific methods to social
problems. I am surely on very thin ice, but I want to say one thing about
science which I believe is true of all reason. Science is in many ways like
that proverbial iceberg of which only one-tenth shows. The part that you
work on is a little bit of an area; the part that you take for granted—that
you do not analyze, that you cannot analyze—is the enormous body of the
experience of our people over centuries. When you get into trouble, when
you and a colleague do not agree that a given experiment has been interpreted right, then you can reason with him. But that is because there is a
great, unanalyzed mass of material on which you do agree, and which you
cannot analyze because you have nothing in terms of which to analyze it,
since it is that which defines the world for us. And my notion is that the
same is true also of all other applications of human reason. You can look
at a little bit of it at a time; you can think about a special set of problems;
but unless this is built upon a community of experience that you do not
have to take apart and examine and analyze—unless what you are debating
is a small fraction of what you hold in common with the man with whom
you may disagree—you will have very little chance of coming to an understanding. That is one reason why I would urge you, as I urge myself, to distrust all the philosophers who claim that by examining science they come to
results in contradiction with common sense. Science is based on common
sense; it cannot contradict it.

This, then, I would say, is the problem of world order. It is to discover
with all the ingenuity, all the skill, and all the fortitude that we possess,
those areas which we have in common with the peoples of the world everywhere, to realize that in those areas reason can apply, because there we are
talking about things of common knowledge and common experience. What
I have been trying to say here is that among these things is science.

[35]

HAROLD E. McCARTHY

Science and Its Critics *

The man whose philosophy of life is based upon the conviction that
the scientific method and the scientific outlook can be and must be extended
into all realms where understanding is sought is finding himself more and
more surrounded by critics. These critics are men who either distrust

* From *The Humanist* XII, No. 2 (1952), 49–55. By permission of the author and
the American Humanist Association.

science completely or who feel that science must be controlled by, directed by, or at least supplemented by non-scientific disciplines, usually revealed religion or dogmatic metaphysics. The scientific temper of mind is not easy to maintain; and where man's security is seriously threatened, even civilized man finds it easy to return to more primitive types of thinking (*e.g.*, magic and supernaturalism, in general), through which a sense of security, if not security itself, may be achieved. Thus it is that the current criticism of science may be, in part, a reflection of the disordered and confused times in which we live. But where the criticisms of science are sincere (whatever forces they may reflect), they can be ignored by the scientific Humanist only at his peril and in the spirit of dogmatism—a spirit which is surely antithetical to the spirit of science.

The following ten criticisms of science have been given expression again and again and in various forms.

I.

Science is narrow and exclusive: it forgets that there are many things (i.e., "intangibles") which cannot be measured with meter sticks, weighed in balances, tested for tensile strength, or otherwise "scientifically" studied.

This general criticism usually rests upon the implicit or explicit identification of science as such with the special methods of the physical sciences, physics in particular. But one who is familiar with several sciences knows that science is not coextensive with physics and that each special science must develop its own empirico-rational procedures with which to deal with the problems that arise in its own particular field of inquiry.

The scientist does not deny, of course, the existence of relative "intangibles"; but he regards such "intangibles" as challenges to the construction of relevant and reliable techniques of study, not as absolutes which are beyond all controlled, empirical investigation. To suppose that the techniques of physics somehow define science is to forget, for instance, that the biologist (not to mention the psychologist) has invented techniques that enable him to study facts which would remain completely "intangible" relative to the specific techniques of physics.

Properly understood, then, science is neither narrow nor exclusive, although, at any given time, it is limited. Its basic strength lies not in any supposed narrowness, but in the multiplicity of its modes of attack and the ingenuity exhibited in the progressive construction of diverse procedures of empirical investigation.

2.

The method of science is essentially analysis rather than synthesis; but analysis, taken alone, is both incomplete and destructive.

The implied dichotomy of analysis and synthesis is a false dichotomy; analysis and synthesis go hand in hand in science. Neither analysis nor synthesis is an end in itself for science, but both are means to that reliable and organized knowledge which defines understanding and which makes possible effective prediction and control. Analysis may sometimes be an indirect instrument of destruction; but what is destroyed by such analysis is only that which is not sound enough to undergo analytical scrutiny and survive. The notion that nothing can undergo analysis without being found defective is the sort of extreme pessimism that is not even supported by ordinary experience. The demand that some principles—be they religious, moral, political, economic—should be accepted without analysis is simply the demand that some principles should be accepted without scrutiny and without criticism and hence on the basis of mere emotion, blind faith, absolute authority, or political opportunism. Such a demand is not only incompatible with the scientific outlook but, taken in itself, gives absolutely no guidance as to just *what* principles should be thus accepted. The demand, say, that democracy should be accepted on faith can always be countered by the demand that communism should be accepted on faith. Where the method is that of unreason, conflict is inevitable.

3.

Science is essentially reductive: To the eye of the scientist man is nothing but an animal, love is nothing but a chemical reaction, the mystic experience is nothing but the boiling over of sexual energies, etc.

It is true that no scientist would deny that man, biologically considered, is a mammal, that love has a chemical aspect, that the mystic experience may have some psycho-sexual roots. But the careful scientific thinker, well aware of the complexities involved in the simplest phenomena, understands fully that the human being, if he is to be understood at all, must be studied from a wide variety of points of view. To the objective observer, man expresses what he is, not only in his biochemical structure, but also in his activities: in work and play, love and war, crime and judicial judgment, art and science, magic and religion. The comprehensive study and understanding of man involves, therefore, the cooperation of the physicist, chemist, biologist, psychologist, sociologist, historian, semanticist, critical philosopher, and art critic.

Speculative philosophers may occasionally claim that man is nothing but an animal, or nothing but a spirit, or nothing but a reflection of the Absolute Self; but such narrow and essentially "reductive" views are completely foreign to the scientific spirit, properly understood.

4.

Science is self-confessedly tentative in spirit and at no time guarantees that without which human beings cannot live—absolute certainty.

It is true that science guarantees no absolute certainties, its justified conviction being that it is never safe to close the door on the possible results of future investigation and future experience. Moreover, science notes that the claim to certainty, when universalized, is essentially self-destructive; those who claim to possess certainties are always attacked by those who claim contrary and incompatible certainties. Nothing, then, breeds unhealthy skepticism (not to mention impotent conflict) more than free-for-all claims to absolute truth.

As for the claim that life cannot be lived without some absolute certainties, the appropriate answer is that life *has* been lived without absolute certainties. It may be true that some people are unhappy without the illusion of certainty, but it is also true that no human being can live rationally until he has freed himself from illusion.

It should be remembered, finally, that in rejecting claims to absolute certainty, science does not leave us with the alternative of absolute uncertainty. Rather, we are left with scientific assurance, which is identical with the process of *making* sure. Although this process has no absolutely final term, it may have at any given time a tentative and relative termination.

5.

Science is thoroughly materialistic.

The charge of being materialistic is an old charge and in most cases is a rhetorical device for setting up negative attitudes. It is difficult to know precisely what the charge actually amounts to.

If the charge is that science studies, or is capable of studying, only matter in motion, the answer is simple: Contemporary scientists are busily investigating all sorts of processes—physical, chemical, biological, psychological, sociological. Indeed, with the aid of the techniques of psychoanalysis, scientists are now exploring both the conscious and unconscious dimensions and determinants of such "immaterial" entities as personality, motivation, and artistic creativity. Thus the subject matter of science is not limited to matter in motion.

If, on the other hand, the charge is that the moral orientation of science is, or must be, crude and unspiritual, the answer is again simple. For what higher and more spiritual goals could any man have than those involved in and implied by the whole enterprise of pure science—cooperation, understanding, respect, truth, and a life guided by reason? Such a goal as eternal bliss in some heavenly hereafter is almost crudely hedonistic in comparison.

6.

Science is essentially pessimistic; it necessarily involves the rejection of the three fundamental human hopes—free will, immortality, and the existence of God.

First of all let us note that science, as science, makes no categorical denials of this kind. The factuality of free will, immortality, and God is, for science, a problem of relative evidence. Science insists only that where reliable evidence is lacking, or inadequate, the most one can do is to suspend judgment or to acknowledge one's hopes as the *hopes* that they are.

The only alternative is that of becoming a dogmatist whose basic premise is that belief can be rational even in the absence of relevant evidence. Such a premise, however, defines precisely what is meant by irrationality; and when universalized, it underwrites any belief, no matter how quixotic and personal.

The scientific faith, on the other hand, is the faith in the guidance of evidence wherever evidence may lead. Such a faith is positive, and only the inveterate cynic would regard such a faith as pessimistic.

7.

Science rejects man's intuitive faculty with the claim that intuition is irrelevant to knowledge.

Broadly speaking, science rules out no "faculty" which leads to reliable knowledge.

With respect to intuition in particular (and those who distrust reason often appear to discredit reason in the interest of the "higher" faculty of intuition), it is well to remember that science, far from turning its back on intuition, recognizes that some of the most important scientific laws, principles, and concepts have been first hit upon "intuitively." However, it must be added that no intuition is self-validating and therefore every intuition must be regarded as a hypothesis to be tested rather than as a conclusion to be recorded.

Einstein has somewhere stated that out of one hundred intuitive insights, ninety-nine fail to withstand scrutiny. The hundredth intuitive insight, however, may be of crucial importance. We could say, then, to paraphrase Whitehead, that science counsels us to seek intuitions, but to distrust them.

8.

Science gives us relative knowledge only; therefore the absolute knowledge man seeks must come from extra-scientific disciplines.

We must recognize at the outset that scientific knowledge is human knowledge, expressive on the one hand of the structure of nature, expressive on the other hand of the nature of man, his needs, and his socio-cultural environment. If this is what is meant by "relative," then scientific knowledge is profoundly relative.

Though a scientist may understand man's yearning for the absolute, he must also recognize that no one has ever really been able to indicate the procedures whereby a human being may transcend his own faculties and facilities and thus assume a superhuman point of view. One can say that the structure of the eye necessarily limits what the eye itself can see, but it should not be forgotten that the possession of an eye is the condition of seeing anything at all.

The recognition that man is man and not God should, then, operate in all that we, as men, do and think. It is most unfortunate that this recognition has sometimes been interpreted to mean that man is not man but a mouse.

9.

Science is strictly intellectualistic and, in the long run, means the elimination of the aesthetic, moral, and religious aspects of human experience.

It is true that, in accordance with the scientific spirit, the man of scientific faith does seek for a rational morality that is grounded in tested experience rather than in revelation, authority, or mere tradition.

In like manner, a man of scientific faith also seeks a religion that is purified of superstition and an art that is something more than an escape from fear, frustration, or boredom. Although a man of science may, in this way, be critical of certain aspects of traditional art, morality, and religion, he neither advocates nor wishes the elimination of the aesthetic, moral, and religious aspects of human experience.

In this connection one may note that no one has expressed the implications of the scientific outlook more vigorously than John Dewey, and no one has been more keenly and continuously concerned with the refinement and enhancement of the aesthetic, moral, and religious dimensions of human experience.[1]

10.

Science is in the process of destroying all of us.

It must be admitted that scientific knowledge of the world in which we live may be used to destroy the world and everything of value in it, including science itself. But it does not follow that ignorance is bliss or that the failure to think is a blessing in disguise. Scientific knowledge, considered only as knowledge, is neutral. Like a hammer, it can be used constructively or destructively. But most working scientists, when not badgered by politicians and appealed to through their political loyalties, are interested only in the constructive use of scientific knowledge.

We may approve the claim that science must be integrated with other human interests and activities. But the further claim that a revival of traditional religion will supply the requisite integration, giving guidance to the development of science and thus bringing to pass a great era of peace and prosperity, is without rational foundation. The claim, indeed, can best be seen for what it is against the background of the religious wars, inquisitions, persecutions, intolerances, and attacks upon scientists which have been an integral part of the development of Christianity, past and present.

In the last analysis, it is peculiarly shortsighted to make science a scapegoat for our own passions and prejudices, irrationalisms, nationalisms, and lusts for economic power. It is these, and not science, which are in the process of destroying all of us ; and these can be coped with only by way of scientific-humanistic reason, not by way of the destruction of science, nor by way of the revival of the theological faith of our militant fathers.

Science, in the last analysis, is something more than method and something more than neutral knowledge. It is a way of life, demanding respect for truth, honesty, and rational evaluation, demanding the profound recognition of human capability, fallibility, and individuality. That science *is* a way of life is testified to by the vigor with which free science has always been attacked by totalitarian regimes, be they communistic, fascistic, or ecclesiastical.

PART D

*

Philosophic Analyses and Syntheses

36

ARISTOTLE

The Origin and Characteristics of Philosophy*

All men by nature desire to know. An indication of this is the delight
we take in our senses; for even apart from their usefulness they are loved
for themselves; and above all others the sense of sight. For not only with
a view to action, but even when we are not going to do anything, we prefer
sight to almost everything else. The reason is that this, most of all the
senses, makes us know and brings to light many differences between things.

By nature animals are born with the faculty of sensation, and from
sensation memory is produced in some of them, though not in others. And
therefore the former are more intelligent and apt at learning than those
which cannot remember; those which are incapable of hearing sounds are
intelligent thought they cannot be taught, e.g. the bee, and any other race
of animals that may be like it; and those which besides memory have this
sense of hearing can be taught.

The animals other than man live by appearances and memories, and
have but little of connected experience; but the human race lives also by
art and reasonings. And from memory experience is produced in men; for
many memories of the same thing produce finally the capacity for a single
experience. Experience is almost identified with science and art, but really
science and art come to men *through* experience; for 'experience made art',
as Polus says, and rightly, 'but inexperience luck'. And art arises, when
from many notions gained by experience one universal judgement about a
class of objects is produced. For to have a judgment that when Callias was
ill of this disease this did him good, and similarly in the case of Socrates
and in many individual cases, is a matter of experience; but to judge that
it has done good to all persons of a certain constitution, marked off in one
class, when they were ill of this disease, e.g. to phlegmatic or bilious people
when burning with fever,—this is a matter of art (*technê*.)

With a view to action experience seems in no respect inferior to art,
and we even see men of experience succeeding more than those who have
theory without experience. The reason is that experience is knowledge of

* From Aristotle, *Metaphysics*, Bk. 1, 980a21 ff. Translated by W. D. Ross, *Aristotle:
Selections* (Modern Students Library) published and copyright by Charles Scribner's Sons,
1927. Pp. 38–43 reprinted here by permission of the publisher.

individuals, art of universals, and actions and productions are all concerned with the individual; for the physician does not cure *man*, except in
an incidental way, but Callias or Socrates or some other called by some
such individual name, who happens to be a man. If then, a man has the
theory without the experience, and knows the universal but does not know
the individual included in this, he will often fail to cure; for it is the individual that is to be cured. But yet we think that *knowledge* and *understanding* belong to art rather than to experience, and we suppose artists to
be wiser than men of experience (which implies that Wisdom depends in
all cases rather on knowledge); and this because the former know the
cause, but the latter do not. For men of experience know that the thing is
so, but do not know why, while the others know the 'why' and the cause.
Hence we think that the master-workers in each craft are more honourable
and know in a truer sense and are wiser than the manual workers, because
they know the causes of the things that are done (we think the manual
workers are like certain lifeless things which act indeed, but act without
knowing what they do, as fire burns,—but while the lifeless things perform
each of their functions by a natural tendency, the labourers perform them
through habit); thus we view them as being wiser not in virtue of being
able to act, but of having the theory for themselves and knowing the causes.
And in general it is a sign of the man who knows, that he can teach, and
therefore we think art more truly knowledge than experience is; for artists
can teach, and men of mere experience cannot.

Again, we do not regard any of the senses as Wisdom; yet surely these
give the most authoritative knowledge of particulars. But they do not tell
us the 'why' of anything—e.g., why fire is hot; they only say that it
is hot.

At first he who invented any art that went beyond the common perceptions of man was naturally admired by men, not only because there was
something useful in the inventions, but because he was thought wise and
superior to the rest. But as more arts were invented, and some were
directed to the necessities of life, others to its recreation, the inventors of
the latter were naturally always regarded as wiser than the inventors of
the former, because their branches of knowledge did not aim at utility.
Hence when all such inventions were already established, the sciences
which do not aim at giving pleasure or at the necessities of life were discovered, and first in the places where men first began to have leisure. This
is why the mathematical arts were founded in Egypt; for there the priestly
caste was allowed to be at leisure.

We have said in the *Ethics* (Bk. VI) what the difference is between art
and science and the other kindred faculties; but the point of our present
discussion is this, that all men suppose what is called Wisdom to deal with
the first causes and the principles of things. This is why, as has been said
before, the man of experience is thought to be wiser than the possessors of
any perception whatever, the artist wiser than the man of experience, the
master-worker than the mechanic, and the theoretical kinds of knowledge

to be more of the nature of Wisdom than the productive. Clearly then Wisdom is knowledge about certain causes and principles.

Since we are seeking this knowledge, we must inquire of what kind are the causes and the principles, the knowledge of which is Wisdom. If we were to take the notions we have about the wise man, this might perhaps make the answer more evident. We suppose first, then, that the wise man knows all things, as far as possible, although he has not knowledge of each of them in detail; secondly, that he who can learn things that are difficult, and not easy for man to know, is wise (sense-perception is common to all, and therefore easy and no mark of Wisdom); again, he who is more exact and more capable of teaching the causes is wiser, in every branch of knowledge; and of the sciences, also, that which is desirable on its own account and for the sake of knowing it is more of the nature of Wisdom than that which is desirable on account of its results, and the superior science is more of the nature of Wisdom than the ancillary; for the wise man must not be ordered but must order, and he must not obey another, but the less wise must obey *him*.

Such and so many are the notions, then, which we have about Wisdom and the wise. Now of these characteristics that of knowing all things must belong to him who has in the highest degree universal knowledge; for he knows in a sense all the subordinate objects. And these things, the most universal, are on the whole the hardest for men to know; for they are furthest from the senses. And the most exact of the sciences are those which deal most with first principles; for those which involve fewer principles are more exact than those which involve additional principles, e.g., arithmetic than geometry. But the science which investigates causes is also the more communicable, for the people who teach are those who tell the causes of each thing. And understanding and knowledge pursued for their own sake are found most in the knowledge of that which is most knowable; for he who chooses to know for the sake of knowing will choose most readily that which is most truly knowledge, and such is the knowledge of that which is most knowable; and the first principles and the causes are most knowable; for by reason of these, and from these, all other things are known, but these are not known by means of the things subordinate to them. And the science which knows to what end each thing must be done is the most authoritative of the sciences, and more authoritative than any ancillary science; and this end is the good in each class, and in general the supreme good in the whole of nature. Judged by all the tests we have mentioned, then, the name in question ['Wisdom'] falls to the same science; this must be the science that investigates the first principles and causes; for the good, i.e., the end and aim, is one of the causes.

37

ERNST MACH

The Economy of Science *

1. It is the object of science to replace, or *save*, experiences, by the reproduction and anticipation of facts in thought. Memory is handier than experience, and often answers the same purpose. This economical office of science, which fills its whole life, is apparent at first glance; and with its full recognition all mysticism in science disappears.

Science is communicated by instruction, in order that one man may profit by the experience of another and be spared the trouble of accumulating it for himself; and thus, to spare posterity, the experiences of whole generations are stored up in libraries.

Language, the instrument of this communication, is itself an economical contrivance. Experiences are analysed, or broken up, into simpler and more familiar precision. The symbols of speech are as yet restricted in their use within national boundaries, and doubtless will long remain so. But written language is gradually being metamorphosed into an ideal universal character. It is certainly no longer a mere transcript of speech. Numerals, algebraic signs, chemical symbols, musical notes, phonetic alphabets, may be regarded as parts already formed of this universal character of the future; they are, to some extent, decidedly conceptual, and of almost general international use. The analysis of colors, physical and physiological, is already far enough advanced to render an international system of color-signs perfectly practical. In Chinese writings, we have an actual example of a true ideographic language, pronounced diversely in different provinces, yet everywhere carrying the same meaning. Were the system and its signs only of a simpler character, the use of Chinese writing might become universal. The dropping of unmeaning and needless accidents of grammar, as English mostly drops them, would be quite requisite to the adoption of such a system. But universality would not be the sole merit of such a character; since to read it would be to understand it. Our children often read what they do not understand; but that which a Chinaman cannot understand, he is precluded from reading.

2. In the reproduction of facts in thought, we never reproduce the facts in full, but only that side of them which is important to us, moved

* From *The Science of Mechanics: A Critical and Historical Account of Its Development*. Translated by Thomas J. McCormack. Second revised and enlarged edition, ed. Charles S. Peirce. Open Court, 1902. Pp. 481–494.

to this directly or indirectly by a practical interest. Our reproductions are invariably abstractions. Here again is an economical tendency.

Nature is composed of sensations as its elements. Primitive man, however, first picks out certain compounds of these elements—those namely that are relatively permanent and of greater importance to him. The first and oldest words are names of "things." Even here, there is an abstractive process, an abstraction from the surroundings of the things, and from the continual small changes which these compound sensations undergo, which being practically unimportant are not noticed. No inalterable thing exists. The thing is an abstraction, the name a symbol, for a compound event; we assign a single word to a changing compound for we need to suggest all the constituent sensations at once. When, later, we come to remark the changeableness, we cannot at the same time hold fast to the idea of the thing's permanence, unless we have recourse to the conception of a thing-in-itself, or other such like absurdity. Sensations are not signs of things; but, on the contrary, a thing is a thought-symbol for a compound sensation of relative fixedness. Properly speaking, the world is not composed of "things" as its elements, but of colors, tones, pressures, spaces, times, in short what we ordinarily call individual sensations.

3. In speaking of cause and effect we arbitrarily give relief to those elements to whose connection we have to attend in the reproduction of a fact in the respect in which it is important to us. There is no cause nor effect in nature; nature has but an individual existence; nature simply *is*. Recurrences of like cases in which A is always connected with B, that is, like results under like circumstances, that is again, the essence of the connection of cause and effect, exist but in the abstraction which we perform for the purpose of mentally reproducing the facts. Let a fact become familiar, and we no longer require this putting into relief of its connecting marks, our attention is no longer attracted to the new and surprising, and we cease to speak of cause and effect. Heat is said to be the cause of the tension of steam; but when the phenomenon becomes familiar we think of the steam at once with the tension proper to its temperature. Acid is said to be the cause of the reddening of tincture of litmus; but later we think of reddening as a property of the acid.

Hume first propounded the question, How can a thing A act on another thing B? Hume, in fact, rejects causality and recognises only a wonted succession in time. Kant correctly remarked that a *necessary* connection between A and B could not be disclosed by simple observation. He assumes an innate idea or category of the mind, a concept of the Understanding (*Verstandesbegriff*), under which the cases of experience are subsumed. Schopenhauer, who adopts substantially the same position, distinguishes four forms of the "principle of sufficient reason"—the logical, physical, and mathematical form, and the law of motivation. But these forms differ only as regards the matter to which they are applied, which may belong either to outward or inward experience.

The natural and common-sense explanation is apparently this. The ideas of cause and effect originally sprang from an endeavor to reproduce facts in thought. At first, the connection of A and B, of C and D, of E and F, and so forth, is regarded as familiar. But after a greater range of experience is acquired and a connection between M and N is observed, it often turns out that we recognise M as *made up of* A, C, E, and N of B, D, F, the connection of which was before a *familiar* fact and accordingly possesses with us a higher authority. This explains why a person of experience regards a new event with different eyes than the novice. The new experience is illuminated by the mass of old experience. As a fact, then, there really does exist in the mind an "idea" under which fresh experiences are subsumed; but that idea has itself been developed from experience. The notion of the *necessity* of the causal connection is probably created by our voluntary movements in the world and by the changes which these indirectly produce, as Hume supposed but Schopenhauer contested. Much of the authority of the ideas of cause and effect is due to the fact that they are developed *instinctively* and involuntarily, and that we are distinctly sensible of having personally contributed nothing to their formation. We may, indeed, say, that our sense of causality is not acquired by the individual, but has been perfected in the development of the race. Cause and effect, therefore, are things of thought, having an economical office. It cannot be said *why* they arise. For it is precisely by the abstraction of uniformities that we know the question "why."

4. In the details of science, its economical character is still more apparent. The so-called descriptive sciences must chiefly remain content with reconstructing individual facts. Where it is possible, the common features of many facts are once for all placed in relief. But in sciences that are more highly developed, rules for the reconstruction of great numbers of facts may be embodied in a *single* expression. Thus, instead of noting individual cases of light-refraction, we can mentally reconstruct all present and future cases, if we know that the incident ray, the refracted ray, and the perpendicular lie in the same plane and that $\sin \alpha / \sin \beta = n$. Here, instead of the numberless cases of refraction in different combinations of matter and under all different angles of incidence, we have simply to note the rule above stated and the values of n,—which is much easier. The economical purpose is here unmistakable. In nature there is no *law* of refraction, only different cases of refraction. The law of refraction is a concise compendious rule, devised by us for the mental reconstruction of a fact, and only for its reconstruction in part, that is, on its geometrical side.

5. The sciences most highly developed economically are those whose facts are reducible to a few numerable elements of like nature. Such is the science of mechanics, in which we deal exclusively with spaces, times, and masses. The whole previously established economy of mathematics stands these sciences in stead. Mathematics may be defined as the economy of counting. Numbers are arrangement-signs which, for the sake of perspicuity and economy, are themselves arranged in a simple system. Numerical operations, it is found, are independent of the kind of objects operated on,

and are consequently mastered once for all. When, for the first time, I have occasion to add five objects to seven others, I count the whole collection through, at once; but when I afterwards discover that I can start counting from 5, I save myself part of the trouble; and still later remembering that that 5 and 7 always count up to 12, I dispense with the numeration entirely.

The object of all arithmetical operations is to *save* direct numeration, by utilizing the results of our old operations of counting. Our endeavor is, having done a sum once, to preserve the answer for future use. The first four rules of arithmetic well illustrate this view. Such, too, is the purpose of algebra, which, substituting relations for values, symbolizes and definitively fixes all numerical operations that follow the same rule. For example, we learn from the equation

$$\frac{x^2 - y^2}{x + y} = x - y$$

that the more complicated numerical operation at the left may always be replaced by the simpler one at the right, whatever numbers x and y stand for. We thus save ourselves the labor of performing in future cases the more complicated operation. Mathematics is the method of replacing in the most comprehensive and *economical* manner possible, *new* numerical operations by old ones done already with known results. It may happen in this procedure that the results of operations are employed which were originally performed centuries ago.

Often operations involving intense mental effort may be replaced by the action of semi-mechanical routine, with great saving of time and avoidance of fatigue. For example, the theory of determinants owes its origin to the remark, that it is not necessary to solve each time anew equations of the form

$$a_1 x + b_1 y + c_1 = 0$$
$$a_2 x + b_2 y + c_2 = 0,$$

from which result

$$x = -\frac{c_1 b_2 - c_2 b_1}{a_1 b_2 - a_2 b_1} = -\frac{P}{N}$$

$$y = -\frac{a_1 c_2 - a_2 c_1}{a_1 b_2 - a_2 b_1} = -\frac{Q}{N},$$

but that the solution may be effected by means of the coefficients, by writing down the coefficients according to a prescribed scheme and operating with them *mechanically*. Thus,

$$\begin{vmatrix} a_1 & b_1 \\ a_2 & b_2 \end{vmatrix} = a_1 b_2 - a_2 b_1 = N$$

and similarly

$$\begin{vmatrix} c_1 & b_1 \\ c_2 & b_2 \end{vmatrix} = P, \text{ and } \begin{vmatrix} a_1 & c_1 \\ a_2 & c_2 \end{vmatrix} = Q.$$

Even a *total* disburdening of the mind can be effected in mathematical operations. This happens where operations of counting hitherto performed are symbolised by mechanical operations with signs, and our brain energy, instead of being wasted on the repetition of old operations, is spared for more important tasks. The merchant pursues a like economy, when, instead of directly handling his bales of goods, he operates with bills of lading or assignments of them. The drudgery of computation may even be relegated to a machine. Several different types of calculating machines are actually in practical use. The earliest of these (of any complexity) was the difference-engine of Babbage, who was familiar with the ideas here presented. . . .

That scientific work should be more useful the more it has been used, while mechanical work is expended in use, may seem strange to us. When a person who daily takes the same walk accidentally finds a shorter cut, and thereafter, remembering that it is shorter, always goes that way, he undoubtedly saves himself the difference of the work. But memory is really not work. It only places at our disposal energy within our present or future possession, which the circumstance of ignorance prevented us from availing ourselves of. This is precisely the case with the application of scientific ideas.

The mathematician who pursues his studies without clear views of this matter, must often have the uncomfortable feeling that his paper and pencil surpass him in intelligence. Mathematics, thus pursued as an object of instruction, is scarcely of more educational value than busying oneself with the Cabala. On the contrary, it induces a tendency toward mystery, which is pretty sure to bear its fruits.

6. The science of physics also furnishes examples of this economy of thought, altogether similar to those we have just examined. A brief reference here will suffice. The moment of inertia saves us the separate consideration of the individual particles of masses. By the force-function we dispense with the separate investigation of individual force-components. The simplicity of reasonings involving force-functions springs from the fact that a great amount of mental work had to be performed before the discovery of the properties of the force-functions was possible. Gauss's dioptrics dispenses us from the separate consideration of the single refracting surfaces of a dioptrical system and substitutes for it the principal and nodal points. But a careful consideration of the single surfaces had to precede the discovery of the principal and nodal points. Gauss's dioptrics simply *saves* us the necessity of often repeating this consideration.

We must admit, therefore, that there is no result of science which in point of principle could not have been arrived at wholly without methods. But, as a matter of fact, within the short span of a human life and with man's limited powers of memory, any stock of knowledge worthy of the name is unattainable except by the *greatest* mental economy. Science itself, therefore, may be regarded as a minimal problem, consisting of the completest possible presentment of facts with the *least possible expenditure of thought*.

7. The function of science, as we take it, is to replace experience. Thus, on the one hand, science must remain in the province of experience, but, on the other, must hasten beyond it, constantly expecting confirmation, constantly expecting the reverse. Where neither confirmation nor refutation is possible, science is not concerned. Science acts and only acts in the domain of *uncompleted* experience. Exemplars of such branches of science are the theories of elasticity and of the conduction of heat, both of which ascribe to the smallest particles of matter only such properties as observation supplies in the study of the larger portions. The comparison of theory and experience may be farther and farther extended, as our means of observation increase in refinement.

Experience alone, without the ideas that are associated with it, would forever remain strange to us. Those ideas that hold good throughout the widest domains of research and that supplement the greatest amount of experience, are the *most scientific*. The principle of continuity, the use of which everywhere pervades modern inquiry, simply prescribes a mode of conception which conduces in the highest degree to the economy of thought.

8. If a long elastic rod be fastened in a vise, the rod may be made to execute slow vibrations. These are directly observable, can be seen, touched, and graphically recorded. If the rod be shortened, the vibrations will increase in rapidity and cannot be directly seen; the rod will present to the sight a blurred image. This is a new phenomenon. But the sensation of touch is still like that of the previous case; we can still make the rod record its movements; and if we mentally retain the *conception* of vibrations, we can still anticipate the results of experiments. On further shortening the rod the sensation of touch is altered; the rod begins to sound; again a new phenomenon is presented. But the phenomena do not all change at once; only this or that phenomenon changes; consequently the accompanying notion of vibration, which is not confined to any single one, is still serviceable, still economical. Even when the sound has reached so high a pitch and the vibrations have become so small that the previous means of observation are not of avail, we still *advantageously* imagine the sounding rod to perform vibrations, and can predict the vibrations of the dark lines in the spectrum of the polarised light of a rod of glass. If on the rod being further shortened *all* the phenomena suddenly passed into *new* phenomena, the conception of vibration would no longer be serviceable because it would no longer afford us a means of supplementing the new experiences by the previous ones.

When we mentally add to those actions of a human being which we can perceive, sensations and ideas like our own which we cannot perceive, the object of the idea we so form is economical. The idea makes experience intelligible to us; it supplements and supplants experience. This idea is not regarded as a great scientific discovery, only because its formation is so natural that every child conceives it. Now, this is exactly what we do when we imagine a moving body which has just disappeared behind a pillar, or a comet at the moment invisible, as continuing its motion and retaining its previously observed properties. We do this that we may not be surprised by its reappearance. We fill out the gaps in experience by the ideas that experience suggests.

9. Yet not all the prevalent scientific theories originated so naturally and artlessly. Thus, chemical, electrical, and optical phenomena are explained by atoms. But the mental artifice atom was not formed by the principle of continuity; on the contrary, it is a product especially devised for the purpose in view. Atoms cannot be perceived by the senses; like all substances, they are things of thought. Furthermore, the atoms are invested with properties that absolutely contradict the attributes hitherto observed in bodies. However well fitted atomic theories may be to reproduce certain groups of facts, the physical inquirer who has laid to heart Newton's rules will only admit those theories as *provisional* helps, and will strive to attain, in some more natural way, a satisfactory substitute.

The atomic theory plays a part in physics similar to that of certain auxiliary concepts in mathematics; it is a mathematical *model* for facilitating the mental reproduction of facts. Although we represent vibrations by the harmonic formula, the phenomena of cooling by exponentials, falls by squares of times, etc., no one will fancy that vibrations in *themselves* have anything to do with the circular functions, or the motion of falling bodies with squares. It has simply been observed that the relations between the quantities investigated were similar to certain relations obtaining between familiar mathematical functions, and these more *familiar* ideas are employed as an easy means of supplementing experience. Natural phenomena whose relations are not similar to those of functions with which we are familiar, are at present very difficult to reconstruct. But the progress of mathematics may facilitate the matter.

As mathematical helps of this kind, spaces of more than three dimensions may be used, as I have elsewhere shown. But it is not necessary to regard these, on this account, as anything more than mental artifices. . . .

This is the case, too, with *all* hypothesis formed for the explanation of new phenomena. Our conceptions of electricity fit in at once with the electrical phenomena, and take almost spontaneously the familiar course, the moment we note that things take place as if attracting and repelling fluids moved on the surface of the conductors. But these mental expedients have nothing whatever to do with the phenomenon *itself*.

[38a]

PIERRE DUHEM

Aim of Scientific Theory

REPRESENTATION VS. EXPLANATION
IN PHYSICAL THEORY

REPRESENTATIVE THEORIES AND THE HISTORY OF PHYSICS *

§ 1. *Role of natural classifications and of explanations in the evolution of physical theories.*

We have proposed that the aim of physical theory is to become a *natural classification,* to establish among diverse experimental laws a logical coordination serving as a sort of image and reflection of the true order according to which the realities escaping us are organized. Also, we have said that on this condition theory will be fruitful and will suggest discoveries.

But an objection immediately arises against the doctrine we are here expounding.

If theory is to be a natural classification, if it is to group appearances in the same way realities are grouped, then is not the surest way to reach this goal to inquire first what these realities are? Instead of constructing a logical system representing experimental laws in as condensed and as exact a form as possible, in the hope that this system will end by being an image of the ontological order of things, would it not make more sense to try to explain these laws and to unveil those hidden things? Moreover, is this not the way in which the masters of science have proceeded? Have they not by striving for the explanation of physical phenomena created those fruitful theories whose very remarkable prophecies did arouse our astonishment? What better can we do than imitate their example and return to the methods [of "explanation"] condemned in our first chapter?

There is no doubt that several of the geniuses to whom we owe modern Physics have built their theories in the hope of giving an explanation of natural phenomena, and that some even have believed they had gotten hold of this explanation; but that, none the less, is no conclusive argument

* From *The Aim and Structure of Physical Theory,* translated by Philip P. Wiener (Princeton University Press, 1953), Pt. I, Ch. III. By permission of the publisher.

against the opinion we have expounded concerning physical theories. Chimerical hopes may have incited admirable discoveries without these discoveries embodying the chimeras which gave birth to them. Bold explorations which have contributed greatly to the progress of geography are due to adventurers who were looking for the golden land; that is not a sufficient reason for inscribing "El Dorado" on our maps of the globe.

Hence, if we want to prove that the search for explanations is a truly fruitful method in Physics, it is not enough to show that a good number of theories have been created by thinkers who strove for such explanations; we have to prove that the search for explanation is indeed the Ariadne's thread which has led them through the confusion of experimental laws and has allowed them to draw the plan of this labyrinth.

Now it is not only impossible to give this proof, but also, as we shall see, even a superficial study of the history of Physics provides abundant arguments to the contrary.

When we analyze a theory created by a physicist who proposes to explain sensible appearances, we do not generally take long to recognize that this theory is formed of two really distinct parts: one is the simply representative part which proposes to classify laws; the other is the explanatory part which proposes to take hold of the reality underlying the phenomena.

Now, very far from it being true that the explanatory part is the reason for the existence of the representative part, the seed from which it grew or the root which nourishes its development, the link between the two parts is nearly always most frail and most artificial. The descriptive part has developed on its own by the proper and autonomous methods of theoretical Physics; the explanatory part has come to this fully formed organism and attached itself to it like a parasite.

It is not to this explanatory part that theory owes its power and fertility; far from it. Everything good in the theory, by virtue of which it appears as a natural classification and confers on it the power to anticipate experience, is found in the representative part; all of that was discovered by the physicist while he forgot about the search for explanation. On the other hand, whatever is false in the theory and contradicted by the facts, is found chiefly in the explanatory part; the physicist has brought error into it, led by his desire to take hold of realities.

Whence the following consequence: When the progress of experimental Physics goes counter to a theory and compels it to be modified or transformed, the purely representative part almost entirely enters the new theory, bringing to it the inheritance of all the valuable possessions of the old theory, whereas the explanatory part falls out in order to give way to another explanation.

Thus, by virtue of a continuous tradition, each theory passes on to the one that follows it a share of the natural classification it was able to construct, as in certain ancient games, each runner handed on the lighted torch to the courier ahead of him; and this continuous tradition assures a perpetuity of life and progress for science.

This continuity of tradition is not visible to the superficial observer on account of the constant breaking out of explanations which arise only to be quelled.

Let us support all we have just said by some examples. They will be provided by the theories about the refraction of light. We shall borrow them from these theories not indeed because they are exceptionally favorable to our thesis, but, on the contrary, because those who study the history of Physics superficially might think that these theories owe their principal progress to the search for explanations.

Descartes has given a theory which *represents* the phenomena of simple refraction; it is the principal object of two admirable treatises on *Dioptrics* and *Meteors,* to which the *Discourse on Method* served as a preface. Based on the constant relation between the sine of the angle of incidence and the sine of the angle of refraction, his theory arranges in a very clear order the properties of lenses of diverse shapes and of optical instruments composed of these lenses; it takes account of the phenomena attending vision, and analyzes the laws of the rainbow.

Descartes has also given an explanation of light effects. Light is only an appearance; the reality is a pressure engendered by the rapid motions of incandescent bodies within a *subtle matter* penetrating all bodies. This subtle matter is incompressible so that the pressure which constitutes light is transmitted in it instantaneously to any distance; no matter how far away a point is from a light source, at the very same instant the latter is lit, the point is lit. This instantaneous transmission of light is an absolutely necessary consequence of the system of physical explanation created by Descartes. Beeckman who did not wish to admit this proposition, and who, in imitation of Galileo, sought to contradict it by means of experiments, rather childish at that, was addressed by Descartes as follows: [1] "To my mind, it [the instantaneous velocity of light] is so certain that if, by some impossibility, it were found guilty of being erroneous, I should be ready to acknowledge to you immediately that I know nothing in philosophy. You have such great confidence in your experiment that you declare yourself ready to hold all of your philosophy false if no lapse of time should separate the instant when one sees the motion of the lantern in the mirror from the instant when one perceives it in his hand; I, on the other hand, declare to you that if this lapse of time could be observed, then my whole philosophy would be completely upset."

Whether Descartes himself created the fundamental law of refraction or borrowed it from Snell, according to Huygens' insinuation, has been a passionately debated question; the answer is doubtful, but it matters little to us. What is certain is that this law and the representative theory based on it are not offspring of the explanation of light phenomena proposed by Descartes; the Cartesian Cosmology has no part in generating them; experiment, induction, and generalization have alone produced them.

And moreover, Descartes never made the attempt to connect the law of refraction with his explanatory theory of light.

It is indeed true that at the beginning of the *Dioptrics,* he develops mechanical analogies concerning this law; he compares the change of direction of the ray which passes from air into water to the change of the path of a ball thrown vigorously and passing from a certain medium into another more resistant one. But these mechanical comparisons, whose logical validity was to be exposed to many criticisms, should rather connect the theory of refraction to the doctrine of *emission,* a doctrine in which a ray of light is compared with a shower of small particles violently projected by the source of light. This explanation, maintained in Descartes' time by Gassendi, and taken up later by Newton, has no analogy with the Cartesian theory of light; it is incompatible with the latter theory.

Thus, the Cartesian explanation of light phenomena and the Cartesian representation of the diverse laws of refraction are simply juxtaposed without any connection or penetration. Whence, the day when the Danish astronomer Römer shows that light is propagated in space with a finite and measurable velocity, the Cartesian explanation of light phenomena collapses completely; but it does not bring down with it even the slightest part of the doctrine which represents and classifies the laws of refraction; the latter continues, even today, to form the major part of our elementary Optics.

.   .   .   .

§ 2. *The opinions of physicists on the nature of physical theories.*

One of the thinkers who have insisted most energetically on the point that physical theories be regarded as condensed representations and not as explanations, Ernst Mach, has written as follows: [2]

"My idea of the economy of thought was developed out of my experience as a professor, and grew out of my practise in teaching. I possessed the idea as early as 1861 when I began my lectures as Privat Docent, and at the time I believed that I was in exclusive possession of the principle,— a conviction which will be found pardonable. But today, on the contrary, I am convinced that at least some presentiment of this idea must have always been a common possession for *all* inquirers who have reflected on the nature of scientific research."

Indeed, since antiquity certain philosophers have very exactly recognized that physical theories were by no means explanations, that their hypotheses were not judgments about the nature of things, that they were only premises intended to provide consequences conforming to experimental laws.[3]

The Greeks were acquainted, properly speaking, with only one physical theory, the theory of celestial motions; that is why it was in dealing with systems of cosmography that they expressed and developed their conception of physical theory. Moreover, other theories that they had carried to a certain degree of perfection, and today emerge again in

Physics, namely, the theory of equilibrium of the lever and Hydrostatics, rested on principles whose nature could not be subject to any doubt; the *axioms* or *demands* of Archimedes were plainly propositions of experimental origin which generalization had transformed; the agreement of their consequences with the facts summarized and ordered the latter without explaining them.

The Greeks clearly distinguished in the discussion of a theory about the motion of the stars what belongs to the physicist—we should say today the metaphysician—and to the astronomer. It belongs to the physicist to decide by reasons drawn from Cosmology what the real motions of the stars are. The astronomer, on the other hand, must not be concerned whether the motions he represents are real or fictions; their sole object is to represent exactly the *relative* displacements of the heavenly bodies.

.   .   .   .

Newton expresses clearly what he thinks about the construction of physical theories, in several passages in his works.

The attentive study of phenomena and their laws permits the physicist to discover by the inductive method appropriate to his science, some of the very general principles from which experimental laws may be deduced; thus the laws of all celestial phenomena are found condensed in the principle of universal gravitation.

Such a condensed representation is not an explanation; the mutual attraction that Celestial Mechanics imagines between any two parts whatsoever of matter permits us to submit all celestial movements to calculation, but the cause itself of this attraction is not laid bare because of that. Must we see in it a primary and irreducible quality of matter? Must we regard it as the result of impulsions produced by a certain ether, as Newton was to judge probable at certain times in his life? These are difficult questions whose solution can be obtained only later. In any case, this problem is the task of the philosopher and not of the physicist; whatever the answer may be, the representative theory constructed by the physicist will keep its full value.

Here is the doctrine stated in a few words in the General Scholium with which the *Mathematical Principles of Natural Philosophy* ends:

"And now we might add something concerning a certain most subtle spirit which pervades and lies hid in all gross bodies; by the force and action of which spirit the particles of bodies attract one another at near distances, and cohere, if contiguous; and electric bodies operate to greater distances, as well repelling as attracting the neighboring corpuscles; and light is emitted, reflected, refracted, inflected, and heats bodies; and all sensation is excited, and the members of animal bodies move at the command of the will, namely, by the vibrations of this spirit, mutually propagated along the solid filaments of the nerves, from the outward organs of sense to the brain, and from the brain into the muscles. But these are things that cannot be explained in few words, nor are we furnished with that sufficiency of experiments which is required to an accurate determination and demonstration of the laws by which this electric and elastic spirit operates."

Later, in the famous Query XXXI at the end (the fourth paragraph from the last) of the second edition of his *Optics,* Newton enunciates with great precision his opinion concerning physical theories; he assigns to them as their object the economic condensation of phenomena:

"To tell us that every species of things is endowed with an occult specifick quality by which it acts and produces manifest effects, is to tell us nothing: But to derive two or three general principles of motion from phaenomena, and afterwards to tell us how the properties and actions of all corporeal things follow from those manifest principles, would be a very great step in Philosophy, though the causes of those principles were not yet discovered: And therefore I scruple not to propose the principles of motion above mentioned, they being of very large extent, and leave their causes to be found out."

Those who shared the proud confidence of the Cartesians or Atomists could not allow such modest limits to be imposed on the claims of Theoretical Physics. . . .

Newton's disciples, however, did not all adhere to the prudent reserve of their master; several could not remain in the narrow confines assigned to them by his method in Physics. Crossing these limits they asserted, as metaphysicians, that mutual attractions were the real and primary qualities of matter and that a phenomenon reduced to these attractions was truly explained. This was the opinion expressed by Roger Cotes in the famous preface he wrote at the head of the second edition of Newton's *Principia.* This was also the doctrine developed by Boscovich that the Leibnizian metaphysics inspired.

However, several of Newton's followers, and not the least distinguished ones, adhered to the method that their illustrious predecessor had so well defined.

Laplace professes utmost confidence in the power of the principle of attraction; this confidence, however, is not a blind one; in some places in the *Exposition du système du Monde,* Laplace indicates that this universal attraction, which in the form of gravity or of molecular attraction coordinates all natural phenomena, is not perhaps the ultimate explanation, and that it may itself depend on a higher cause. This cause, it is true, seems to be relegated by Laplace to an unknowable domain. In any case, he recognizes with Newton that the quest for this cause, if at all possible, constitutes a problem distinct from the one which physical and astronomical theories solve: He asks:[4] "Is this principle a fundamental law of nature? Is it only a general effect of an unknown cause? Here, we are stopped by our ignorance of the intimate properties of matter, depriving us of any hope of answering these questions satisfactorily." Again, he says (*op. cit.,* I.V. ch. V): "Is the principle of universal gravity a fundamental law of nature or but the general effect of an unknown cause? May we not reduce the attractions to this principle? Newton, more circumspect than several of his disciples, did not pronounce judgment on these matters where our ignorance of the properties of matter does not permit us to give any satisfactory answer."

Ampère, a more profound philosopher than Laplace, sees with perfect clarity the importance of regarding a physical theory as independent of any metaphysical explanation; in fact, that is the way to keep out of Physics the divisive quarrels of the diverse cosmological schools; at the same time, Physics remains acceptable to minds who profess incompatible philosophical opinions; and yet, very far from blocking the inquiries of those who would lay claim to giving an explanation of phenomena, we expedite their task. We condense in a small number of very general propositions the countless laws they are to explain, so that it suffices for them to explain these few propositions in order to get at anything mysteriously contained in that enormous collection of laws:

"The chief importance [5] of the formulas which are thus immediately concluded from some general facts given by a sufficient number of observations so that their certainty cannot be contested, is that they remain independent both of the hypotheses used by their authors in the search for these formulas and of those hypotheses which may be substituted subsequently. The expression of universal attraction deduced from Kepler's laws does not depend on the hypotheses that a few authors have ventured concerning a mechanical cause they wished to assign to it. The theory of heat really rests on general facts immediately given to observation; and the equation deduced from these facts being confirmed by the agreement of the results drawn from the equation with those given by experience, should be regarded as expressing the true laws of the propagation of heat, by both those who attribute heat to a radiation of calorific molecules as well as by those who explain the same phenomenon by having recourse to the vibrations of a fluid pervading space; only it is necessary that the former show how the equation in question results from their way of looking at things, and that the latter deduce it from the general formula of vibratory motions, not for the sake of adding anything to the certainty of this equation but for maintaining their own respective hypotheses. The physicist who has not taken sides in this regard accepts this equation as the exact representation of the facts without worrying about the way it may result from either one of the above explanations."

Fourier, moreover, shares Ampère's judgment concerning the theory of heat; in fact, here is how he expresses himself in the *Discours Préliminaire* which prefaces his immortal work: [6]

"The fundamental causes are not known to us, but they are subject to simple and constant laws that may be discovered by observation, and the study of these is the object of Natural Philosophy.

"Heat, like gravity, penetrates every substance in the universe; its rays fill every part of space. The aim of our work is to expound the mathematical laws that this element follows. This theory will henceforth form one of the most important branches of Physics.

". . . The principles of this theory are deduced, like those of Mechanics, from a small number of fundamental facts whose cause is not considered by mathematicians but which are accepted by them as resulting from common observations and confirmed by all the experiments."

Fresnel does not assign, any more than Ampère or Fourier, any metaphysical explanation as the aim of theory. He sees in theory a powerful means of discovery because it is a summary and classified representation of experimental knowledge: "It is not useless [7] to unite facts under the same viewpoint by tying them to a small number of general principles. That is the means for grasping laws more easily, and I think that efforts of this kind may contribute as much as the observations themselves to the advancement of science."

The rapid development of Thermodynamics in the middle of the nineteenth century reinstates favorably the hypotheses Descartes had first formulated concerning the nature of heat; Cartesian and atomistic opinions received renewed vitality, and the hope of constructing explanatory theories was revived in the thought of more than one physicist.

However, some of the more important physicists, creators of the new doctrine, did not let themselves become intoxicated by this hope; among them, and of the first rank, was Robert Mayer whom it is appropriate to quote: "Concerning the intimate nature of heat," he wrote to Griesinger,[8] "or of electricity, etc., I know nothing, any more than I know the *intimate nature* of any matter whatsoever, or of anything else."

The first contributions of Macquorn Rankine to the progress of the mechanical theory of heat had been attempts at explanation; but his ideas soon evolved and, in a short paper of his,[9] too little known, he traced very clearly the characteristics which distinguish a representative theory— called by him *abstractive theory*—from an explanatory theory—designated by the name *hypothetical theory*.

Let us quote some passages from this work:

"An essential distinction exists between two stages in the process of advancing our knowledge of the laws of physical phenomena. The first stage consists in observing the relations of phenomena, whether of such as occur in the ordinary course of nature, or of such as are artificially produced in experimental investigations, and in expressing the relations so observed by propositions called formal laws. The second stage consists in reducing the formal laws of an entire class of phenomena to the form of a science; that is to say, in discovering the most simple system of principles, from which all the formal laws of the class of phenomena can be deduced as consequences.

"Such a system of principles, with its consequences methodically deduced, constitutes the *physical theory* of a class of phenomena. . . .

"Two methods of framing a physical theory may be distinguished, characterised chiefly by the manner in which classes of phenomena are defined. They may be termed, respectively, the *abstractive* and the *hypothetical* methods.

"According to the *abstractive* method, a class of objects or phenomena is defined by describing, or otherwise making to be understood, and assigning a name or symbol to, that assemblage of properties which is common to all the objects or phenomena composing the class, as perceived by the senses, without introducing anything hypothetical.

"According to the *hypothetical* method, a class of objects or phenomena is defined, according to a conjectural conception of their nature, as being constituted, in a manner not apparent to the senses, by a modification of some other class of objects or phenomena whose laws are already known. Should the consequences of such a hypothetical definition be found to be in accordance with the results of observation and experiment, it serves as the means of deducing the laws of one class of objects or phenomena from those of another." For example, it is in this way that we shall derive the laws of light or heat from the laws of Mechanics.

Rankine thinks that hypothetical theories will be gradually replaced by abstractive theories; however, he believes "that a hypothetical theory is necessary, as a first step, in order to put simplicity and order into the expression of phenomena before it is possible to make any progress in the construction of an abstract theory." We have seen in the preceding section that this assertion was scarcely confirmed by the history of physical theories. . . .

Towards the end of the nineteenth century, hypothetical theories which were offered as more or less probable explanations of phenomena were extraordinarily multiplied. The noise of their battles and the fracas of their collapse have wearied physicists and led them gradually back to the sound doctrines Newton had expressed so forcefully. Renewing the interrupted tradition, Ernst Mach [10] has defined Theoretical Physics as an abstract and condensed representation of natural phenomena. G. Kirchhoff [11] has offered as the aim of Mechanics "to describe as completely and as simply as possible the motions produced in nature."

Therefore, if some very great physicists may have taken pride in the powerful method that they employed to the point of exaggerating its scope, if they could believe that their theories would reveal the metaphysical nature of things, many discoverers who arouse our admiration have been more modest and more farsighted. They have recognized that physical theory was not an explanation, but a simplified and orderly representation grouping laws according to a classification becoming more and more complete, more and more natural.

EMILE MEYERSON

Law and Causal Explanation *

From the preceding pages this conclusion, it seems, stands out: it is not true that the sole end of science is action, nor that it is solely governed by the desire for economy in this action. Science also wishes to make us *understand* nature. It tends, indeed, according to Le Roy's expression, toward the "progressive rationalization of reality." [1]

Science has, in truth, been established with the almost complete certainty that nature is regulated, but also with the tenacious hope that it will manifest itself as intelligible. In every chapter of science these two principles have been applied simultaneously and continue to be so applied. Their action is irrevocably entangled, because they pass and repass their acquisitions to each other; not only, as has been said, do empirical facts serve to establish theories which bring about the discovery of new facts, but also considerations of conservation, of identity, intervene at every step in empirical science, which is, in spite of appearances, saturated with these *a priori* elements.

Science is not *positive* and does not even contain positive data in the precise meaning which Auguste Comte and his adherents have given to this term—that is, data "stripped of all ontology." Ontology is of a piece with science itself and cannot be separated from it. Those who pretend to separate them are unconsciously using a current metaphysical system, a common sense more or less transformed by science of the past, which is familiar to them. The positivist plan is, therefore, truly chimerical. Not only does it correspond neither to modern science nor to any which humanity has known at any epoch of evolution, but it implies and demands such a modification, such an unsettling of our habits of thought, that we have infinite difficulty in conceiving it and especially in measuring all of its consequences. Indeed, the only means of doing away with every ontology would consist in accomplishing that operation at the very beginning of physics, by dissolving the object and returning to the immediate data of

* From *Identity and Reality* by Emile Meyerson. Authorized translation by Kate Loewenberg, London: George Allen & Unwin, Ltd. New York: The Macmillan Co., 1930. Pp. 384–395 of Ch. XII Conclusions. By permission of the publishers. References like "the preceding pages" or in parentheses are to pages in *Identity and Reality, op. cit.*

Bergson, in order to try afterwards to establish direct relations between these data, without passing through the hypothesis of an objective existence. Is such a science possible? Malebranche expressly denied it. He attempted to show that in no case could one pretend to measure sensations directly by one another, as subjective phenomena; and that all comparison of these presupposes a preliminary reduction to objective causes, and therefore a subjection of them to fixation in time and space.[2] This seems to be an impregnable deduction. We saw (p. 341) that a purely qualitative science, which was still substantialistic, though capable of setting up *scales,* could no longer *measure.* With still greater reason would this be so in the science that is truly phenomenalistic, from which the very quality itself, viewed as substratum, would be excluded. And yet must the possibility of a science of this kind be radically denied, and its entire uselessness from the point of view of prevision be asserted? What makes one hesitate before this absolute negation is precisely the novelty, the unknown factor in the proposed method. Without further attempt to go to the bottom of this question, which would be too great a digression from the subject of this book, let us observe, once again, how greatly science thus constituted, supposing even that it were possible, would depart from all that we know. It would certainly no longer be physics, but rather a sort of psycho-physics pushed to the extreme; it would, indeed, be infinitely more than all we know under this name, removed from physics, since modern psycho-physics, it is easily understood, presupposes physics as a basis, and consequently the whole ontological world of common sense and of science.—The ontological character of scientific explanation is ineffaceable. Doubtless, through the unity of matter it finally ends in uniform and empty space. But here there is destruction of reality, of the whole external world; and in this destruction, it goes without saying, law also has been abolished, for there being no longer any diversity either in time or in space, there is no longer any phenomenon, and therefore nothing which law may rule.[3] Therefore, and contrary to what is sometimes supposed believable, there is not, there cannot be, in the natural evolution of scientific theories, any phase where ontological reality would disappear, and at the same time the concept of conformity to law remain standing. Their disappearance is certainly *simultaneous,* and if we take the world of scientific theory at the moment, so to speak, when it is going to evolve into non-entity, we shall find it as ontological as that of the reality of common sense; the singular points of the ether, in so far as we differentiate them from their medium by any means whatsoever, will be just as real, just as much *objects,* and even more fundamentally independent of us and our sensation than anything in our perception. Explanatory science, indeed, rejoins absolute idealism or solipsism, but it is only in complete acosmism that these two ways encounter each other. Between these two parallel lines, along which science and philosophy, each one by itself, tend to destroy reality, one cannot imagine any point in common, except one situated in infinity.

This explains a peculiar characteristic of physicists' research into the constitution of matter, a characteristic which is certainly of a nature to strike the attention of the philosopher—to wit, the unconscious certainty, one might almost say the alacrity, which the scientist shows in this domain, whereas to the philosopher, his conclusions appear formidable, extravagant in the literal sense of the word, completely departing from the ordinary plan of experimental research. How does it happen, then, that the physicist does not possess this feeling at all, that he has, on the contrary, the very distinct impression of being in his own domain and of following his customary methods? It is because, starting from a conception of the world such as our naïve perception offers, he has never transformed it except by putting into play the very rules according to which this conception was constituted. He has continually substituted the invisible for the visible, but what he has created is of the same order as what he has destroyed. He simply treats the atom as the biologist treats the microbe, the first is compared to a billiard ball as the second is compared to an animal.

With all the more reason the scientist feels himself protected from doubt in less extreme, less exposed parts of his domain; and it is not astonishing that this security has at times been envied by the philosopher. This is why frequently renewed attempts have been made to extract a real philosophy from science with the help of processes of extrapolation and generalization. The progress and ultimate end of this kind of enterprise may be traced in advance to a certain extent. Indeed, in creating science, man has constantly obeyed his causal instinct; starting from sensation, he has unceasingly tried to explain it, to make it yield to the exigencies of his reason. Therefore, what will be most general in science will necessarily be also a form of these exigencies, and, consequently, a conception saturated with the *a priori*: a causal hypothesis such as that of the persistence of qualities and especially the atomic or mechanical theory. And so it is that believing to generalize the results of experience we succeed paradoxically in liberating our conceptions, prior to experience, from the restrictions imposed by experience.

It goes without saying that in pressing his thought into the ontological mould, in giving to it the form of an hypothesis about the reality of things, the scientist, just like the commonsense man, acts in an entirely unconscious manner. It is not astonishing, therefore, to see him unacquainted with the process which he is applying—nay, even with the metaphysical tendency which is pushing him on. No more than any other man does the scientist see himself thinking. Doubtless, if he has peculiarly powerful gifts, he may succeed, by a slow and patient analysis, in sometimes recognizing the true path which his thought has followed; but the fact of being a scientist, nay, even a great scientist, has nothing to do with it. Indeed, the distinctive quality of a great scientist is a powerful scientific instinct, a sort of divination which allows him to touch the high places only. The discovery, it has often been noticed, comes to him suddenly—after long labour, of course; it is a flash, a revelation: is it astonishing that he has not been able to trace its genesis? And so it follows that we must not look to the scientist for the principles which have really guided his thought; we must not even believe him on his word when he tries to state them. He may have discovered these principles in almost any other way than by a patient analysis of his own thought. He has most often found them already fashioned in some book; they penetrated him without his knowledge, because they pervaded the intellectual atmosphere surrounding him.

This explains how one can go astray in searching for the principles of science, even on the supposition that one is following closely the scientists; their methodical ways are cheerfully accepted, without questioning whether the aforesaid methods had ever really been applied by the scientists themselves. It is this error, we think, which is at the bottom of the affirmation according to which, as a very eminent contemporary philosopher says, "Mathematical physics turns aside from the essence of things and their inner substantiality in order to turn toward their numerical order and connection, and their functional and mathematical structure." [4]

Declarations of this sort may certainly be found in the creators of modern physical science—in Kepler, in Newton, even in Descartes, in Boyle, and in Boscovich. But if, on the other hand, we consider without prejudice and on its merits their work as scientists, we easily perceive that it offers a quite different picture. Thus Boscovich seems, indeed, according to the title of his *Theoria,* to reduce the concept of force to that of law. But it is clear, when one reaches the heart of the work, that he considers this force to be, on the contrary, a real being, a *thing,* the true essence of nature, which he has sought for and found; his argumentation against the corpuscular theory would have no meaning if this were not so. Boyle, we have seen, was one of the strictest atomists known to the history of science at any time; he invented the term "corpuscular" for the particular form of the theory which he adopted and which he constantly used. His foregone conclusion from this point of view greatly impressed his contemporaries, such as Spinoza and Leibniz;[5] and it is clear that in attempting to reduce a change of colour to the displacement of molecules, as he did many times, he was not concerned simply with the rule of a phenomenon, but with its true nature, its essence, and its cause. And as to Descartes, it is certain that he sought for the essence of things as eagerly as the scholastics, but, unlike these latter, he found it in space; surely no one has been more affirmative, more apodictic than he in this respect. In spite of appearances the situation was the same with Kepler and with Newton. Kepler, while seeking for the laws of planetary attraction, sought at the same time for its cause, and formulated a whole theory on this subject. Newton, in spite of the *hypotheses non fingo,* based his *Opticks* on the theory of emission. His famous definition of mass by density can only be explained, as Rosenberger has justly shown,[6] by strongly entrenched atomistic convictions. And it is reasonable to doubt whether, in eliminating every real hypothesis, he ever conceived the action of gravitation as a pure and simple law; on the contrary, he openly accepted in the first place the partly theological hypothesis of More, attempting to give it a more scientific appearance by the assumption of a particular medium, and afterward allowed Cotes, in the preface to the second edition of *Principia*, to speak of force acting at a distance as of a real being.[7]

This situation is so apparent that, in building up anti-substantialistic conceptions of science, it could not be entirely ignored. The difficulty has generally been avoided by treating the works and the attempts in question as simple digressions, by pretending to believe that it was a question of parts which were not essential to the whole of the work and which could be easily detached. Now it is certain that, on the contrary, such an operation would be extremely difficult, even for Newton, whose *Opticks* and *Principia* would be deprived of some of their most essential chapters. And if one tried to do it for Descartes, all his *Principia* would have to be effaced. Evidently the scientific work of these great scientists holds together and is ordered in quite a different sense from the statements of method which are cited.

We saw at the beginning of this book [8] that the primitive source of what might be called the positivist error lies in the confusion between law and cause, in the misunderstanding of the truth, that in explaining a phenomenon by a law we are only using a synecdoche. The fact, however, that many scientists have made statements condemning all search for essence and for cause is susceptible, we believe, of more direct psychological explanations. It must be noted that it is a very simple principle, which can be expressed under a precise form like that finally given it by Comte, and for that very reason it is tempting in itself. Moreover, it flatters the scientist's pride, since it makes his chosen field appear to be in a manner sovereign, and entirely independent of the other pursuits of human thought. It is conceivable that it was on these last grounds that positivism conquered the nineteenth century, an epoch distinguished for the fruitfulness of experimental research. But it is not at all astonishing that this conception in a way surreptitiously seduced many minds before that time. One should rather be astonished at the contrary, and, indeed, if this conception did not appear sooner, if, when sometimes formulated very distinctly (as it was, for instance, by Berkeley) it again disappeared, immediately forgotten, it is not, as has frequently been said, because of a kind of vicious propensity of the human mind toward ontology, but rather because it is entirely contrary to the real advance of the intellect as much in the individual thinker as in the whole evolution of science. What would have happened in the past if humanity, seeking the impossible, had adopted Berkeley's or Comte's point of view and considered that there is no cause beyond law or that it ought not to be sought for? The great idealistic philosopher prudently abstained from applying his principle. But Auguste Comte expressed himself with greater precision. Thus he praised Fourier for having dealt with heat without trying to know whether it was matter or movement.[9] He denied that the undulatory theory or any other could ever possess "any real usefulness in guiding our minds in the effective study of optics"; [10] he considered that the "pretended optical interferences or the analogous crossings in acoustics" were "essentially subjective phenomena," the contrary opinion of physicists being "a serious illusion"; [11] he affirmed that all comparison between light, sound, or motion will always be "an arbitrary assumption"; [12] he condemned in general as due "to the prolonged preponderance of the old philosophical mind" all tendencies attempting to establish relations between what to-day we call the different forms of energy.[13] Moreover, it is easy to ascertain that these errors of the founder of positivism are in no way accidental. Starting from the utilitarian concept of science, as we saw in Chapter I, one can justify explicative hypotheses, if necessary. However, it becomes difficult to explain the physicist's predilection for atomic conceptions; and we see that Comte's anathema against the undulatory theory, etc., is really a part of his doctrine.

Principles of positivism, or, at any rate, analogous principles, have since been adopted, at least in appearance, by many scientists, who have often felt bound to protest, like Comte, against atomic theories; but, as a matter of fact, and in spite of the aid given to this tendency by the great and legitimate authority of Mach, it remains to-day, as it did during the nineteenth century, without the least influence on the progress of science. The scientists of the beginning of the twentieth century continue to build up atomic theories just as their predecessors have done. All, doubtless, do not believe in the truth of the theories which they imagine or which they follow; but all believe in their utility. All see in them, for want of something better, an instrument of research of great value, "working hypotheses." These play an extremely important rôle. Bacon believed that one could arrive at scientific discoveries by mechanical processes of induction, so to speak; he went to great lengths in elaborating detailed plans the use of which would leave little to be attributed "to the penetration and vigour of minds," making them, on the contrary, "all nearly equal." [14] It is incontestable that certain rules stated by Bacon (such as, for example, those of concomitant variations) are useful in scientific reasoning. But his tables or schemes, one may boldly affirm, have never been employed in a constant manner by a scientist worthy of that name; at any rate, no scientific discovery, great or small, is due to their application.[15] It would seem that one cannot better refute Bacon's opinions than by citing those of three eminent men, counted amongst the creators of that especially experimental science, the chemistry of the end of the eighteenth century and the first half of the nineteenth. "To attempt an experiment," says Berthollet, "one must have an end, be guided by an hypothesis." [16] Humphry Davy affirms that "it is only in forming theories and in comparing them with facts that we can hope to discover the true system of nature." [17] And Liebig, after having declared that between experiments in Bacon's sense and true scientific research "there is the same relation as between the noise a child produces by striking on a drum and music," [18] shows that, on the contrary, it is the scientific imagination which plays the most important rôle in discoveries, and that experiment, like the calculus, only aids in the process of thought.

Among our contemporaries, Poincaré, in his Report to the *Congrès International de Physique de 1900,* stated that to wish to experiment without preconceived ideas would be to render all experiment sterile, and, moreover, that it is impossible to free oneself from ideas of this kind; [19] and Duhem showed the close dependence of experiments upon scientific theories [20] and made clear the impossibility of the famous *experimentum crucis,* which plays such an important part in the Baconian theory.[21]

As to the "working hypotheses," the only point of view which directly interests the scientist is their fertility, their aptitude for making him discover relations between phenomena which he had not suspected. What assumptions have ever equalled from this point of view the utility of mechanical hypotheses? In the entire domain of science, which they fill, they have produced, and are producing, a prodigious harvest of discoveries of the highest value. Where scientists in the first place have thought there was only a quite superficial similitude, subsequent research has sometimes brought to light in a most unexpected manner a more profound analogy. Let us recall how sceptical people were at first about Kekulé's hypothesis concerning the structure of the components of carbon and the position of atoms in the molecule; and even when it was proved that this description explained admirably an immense series of phenomena, which, until then, constituted a kind of impenetrable jungle, to many it still seemed grossly inadequate. And yet what an astonishing extension and verification of these theories were Le Bel's and van't Hoff's discoveries about the asymmetric atom of carbon! [22] Who does not marvel at the rôle of the atomic hypotheses in the recent progress of electricity and at the alliance of chemistry with it through the efforts of Svante Arrhenius? And is it not surprising to notice that the greater part of irreversible phenomena, which by their nature seem to elude causal explanations, appear traced, so to speak, to a mechanical phenomenon, viz. friction, to the point that physicists are now convinced that it is more than a simple analogy— something which reveals the intimate nature of things.[23] We have cited only recent, almost contemporary, examples, but there were just as many in the past, as, for instance, only to mention one illustrious example, the so brilliantly realized previsions which were deduced from Fresnel's theorem.[24]

So also the history of sciences shows us that, thanks to atomic conceptions, humanity has really foreseen to some extent certain important scientific truths, and developed a kind of prescience. When the Greek atomists affirmed that air, like any other substance, must be composed of discrete parts, it was a pure *a priori* conception. No fact was known at that time to confirm this opinion; on the contrary, everything seemed to show that air is a continuum. But we can now prove experimentally that this last opinion is untenable, that the gases really have a structure, are discontinuous.[25] So also the chemists of the nineteenth century, by attaching a tenacious hope to the hypothesis of the unity of matter, were in opposition to the best established experimental facts which formed the very basis of their own doctrine. And yet phenomena relating to cathode rays, to radiant matter, etc., are tending to furnish an experimental foundation to this hypothesis. What is taking place as regards the reversibility of chemical reactions is of the same order. It is certain (Berthollet's ideas on this having had almost no influence on the progress of science) that this notion was absolutely foreign to the mind of a chemist in the middle of the nineteenth century; and nothing was less justifiable from this point of view than the use of the sign of equality to unite the two terms of what is called a "chemical equation" (p. 225). This sign, a palpable manifestation of the causal tendency, expressed a postulate or, if you will, a hope, which, in the light of the then prevailing theories, was unrealizable or rather absurd, since it was understood that the two sides of the equation indicated, one the initial state and the other the final state of the phenomenon, which always had to take place in the same direction, without hope of return. It is all the more astonishing to state that this almost chimerical hope has, in a certain measure, been realized: chemical reactions appear to us to-day as generally reversible and we can, in fact, replace the equation sign (the meaning of which was distorted), by van't Hoff's two arrows.

But the most striking, the most marvellous phenomenon of this order, is the existence of the principles of conservation. In virtue of the causal tendency, humanity had a presentiment of them; it had formed the concept of the atom-substance long before any experiment on the conservation of matter, and it vaguely conceived mechanical systems as implying the persistence of motion before inertia and the conservation of energy. So if, on the one hand, these principles seem simply to formulate a knowledge that humanity had always possessed, on the other hand, they surpass, so to speak, the very limits of the hope it had a right to conceive. Thus heat and light might well have been movements, conforming to the postulate of universal mechanism, without any possibility of converting these movements of particles into movements of mass, or vice versa. This was approximately the conception of Leibniz and Huygens, and, in general, of most mechanistic physicists before the establishment of the conservation of energy. This last discovery is a quite unexpected confirmation. In the same way the most determined mechanist would never have dared to hope in the nineteenth century, before the work of Gouy, that the agitation of molecules could ever be made directly visible by its most immediate mechanical effects. These surprising agreements attracted the attention of thinkers. We saw (Chapter II, p. 91) that Cournot, in stating the perennial character of atomic theories, had concluded that it was possible that its inventors had "immediately fallen on the very key of natural phenomena." At other times he thought that he could infer from the conservation of the weight of matter that the idea of substance is not merely a logical abstraction, but that it has "its foundation in the essence of bodies." [26] Many remarks of contemporary physicists may be cited in which they express their astonishment at the agreement between the conceptions of the mind and the results of experimental research. Poincaré's observation on irreversible phenomena, which we have noted earlier, belongs to this region of ideas. At another time this eminent theorist marvels rightly at the surprising analogy between electric oscillation and the motion of the pendulum.[27] Boltzmann states that "all the consequences of the mechanical theory of heat, even those belonging to the most incongruous domains, have been confirmed by experiment; it may even be said that they agree most strangely, even in their finest shades, with the pulse of nature." [28] Hertz, in the beginning of his mechanics, declares that in a general manner, in order that we may form images of things, the logical consequences of these images must indeed be images of the consequences which things really produce in nature. There must, therefore, be agreement between nature and our minds.[29]

It was consequently wrong to have called, as we did, causal hypotheses, simple instruments of research, "working" hypotheses. They are more than the scaffolding destined to disappear when the building is constructed. They have their own value; they correspond certainly to something very profound and very essential in nature itself.

And so, and this is very important to notice, the agreement between the postulates of our mind and phenomena goes beyond pure conformity to law. Nature not only shows itself to be ordered, but, even to a certain point, really intelligible.

.   .   .   .

[38c]

MORITZ SCHLICK

Description and Explanation *

The first step towards a knowledge of nature consists in the description of nature which is equivalent to the establishment of the facts. And this, in turn, consists in stating, by means of words or symbols, how the facts described are composed of elements, each of which is denoted by the customary symbol (name). For this purpose, certain primitive acts of recognition are always necessary, so that each component can be identified as belonging to a definite class and assigned to a corresponding symbol.

The next step towards a knowledge of nature—explanation—is char-

* From *Philosophy of Nature* by Moritz Schlick. Translated by Amethe von Zeppelin. New York: Philosophical Library. Copyright, 1949, by Philosophical Library, Inc. Ch. 3, pp. 17-21, reprinted by permission of the publisher.

acterized by the fact that a symbol (concept) which is employed in the description of nature is replaced by a combination of symbols which have already been used in another context. In point of fact, progress in knowledge consists in the discovery that a substitution of this kind is possible. Thus it is a chemical discovery when, instead of the word "water", we can say: "combination of H and O in proportionate weights of 1 : 8"; and it is a physical explanation when, instead of speaking of the heat of a body, we can speak of the energy of motion of its smallest particles. And so on. The advantage of this new kind of description lies in the fact that, with its assistance, the ways of behaviour of the things thus designated, can be predicted—inasmuch as this behaviour can be deduced from the behaviour already known, of those things which are denoted by the concepts used in the explanation. If, for example, heat be explained as a form of motion of the smallest particles, we can, as a result, attribute all phenomena of heat to the properties of the invisible motion of a host of the smallest particles, and thereby predict phenomena of heat which had previously been unknown to us. It is obvious that in the progress of knowledge, the number of concepts necessary for a description of nature, will become increasingly reduced; so that what is denoted by the term "world-picture" will become more and more unified. The world will become a *"Uni*-verse". It is evident from their attempts to reduce the multiplicity of the Universe to a single principle, that even the Greek philosophers of antiquity were conscious in a dim way, of the ultimate goal of knowledge. This idea was at the root of Thales' theory that water is the primal substance of the world; while for Anaximenes and Heraclitus, air and fire respectively, filled this role.

Explanation means the discovery of like in unlike—of identity in difference. And inasmuch as explanation reduces different species of natural phenomena to the same domain, these different species are included as special cases in the latter. Hence we may say, that explanation is the inclusion of the special in the general. Thus, heat and sound, for example, are both explained in so far as they are regarded as special cases of the motion of the smallest particles.

In the first stages of scientific thought, the discovery of the similar in the dissimilar was interpreted as the discovery of a constant, an invariant—something which remains identical with itself and which, while it is the basis of all variety and change, has no part in them. This constant was called *substance*, and was supposed to occur in a multitude of apparent forms and to be subjected to a variety of processes without its essential nature being altered thereby. This primitive concept of substance, the logical deficiencies of which will become evident later, was even then inadequate. For how this substance came to be differentiated and to undergo such transformations, remained unexplained. Change itself must be rendered intelligible by the discovery in it of the unchanging, or invariable— and for this purpose, the concept of law is necessary.

"General descriptions" constitute a preliminary stage in the procedure (e.g. "a stone which is thrown, falls to the ground"). These general descriptions may even be termed laws; but they still do not constitute an *explanation* of the processes described. Such an explanation can only be achieved when a number of laws of the kind are united in a single law, and when one is recognized as a special case of the other. In that case, *one and the same formula* will describe a number, or indeed, an arbitrary number, of processes. This is the essence of Meyerson's interpretation of the rôle which "identity" plays in the explanation of nature. An explanation is perfect only when this formula is specified with the help of the mathematical concept of "function." For it is only with the help of a formula of this kind that it is possible to obtain a description which is complete in all details.

Galileo was the original creator of this kind of exact natural knowledge. We will first attempt to get a clear idea of the essential character of the natural law which was enunciated by him as the law of falling bodies. We imagine a freely falling body, whose velocity v is measured at many points on its path. We divide these velocities by the time t which the body has taken in order to reach the corresponding points on its path. The quotient will show the same number each time (called g), although the numerator and denominator are constantly changing during the fall. Thus the quotient represents the constant element in the change, or the invariable in the variable. Generally speaking, the formulation of a law concerning any natural process consists in stating the *particular combination* (function) of those variable magnitudes or quantities describing the process, *which remains constant during the whole process*. Galileo "explains" *why* the falling body had traversed a certain distance in a certain time. Newton again, explains Galileo's law, inasmuch as he shows it to be a special case of the law of gravitation. And Einstein explains the law of gravitation inasmuch as he reduces it to a general principle of inertia.

The explanation of nature means a description of nature by means of laws. The function of laws (the meaning of laws) is to *de*-scribe and not to *pre*-scribe. They relate what actually occurs, and not what ought to occur. And when necessity is ascribed to the laws of nature, this means that they are universally valid, and not that they exert force. The laws of a country or State, are forms of compulsion for the citizens of that State. But to speak of compulsion, or force, in the case of the laws of nature, is absurd. One is misled into doing so, because of the ambiguity of the word "law"—and this, in turn, is due to the half-conscious use of a psychological model.

Psychological models of this kind, in which natural processes are conceived of in accordance with the pattern of psychic events, constitute the basis of the mythical explanation of the world, and of the animistic conception of nature. They are also responsible for a number of metaphysical systems, like that of Schopenhauer, for whom natural processes represented the manifestations of a hidden Will. Bergson's life force (élan vital) plays a similar rôle and likewise represents a primitive psychological model. It is characteristic of both these philosophers that they set up, in opposition to the scientific explanation of nature by means of laws, a philosophical knowledge which they claimed was deeper. This deeper philosophical knowledge does not consist in description, but in a real coalescence with the subject-matter of which knowledge is sought. Only thus, in their opinion, can true understanding be attained. But these philosophers do not realize that description by means of laws achieves all that can possibly be demanded of knowledge; and that psychologically intuitive models only *apparently* advance the understanding of nature—in reality they obstruct it more than does the use of a mechanical model. The word "force" also— the meaning of which we shall analyse later—owes its introduction into science, to a psychological model.[1]

[39]

PHILIPP FRANK

Why Do Scientists and Philosophers So Often Disagree About the Merits of a New Theory? *

If, in seeking an answer to the question that heads this chapter, we put the preliminary question, "Do they really disagree?" my answer is: At the beginning they do, mostly, but by and by the disagreement weakens and finally the philosophers come to agree too completely. Frequently just at this moment the physical theory in question turns out to be doubtful to the physicist. He advances a new theory and the whole cycle of disagreement and agreement begins again. If we succeed in understanding this periodically recurrent cycle we have performed a great step toward the understanding of the interaction between science and philosophy.

The divergences between physicists and philosophers have become very clear recently. We have only to glance at the discussions about space, time, and causality connected with relativity and the quantum theory to see this. There are a great many people who believe that these divergencies are characteristics of our twentieth-century physics. In order to counteract this erroneous impression I shall start by discussing the attitude of scientists and philosophers toward the Copernican world system at a time when it was news. My point is that the dispute of that time was of the same character as the dispute of today.

Copernicus published his system in the middle of the sixteenth century. A century afterwards this system was condemned by the Roman Inquisition as "philosophically false." During this century the Copernican system

* Reprinted by permission of the author and publishers from Philipp Frank, *Modern Science and Its Philosophy*, ch. 12, pp. 207–215. Cambridge, Mass.: Harvard University Press, Copyright, 1949, by The President and Fellows of Harvard College.

was taught in the universities and presented in the official textbooks as a remarkable achievement in science which was—unfortunately—"philosophically false." This attitude is illustrated by some sentences from a textbook of astronomy of 1581 written by the Jesuit C. Clavius:

> One may doubt whether it would be preferable to follow Ptolemy or Copernicus. For both are in agreement with the observed phenomena. But Copernicus' principles contain a great many assertions that are absurd. He assumes, for instance, that the earth is moving with a triple motion which I cannot understand. For according to the philosophers a simple body like the earth can have only a simple motion.

After setting forth a number of arguments of the same type the author concludes:

> Therefore it seems to me that Ptolemy's geocentric doctrine must be preferred to Copernicus' doctrine.

In spite of the agreement with the observed facts the Copernican system had to be rejected because it was in contradiction with certain principles which were regarded as firmly established. For instance, a simple body like the earth can have only a simple motion, such as a rectilinear or circular one. Or, to quote a second principle of the same type: We see that every piece of earth falls downwards along a straight line; therefore the earth as a whole cannot possess a circular motion. For it was an established principle that to every particular kind of matter there corresponded a particular type of motion.

All these principles were parts of Aristotelian physics. They originated from generalizations of observation, just like any physical theorems. They belonged, however, to an earlier state of physical science. At the time of Copernicus they were already in a state of "fossilization"; they were believed to be eternal truths which could be derived from pure reason. Every statement of science that was in disagreement with these principles of Aristotelian physics was called "philosophically false." In this sense the Copernican system could be declared "mathematically true" but "philosophically false." This meant only that it was in agreement with the observed facts but in disagreement with the principles of Aristotelian philosophy or physics—physics being a part of philosophy.

It may be objected that this was the opinion of a Jesuit and orthodox believer in scholastic philosophy. I shall quote, therefore, the statement of a very progressive man of that time. Francis Bacon has been called in the textbooks of philosophy the very father of empirical science. He says, in 1622:

> In the system of Copernicus there are found many and great inconveniences; for both the loading of the earth with a triple motion is very incommodious and the separation of the sun from the company of the planets with which it has so many passions in common is likewise a difficulty and the introduction of so much immobility into nature by representing the sun and the stars as immovable . . . all these are the speculations of one, who cares not what fictions he introduces into nature, provided his calculations answer.

If we compare this judgment of an empirical philosopher with that of the follower of Aristotle we perceive this difference: the self-confident statements of Aristotelian physics now have faded into rather vague statements of so-called common sense. We no longer derive from profound metaphysical principles the conclusion that the sun must possess the same type of motion as the planets, since it is of the same nature. It is just a "difficulty" to separate the sun from the company of the stars, since they look so similar.

The philosopher's attitude toward physical science had, however, remained essentially unchanged: physical theorems that are in contradiction with certain established general principles have to be rejected, even if these physical theorems are in agreement with all observed facts. The scholastic philosopher just as well as the advocate of empiricism upheld the distinction between "scientific truth" and "philosophic truth." The truth of a physical theorem in the first sense has to be checked by experiments. The truth in the second (the philosophic) sense depends upon whether the theorem is compatible with certain established principles.

In this sense the Copernican system was declared to be "mathematically true" but "philosophically false." And this severe judgment has been passed again and again by philosophers upon new physical theories. Let us direct our attention to Bacon's characterization of Copernicus' personality:

Copernicus was a man who did not care what fictions he introduced into nature provided his calculations answer.

We cannot help remembering how many philosophic reviewers have charged the authors of recent physical theories (particularly relativity and quantum theory), with the same thing. We can perhaps understand this divergence in the attitude of philosophers and physicists most clearly if we examine the example of Newton's physics. For in this case we are able to pursue the fate of a great theory from its birth to its death.

As a starting point I quote a judgment on Newton by a great philosopher who was Newton's contemporary—Bishop Berkeley. The point he makes is again the difference between two ways of judging a physical theory: either by its agreement with general principles (the philosophic criterion) or by the agreement of its consequences with observations (the scientific criterion). In his book *The Analyst,* which is devoted mostly to a criticism of Newton's doctrine, Berkeley puts the rhetorical question:

Whether there can be science of the conclusion when there is no evidence of the principle? And whether a man can have evidence of the principles without understanding them? And therefore whether the mathematicians of the present age act like men of science in taking so much more pains to apply their principles than to understand them?

This sounds like a twentieth-century philosopher criticizing Einstein. It may perhaps be objected that Berkeley was not competent to pass judgment on a scientist like Newton. However, a man like Leibniz, equally

competent as scientist and philosopher, considered both Newton's law of
inertia and his law of gravitation philosophically false and even absurd.

Two traits in these laws seemed to be incompatible with the established principles of philosophy. According to Newton a moving body keeps
its direction with respect to the empty space. This was regarded as absurd.
How could the empty space exert any action? Moreover, the law of gravitation assumed that material bodies attracted each other at any distance
and instantaneously. This action at a distance was incompatible with
Aristotelian philosophy as well as with the "mechanistic" and "geometric"
philosophy of Democritus or Descartes. For a material body could only
be set in motion by contact with a second body, by push or pull.

Newton himself did not believe that his force of attraction was a
causal explanation of the motion of planets. He expected always to find a
derivation of these laws from general principles which were connected
with a medium exerting an impact upon the planets. He compared himself to a man who could explain the operation of a piece of clockwork.
Such a man can describe the mechanism by which the fall of a weight is
transformed into the motion of the hands. But if you ask such a man how
the weight manages to fall he would be at a loss. Nonetheless, you are
forced to admit that he has given you a better understanding of the clockwork than you had before.

This attitude is defined in Newton's famous dictum, *"Hypotheses non
fingo*—I don't set up hypotheses." This word has been frequently mis-
interpreted. For from our present viewpoint Newton's law of gravitation
is a hypothesis too. Newton disappointed his most ardent followers in the
question of the action at a distance as well as in the question of the
corpuscular theory of light. He was always convinced that this theory was
not the negation of the undulatory theory but would have to incorporate
some elements of the latter. In short, Newton was not a faithful
Newtonian.

The great success of Newton's physics was based upon the wide range
of observable facts embraced and by the simplicity and elegance of the
mathematical methods employed. It was justified by its consequences, or,
to speak in the language of the Middle Ages, by its mathematical truth.
But the "philosophic truth" of Newton's principles was regarded as
very doubtful by his contemporaries. Not only "pure" philosophers but
scientists also passed the judgments that these principles were obscure
or even absurd.

But presently the confirmation of these principles by the increasing
range of physical facts that could be derived from them changed the
attitude of the philosophers too. If we examine the general opinion toward
the end of the eighteenth century we notice a complete revolution. The law
of inertia and the law of gravitation were no longer regarded as absurd;
on the contrary, they were declared more and more to be self-evident,
derivable from pure reason, the only way in which the human mind can
understand nature.

As an example of this changed attitude we can point to Immanuel Kant's "Metaphysical Elements of Natural Science," which was published in 1786. We find in this book all the theorems of Newton's *Mathematical Principles of Natural Philosophy,* but they are transformed, so to speak, into a petrified state. Newton had invented bold generalizations in order to cover a large range of facts that had formerly defied all attempts at rational approach. All of these general statements, which seemed to Newton's contemporaries so new, so amazing, so absurd, are now quoted as self-evident. Kant claimed to have demonstrated that the law of inertia can be derived from pure reason; he claimed that the recognition of that law is the only assumption under which nature is conceivable to human reason.

One may say that this was merely the opinion of a philosopher who was a product of the German inclination toward a foggy metaphysics. But when we look at the great advocates of empirical philosophy in the nineteenth century we find almost the same opinion. We may choose as an example the British champion of empirical and mechanistic philosophy in the middle of the nineteenth century, Herbert Spencer. In his standard work, *Synthetic Philosophy,* he expresses himself about the law of inertia. He says:

This law means that motion like matter is indestructible. This indestructibility is not inductively inferred, but is a necessity of thought. For destructibility cannot be conceived at all . . . it is a pseudo-idea. To say that something can become nothing would establish a relation between two terms of which one (nothing) is absent from consciousness, which is impossible.

This was written in 1860.

But we may leave the philosophers and examine the attitude of the scientists of that period. We soon notice that their attitude is strongly influenced by the success claimed by the philosophers. The scientists would not exactly say that Newton's principles of mechanics could be derived from pure reason, but they would fervently proclaim that no physical theory is satisfactory which fails to prove that the observed phenomena are derivable from Newton's laws. Without this proof no theory could be regarded as a real step toward the understanding of nature. I quote two striking examples. About the middle of the nineteenth century, in 1847, Helmholtz published his famous paper, "On the Conservation of Energy." [1] He was a great physicist who was also a great physiologist and psychologist. He said:

The task of physical science is finally to reduce all phenomena of nature to forces of attraction and repulsion the intensity of which is dependent only upon the mutual distance of material bodies. Only if this problem is solved are we sure that nature is conceivable.

Perhaps still more impressive are the statements of the well-known physiologist Du Bois-Reymond. He gave, in 1872, an address "On the Limitations of Natural Science." This speech was widely discussed in the last quarter of the nineteenth century. Du Bois-Reymond said:

The cognition of nature is the reduction of changes in the material world to the motions of atoms, acted upon by central forces, independent of time . . . It is a psychological fact of experience that wherever such a reduction is successfully carried through our need for causality feels satisfied *for the time being.*

Is this not an amazing fact in the history of human mind? As Newton set up his theory the introduction of the central forces of attraction was regarded as a particularly weak point of this theory. It was accused of requiring the introduction of an element that is philosophically absurd. But what happened about a hundred years later? It was claimed as a "psychologic fact" that just the same thing—the reduction of a group of phenomena to the action of central forces—satisfies our need for causal understanding. And the derivation of physical theorems from the action of these forces, which were formerly condemned as unconceivable, was now the guarantee that nature is conceivable.

What is the point of all these considerations? By examining the changes in the appreciation of Newton's laws we are able to find out and to understand the origin and the formation of established philosophic principles. Both the law of inertia and the law of gravitation originated as physical hypotheses that enabled the physicist to describe and predict a large group of observable phenomena in a very convenient way. These laws were justified by the success of this enterprise—that is to say, by their effects—but they could not be recognized as compatible with established philosophic principles. They were, if we apply the language of the Church in its struggle against Copernicus, "philosophically false" and merely "mathematically true."

But what was the situation in the middle of the nineteenth century? Now, the same laws, the law of inertia as well as the law of gravitation, became themselves established philosophic principles, with which all physical theorems had to be in agreement. A physical theorem was now by definition "philosophically true" if it could be derived from Newton's laws. We understand now very well that these "established philosophic principles" are nothing else than physical hypotheses in a state of petrifaction.

It may be asked why we should call it "petrifaction." A physical theory can be changed when new facts are discovered that are not embraced by this theory in a convenient way. But a philosophic principle which is derived from pure reason can never be changed or even modified. If Kant and Spencer are right, that the principle of inertia can be demonstrated by purely mental operations, no future discovery of new physical phenomena can bring about any modification of this principle. The transformation of a physical hypothesis into a philosophic principle is therefore a petrifaction of that hypothesis.

And now it seems very plausible that the philosophic principles of earlier periods are of the same origin. Aristotle's principles of physics were originally also generalizations that covered in a convenient way a certain group of observed facts. When Copernicus and Galileo advanced their new physical theories they were declared to be "philosophically false." This meant only that they were in contradiction with the petrifactions of Aristotelian physics.

In the same way we can now understand the widespread claim that the theory of relativity and the quantum theory are valuable descriptions of observed facts but give us neither a causal understanding nor a description of physical reality. To put it briefly, they are taxed with being only mathematically true but philosophically false or even absurd. This means in this case only that they are in contradiction with the petrifactions of Newton's physics. Or in other words, in twentieth-century physics we are confronted with new experimental facts and have to change the hypotheses of Newton's physics. This is possible as long as these hypotheses are not petrified. But once Newton's laws are regarded as philosophic principles which can be deduced from pure reason they can no longer be changed. Now every modification of Newton's laws will be "philosophically false."

But knowing the origin of philosophic principles we need not be terrorized by the verdict "philosophically false." It means only that the new physical laws are in contradiction with the old physical laws which appear now disguised as philosophic principles with pretensions of eternal validity. The old physical theory was a good description of a restricted group of facts. But to cover the new facts the old theory became inconvenient. It is natural to drop it, if an obsolete physical theory does not pretend to be an "eternal philosophy."

This very simple state of affairs has often been described by the pretentious term "crisis of physics," or even "crisis of science."

And now we can answer with a few words the question put in the title of this chapter. Why do philosophers and scientists so often disagree about the merit of a new theory? They mostly disagree because the new theory seems to be in contradiction to established philosophic principles. Moreover—and this is my chief point—this disagreement arises from necessity, for the established philosophic principles are mostly petrifactions of physical theories that are no longer appropriate to embrace the facts of our actual physical experience.

40

ARTHUR PAP

Does Science Have Metaphysical Presuppositions? *

a. What is a "Presupposition"?

Suppose an honorable citizen who prides himself on perfect soberness and rationality becomes so ecstatic over the ideal life which he thinks he lives that he decides to write an ode to soberness. Naturally, he deprecates, in that ode, the sentimental way of living. It may be expected that the sentimentalists, in reading his ode, will smile and whisper into one another's ears "isn't he sentimental about soberness and rationality, though!" Many a metaphysician of our time reacts to the positivistic worship of science, which is usually accompanied by contempt for metaphysics, somewhat the way the sentimentalists would react to that ode to soberness and rationality: the scientists themselves are metaphysicians, they say, only they are not aware of their own metaphysical presuppositions.

In evaluating this pretty bold claim, our first task will be to unfold the various meanings of the word "presupposition." Being human, one might say, presupposes the possession of two legs; or, legal marriage presupposes the attainment of a certain specified age. It is easy to see that in uses of this sort "presupposition" means "necessary condition": p presupposes $q =_{df} p$ implies q, or, which is the same, not–q implies not–p. On the other hand, when we say "p presupposes q" we certainly do not mean that q is a sufficient condition for p. Nobody would say that having two legs presupposes being human, for we know that it is not necessary to be human for that; one might be a bird, for example. It would be mistaken, therefore, to conceive of the relation of a presupposition to those propositions which somehow rest on it as of the relation of premiss to conclusion: it is the consequence which is presupposed by the premiss, in the sense that the premiss cannot be true *unless* the consequence is true, not the other way around. Let us, now, pick out a proposition which a metaphysician might claim to be presupposed by science without nonetheless belonging to science: the principle of causality, in the simple form "every event has a cause." Could it be said that any specific causal law, such as "a deficient supply of vitamin B causes poor eyesight," presupposes this principle?

* From *Elements of Analytic Philosophy* by Arthur Pap. New York: The Macmillan Co., 1949. Copyright, 1949, by The Macmillan Co. Pp. 402–408 reprinted by permission of the author and publisher.

Surely not, for "some events are uncaused" is certainly consistent with "this event has a cause." Let us try another proposition which a follower of Kant might wish to call a presupposition of empirical science: there are physical constants. Well, by an elementary rule of deductive inference, a singular statement of the form "this has the property P" entails the existential statement "there are things that have the property P." Now, physicists have discovered many physical constants: the acceleration of gravity is a constant near the surface of the earth, the atomic weight of an element is a constant, the quantity pV/T, calculated for a mol of an ideal gas, is a constant (called "the universal gas constant"), etc. Unless there were physical constants, none of these statements could be true, hence it is correct to say that they presuppose the existence of physical constants. Only, we cannot help asking why such a presupposition should be called "metaphysical"? Is any existential statement that has been verified by a singular scientific statement a metaphysical truth? Are we talking metaphysics, then, when we say "there are reptiles," "there are gases that are lighter than air," etc.? If not, how would those who believe that science is built on metaphysical foundations distinguish the metaphysical consequences of scientific propositions from those consequences that are likewise to be classified as scientific propositions? [1]

However, there are other senses of the verb "to presuppose," maybe no less common than the one just discussed. One might say, for example, that analytical mechanics presupposes the calculus. Does this mean that the laws of mechanics would have to be abandoned if, say, the rules of differentiation turned out one day to be infected with a fatal inconsistency? Not quite, for it might be possible to establish the laws of mechanics without the help of the differential calculus. Thus, once the constancy of the acceleration of gravity is experimentally established, the law "$s = \frac{1}{2}gt^2$" may be derived from the definitions of acceleration and velocity as time derivatives by merely applying the rules of differentiation in two successive steps. However, if the calculus should become unavailable as an instrument of deduction, the proportionality of fallen height to the square of the time of fall could still be verified by experiment. In this usage, then, the fact that q is presupposed by p does not imply that the falsity of q entails the falsity of p. What is meant is rather this: if q were false, then the belief in p would cease to be grounded, since q belonged to the premises or to the rules of inference on the basis of which p was inferred. q, here, is not a necessary condition for p, since p might still be true even though q is false; in fact, while a belief in p may have been partially grounded in the assumed truth of q, one could still have good reasons for believing p to be true, if q were false. The relationship designated by "x presupposes y" in this usage is, indeed, none other than the relation of an inferred conclusion to a part of its premises. The fact that all men are mortal is neither a sufficient condition nor a necessary condition for the fact that, say, Jesus Christ is mortal. It is not a sufficient condition since one would moreover have to be agreed that Jesus Christ was a man, and it is not a necessary condition, since obviously the mortality of Christ would be consistent with the immortality of some men. Still, somebody might argue against the credibility of the divinity of Christ by referring to the fact that all men are bound to die, whereupon, logically speaking, two alternative rebuttals would be open to the orthodox believer: he could say "you presuppose in your argument that all men are mortal" or "you presuppose in your argument that Jesus Christ was human, which I deny, holding him to be divine."

This is also the sense in question when it is said that some sciences presuppose others. In deriving physical laws from certain selected physical axioms, the physicist uses the truths of Euclidian geometry, for example, as (for the most part unexpressed) premises, and in this sense physics may be said to presuppose geometry. But this does not mean that the physical propositions derived with the help of geometry would necessarily be false if the propositions of geometry turned out to be false. If I calculate the magnitude of a certain force from the magnitudes of its rectangular vector components by using the Pythagorean theorem, and the latter turned out to be false, my calculation would, indeed, become unfounded. But inasmuch as the derived proposition of measurement could be verified without the use of the Pythagorean theorem, the truth of the latter is not a necessary condition for the truth of the former. It is evidently also in this sense that logic is presupposed by all the sciences: if we have no good reason for believing the principles of inference to be true, then we have no good reason for believing any proposition known by inference only to be true, no matter what subject-matter the inferred proposition may be about. To be sure, any empirical proposition presupposes the principles of logic also in the first sense of "presupposition," the sense of necessary condition: for the negation of a logical truth is a contradiction, and a contradiction entails any proposition, hence also the negation of any given empirical proposition.

Now, it is conceivable that this is the sense of "presupposition" that is intended when it is said that science makes metaphysical presuppositions. Consider such principles as "all physical magnitudes are continuous functions" or "if several laws are consistent with the data of measurement, the simplest law is the true law." The first principle—which, by the way, progressive metaphysicians, aware of the discontinuities disclosed by quantum physics, would not wish to defend any more—might be said to express a *reason* for the possibility of the graphical procedure of representing physical magnitudes by coordinates and numerical laws connecting diverse physical magnitudes by continuous curves. Obviously, if it were false—and we know nowadays that it is false, since energy can be radiated only in integral multiples of the so-called "elementary quantum of action" —all physical laws believed to be true might still be true. All we can say is that if it were not for the assumption of its truth, the scientist would be less confident in the application of the graphical method of determining numerical laws. The same is to be said of the second of the above mentioned principles. Whatever the scientist's reasons may be for believing in the simplicity of nature, this belief itself is certainly a circumstance which partially explains what he actually does—why, for example, he ascribes deviations from the simple law to errors arising from a variety of sources, and assumes unhesitatingly that we would see perfect order were we only perfect observers. However, it is important to distinguish the beliefs whose verification is the goal of scientific inquiries from the beliefs which the scientist *expresses* by his activities and which motivate his behavior as scientist. A striking example is the so-called principle of uniformity "same cause, same effect": it has been remarked that if an experiment, designed to prove a generalization "if A, B, C, then D," is repeated several times under varied conditions, it is in order to make sure that A, B, C really are the essential conditions on which the effect D depends, and that the appearance of such a dependence was not due to some "accidental" circumstance. But it would never occur to the scientist for a moment that the mere place or time of the experiment could make any difference to the effect; a law formulated as "other things being equal, if A, B, C then D" is to be read as "other things being equal, then for any time and place, if A, B, C then D." This conviction of the causal irrelevancy of mere position in space and time [1] explains why the scientist often regards one or two experiments as sufficient proof for a very general conclusion. Obviously, there would be an absurdity in the undertaking of a series of experiments for the purpose of verifying the causal irrelevancy of mere spatial and temporal position. And one might say that "same cause, same effect" is a belief, tacitly adhered to by the scientist, which explains the scientist's behavior, particularly the confidence with which he generalizes from a small number of experiments.

But here again we must ask: what additional information is conveyed, if it is said that such beliefs which the scientist manifests by what he does are "metaphysical"? Is any belief which motivates scientific procedure and which is not itself subjected to empirical test to be called "metaphysical"? Is it, then, a metaphysical belief that events are predictable, or that they obey simple laws? But that there is a simple relation, say, between the angle of incidence and the angle of reflection of a light ray, or that an inflation after a long war is predictable—these are not metaphysical beliefs? In that case a "metaphysical" belief seems to amount simply to a very *general* belief. Now, nobody would deny that men would behave differently if they changed certain general beliefs more or less unconsciously entertained; why should it be otherwise with the sort of behavior we call "scientific inquiry"? If the metaphysicians who deny that science stands on its own feet mean anything as obviously true as this, why not say so? Nobody could seriously disagree with them.

Once again, the distinction between logical analysis and psychology must be emphasized. As logical analysts we are interested in clarifying the nature of scientific assertions and the methods by which scientific assertions are validated. This need not at all prevent us from being also interested in the *psychology* of scientific inquiry, the various motivating forces that impel the scientists to do what they do. However, we should not confuse these entirely different pursuits that might attract the spectator of science. It is one thing to say that the firm belief in a "deterministic universe," let us say, motivated Laplace to perfect astronomy with mathematical tools. It is different to contend that the propositions of astronomy logically depend on the validity of such sweeping beliefs.

These considerations suggest a third sense of "presupposition" which, in contrast to the other senses mentioned so far, is perhaps more psychological than logical. Assuming that a man's behavior is purposive rather than blind, we can infer from the way he behaves that he holds such and such beliefs, inasmuch as it would not be rational for him to act the way he acts unless he held those beliefs. Thus, from the mere fact that a lawyer in court cross-questions a certain witness we may infer that the lawyer believes the witness may be able to produce convincing, or at least relevant, evidence. The belief in question is a *causal condition* of the lawyer's behavior; unless the lawyer held that belief, he would behave differently. If an onlooker said "the lawyer *presupposes* that . . ." this is undoubtedly what he would mean: unless the lawyer believed . . . to be true, his actions would be pointless, irrational. Suppose, now, a philosopher made the following comment on the behavior of lawyers in court: "all lawyers presuppose the principle that convincing evidence may be produced by the procedure of cross-questioning witnesses. Unlike such propositions as 'Mr. *X* committed the murder' or 'Mr. *X* was run over by the car without premeditation' this principle is never debated in any court session; it is just taken for granted, all judical investigations are based on it, and it is therefore a metaphysical presupposition of legal practice." If one wonders what additional information is conveyed by the grand conclusion that this proposition is a "metaphysical" presupposition, one should likewise wonder what information is conveyed by such statements as "it is a metaphysical presupposition of science that the world is predictable, that there is, for any observed coexistence of properties or sequence of events, a law which explains it, etc." For all these propositions merely express beliefs or hopes which motivate the scientist to do what he does.

In all the different senses of "presupposition" which we have discussed, a presupposition is a proposition, something of which it is meaningful to assert truth or falsehood. Sometimes, however, it is said that science presupposes metaphysical *concepts*, such as substance, event, property, relation. Such concepts which distinguish themselves at first glance by their abstractness and universality are at times also called "categories." Now, it was in our very first chapter that we called attention to the distinction between concepts that are specific to some one science and concepts that are employed in all the sciences. If by a metaphysical concept, then, be meant such a universally employed concept, whose meaning is normally taken for granted by the scientist and the man in the street but is a puzzle to the logical analyst, there is no doubt but that such "categories" may be found in all the sciences.

.   .   .   .

41

CHARLES S. PEIRCE

The Doctrine of Necessity Examined *

In *The Monist* for January, 1891, I endeavored to show what elementary ideas ought to enter into our view of the universe. I may mention that on those considerations I had already grounded a cosmical theory, and from it had deduced a considerable number of consequences capable of being compared with experience. This comparison is now in progress, but under existing circumstances must occupy many years.

I propose here to examine the common belief that every single fact in the universe is precisely determined by law. It must not be supposed that this is a doctrine accepted everywhere and at all times by all rational men. Its first advocate appears to have been Democritus, the atomist, who was led to it, as we are informed, by reflecting upon the "impenetrability, translation, and impact of matter (ἀντιτυπία καὶ φορὰ καὶ πληγὴ τῆς ὕλης)." That is to say, having restricted his attention to a field where no influence other than mechanical constraint could possibly come before his notice, he straightway jumped to the conclusion that throughout the universe that was the sole principle of action,—a style of reasoning so usual in our day with men not unreflecting as to be more than excusable in the infancy of thought. But Epicurus, in revising the atomic doctrine and repairing its defences, found himself obliged to suppose that atoms swerve from their courses by spontaneous chance; and thereby he conferred upon the theory life and entelechy. For we now see clearly that the peculiar function of the molecular hypothesis in physics is to open an entry for the calculus of probabilities. Already, the prince of philosophers [Aristotle] had re-

* From *The Monist* (April, 1892), pp. 321–337; reprinted in *Chance, Love, and Logic: Philosophical Essays by the late Charles S. Peirce The Founder of Pragmatism*, edited by Morris R. Cohen, with a Supplementary Essay on The Pragmatism of Peirce by John Dewey (New York: Harcourt, Brace & Co., 1923; Peter Smith, 1949). Also, cf. *Collected Papers of Charles Sanders Peirce*, edited by Charles Hartshorne and Paul Weiss (6 volumes, Harvard University Press, 1931–35), 6.35–65; *Classic American Philosophers*, ed. Max H. Fisch (New York, 1951), Ch. I on Peirce with Introduction by Arthur W. Burks; *Studies in the Philosophy of C. S. Peirce*, edited by Philip P. Wiener and Frederic H. Young (Harvard University Press, 1952) contains 24 essays by leading Peirce scholars. The works of Justus H. Buchler, James K. Feibleman, Thomas A. Goudge, and W. B. Gallie on Peirce's philosophy should be consulted. Max H. Fisch has brought M. R. Cohen's Bibliography of Peirce's published writings up to date in *Studies in the Philosophy of C. S. Peirce*, Appendix V.

peatedly and emphatically condemned the dictum of Democritus (especially in the "Physics," [of Aristotle] Book II, chapters iv, v, vi), holding that events come to pass in three ways, namely, (1) by external compulsion, or the action of efficient causes, (2) by virtue of an inward nature, or the influence of final causes, and (3) irregularly without definite cause, but just by absolute chance; and this doctrine is of the inmost essence of Aristotelianism. It affords, at any rate, a valuable enumeration of the possible ways in which anything can be supposed to have come about. The freedom of the will, too, was admitted both by Aristotle and by Epicurus. . . .

The proposition in question is that the state of things existing at any time, together with certain immutable laws, completely determine the state of things at every other time (for a limitation to *future* time is indefensible). Thus, given the state of the universe in the original nebula, and given the laws of mechanics, a sufficiently powerful mind could deduce from these data the precise form of every curlicue of every letter I am now writing.

Whoever holds that every act of the will as well as every idea of the mind is under the rigid governance of a necessity co-ordinated with that of the physical world, will logically be carried to the proposition that minds are part of the physical world in such a sense that the laws of mechanics determine everything that happens according to immutable attractions and repulsions. In that case, that instantaneous state of things from which every other state of things is calculable consists in the positions and velocities of all the particles at any instant. This, the usual and most logical form of necessitarianism, is called the mechanical philosophy.

When I have asked thinking men what reason they had to believe that every fact in the universe is precisely determined by law, the first answer has usually been that the proposition is a "presupposition" or postulate of scientific reasoning. Well, if that is the best that can be said for it, the belief is doomed. Suppose it be "postulated": that does not make it true, nor so much as afford the slightest rational motive for yielding it any credence. It is as if a man should come to borrow money, and when asked for his security, should reply he "postulated" the loan. To "postulate" a proposition is no more than to hope it is true. There are, indeed, practical emergencies in which we act upon assumptions of certain propositions as true, because if they are not so, it can make no difference how we act. But all such propositions I take to be hypotheses of individual facts. For it is manifest that no universal principle can in its universality be comprised in a special case or can be requisite for the validity of any ordinary inference. To say, for instance, that the demonstration by Archimedes of the property of the lever would fall to the ground if men were endowed with free-will, is extravagant; yet this is implied by those who make a proposition incompatible with the freedom of the will the postulate of all inference. Considering, too, that the conclusions of science make no pretence to being more than probable, and considering that a probable inference can at most only suppose something to be most frequently, or otherwise approximately,

true, but never that anything is precisely true without exception throughout the universe, we see how far this proposition in truth is from being so
postulated.

But the whole notion of a postulate being involved in reasoning apper-
tains to a by-gone and false conception of logic. Non-deductive, or ampliative inference, is of three kinds: induction, hypothesis, and analogy. If
there be any other modes, they must be extremely unusual and highly
complicated, and may be assumed with little doubt to be of the same nature
as those enumerated. For induction, hypothesis, and analogy, as far as their
ampliative character goes, that is, so far as they conclude something not
implied in the premises, depend upon one principle and involve the same
procedure. All are essentially inferences from sampling. Suppose a ship
arrives at Liverpool laden with wheat in bulk. Suppose that by some
machinery the whole cargo be stirred up with great thoroughness. Suppose
that twenty-seven thimblefuls be taken equally from the forward, mid-
ships, and aft parts, from the starboard, center, and larboard parts, and
from the top, half depth, and lower parts of her hold, and that these being
mixed and the grains counted, four-fifths of the latter are found to be of
quality A. Then we infer, experientially and provisionally, that approximately four-fifths of all the grain in the cargo is of the same quality. I say
we infer this *experientially* and *provisionally*. By saying that we infer it
experientially, I mean that our conclusion makes no pretension to knowledge of wheat-in-itself, our ἀλήθεια, as the derivation of that word implies,
has nothing to do with *latent* wheat. We are dealing only with the matter
of possible experience,—experience in the full acceptation of the term as
something not merely affecting the senses but also as the subject of thought.
If there be any wheat hidden on the ship, so that it can neither turn up in
the sample nor be heard of subsequently from purchasers,—or if it be
half-hidden, so that it may, indeed, turn up, but is less likely to do so than
the rest,—or if it can affect our senses and our pockets, but from some
strange cause or causelessness cannot be reasoned about,—all such wheat
is to be excluded (or have only its proportional weight) in calculating that
true proportion of quality A, to which our inference seeks to approximate.
By saying that we draw the inference *provisionally*, I mean that we do not
hold that we have reached any assigned degree of approximation as yet,
but only hold that if our experience be indefinitely extended, and if every
fact of whatever nature, as fast as it presents itself, be duly applied, according to the inductive method, in correcting the inferred ratio, then our approximation will become indefinitely close in the long run; that is to say,
close to the experience *to come* (not merely close by the exhaustion of a
finite collection) so that if experience in general is to fluctuate irregularly
to and fro, in a manner to deprive the ratio sought of all definite value,
we shall be able to find out approximately within what limits it fluctuates,
and if, after having one definite value, it changes and assumes another, we
shall be able to find that out, and in short, whatever may be the variations
of this ratio in experience, experience indefinitely extended will enable us

to detect them, so as to predict rightly, at last, what its ultimate value may be, if it have any ultimate value, or what the ultimate law of succession of values may be, if there be any such ultimate law, or that it ultimately fluctuates irregularly within certain limits, if it do so ultimately fluctuate. Now our inference, claiming to be no more than thus experiential and pro-visional, manifestly involves no postulate whatever.

For what is a postulate? It is the formulation of a material fact which we are not entitled to assume as a premise, but the truth of which is requisite to the validity of an inference. Any fact, then, which might be supposed postulated, must either be such that it would ultimately present itself in experience, or not. If it will present itself, we need not postulate it now in our provisional inference, since we shall ultimately be entitled to use it as a premise. But if it never would present itself in experience, our conclusion is valid but for the possibility of this fact being otherwise than assumed, that is, it is valid as far as possible experience goes, and that is all that we claim. Thus, every postulate is cut off, either by the provision-ality or by the experientiality of our inference. For instance, it has been said that induction postulates that, if an indefinite succession of samples be drawn, examined, and thrown back each before the next is drawn, then in the long run every grain will be drawn as often as any other, that is to say, postulates that the ratio of the numbers of times in which any two are drawn will indefinitely approximate to unity. But no such postulate is made; for if, on the one hand, we are to have no other experience of the wheat than from such drawings, it is the ratio that presents itself in those drawings and not the ratio which belongs to the wheat in its latent exist-ence that we are endeavoring to determine; while if, on the other hand, there is some other mode by which the wheat is to come under our knowl-edge, equivalent to another kind of sampling, so that after all our care in stirring up the wheat, some experiential grains will present themselves in the first sampling operation more often than others in the long run, this very singular fact will be sure to get discovered by the inductive method, which must avail itself of every sort of experience; and our inference, which was only provisional, corrects itself at last. Again, it has been said, that induction postulates that under like circumstances like events will happen, and that this postulate is at bottom the same as the principle of universal causation. But this is a blunder, or *bévue*, due to thinking exclu-sively of inductions where the concluded ratio is either 1 or 0. If any such proposition were postulated, it would be that under like circumstances (the circumstances of drawing the different samples) different events occur in the same proportions in all the different sets,—a proposition which is false and even absurd. But in truth no such thing is postulated, the experiential character of the inference reducing the condition of validity to this, that if a certain result does not occur, the opposite result will be manifested, a condition assured by the provisionality of the inference. But it may be asked whether it is not conceivable that every instance of a certain class destined to be ever employed as a datum of induction should have one character, while every instance destined not to be so employed should have the opposite character. The answer is that in that case, the instances excluded from being subjects of reasoning would not be experienced in the full sense of the word, but would be among these *latent* individuals of which our conclusion does not pretend to speak.

To this account of the rationale of induction I know of but one objection worth mention: it is that I thus fail to deduce the full degree of force which this mode of inference in fact possesses; that according to my view, no matter how thorough and elaborate the stirring and mixing process had been, the examination of a single handful of grain would not give me any assurance, sufficient to risk money upon that the next handful would not greatly modify the concluded value of the ratio under inquiry, while, in fact, the assurance would be very high that this ratio was not greatly in error. If the true ratio of grains of quality A were 0.80 and the handful contained a thousand grains, nine such handfuls out of every ten would contain from 780 to 820 grains of quality A. The answer to this is that the calculation given is correct when we know that the units of this handful and the quality inquired into have the normal independence of one another, if for instance the stirring has been complete and the character sampled for has been settled upon in advance of the examination of the sample. But in so far as these conditions are not known to be complied with, the above figures cease to be applicable. Random sampling and predesignation of the character sampled for should always be striven after in inductive reasoning, but when they cannot be attained, so long as it is conducted honestly, the inference retains some value. When we cannot ascertain how the sampling has been done or the sample-character selected, induction still has the essential validity which my present account of it shows it to have.

I do not think a man who combines a willingness to be convinced with a power of appreciating an argument upon a difficult subject can resist the reasons which have been given to show that the principle of universal necessity cannot be defended as being a postulate of reasoning. But then the question immediately arises whether it is not proved to be true, or at least rendered highly probable, by observation of nature.

Still, this question ought not long to arrest a person accustomed to reflect upon the force of scientific reasoning. For the essence of the necessitarian position is that certain continuous quantities have certain exact values. Now, how can observation determine the value of such a quantity with a probable error absolutely *nil*? To one who is behind the scenes, and knows that the most refined comparisons of masses, lengths, and angles, far surpassing in precision all other measurements, yet fall behind the accuracy of bank-accounts, and that the ordinary determinations of physical constants, such as appear from month to month in the journals, are about on a par with an upholsterer's measurements of carpets and curtains, the idea of mathematical exactitude being demonstrated in the laboratory will appear simply ridiculous. There is a recognized method of estimating the probable magnitudes of errors in physics,—the method of least squares. It is universally admitted that this method makes the errors smaller than they really are; yet even according to that theory an error indefinitely small is indefinitely improbable; so that any statement to the effect that a certain continuous quantity has a certain exact value, if well-founded at all, must be founded on something other than observation.

Still, I am obliged to admit that this rule is subject to a certain quali-fication. Namely, it only applies to continuous * quantity. Now, certain kinds of continuous quantity are discontinuous at one or at two limits, and for such limits the rule must be modified. Thus, the length of a line cannot be less than zero. Suppose, then, the question arises how long a line a cer-tain person had drawn from a marked point on a piece of paper. If no line at all can be seen, the observed length is zero; and the only conclusion this observation warrants is that the length of the line is less than the smallest length visible with the optical power employed. But indirect observa-tions,—for example, that the person supposed to have drawn the line was never within fifty feet of the paper,—may make it probable that no line at all was made, so that the concluded length will be strictly zero. In like manner, experience no doubt would warrant the conclusion that there is absolutely *no* indigo in a given ear of wheat, and absolutely *no* attar in a given lichen. But such inferences can only be rendered valid by positive experiential evidence, direct or remote, and cannot rest upon a mere in-ability to detect the quantity in question. We have reason to think there is no indigo in the wheat, because we have remarked that wherever indigo is produced it is produced in considerable quantities, to mention only one argument. We have reason to think there is no attar in the lichen, because essential oils seem to be in general peculiar to single species. If the question had been whether there was iron in the wheat or the lichen, though chemical analysis should fail to detect its presence, we should think some of it probably was there, since iron is almost everywhere. Without any such information, one way or the other, we could only abstain from any opinion as to the presence of the substance in question. It cannot, I conceive, be maintained that we are in any *better* position than this in regard to the presence of the element of chance or spontaneous departures from law in nature.

Those observations which are generally adduced in favor of mechani-cal causation simply prove that there is an element of regularity in nature, and have no bearing whatever upon the question of whether such regularity is exact and universal, or not. Nay, in regard to this *exactitude*, all observa-tion is directly *opposed* to it; and the most that can be said is that a good deal of this observation can be explained away. Try to verify any law of nature, and you will find that the more precise your observations, the more certain they will be to show irregular departures from the law. We are accustomed to ascribe these, and I do not say wrongly, to errors of observa-tion; yet we cannot usually account for such errors in any antecedently

---

Continuous is not exactly the right word, but I let it go to avoid a long and irrelevant discussion.

probable way. Trace their causes back far enough, and you will be forced to admit they are always due to arbitrary determination, or chance.

But it may be asked whether if there were an element of real chance in the universe it must not occasionally be productive of signal effects such as could not pass unobserved. In answer to this question, without stopping to point out that there is an abundance of great events which one might be tempted to suppose were of that nature, it will be simplest to remark that physicists hold that the particles of gases are moving about irregularly, substantially as if by real chance, and that by the principles of probabilities there must occasionally happen to be concentrations of heat in the gases contrary to the second law of thermodynamics, and these concentrations, occurring in explosive mixtures, must sometimes have tremendous effects. Here, then, is in substance the very situation supposed; yet no phenomena ever have resulted which we are forced to attribute to such chance concentration of heat, or which anybody, wise or foolish, has ever dreamed of accounting for in that manner.

In view of all these considerations, I do not believe that anybody, not in a state of case-hardened ignorance respecting the logic of science, can maintain that the precise and universal conformity of facts to law is clearly proved, or even rendered particularly probable, by any observations hitherto made. In this way, the determined advocate of exact regularity will soon find himself driven to *a priori* reasons to support his thesis. These received such a socdolager from Stuart Mill in his Examination of Hamilton, that holding to them now seems to me to denote a high degree of imperviousness to reason; so that I shall pass them by with little notice.

To say that we cannot help believing a given proposition is no argument, but it is a conclusive fact if it be true; and with the substitution of "I" for "we," it is true in the mouths of several classes of minds, the blindly passionate, the unreflecting and ignorant, and the person who has overwhelming evidence before his eyes. But that which has been inconceivable to-day has often turned out indisputable on the morrow. Inability to conceive is only a stage through which every man must pass in regard to a number of beliefs,—unless endowed with extraordinary obstinacy and obtuseness. His understanding is enslaved to some blind compulsion which a vigorous mind is pretty sure soon to cast off.

Some seek to back up the *a priori* position with empirical arguments. They say that the exact regularity of the world is a natural belief, and that natural beliefs have generally been confirmed by experience. There is some reason in this. Natural beliefs, however, if they generally have a foundation of truth, also require correction and purification from natural illusions. The principles of mechanics are undoubtedly natural beliefs; but, for all that, the early formulations of them were exceedingly erroneous. The general approximation to truth in natural beliefs is, in fact, a case of the general adaptation of genetic products to recognizable utilities or ends. Now, the adaptations of nature, beautiful and often marvelous as they verily are, are never found to be quite perfect; so that the argument is

quite *against* the absolute exactitude of any natural belief, including that
of the principle of causation.

Another argument, or convenient commonplace, is that absolute chance
is *inconceivable*. (This word has eight current significations. The *Century
Dictionary* enumerates six.) Those who talk like this will hardly be persuaded to say in what sense they mean that chance is inconceivable. Should
they do so, it would easily be shown either that they have no sufficient
reason for the statement or that the inconceivability is of a kind which
does not prove that chance is non-existent.

Another *a priori* argument is that chance is unintelligible; that is to
say, while it may perhaps be conceivable, it does not disclose to the eye
of reason the how or why of things; and since a hypothesis can only be
justified so far as it renders some phenomenon intelligible, we never can
have any right to suppose absolute chance to enter into the production of
anything in nature. This argument may be considered in connection with
two others. Namely, instead of going so far as to say that the supposition
of chance can *never* properly be used to explain any observed fact, it may
be alleged merely that no facts are known which such a supposition could
in any way help in explaining. Or again, the allegation being still further
weakened, it may be said that since departures from law are not unmistak-
ably observed, chance is not a *vera causa*, and ought not unnecessarily to
be introduced into a hypothesis.

These are no mean arguments, and require us to examine the matter
a little more closely. Come, my superior opponent, let me learn from your
wisdom. It seems to me that every throw of sixes with a pair of dice is a
manifest instance of chance.

"While you would hold a throw of deuce-ace to be brought about by
necessity?" (The opponent's supposed remarks are placed in quotation
marks.)

Clearly one throw is as much chance as another.

"Do you think throws of dice are of a different nature from other
events?"

I see that I must say that *all* the diversity and specificalness of events
is attributable to chance.

"Would you, then, deny that there is any regularity in the world?"

That is clearly undeniable. I must acknowledge there is an approximate regularity, and that every event is influenced by it. But the diversification, specificalness, and irregularity of things I suppose is chance. A
throw of sixes appears to me a case in which this element is particularly
obtrusive.

"If you reflect more deeply, you will come to see that *chance* is only
a name for a cause that is unknown to us."

Do you mean that we have no idea whatever what kind of causes could
bring about a throw of sixes?

"On the contrary, each die moves under the influence of precise
mechanical laws."

But it appears to me that it is not these *laws* which made the dice turn up sixes; for these laws act just the same when other throws come up. The chance lies in the diversity of throws; and this diversity cannot be due to laws which are immutable.

"The diversity is due to the diverse circumstances under which the laws act. The dice lie differently in the box, and the motion given to the box is different. These are the unknown causes which produce the throws, and to which we give the name of chance; not the mechanical law which regulates the operation of these causes. You see you are already beginning to think more clearly about this subject."

Does the operation of mechanical law not increase the diversity?

"Properly not. You must know that the instantaneous state of a system of particles is defined by six times as many numbers as there are particles, three for the co-ordinates of each particle's position, and three more for the components of its velocity. This number of numbers, which expresses the amount of diversity in the system, remains the same at all times. There may be, to be sure, some kind of relation between the co-ordinates and component velocities of the different particles, by means of which the state of the system might be expressed by a smaller number of numbers. But, if this is the case, a precisely correspondingly relationship must exist between the co-ordinates and component velocities at any other time, though it may doubtless be a relation less obvious to us. Thus, the intrinsic complexity of the system is the same at all times."

Very well, my obliging opponent, we have now reached an issue. You think all the arbitrary specifications of the universe were introduced in one dose, in the beginning, if there was a beginning, and that the variety and complication of nature has always been just as much as it is now. But I, for my part, think that the diversification, the specification, has been continually taking place. Should you condescend to ask me why I so think, I should give my reasons as follows:

(1) Question any science which deals with the course of time. Consider the life of an individual animal or plant, or of a mind. Glance at the history of states, of institutions, of language, of ideas. Examine the successions of forms shown by paleontology, the history of the globe as set forth in geology, of what the astronomer is able to make out concerning the changes of stellar systems. Everywhere the main fact is growth and increasing complexity. Death and corruption are mere accidents or secondary phenomena. Among some of the lower organisms, it is a moot point with biologists whether there be anything which ought to be called death. Races, at any rate, do not die out except under unfavorable circumstances. From these broad and ubiquitous facts we may fairly infer, by the most unexceptionable logic, that there is probably in nature some agency by which the complexity and diversity of things can be increased; and that consequently the rule of mechanical necessity meets in some way with interference.

(2) By thus admitting pure spontaneity or life as a character of the

universe, acting always and everywhere though restrained within narrow bounds by law, producing infinitesimal departures from law continually, and great ones with infinite infrequency, I account for all the variety and diversity of the universe, in the only sense in which the really *sui generis* and new can be said to be accounted for. The ordinary view has to admit the inexhaustible multitudinous variety of the world, has to admit that its mechanical law cannot account for this in the least, that variety can spring only from spontaneity, and yet denies without any evidence or reason the existence of this spontaneity, or else shoves it back to the beginning of time and supposes it dead ever since. The superior logic of my view appears to me not easily controverted.

(3) When I ask the necessitarian how he would explain the diversity and irregularity of the universe, he replies to me out of the treasury of his wisdom that irregularity is something which from the nature of things we must not seek to explain. Abashed at this, I seek to cover my confusion by asking how he would explain the uniformity and regularity of the universe, whereupon he tells me that the laws of nature are immutable and ultimate facts, and no account is to be given of them. But my hypothesis of spontaneity does explain irregularity, in a certain sense; that is, it explains the general fact of irregularity, though not, of course, what each lawless event is to be. At the same time, by thus loosening the bond of necessity, it gives room for the influence of another kind of causation, such as seems to be operative in the mind in the formation of associations, and enables us to understand how the uniformity of nature could have been brought about. That single events should be hard and unintelligible, logic will permit without difficulty: we do not expect to make the shock of a personally experienced earthquake appear natural and reasonable by any amount of cogitation. But logic does expect things *general* to be understandable. To say that there is a universal law, and that it is a hard, ultimate, unintelligible fact, the why and wherefore of which can never be inquired into, at this a sound logic will revolt; and will pass over at once to a method of philosophizing which does not thus barricade the road of discovery.

(4) Necessitarianism cannot logically stop short of making the whole action of the mind a part of the physical universe. Our notion that we decide what we are going to do, if as the necessitarian says, it has been calculable since the earliest times, is reduced to illusion. Indeed, consciousness in general thus becomes a mere illusory aspect of a material system. What we call red, green, and violet are in reality only different rates of vibration. The sole reality is the distribution of qualities of matter in space and time. Brain-matter is protoplasm in a certain degree and kind of complication,—a certain arrangement of mechanical particles. Its feeling is but an inward aspect, a phantom. For, from the positions and velocities of the particles at any one instant, and the knowledge of the immutable forces, the positions at all other times are calculable; so that the universe of space, time, and matter is a rounded system uninterfered with from elsewhere. But from the state of feeling at any instant, there is no reason

to suppose the states of feeling at all other instants are thus exactly calculable; so that feeling is, as I said, a mere fragmentary and illusive aspect
of the universe. This is the way, then, that necessitarianism has to make
up its accounts. It enters consciousness under the head of sundries, as a
forgotten trifle; its scheme of the universe would be more satisfactory if
this little fact could be dropped out of sight. On the other hand, by supposing the rigid exactitude of causation to yield, I care not how little,—be
it but by a strictly infinitesimal amount,—we gain room to insert mind into
our scheme, and to put it into the place where it is needed, into the position
which, as the sole self-intelligible thing, it is entitled to occupy, that of the
fountain of existence; and in so doing we resolve the problem of the connection of soul and body.

(5) But I must leave undeveloped the chief of my reasons, and can
only adumbrate it. The hypothesis of chance-spontaneity is one whose inevitable consequences are capable of being traced out with mathematical
precision into considerable detail. Much of this I have done and find the
consequences to agree with observed facts to an extent which seems to me
remarkable. But the matter and methods of reasoning are novel, and I
have no right to promise that other mathematicians shall find my deductions as satisfactory as I myself do, so that the strongest reason for my
belief must for the present remain a private reason of my own, and cannot
influence others. I mention it to explain my own position; and partly to
indicate to future mathematical speculators a veritable goldmine, should
time and circumstances and the abridger of all joys prevent my opening
it to the world.

If now I, in my turn, inquire of the necessitarian why he prefers to
suppose that all specification goes back to the beginning of things, he will
answer me with one of those last three arguments which I left unanswered.

First, he may say that chance is a thing absolutely unintelligible, and,
therefore, that we never can be entitled to make such a supposition. But
does not this objection smack of naïve impudence? It is not mine, it is
his own conception of the universe which leads abruptly up to hard,
ultimate, inexplicable, immutable law, on the one hand, and to inexplicable
specification and diversification of circumstances on the other. My view, on
the contrary, hypothetises nothing at all, unless it be hypothesis to say
that all specification came about in some sense, and is not to be accepted
as unaccountable. To undertake to account for anything by saying boldly
that it is due to chance would, indeed, be futile. But this I do not do.
I make use of chance chiefly to make room for a principle of generalization, or tendency to form habits, which I hold has produced all regularities. The mechanical philosopher leaves the whole specification of
the world utterly unaccounted for, which is pretty nearly as bad as to
boldly attribute it to chance. I attribute it altogether to chance, it is true,
but to chance in the form of a spontaneity which is to some degree regular.
It seems to me clear at any rate that one of these two positions must be
taken, or else specification must be supposed due to a spontaneity which

develops itself in a certain and not in a chance way, by an objective logic like that of Hegel. This last way I leave as an open possibility, for the present; for it is as much opposed to the necessitarian scheme of existence as my own theory is.

Secondly, the necessitarian may say there are, at any rate, no observed phenomena which the hypothesis of chance could aid in explaining. In reply, I point first to the phenomenon of growth and developing complexity, which appears to be universal, and which though it may possibly be an affair of mechanism perhaps, certainly presents all the appearance of increasing diversification. Then, there is variety itself, beyond comparison the most obtrusive character of the universe: no mechanism can account for this. Then, there is the very fact the necessitarian most insists upon, the regularity of the universe which for him serves only to block the road of inquiry. Then, there are the regular relationships between the laws of nature,—similarities and comparative characters, which appeal to our intelligence as its cousins, and call upon us for a reason. Finally, there is consciousness, feeling, a patent fact enough, but a very inconvenient one to the mechanical philosopher.

Thirdly, the necessitarian may say that chance is not a *vera causa,* that we cannot know positively there is any such element in the universe. But the doctrine of the *vera causa* has nothing to do with elementary conceptions. Pushed to that extreme, it at once cuts off belief in the existence of a material universe; and without that necessitarianism could hardly maintain its ground. Besides, variety is a fact which must be admitted; and the theory of chance merely consists in supposing this diversification does not antedate all time. . . .

[42]

RICHARD VON MISES

Causality and Probability*

PROBABILITY

1. *Frequency.* Among the various alternate forms in which language expresses the causal connection between two events A, B is the following. Equivalent to "A is the cause of B" or "B follows from A" one finds the proposition: "From the occurrence of A the occurrence of B can be predicted." Lending to the causal connection, as is customary, the character

* By permission of the author and publishers of Richard von Mises, *Positivism: A Study in Human Understanding*, ch. 14, pp. 163–176. Cambridge, Mass.: Harvard University Press, Copyright, 1951, by The President and Fellows of Harvard College.

of "necessity," one may add: "with certainty," or "for sure." This is the point where another parlance branches off and gradually leads out of the area of causality: one may speak of uncertain, or more or less certain, or of only "probable" predictions.

The most important difference between probability and the causal relation is that the former is graduated. One speaks of higher or lower probability and thus one can correlate these attenuated causal judgments to measure, and hence to arithmetic. Another less striking characteristic is that if one deals with predictions (primarily with uncertain ones), one often pays more attention to the effect B than to the cause A and the latter is often not even mentioned explicitly. Thus it is predicted that the event B will occur with this or that probability, without indicating any specific premise A; the implication is then that the totality of all present circumstances is assumed as the cause of the future event. But there is, of course, in the area of "uncertain" causal statements also the complete form: If this die is handled in such and such a manner, it is very probable that. . . .

When one studies the meaning of probability judgments, i.e., attempts to describe experiences to which such a statement points, one will certainly find that they consist of connections which at times take place and at other times do not. At the basis there is, just as in the case of the causal judgment, the primitive idea of "repeatability under the same circumstances." But while the causal statement assumes a succession of B upon A without exception, the probability statement is the indication of a state in which B in some cases follows the occurrence of A, and in other cases does not. This shows clearly that here—as opposed to the strict causal judgment—a certain graduation is possible corresponding to the higher or lower frequency of cases of one kind or the other. Aristotle understood this and explained: "The probable is that which happens frequently" (where "probable" is used in the sense of "highly probable").

In many popular explanations of the concept of probability it is not the number of observed verifications that is given as a measure of the probability, but rather the number of *reasons*, of motives, which are favorable to the assumption in question. The prediction that it will rain tomorrow is indeed made more probable if not only the barometer at the place in question has dropped, but also the distribution of air pressure in a wider vicinity and, further, the over-all weather situation indicate rain; hence there are three reasons for it. But these single "reasons" are themselves not causes in the sense of exceptionless correlation, as the causal judgment requires (otherwise their number would make no difference); between them and the occurrence of rain there also is only a probability relation. In this manner, therefore, one probability judgment is merely reduced to the concurrence of several probability relations, and the question still remains to what degree each of the latter is to be taken into account. Thus one cannot avoid evaluating the probability of a statement (in so far as a measure can be assigned to it at all), in the last analysis, by the frequency of cases in which the assertion in question holds true.

The observation of couples of events, A, B, *which are loosely con-nected with each other in such a way that* B *follows* A *in some cases and in others does not, leads to the probability concept. The frequency of the occurrence of the successor* B *to* A *provides an estimate for the probability. On the whole, the prerequisites for the concept of probability, its imper-fections, and its practical usefulness are subject to the same considerations as those advanced in Chapter 13 about the causality concept.*

2. *Subjective Probability.* In philosophical literature one will often find vigorous objections to the above-outlined reduction of probability measure to the frequency of events, and even to the principle of relating the probability concept to observable events at all. The point of view of Sigwart's *Logic* may be taken as representative of the whole of school phi-losophy. According to him, probability theory deals with the study of cer-tain *forms of inferences,* and hence is a part of logic. His line of thought is about as follows.

In some problems a discussion following the customary rules of logic arrives in the first place at a so-called disjunctive judgment, i.e., to a sen-tence of the form: "*A* is either *b* or *c*" (*A* is the subject; *b* and *c* are predi-cates). Then, he says, "on the grounds of the ratio of the amount of know-ing to the amount of not-knowing on which the disjunctive judgment is based," one can derive a "measure of subjective expectation" and that is the probability of *b* or *c,* respectively. For example, about a person *P* it can logically be asserted that within the next year he will or will not die. One of the two alternatives is certainly true and each of them has a certain probability. The knowing or not-knowing on which the disjunctive judg-ment is based—at least so one would think—consists of the experience that all men eventually die; but from that one can surely not derive a "measure of expectation" for the case of *P.* Hence it is apparent that Sig-wart must have in mind a different kind of knowledge; this can only be knowledge of the age, the state of health, the occupation, etc., of *P* and on the other hand the collected experience about the length of life of other men with the same characteristic properties. From the totality of *this* knowledge one may, perhaps, derive a statement such as the following: The probability of *P*'s death in the next year is very small. The mere fact of replacing "probability" by "measure of subjective expectation" offers no advantage. If somebody is asked in what way the probability judgment enunciated is related to the knowledge it is based on, he can hardly reply anything else than this: Among a great number of persons of the category in question only a small number die within a year.

Terming the judgment a "subjective" one can only mean that some-body else called upon to judge has at his disposal more or less knowledge about *P* and the life span of the corresponding group and will therefore pass a different judgment. If, e.g., it is known that *P* comes from a sick family, and if something about the rate at which the sickness is hereditary is known, this may change the probability judgment. In no case, however, can there be a connection between the experiential knowledge and the probability statement other than that given by the frequency relation.

Often the "subjective" or "logical" theory of probability is supplemented by theorems that are supposed to tell when the alternatives of a disjunction are equally probable (or are called that way). Thus C. Stumpf says,

Those cases are equally possible about which we are in equal ignorance. And since ignorance can be set equal in its measure only if we know absolutely nothing about which alternative will happen, we can more specifically substitute this explanation for it.

In brief this means: The alternatives of a disjunction are equally probable if we know absolutely nothing about the possibility of their occurrence. But what sort of ignorance is meant here? In the case of a correct die, as well as in the case of one whose center of gravity is displaced in a known way, we certainly know "absolutely nothing" about what the next throw will show. If the ignorance refers to a specific single trial, then with *every* die the six possibilities should be equally probable. But if it means that one must not know anything that distinguishes the six faces of the die, this is never true, since we know at least that the six faces bear different numbers. Hence nothing is left but to demand that nothing should be known that would lead to the conclusion that one face will fall more frequently than another—which leads us back to the frequency concept.

The "subjective" or "logical" theory of probability, preferred by school philosophy, seeks in vain for a basis of probability measurement that would be different from the frequency of the occurrence of the event in question. Even the explanation of equal probability of alternative cases is not possible without reference to the frequency.

3. *Probability Calculus.* When in the framework of the positivistic conception of science we deal with a general concept such as that of probability, we see two possible approaches. In the first place, we may examine what it is that is referred to by the word "probable" and similar expressions in everyday language, including nonspecialized scientific literature. On the other hand, we may try to construct an exact theory serving for the description of an area of facts to which the linguistic expressions in question point. The problem, however, that school philosophy regards as the only important one does not concern us, namely, to find the "true and real essence" of probability, to expose its "pure idea," which is supposed to exist somewhere and to be hidden somehow in the imperfect expressions of everyday language.

In the discussion of causality we had to limit ourselves to the first of these two approaches. For we know of no special discipline in which the general concept of causality plays a special role—unless one counts as such the whole of physics (whose relation to the idea of causality and probability will be discussed in the next chapter).

The situation is a little different concerning the various applications of the probability concept. Surely there is no sphere of human life in which expressions such as "presumable," "probable," "easily possible," or "hardly possible" are not customarily used. One even speaks of the probability of a past occurence, whereby one thinks vaguely of the frequency with which such an event would happen as a consequence of known premises in case these premises should be realized repeatedly. But it is a fruitless endeavor to try to account for such ways of speaking in the form of an exact theory. Everyday language is simply not precise; it does not contain rigorous conventions of correlation (Chapter 3) and it is vain to search for the *exact* meaning of a sentence (which may be quite connectible with the rules of ordinary language) such as: It is less probable that we shall have war next year than that there will be an earthquake in the same space of time.

But there exists a special area of experience in which all ideas connected with frequency and similar concepts, and hence also with probability, are quite easily susceptible of a treatment of higher precision. That is the sphere of mass phenomena and repetitive events. Among these a simple, repeatable game of chance, such as the dice game, is the best-known type. If one says that the six faces of a certain die fall with equal probability, this has a comparatively precise meaning; it means that on continual throwing, each of the six sides falls equally often, on the average. From the mathematical point of view the expression "on the average" is still in need of a more precise definition. But it is apparent that in occurrences of this kind the main source of indeterminacy and lack of precision, otherwise a property of the probability parlance, does not exist. In the first place, one can pretty easily state here what events must precede the observed effect: the putting of the die into the cup; the shaking of the cup; the throwing of the die. In the second place, the procedure can without difficulty be repeated at will as often as one wishes and almost without alteration; and in the third place, the effect of each trial (appearance of a specific face) is unambiguously determinable. These circumstances form the basis of an exact theory of probability, usually called the *calculus of probability*.

Clearly such a theory can cover only a small part of those occurrences to which, in ordinary language, the word "probable" is applied. It is the theory of a specific class of observable phenomena, namely, the class of mass phenomena and repeatable events, in the same sense in which thermodynamics is the theory of the phenomena of heat. The whole thing has nothing to do with a search for the "true meaning" of the word "probability."

Out of all the cases in which the various probability expressions of everyday language are used, one special group may be singled out in which the probability concept can be given a precise meaning. This is the starting point of the so-called calculus of probability, which then becomes the exact theory of mass phenomena and repetitive events, in the same sense in which mechanics is the theory of the phenomena of motion, or geometry, the theory of the phenomena of space.

4. *The Limiting Value of Frequency*. It will be useful for us to go into a few more details concerning the transition from the vague probability concept of ordinary language to the exact theory of repeatable events, and thence to the calculus of probability.

The first difficulty is to give a precise meaning to the words "frequency" or "average frequency" of the occurrence of an event. For this we have certain analogies in other areas of exact science, e.g., in the way the concepts of velocity and of specific weight are defined in mechanics. Velocity we call—imprecisely—the ratio of the displacement of a particle to the time used for it. But what displacement and what time are to be taken if one wants to specify the velocity with which a falling body arrives on the ground? Analogously, specific weight (or density) is—roughly speaking—defined as the ratio of the weight (or mass) to the volume of a body; but if we say that the density of the earth increases steadily with depth or with the distance from the surface, to what ratios do we refer?

All such questions have been solved completely for physics since the days of Leibniz and Newton. The infinitesimal calculus represents a closed, consistent system of tautological constructions which lead, among other things, to the concept of the differential quotient. It can be used to provide a refined picture of many situations given in experience. We imagine that the path traversed by a moving particle is representable by a mathematical function of time and that this function belongs to those which are "differentiable." Then the velocity at a specific moment may be defined as the differential quotient, i.e., as the limiting value which the ratio of displacement to time approaches as both the numerator and the denominator of the quotient tend to zero. Analogously, the density at a point of an arbitrary medium is defined in the following way. One takes a small piece of the body around the point in question, and lets its dimensions diminish successively more and more; in every phase of this process one forms for the piece under consideration the ratio of mass to volume and one assumes that in the "transition to zero," i.e., as both numerator and denominator of the quotient approach zero, the ratio becomes equal to a certain limiting value. This value is then called the density of the body at the point under consideration.

The problem of making the concept of "frequency" mathematically precise is solved in a similar fashion. If among n observations the event considered happens m times, the quotient m/n is called the (relative) frequency within the trial sequence of length n. If, then, one wants to speak of frequency as such, without specification of the length of sequence of trials, one must imagine that the trials can be continued ad libitum. Furthermore, it is assumed that when the numerator and denominator of the fraction m/n become bigger and bigger, the quotient approaches a certain limiting value. We then consider this limiting value as the measure of the frequency of the whole sequence and, according to what was said above, as the measure of the probability. S. D. Poisson recognized that this assumption is an appropriate picture of reality, at least in very many applications. He wrote in the introduction to his work of 1837, *Sur la probabilité des jugements,* one of the standard works of classical probability theory:

All things in nature are subject to a universal law . . . This consists of the fact that if one observes very considerable numbers of events of the same kind . . . one will find among those numbers very nearly constant ratios. For every class of observations these ratios have a special value from which they deviate less and less as the series of observed events grows in length, and they would attain this value rigorously if it were possible to extend the series to infinity.

The present author (1919) made the definition of probability as the limiting value of the relative frequency the basis of a rational calculus of probability, which follows methodically the same lines as geometry or mechanics or similar branches of science.

We need not stress here once more explicitly that such a mathematical definition of probability will never be able to do justice to all customary applications of the word "probability." Expressions such as "force" or "work" in mechanics also denote concepts that correspond only in comparatively rare cases to what is denoted by these words in ordinary language.

As a basis of an exact theory of repeated events and mass phenomena one may choose a probability concept defined as the limiting value of the relative frequency of an event in a sequence of trials continued indefinitely.

5. *The Complete Theory.* Our definition of mathematical probability has the immediate advantage that it yields a reasonable addition theorem for the probability calculus. If one calls an infinite sequence of trials in which several different results (events) may occur (e.g., an ideal game with dice that do not wear out) a *collective,* it follows from the definition that the probability for the assumption that *within one* collective one of several mutually exclusive results occurs is equal to the sum of the probabilities of the individual results. For example, the probability of throwing an even number with a single die is equal to the sum of the probabilities of the occurrence of a 2, a 4, and a 6. A theory that does not use the concept of the collective and of the frequency within a collective cannot even state correctly the addition theorem. For the probabilities of *arbitrary* "mutually exclusive" events can have any sum, even bigger than 1.

Perhaps the most important insight supplied by the derivation of the probability concept from the frequency within a collective is the following. One may ask the question: Is there a definite, measurable probability for the assumption that a certain specified individual, John Smith, of New York, is going to die within a year? From the point of view of our theory the answer is a clear-cut "no." Only within a class, within a precisely defined group of persons, which can be considered as unlimited, does there exist a frequency of deaths; and we can speak of a limiting value only if we think of an indefinite continuation of observations within the group.

But the individual, John Smith, is a member of many different classes, e.g., of the class of "men and women in New York 40 years of age" or of the class of "men in the United States in normal jobs, not over 40 years of age, and insured for 5 years." The probability of death in these two classes will, in general, be different and each of the two numbers (and many others) can be taken as John Smith's probability of death. If one thinks that a "true," and hence uniquely determined, number can be found by including in the definition of the class as many properties of John Smith as possible one does not get any result. For by *all* his properties only the one individual and no other one is determined, and thus any possibility of computing a frequency vanishes.

Besides the addition theorem for probabilities of mutually exclusive events within a collective, there is a need in probability calculus for a "multiplication rule." This rule states, e.g., that the probability of throwing a 5 and a 6 in succession is equal to the product of the probabilities of 5 and of 6. In order to derive the multiplicative law, which expresses a well-known empirical fact, in a sufficiently general form, one has to subject the collective to another axiom besides the one that requires the existence of a limiting value of the relative frequency. The second axiom demands that the succession of the various labels or trial results within a collective is in a specific sense "random." This requirement can be brought into a precise form by asking that in a subsequence of all trials, selected without knowledge of the trial results, the limiting values of the frequencies of the various possible results are the same as those in the total sequence forming the collective. The empirical fact expressed by the "axiom of randomness" in an idealized form is that it is practically impossible in a continued game of chance, e.g., roulette, to change one's chances of winning for an unlimited duration of the game by a calculated selection of parties (or of stakes), i.e., by a so-called gambling system. Originally objections were raised to this formulation of the axiom of randomness within the framework of the mathematical (tautological) theory. Later, however, owing to the work of A. Wald, A. H. Copeland, and W. Feller, a consistency proof for the probability calculus as based upon the two axioms, existence of a limited frequency and randomness of succession, was successfully carried out.

Finally, our conception bears out the analogy between the probability calculus and the rational theories of other areas as far as the nature of its problems is concerned. According to the classical point of view represented by Laplace, which in more recent times was adopted without reservation, even by H. Poincaré (1912), it is the outright task of probability theory to compute the probability of any describable event. But nobody claims today that it is the task of geometry to determine the distance of two well-described points on the surface of the earth. One realizes rather that geometry deals only with *relations* among spatial quantities and shows how to compute the length of the side of a triangle only if other lengths, etc., are given beforehand. Thus a rational theory of probability enables us to calculate unknown probabilities only from given probabilities. The general problem can be formulated in this manner: In every single case the probabilities within certain initial collectives are taken for granted, and then, by means of theorems derived tautologically from the axioms, the probabilities within specific, derived collectives can be computed. In the foregoing example for the addition theorem, the initial collective consisted of the gambling results of a die, hence of a sequence formed by the numbers 1 to 6; the end collective, of a sequence of "even" and "odd." Once the six probabilities p_1 to p_6 of the first-mentioned collective are given, the latter ones are found as the two partial sums $p_1 + p_3 + p_5$ for the odd, and $p_2 + p_4 + p_6$ for the even results.

Based upon the concept of the collective and the two axioms, existence of a limiting frequency and randomness of the succession of results, a consistent mathematical probability theory can be constructed, which—in analogy to geometry, mechanics, etc.—forms an exact rational theory of the mass phenomena and repetitive events.

6. *Trangression of the Borderline.* It is a well-known phenomenon that people often try to apply a theory, once it has found a certain recognition and proved its usefulness, far beyond its range of validity. In so far as this attempt belongs to what we have called (Chapter 1, 3) "change of usage," it is a regular procedure and may work out to the advantage of the evolution of science. But this endeavor often overshoots its mark, as many examples show. The usefulness of the energy principle in wide areas of physics and chemistry led the chemist Wilhelm Ostwald to the idea of making energetics a *Weltanschauung,* i.e., of extending its application to all possible observable phenomena. He went so far as to suggest a measure for the subjective feeling of happiness of men in a formula containing certain quantities of energy (see Chapter 26, 7).

In the calculus of probability there has always been a strong tendency to transgress boundaries and this trend has received a new impetus since the frequency conception has become more and more prevalent. Among older instances we mention that Laplace tried to compute the advantages and disadvantages of monarchistic and republican rule; the mathematician A. A. Markoff, the credibility of the Bible; the philosopher E. Hartmann, the answer to the question whether there are spiritual causes of natural phenomena; and for all this the formulas of probability calculus ought to serve! One may perhaps in those cases use the probability expressions of everyday language, just as one may colloquially speak of an energy of the feeling of happiness, but the prerequisites for the application of the exact probability concept are in no way satisfied.

We are primarily interested here in the repeated attempts at using the probability calculus for the so-called solution of the problem of induction. E. Zilsel made such an attempt on the basis of the classical conception of probability, and H. Reichenbach, on the basis of the frequency theory. We know (Chapter 12, 7, Chapter 13, 5) that the cardinal problem in any treatment of induction is to discuss how the transition from accumulated unprecise and even partly inconsistent observations to a specific exact theory of the domain in question can be performed. Reichenbach starts by formulating a rule which he calls the fundamental rule of induction and in which only a single collective or mass phenomenon is taken into consideration. It runs as follows: If in a finite sequence of n observations an event occurs m times, hence with a frequence $m/n = p$, and if otherwise nothing is known, then we "posit" that the limiting value of the frequency (as m and n tend to infinity) is equal to $p \pm \varepsilon$, where ε is a small unknown positive quantity. Analogously one could say: If the measurement of the side of a triangle yields the value l, we "posit" that its length is $l \pm \varepsilon$. There is nothing much to say against such propositions, except that they are obvious. More correctly and more generally, one might state that for the data going into a problem within an exact theory one chooses values which are based upon necessarily imperfect measurement and that one has to take that lack of precision into account in retransforming the theoretical results to statements about reality.

But Reichenbach gives his induction rule—and here lies the transgression of the limits of the theory—a much more general interpretation. In the first place, it is supposed to be applicable to happenings of everyday life, e.g., when one wants to judge whether on a certain day a train is going to leave on time. In our opinion there is in such a case no possibility of computing in a reasonable manner the number n of observations and the number m of events, from which $p = m/n$ results, however rough the approximation. For even on the first day of the introduction of the timetable, or even on the day the railroad starts operating, one forms a "probability judgment," which is based upon various considerations, e.g., upon one's opinion about the possibility of a strike, or of an accident, and upon experiences of a more general kind about the reliability of people throughout the country, etc. Each of these considerations is very vaguely connected, in the manner mentioned in Section 1, with some frequency of experiences. And after all, what can the traveler do with the information that the probability of a train leaving on time is between 0.374 and 0.376? Is there any sense in thinking of a several-hundredfold repetition of exactly the same situation where in 37 per cent of the cases the train leaves on time? Obviously, this represents an example in which, although customary parlance allows the use of the word "probability" on the grounds of a vague and unclear idea of the countability of cases, the application of elementary or higher mathematics, the formation of a quotient and its limiting value, and the introduction of accuracy limits $\pm \varepsilon$, etc., are completely out of place.

Even more striking is the attempted application of the "rule of induction" to the problem of induction itself. Reichenbach defends seriously the view that the number of successful and unsuccessful instances of testing of a physical theory, such as the theory of relativity, can be counted, and each one of them can be given a definite "weight," e.g., the red shift counts $+ 3$, the deviation of a light ray by the sun, $+ \frac{1}{2}$, the motion of the perihelion of Mercury, $+$ 5, etc. Here the most elementary prerequisites of counting are not satisfied, for 1 thought plus 1 thought by no means always equals 2 thoughts. Calculations that operate with "numbers" of thoughts, of successful instances of testing, etc., are model examples of nonconnectibility with the most elementary rules of language—not to mention the fact that a theory which definitely breaks down in the case of one single phenomenon must be rejected, and not be given the probability 0.99 if one can quote 99 instances in which it holds true. At any rate, in this way, one is not capable of reducing the question of the usefulness of a theoretical idea in any physical area to a question of probability calculus. It must be noticed that even in unprecise colloquial talk physicists hardly ever use the expression that a *theory* has a greater or smaller numerical probability. The physicist judges the usefulness, the possible acceptance or rejection of a theory by various criteria quite different from the ones above —to mention but one example: by the point of view of economy of thought (Chapter 12, 3). It is only within the framework of *one* theory which is taken for granted, and when all that remains to do is determine the value of a constant factor, that one can apply the concepts of the probability calculus to a sequence of uniform trials and then compute the probability for different possible values of the constant (so-called error theory).

It has been pointed out above that we consider as the legitimate domain of the calculus of probability the problems concerning mass phenomena and repetitive events. In other words, we hold that any statement of the probability calculus is nothing else than a proposition on certain infinite sequences of numbers or signs which stand for well-defined events or occurrences. There is no doubt that one may try to build up another theory, also connected with the colloquial usage of the term "probability," which concerns itself with the psychological problem of *plausibility* or *degree of confirmation* of a single statement or of entire systems. The mathematician G. Pólya has given some fundamentals of such a theory whose main characteristic is that no numerical value can be ascribed to the plausibility of a statement. In contrast to this, R. Carnap, once a follower of logical empiricism, thinks that he can apply not only numerical values, but even rules of classical probability calculus to degree of confirmation. This means, essentially, that he *counts* statements, judgments, confirmations, as Reichenbach does (see above). The ultimate goal of the confirmation calculus is again to give a mathematical foundation to the procedure of induction (inductive logic, see Chapter 13, 5). Our point of view may be summarized as follows.

The calculus of probability, which, like geometry, mechanics, etc., is the exact theory of a specific area of phenomena and which is itself derived from an empirical basis by means of induction, cannot serve to justify or rationalize the alleged inductive "inference" within the range of other areas of facts. The transition from observations to general theoretical statements cannot be mathematicized at all; it is not a logical conclusion, but a choice of that precise description of observed facts which one believes will stand up in the face of future observations, but which can be altered at any time for various reasons.

7. *Different Points of View.* Many mathematicians who are under the influence of school philosophy reject the conception of a probability calculus based upon the concept of the collective as a "purely empirical" point of view. Others object that the collective as an infinite sequence of observations does not exist in reality, and hence that the theory is too abstract and could not be used for the description of real phenomena. To answer both of these objections one need only point to the repeatedly mentioned analogy with all other branches of exact science. There exists no infinitely long straight line of infinitely small cross-sectional area; nevertheless, geometry, which works with this and similar concepts, is useful for the explanation of phenomena of space—and is on the other hand not a "purely empirical" science.

Of course, one cannot say anything against someone's treating the tautological part of the theory of any area of experience in such a way that he gives a comprehensive exposition without referring back to the empirical starting point. But then he must not enunciate the results of his calculations in a form which gives the impression that these considerations represent statements about certain real phenomena. The typical flaw in the thinking of the older presentation of the calculus of probability may be illustrated by the following example.

Forming with the signs "o" and "1" (or any other two signs) all those combinations which consist of a total of n signs, one gets a group of 2^n different combinations. It is found that, if one takes n as a very large number, the great majority of combinations belonging to the group consists of approximately $n/2$ zeros and $n/2$ ones. More precisely, Jacob Bernoulli (1713) derived the following theorem: The larger n is, the larger is the fraction of those combinations in which the number of zeros or of ones deviates from $n/2$ by less than, say, 0.1 per cent. Obviously, this is a purely arithmetic property of numbers and it is connected with reality only in so far as is any arithmetic theorem (Chapter 11, 1). But Bernoulli himself and most textbooks state the result in such a way that it says: if one throws a "true" coin for heads and tails and carries out a long enough sequence of trials, it is almost certain that the number of heads will deviate by less than 0.1 per cent from half the number of trials. All we have to remark here is: The transition from the arithmetic theorem to this statement about reality can be justified only by defining a "true" coin as one for which the probabilities of the two alternatives are $\frac{1}{2}$ each, hereby using the probability concept suggested by us, which establishes a connection with the frequency of occurrence of an event. A special variety of the confusion here is the idea that the derivation of the arithmetic theorem actually "mathematically *proves*" the fact that an event possessing the probability $\frac{1}{2}$ will in a long sequence of trials almost certainly occur with a frequency approximately equal to $\frac{1}{2}$, even if one did not previously define the probability by means of the frequency in a sequence of trials.

The calculus of probability is particularly interesting, from the point of view of the general topics treated in this book, because in this special discipline almost all fundamental questions that have played a role in the history of the inductive sciences are still under discussion. From the naïve empiricist on the one hand, who does not admit any exact concepts but accepts only the conceptual spheres vaguely delineated by the words of everyday language, up to the no less naïve "pure theoreticians," in whose mind all of science dissolves into separate systems of tautological transformations, every point of view is still represented today. There still are, e.g., the followers of the classical theory according to which everything depends upon the a priori recognition of equally possible cases, and they speak of "free formation of expectation," of "indifferent ranges," and of "compulsory, nonarbitrary construction of assumptions of equal right." Others again find that with the use of exact concepts "probability can no longer be a guide in practical life," or they predict the near approach of the breakdown of the whole of science if it continues to prove to be so unrealistic.

More recently the view has been defended that for the treatment of the problems of probability theory customary logic that knows only true and false judgments is not sufficient and that one has to create a special "logic of probability." To each judgment, according to this, there should be correlated a number between zero and one as its "probability value." It is not stated what value the correlation of the value number itself has. There is little doubt that it is possible to give to a part of the tautological considerations within the calculus of probability the external form of a "multivalued logic"; but that cannot have any essential influence upon the meaning and the results of the theory.

In the contemporary discussion of the foundation of probability theory all the various points of view are represented that have played a role in the evolution of the inductive sciences: a-priorism, pure empiricism, the idea that statements about phenomena which are not taken into consideration in the definition of the basic concepts can be "proved mathematically," and finally the tendency to transgress all limits of validity of the theory by giving to the names of the basic concepts retroactively the widest interpretation. It may be expected that for this sector of the world of experience (the area of mass phenomena and repetitive events) also clarification will be reached gradually, which in other fields such as those of spatial phenomena, the phenomena of motion, heat processes, etc., has either already been reached or is actually in progress.

•

RUDOLF CARNAP

Empiricism, Semantics, and Ontology *

1. The Problem of Abstract Entities

Empiricists are in general rather suspicious with respect to any kind of abstract entities like properties, classes, relations, numbers, propositions, etc. They usually feel much more in sympathy with nominalists than with realists (in the medieval sense). As far as possible they try to avoid any reference to abstract entities and to restrict themselves to what is sometimes called a nominalistic language, i.e., one not containing such references. However, within certain scientific contexts it seems hardly possible to avoid them. In the case of mathematics, some empiricists try to find a way out by treating the whole of mathematics as a mere calculus, a formal system for which no interpretation is given or can be given. Accordingly, the mathematician is said to speak not about numbers, functions, and infinite classes, but merely about meaningless symbols and formulas manipulated according to given formal rules. In physics it is more difficult to shun the suspected entities, because the language of physics serves for the communication of reports and predictions and hence cannot be taken as a mere calculus. A physicist who is suspicious of abstract entities may perhaps try to declare a certain part of the language of physics as uninterpreted and uninterpretable, that part which refers to real numbers as space-time coordinates or as values of physical magnitudes, to functions, limits, etc. More probably he will just speak about all these things like anybody else but with an uneasy conscience, like a man who in his everyday life does with qualms many things which are not in accord with the high moral principles he professes on Sundays. Recently the problem of abstract entities has arisen again in connection with semantics, the theory of meaning and truth. Some semanticists say that certain expressions designate certain entities, and among these designated entities they include not only concrete material things but also abstract entities, e.g., properties as designated

* From *Revue Internationale de Philosophie* IV, no. 11 (Jan., 1950), pp. 20–40. Reprinted by permission of the author and editor (Jean Lameere). The author has made some minor changes in the formulations to the effect that the term "framework" is now used only for the system of linguistic expressions, and not for the system of the entities in question.

by predicates and propositions as designated by sentences.[1] Others object strongly to this procedure as violating the basic principles of empiricism and leading back to a metaphysical ontology of the Platonic kind.

It is the purpose of this article to clarify this controversial issue. The nature and implications of the acceptance of a language referring to abstract entities will first be discussed in general; it will be shown that using such a language does not imply embracing a Platonic ontology but is perfectly compatible with empiricism and strictly scientific thinking. Then the special question of the role of abstract entities in semantics will be discussed. It is hoped that the clarification of the issue will be useful to those who would like to accept abstract entities in their work in mathematics, physics, semantics, or any other field; it may help them to overcome nominalistic scruples.

2. *Linguistic Framework of Entities*

Are there properties, classes, numbers, propositions? In order to understand more clearly the nature of these and related problems, it is above all necessary to recognize a fundamental distinction between two kinds of questions concerning the existence or reality of entities. If someone wishes to speak in his language about a new kind of entities, he has to introduce a system of new ways of speaking, subject to new rules; we shall call this procedure the construction of a linguistic *framework* for the new entities in question. And now we must distinguish two kinds of questions of existence: first, questions of the existence of certain entities of the new kind *within the framework*; we call them *internal questions*; and second, questions concerning the existence or reality of the *system of entities as a whole*, called *external questions*. Internal questions and possible answers to them are formulated with the help of the new forms of expressions. The answers may be found either by purely logical methods or by empirical methods, depending upon whether the framework is a logical or a factual one. An external question is of a problematic character which is in need of closer examination.

The world of things. Let us consider as an example the simplest kind of entities dealt with in the everyday language: the spatio-temporally ordered system of observable things and events. Once we have accepted the thing-language with its framework for things, we can raise and answer internal questions, e.g., "Is there a white piece of paper on my desk?," "Did King Arthur actually live?," "Are unicorns and centaurs real or merely imaginary?," and the like. These questions are to be answered by empirical investigations. Results of observations are evaluated according to certain rules as confirming or disconfirming evidence for possible answers. (This evaluation is usually carried out, of course, as a matter of habit rather than a deliberate, rational procedure. But it is possible, in a rational reconstruction, to lay down explicit rules for the evaluation. This is one of the main tasks of a pure, as distinguished from a psychological epistemology.) The concept of reality occurring in these internal questions is an empirical, scientific, non-metaphysical concept. To recognize something as a real thing or event means to succeed in incorporating it into the system of things at a particular space-time position so that it fits together with the other things recognized as real, according to the rules of the framework.

From these questions we must distinguish the external question of the reality of the thing world itself. In contrast to the former questions, this question is raised neither by the man in the street nor by scientists, but only by philosophers. Realists give an affirmative answer, subjective idealists a negative one, and the controversy goes on for centuries without ever being solved. And it cannot be solved because it is framed in a wrong way. To be real in the scientific sense means to be an element of the system; hence this concept cannot be meaningfully applied to the system itself. Those who raise the question of the reality of the thing world itself have perhaps in mind not a theoretical question as their formulation seems to suggest, but rather a practical question, a matter of a practical decision concerning the structure of our language. We have to make the choice whether or not to accept and use the forms of expression in the framework in question.

In the case of this particular example, there is usually no deliberate choice because we all have accepted the thing language early in our lives as a matter of course. Nevertheless, we may regard it as a matter of decision in this sense: we are free to choose to continue using the thing language or not; in the latter case we could restrict ourselves to a language of sense-data and other "phenomenal" entities, or construct an alternative to the customary thing language with another structure, or, finally, we could refrain from speaking. If someone decides to accept the thing language, there is no objection against saying that he has accepted the world of things. But this must not be interpreted as if it meant his acceptance of a *belief* in the reality of the thing world; there is no such belief or assertion or assumption, because it is not a theoretical question. To accept the thing world means nothing more than to accept a certain form of language, in other words, to accept rules for forming statements and for testing, accepting, or rejecting them. The acceptance of the thing language leads, on the basis of observations made, also to the acceptance, belief, and assertion of certain statements. But the thesis of the reality of the thing world cannot be among these statements, because it cannot be formulated in the thing language or, it seems, in any other theoretical language.

The decision of accepting the thing language, although itself not of a cognitive nature, will nevertheless usually be influenced by theoretical knowledge, just like any other deliberate decision concerning the acceptance of linguistic or other rules. The purposes for which the language is intended to be used, for instance, the purpose of communicating factual knowledge, will determine which factors are relevant for the decision. The efficiency, fruitfulness, and simplicity of the use of the thing language may be among the decisive factors. And the questions concerning these qualities are indeed of a theoretical nature. But these questions cannot be identified with the question of realism. They are not yes-no questions but questions of degree. The thing language in the customary form works indeed with a high degree of efficiency for most purposes of everyday life. This is a matter of fact, based upon the content of our experiences. However, it would be wrong to describe this situation by saying: "The fact of the efficiency of the thing language is confirming evidence for the reality of the thing world"; we should rather say instead: "This fact makes it advisable to accept the thing language."

The system of numbers. As an example of a system which is of a logical rather than a factual nature let us take the system of natural numbers. The framework for this system is constructed by introducing into the language new expressions with suitable rules: (1) numerals like "five" and sentence forms like "there are five books on the table"; (2) The general term "number" for the new entities, and sentence forms like "five is a number"; (3) expressions for properties of numbers (e.g., "odd," "prime"), relations (e.g., "greater than,") and functions (e.g., "plus,") and sentence forms like "two plus three is five"; (4) numerical variables ("m," "n," etc.) and quantifiers for universal sentences ("for every n, . . .") and existential sentences ("there is an n such that . . .") with the customary deductive rules.

Here again there are internal questions, e.g., "Is there a prime number greater than hundred?" Here, however, the answers are found, not by empirical investigation based on observations, but by logical analysis based on the rules for the new expressions. Therefore the answers are here analytic, i.e., logically true.

What is now the nature of the philosophical question concerning the existence or reality of numbers? To begin with, there is the internal question which, together with the affirmative answer, can be formulated in the new terms, say, by "There are numbers" or, more explicitly, "There is an n such that n is a number." This statement follows from the analytic statement "five is a number" and is therefore itself analytic. Moreover, it is rather trivial (in contradistinction to a statement like "There is a prime number greater than a million," which is likewise analytic but far from trivial), because it does not say more than that the new system is not empty; but this is immediately seen from the rule which states that words like "five" are substitutable for the new variables. Therefore nobody who meant the question "Are there numbers?" in the internal sense would either assert or even seriously consider a negative answer. This makes it plausible to assume that those philosophers who treat the question of the existence of numbers as a serious philosophical problem and offer lengthy arguments on either side, do not have in mind the internal question. And, indeed, if we were to ask them: "Do you mean the question as to whether the framework of numbers, *if* we were to accept it, would be found to be empty or not?," they would probably reply: "Not at all; we mean a question *prior* to the acceptance of the new framework." They might try to explain what they mean by saying that it is a question of the ontological status of numbers; the question whether or not numbers have a certain metaphysical characteristic called reality (but a kind of ideal reality, different from the material reality of the thing world) or subsistence or status of "independent entities." Unfortunately, these philosophers have so far not given a formulation of their question in terms of the common scientific language. Therefore our judgement must be that they have not succeeded in giving to the external question and to the possible answers any cognitive content. Unless and until they supply a clear cognitive interpretation, we are justified in our suspicion that their question is a pseudo-question, that is, one disguised in the form of a theoretical question while in fact it is non-theoretical; in the present case it is the practical problem whether or not to incorporate into the language the new linguistic forms which constitute the framework of numbers.

The system of propositions. New variables, "p," "q," etc., are introduced with a rule to the effect that any (declarative) sentence may be substituted for a variable of this kind; this includes, in addition to the sentences of the original thing language, also all general sentences with variables of any kind which may have been introduced into the language. Further, the general term "proposition" is introduced. "p is a proposition" may be defined by "p or not p" (or any other sentence form yielding only analytic sentences). Therefore, every sentence of the form ". . . is a proposition" (where any sentence may stand in the place of the dots) is analytic. This holds, for example, for the sentence:

(*a*) "Chicago is large is a proposition."

(We disregard here the fact that the rules of English grammar require not a sentence but a that-clause as the subject of another sentence; accordingly, instead of (*a*) we should have to say "That Chicago is large is a proposition.") Predicates may be admitted whose argument expressions are sentences; these predicates may be either extensional (e.g., the customary truth-functional connectives) or not (e.g., modal predicates like "possible," "necessary," etc.). With the help of the new variables, general sentences may be formed, e.g.

(*b*) "For every p, either p or not-p."

(*c*) "There is a p such that p is not necessary and not-p is not necessary."

(*d*) "There is a p such that p is a proposition."

(*c*) and (*d*) are internal assertions of existence. The statement "There are propositions" may be meant in the sense of (*d*); in this case it is analytic (since it follows from (*a*)) and even trivial. If, however, the statement is meant in an external sense, then it is non-cognitive.

It is important to notice that the system of rules for the linguistic expressions of the propositional framework (of which only a few rules have here been briefly indicated) is sufficient for the introduction of the framework. Any further explanations as to the nature of the propositions (i.e., the elements of the system, the values of the variables "p," "q," etc.) are theoretically unnecessary because, if correct, they follow from the rules. For example, are propositions mental events (as in Russell's theory)? A look at the rules shows us that they are not, because otherwise existential statements would be of the form: "If the mental state of the person in question fulfils such and such conditions, then there is a p such that . . .". The fact that no references to mental conditions occur in existential statements (like (c), (d), etc.) shows that propositions are not mental entities. Further, a statement of the existence of linguistic entities (e.g., expressions, classes of expressions, etc.) must contain a reference to a language. The fact that no such reference occurs in the existential statements here, shows that propositions are not linguistic entities. The fact that in these statements no reference to a subject (an observer or knower) occurs (nothing like: "There is a p which is necessary for Mr. X"), shows that the propositions (and their properties, like necessity, etc.) are not subjective. Although characterizations of these or similar kinds are, strictly speaking, unnecessary, they may nevertheless be practically useful. If they are given, they should be understood, not as ingredient parts of the system, but merely as marginal notes with the purpose of supplying to the reader helpful hints or convenient pictorial associations which may make his learning of the use of the expressions easier than the bare system of the rules would do. Such a characterization is analogous to an extra-systematic explanation which a physicist sometimes gives to the beginner. He might, for example, tell him to imagine the atoms of a gas as small balls rushing around with great speed, or the electromagnetic field and its oscillations as quasi-elastic tensions and vibrations in an ether. In fact, however, all that can accurately be said about atoms or the field is implicitly contained in the physical laws of the theories in question.[2]

The system of thing properties. The thing language contains words like "red," "hard," "stone," "house," etc., which are used for describing what things are like. Now we may introduce new variables, say "f," "g," etc., for which those words are substitutable and furthermore the general term "property." New rules are laid down which admit sentences like "Red is a property," "Red is a color," "These two pieces of paper have at least one color in common" (i.e., "There is an f such that f is a color, and . . ."). The last sentence is an internal assertion. It is of an empirical, factual nature. However, the external statement, the philosophical statement of the reality of properties—a special case of the thesis of the reality of universals—is devoid of cognitive content.

The systems of integers and rational numbers. Into a language containing the framework of natural numbers we may introduce first the (positive and negative) integers as relations among natural numbers and then the rational numbers as relations among integers. This involves introducing new types of variables, expressions substitutable for them and the general terms "integer" and "rational number."

The system of real numbers. On the basis of the rational numbers, the real numbers may be introduced as classes of a special kind (segments) of rational numbers (according to the method developed by Dedekind and Frege). Here again a new type of variables is introduced, expressions substitutable for them (e.g., "$\sqrt{2}$"), and the general term "real number."

The spatio-temporal coordinate system for physics. The new entities are the space-time points. Each is an ordered quadruple of four real numbers, called its coordinates, consisting of three spatial and one temporal coordinates. The physical state of a spatio-temporal point or region is described either with the help of qualitative predicates (e.g., "hot") or by ascribing numbers as values of a physical magnitude (e.g., mass, temperature, and the like). The step from the system of things (which does not contain space-time points but only extended objects with spatial and temporal relations between them) to the physical coordinate system is again a matter of decision. Our choice of certain features, although itself not theoretical, is suggested by theoretical knowledge, either logical or factual. For example, the choice of real numbers rather than rational numbers or integers as coordinates is not much influenced by the facts of experience but mainly due to considerations of mathematical simplicity. The restriction to rational coordinates would not be in conflict with any experimental knowledge we have, because the result of any measurement is a rational number. However, it would prevent the use of ordinary geometry (which says, e.g., that the diagonal of a square with the side 1 has the irrational value $\sqrt{2}$) and thus lead to great complications. On the other hand, the decision to use three rather than two or four spatial coordinates is strongly suggested, but still not forced upon us, by the result of common observations. If certain events allegedly observed in spiritualistic séances, e.g., a ball moving out of a sealed box, were confirmed beyond any reasonable doubt, it might seem advisable to use four spatial coordinates. Internal questions are here, in general, empirical questions to be answered by empirical investigations. On the other hand, the external questions of the reality of physical space and physical time are pseudo-questions. A question like "Are there (really) space-time points?" is ambiguous. It may be meant as an internal question; then the affirmative answer is, of course, analytic and trivial. Or it may be meant in the external sense: "Shall we introduce such and such forms into our language?"; in this case it is not a theoretical but a practical question, a matter of decision rather than assertion, and hence the proposed formulation would be misleading. Or finally, it may be meant in the following sense: "Are our experiences such that the use of the linguistic forms in question will be expedient and fruitful?" This is a theoretical question of a factual, empirical nature. But it concerns a matter of degree; therefore a formulation in the form "real or not?" would be inadequate.

3. *What does Acceptance of Kind of Entities Mean?*

Let us now summarize the essential characteristics of situations involving the introduction of a new kind of entities, characteristics which are common to the various examples outlined above.

The acceptance of a new kind of entities is represented in the language by the introduction of a framework of new forms of expressions to be used according to a new set of rules. There may be new names for particular entities of the kind in question; but some such names may already occur in the language before the introduction of the new framework. (Thus, for example, the thing language contains certainly words of the type of "blue" and "house" before the framework of properties is introduced; and it may contain words like "ten" in sentences of the form "I have ten fingers" before the framework of numbers is introduced.) The latter fact shows that the occurrence of constants of the type in question—regarded as names of entities of the new kind after the new framework is introduced—is not a sure sign of the acceptance of the new kind of entities. Therefore the introduction of such constants is not to be regarded as an essential step in the introduction of the framework. The two essential steps are rather the following. First, the introduction of a general term, a predicate of higher level, for the new kind of entities, permitting us to say of any particular entity that it belongs to this kind (e.g., "Red is a *property*," "Five is a *number*.") Second, the introduction of variables of the new type. The new entities are values of these variables; the constants (and the closed compound expressions, if any) are substitutable for the variables.[3] With the help of the variables, general sentences concerning the new entities can be formulated.

After the new forms are introduced into the language, it is possible to formulate with their help internal questions and possible answers to them. A question of this kind may be either empirical or logical; accordingly a true answer is either factually true or analytic.

From the internal questions we must clearly distinguish external questions, i.e., philosophical questions concerning the existence or reality of the total system of the new entities. Many philosophers regard a question of this kind as an ontological question which must be raised and answered *before* the introduction of the new language forms. The latter introduction, they believe, is legitimate only if it can be justified by an ontological insight supplying an affirmative answer to the question of reality. In contrast to this view, we take the position that the introduction of the new ways of speaking does not need any theoretical justification because it does not imply any assertion of reality. We may still speak (and have done so) of "the acceptance of the new entities" since this form of speech is customary; but one must keep in mind that this phrase does not mean for us anything more than acceptance of the new framework, i.e. of the new linguistic forms. Above all, it must not be interpreted as referring to an assumption, belief, or assertion of "the reality of the entities." There is no such assertion. An alleged statement of the reality of the system of entities is a pseudo-statement without cognitive content. To be sure, we have to face at this point an important question; but it is a practical, not a theoretical question; it is the question of whether or not to accept the new linguistic forms. The acceptance cannot be judged as being either true or false because it is not an assertion. It can only be judged as being more or less expedient, fruitful, conducive to the aim for which the language is intended. Judgments of this kind supply the motivation for the decision of accepting or rejecting the kind of entities.[4]

Thus it is clear that the acceptance of a linguistic framework must not be regarded as implying a metaphysical doctrine concerning the reality of the entities in question. It seems to me due to a neglect of this important distinction that some contemporary nominalists label the admission of variables of abstract types as "platonism."[5] This is, to say the least, an extremely misleading terminology. It leads to the absurd consequence, that the position of everybody who accepts the language of physics with its real number of variables (as a language of communication, not merely as a calculus) would be called platonistic, even if he is a strict empiricist who rejects platonic metaphysics.

A brief historical remark may here be inserted. The non-cognitive character of the questions which we have called here external questions was recognized and emphasized already by the Vienna Circle under the leadership of Moritz Schlick, the group from which the movement of logical empiricism originated. Influenced by ideas of Ludwig Wittgenstein, the Circle rejected both the thesis of the reality of the external world and the thesis of its irreality as pseudo-statements;[6] the same was the case for both the thesis of the reality of universals (abstract entities, in our present terminology) and the nominalistic thesis that they are not real and that their alleged names are not names of anything but merely *flatus vocis*. (It is obvious that the apparent negation of a pseudo-statement must also be a pseudo-statement.) It is therefore not correct to classify the members of the Vienna Circle as nominalists, as is sometimes done. However, if we look at the basic anti-metaphysical and pro-scientific attitude of most nominalists (and the same holds for many materialists and realists in the modern sense), disregarding their occasional pseudo-theoretical formulations, then it is, of course, true to say that the Vienna Circle was much closer to those philosophers than to their opponents.

4. *Abstract Entities in Semantics*

The problem of the legitimacy and the status of abstract entities has recently again led to controversial discussions in connection with semantics. In a semantical meaning analysis certain expressions in a language are often said to designate (or name or denote or signify or refer to) certain extralinguistic entities.[7] As long as physical things or events (e.g., Chicago or Caesar's death) are taken as designata (entities designated), no serious doubts arise. But strong objections have been raised, especially by some empiricists, against abstract entities as designata, e.g., against semantical statements of the following kind:

(1) "The word 'red' designates a property of things";
(2) "The word 'color' designates a property of properties of things";

(3) "The word 'five' designates a number";
(4) "The word 'odd' designates a property of numbers";
(5) "The sentence 'Chicago is large' designates a proposition."

Those who criticize these statements do not, of course, reject the use of the expressions in question, like "red" or "five"; nor would they deny that these expressions are meaningful. But to be meaningful, they would say, is not the same as having a meaning in the sense of an entity designated. They reject the belief, which they regard as implicitly presupposed by those semantical statements, that to each expression of the types in question (adjectives like "red," numerals like "five," etc.) there is a particular real entity to which the expression stands in the relation of designation. This belief is rejected as incompatible with the basic principles of empiricism or of scientific thinking. Derogatory labels like "Platonic realism," "hypostatization," or " 'Fido'-Fido principle" are attached to it. The latter is the name given by Gilbert Ryle [8] to the criticized belief, which, in his view, arises by a naive inference of analogy: just as there is an entity well known to me, viz. my dog Fido, which is designated by the name "Fido," thus there must be for every meaningful expression a particular entity to which it stands in the relation of designation or naming, i.e., the relation exemplified by "Fido"-Fido. The belief criticized is thus a case of hypostatization, i.e., of treating as names expressions which are not names. While "Fido" is a name, expressions like "red," "five," etc., are said not to be names, not to designate anything.

Our previous discussions concerning the acceptance of frameworks enables us now to clarify the situation with respect to abstract entities as designata. Let us take as an example the statement:

(a) " 'Five' designates a number."

The formulation of this statement presupposes that our language L contains the forms of expressions which we have called the framework of numbers, in particular, numerical variables and the general term "number." If L contains these forms, the following is an analytic statement in L:

(b) "Five is a number."

Further, to make the statement (a) possible, L must contain an expression like "designates" or "is a name of" for the semantical relation of designation. If suitable rules for this term are laid down, the following is likewise analytic:

(c) " 'Five' designates five."

(Generally speaking, any expression of the form " '. . .' designates . . ." is an analytic statement provided the term ". . ." is a constant in an accepted framework. If the latter condition is not fulfilled, the expression is not a statement.) Since (a) follows from (c) and (b), (a) is likewise analytic.

Thus it is clear that *if* someone accepts the framework of numbers, then he must acknowledge (c) and (b) and hence (a) as true statements. Generally speaking, if someone accepts a framework of entities, then he is bound to admit its entities as possible designata. Thus the question of the admissibility of entities of a certain type or of abstract entities in general as designata is reduced to the question of the acceptability of the linguistic framework for those entities. Both the nominalistic critics, who refuse the status of designators or names to expressions like "red," "five," etc., because they deny the existence of abstract entities, and the skeptics, who express doubts concerning the existence and demand evidence for it, treat the question of existence as a theoretical question. They do, of course, not mean the internal question; the affirmative answer to *this* question is analytic and trivial and too obvious for doubt or denial, as we have seen. Their doubts refer rather to the system of entities itself; hence they mean the external question. They believe that only after making sure that there really is a system of entities of the kind in question are we justified in accepting the framework by incorporating the linguistic forms into our language. However, we have seen that the external question is not a theoretical question but rather the practical question whether or not to accept those linguistic forms. This acceptance is not in need of a theoretical justification (except with respect to expediency and fruitfulness), because it does not imply a belief or assertion. Ryle says that the "Fido"-Fido principle is "a grotesque theory." Grotesque or not, Ryle is wrong in calling it a theory. It is rather the practical decision to accept certain frameworks. Maybe Ryle is historically right with respect to those whom he mentions as previous representatives of the principle, viz. John Stuart Mill, Frege, and Russell. If these philosophers regarded the acceptance of a system of entities as a theory, an assertion, they were victims of the same old, metaphysical confusion. But it is certainly wrong to regard *my* semantical method as involving a belief in the reality of abstract entities, since I reject a thesis of this kind as a metaphysical pseudo-statement.

The critics of the use of abstract entities in semantics overlook the fundamental difference between the acceptance of a system of entities and an internal assertion, e.g., an assertion that there are elephants or electrons or prime numbers greater than a million. Whoever makes an internal assertion is certainly obliged to justify it by providing evidence, empirical evidence in the case of electrons, logical proof in the case of the prime numbers. The demand for a theoretical justification, correct in the case of internal assertions, is sometimes wrongly applied to the acceptance of a system of entities. Thus, for example, Ernest Nagel [9] asks for "evidence relevant for affirming with warrant that there are such entities as infinitesimals or propositions." He characterizes the evidence required in these cases—in distinction to the empirical evidence in the case of electrons—as "in the broad sense logical and dialectical." Beyond this no hint is given as to what might be regarded as relevant evidence. Some nominalists regard the acceptance of abstract entities as a kind of superstition or myth, populating the world with fictitious or at least dubious entities, analogous to the belief in centaurs or demons. This shows again the confusion mentioned, because a superstition or myth is a false (or dubious) internal statement.

Let us take as example the natural numbers as cardinal numbers, i.e., in contexts like "Here are three books." The linguistic forms of the framework of numbers, including variables and the general term "number" are generally used in our common language of communication; and it is easy to formulate explicit rules for their use. Thus the logical characteristics of this framework are sufficiently clear (while many internal questions, i.e., arithmetical questions, are, of course, still open). In spite of this, the controversy concerning the external question of the ontological reality of the system of numbers continues. Suppose that one philosopher says: "I believe that there are numbers as real entities. This gives me the right to use the linguistic forms of the numerical framework and to make semantical statements about numbers as designata of numerals." His nominalistic opponent replies: "You are wrong; there are no numbers. The numerals may still be used as meaningful expressions. But they are not names, there are no entities designated by them. Therefore the word "number" and numerical variables must not be used (unless a way were found to introduce them as merely abbreviating devices, a way of translating them into the nominalistic thing language)." I cannot think of any possible evidence that would be regarded as relevant by both philosophers, and therefore, if actually found would decide the controversy or at least make one of the opposite theses more probable than the other. (To construe the numbers as classes or properties of the second level, according to the Frege-Russell method does, of course, not solve the controversy, because the first philosopher would affirm and the second deny the existence of the system of classes or properties of the second level.) Therefore I feel compelled to regard the external question as a pseudo-question, until both parties to the controversy offer a common interpretation of the question as a cognitive question; this would involve an indication of possible evidence regarded as relevant by both sides.

There is a particular kind of misinterpretation of the acceptance of abstract entities in various fields of science and in semantics, that needs to be cleared up. Certain early British empiricists (e.g., Berkeley and Hume) denied the existence of abstract entities on the ground that immediate experience presents us only with particulars, not with universals, e.g., with this red patch, but not with Redness or Color-in-General; with this scalene triangle, but not with Scalene Triangularity or Triangularity-in-General. Only entities belonging to a type of which examples were to be found within immediate experience could be accepted as ultimate constituents of reality. Thus, according to this way of thinking, the existence of abstract entities could be asserted only if one could show either that some abstract entities fall within the given, or that abstract entities can be defined in terms of the types of entity which are given. Since these empiricists found no abstract entities within the realm of sense-data, they either denied their existence, or else made a futile attempt to define universals in terms of particulars. Some contemporary philosophers, especially English philosophers following Bertrand Russell, think in basically similar terms. They emphasize a distinction between the data (that which is immediately given in consciousness, e.g. sense-data, immediately past experiences, etc.) and the constructs based on the data. Existence or reality is ascribed only to the data; the constructs are not real entities; the corresponding linguistic expressions are merely ways of speech not actually designating anything (reminiscent of the nominalists' *flatus vocis*). We shall not criticize here this general conception. (As far as it is a principle of accepting certain entities and not accepting others, leaving aside any ontological, phenomenalistic and nominalistic pseudo-statements, there cannot be any theoretical objection to it.) But if this conception leads to the view that other philosophers or scientists who accept abstract entities thereby assert or imply their occurrence as immediate data, then such a view must be rejected as a misinterpretation. References to space-time points, the electro-magnetic field, or electrons in physics, to real or complex numbers and their functions in mathematics, to the excitatory potential or unconscious complexes in psychology, to an inflationary trend in economics, and the like, do not imply the assertion that entities of these kinds occur as immediate data. And the same holds for references to abstract entities as designata in semantics. Some of the criticisms by English philosophers against such references give the impression that, probably due to the misinterpretation just indicated, they accuse the semanticist not so much of bad metaphysics (as some nominalists would do) but of bad psychology. The fact that they regard a semantical method involving abstract entities not merely as doubtful and perhaps wrong, but as manifestly absurd, preposterous and grotesque, and that they show a deep horror and indignation against this method, is perhaps to be explained by a misinterpretation of the kind described. In fact, of course, the semanticist does not in the least assert or imply that the abstract entities to which he refers can be experienced as immediately given either by sensation or by a kind of rational intuition. An assertion of this kind would indeed be very dubious psychology. The psychological question as to which kinds of entities do and which do not occur as immediate data is entirely irrelevant for semantics, just as it is for physics, mathematics, economics, etc., with respect to the examples mentioned above.[10]

5. *Conclusion*

For those who want to develop or use semantical methods, the decisive question is not the alleged ontological question of the existence of abstract entities but rather the question whether the use of abstract linguistic forms or, in technical terms, the use of variables beyond those for things (or phenomenal data), is expedient and fruitful for the purposes for which semantical analyses are made, viz. the analysis, interpretation, clarification, or construction of languages of communication, especially languages of science. This question is here neither decided nor even discussed. It is not a question simply of yes or no, but a matter of degree. Among those philosophers who have carried out semantical analyses and thought about suitable tools for this work, beginning with Plato and Aristotle and, in a more technical way on the basis of modern logic, with C. S. Peirce and Frege, a great majority accepted abstract entities. This does, of course, not prove the case. After all, semantics in the technical sense is still in the initial phases of its development, and we must be prepared for possible fundamental changes in methods. Let us therefore admit that the nominalistic critics may possibly be right. But if so, they will have to offer better arguments than they did so far. Appeal to ontological insight will not carry much weight. The critics will have to show that it is possible to construct a semantical method which avoids all references to abstract entities and achieves by simpler means essentially the same results as the other methods.

The acceptance or rejection of abstract linguistic forms, just as the acceptance or rejection of any other linguistic forms in any branch of science, will finally be decided by their efficiency as instruments, the ratio of the results achieved to the amount and complexity of the efforts required. To decree dogmatic prohibitions of certain linguistic forms instead of testing them by their success or failure in practical use, is worse than futile; it is positively harmful because it may obstruct scientific progress. The history of science shows examples of such prohibitions based on prejudices deriving from religious, mythological, metaphysical, or other irrational sources, which slowed up the developments for shorter or longer periods of time. Let us learn from the lessons of history. Let us grant to those who work in any special field of investigation the freedom to use any form of expression which seems useful to them; the work in the field will sooner or later lead to the elimination of those forms which have no useful function. *Let us be cautious in making assertions and critical in examining them, but tolerant in permitting linguistic forms.*

[43b]

HERBERT FEIGL

Confirmability and Confirmation

SOME COMMENTS ON THE EMPIRICIST CRITERION
OF MEANING AND RELATED ISSUES *

The discussions of the last twenty years concerning the empiricist criterion of factual meaningfulness have increasingly emphasized the need for a more liberal formulation. Positivists, old and new, adamant in their repudiation of metaphysics, have tended to overshoot their goal. The

* From *Revue Internationale de Philosophie* V (1951), pp. 268–279. Reprinted by permission of the author and editor (Jean Lameere).

motivation was of course understandable and, on the whole, admirable. The decision to eliminate from scientific and philosophical discourse the kind of problems which, because of their very conception cannot possibly be solved in a responsible manner, had an eminently salutary and cathartic effect. There is certainly no point in worrying one's head about questions which are supposed to concern matters of fact and yet cannot conceivably be answered (at least partially or indirectly) by appeal to the data of observation. We are all too familiar with the dialectic devices designed to protect the claims of transcendent knowledge against refutation. Such devices have been utilized in the arguments not only of outright theology and metaphysics but frequently enough also in the frontal areas of the expanding scientific enterprise itself. Speculations, about absolute space and time, substance, the ether, causal necessity, entelechies, telefinalities, group-minds, etc. are apt to become devoid of whatever (no matter how vaguely) specifiable meaning they may have had to begin with. They are rendered proof against disproof by a simple but often rather concealed or unwitting decision to make them immune against the outcome of any conceivable test.

If the empiricist criterion of meaningfulness merely eliminates such in-principle-unanswerable questions, there can be no quarrel with it. At least there can be no objection from anyone holding a scientific outlook in philosophy. It is of course regrettable to have aroused ire and indignation on the part of the tender-minded and other-wordly thinkers. But, contemporary empiricism, pragmatism, positivism and naturalism in their various forms are all continuous with the ideas of the enlightenment of the eighteenth century and cannot possibly help offending those engaged in the search for absolutes or in the quest for certainty. Whatever significance unanswerable questions may appear to have is easily explained in terms of their purely formal structures or their expressive and evocative (pictorial, emotional, motivative) functions.

The meaning of words and sentences depends upon the kind of use to which we put them. An isolated spoken or printed sentence may mean anything at all—or nothing—depending on the rules according to which these words are made to function. Confronted with a given assertion, the first task in ascertaining its meaning consists in finding out how the speaker or writer uses his words in connection with other words of his vocabulary and how (some of) the words of his language are related to the data of experience. To illustrate first by a perfectly obvious example: An old facetious German "rule" for weather prediction, when stripped of its trappings, reads: "The weather will either change or remain the same." It scarcely needs to be pointed out that this assertion is a substitution instance of the law of the excluded middle and thus a glaring tautology. If there had been a serious intention to pronounce a law of nature (a genuinely synthetic general proposition), one can immediately see that this intention was not fulfilled by the given formulation—always taking for granted that the terms occurring in it are taken in their usual meanings.

If some of the "laws" of physics were to be understood in the manner in which Poincaré and other conventionalists construe them, they would indeed reduce to purely analytic propositions. Similar dangers of confusion are well known in the attempts of some older psychologies to formulate a law of human motivation in terms of the pleasure principle, and in the formulation of some of the laws of economics and sociology. It is a matter of purely terminological decision whether we choose to characterize analytic propositions as factually meaningless or as the null-case (lower limit) of factual content. At any rate it is indispensable first to find out, by the use of the sort of procedure that might be called "socratic," "dialectical," "casuistic" or "diagnostic," just what, if anything, the assertion achieves in asserting. Formal analysis in the sense of a reconstruction within an ideal language merely consolidates and systematizes the results first disclosed by the socratic procedure of informal explication.

Another example will bring out the essentials of the diagnostic method as regards transcendent metaphysical assertions. Newton's conception of absolute space was subjected to a searching scrutiny already by Leibniz. To be sure, the famous correspondence on this issue between Leibniz and Clarke (Newton's disciple) is replete with theological and metaphysical arguments on both sides. Yet it is obvious that in some phases of the dispute Leibniz proceeded deliberately, and strikingly like a pragmatist or positivist. He asked in effect what conceivable difference in observable consequences there could be between the assertion and the denial of the existence of absolute space. (It should be remembered that the issue concerned exclusively the space of kinematics. In regard to the dynamic aspects of space Newton not only made a meaningful assertion but was—at the time—even justified in his assertion of a privileged coordinate system, or, as he *should* have put it, a *class* of such systems). Clarke had no other way out than to remove the concept of absolute space beyond the possibility of any sort of test whatever. We find the same sort of situation again at the beginning of our century when Lorentz, Fitzgerald and others protected the ether-hypothesis (a latter-day incarnation of Newton's absolute space) by special safeguards from refutation. These theorists did not—but Einstein did—realize that thereby electro-dynamics had come to include a set of sentences which were not only superfluous but strictly speaking devoid of factual meaning. (Some of the earlier versions of the ether-hypothesis were of course meaningful, but were proved false by the joint evidence of a number of fairly decisive experiments). The diagnostic procedure reveals in this instance as well as in many others that confirmability, i.e. at least indirect and/or incomplete testability-in-principle is *logically* excluded by some of the assumptions of the system of which the assertion under scrutiny is a part. In other words, factual meaninglessness can be charged against an assertion only if the premises of the hypothetico-deductive system stand in contradiction with the very idea of a test which would either confirm or disconfirm the assertion in question.

Conceived along these lines the empiricist meaning criterion draws a perfectly sharp distinction between sense and non-sense. I believe that Professor Hempel's scruples (15) [1] do not apply to the criterion if it is understood in this way. For example, I cannot take very seriously the qualms about the meaning of statements involving the use of irrational numbers. Since the assumption of the ubiquitous limits of exact measurement is inconsistent with the ascertainment of precise numerical values (rational or irrational) for any physical magnitude, there is indeed "no difference that makes a difference" and hence no difference in *factual* meaning. The use of the system of real numbers in physics is therefore to be regarded as a convention whose sole justification lies in the expedience of the *formal* aspects of mathematical representation and computation, rather than in any empirically discernible fact.

As regards the introduction of theoretical constructs, we must first decide whether they are explicitly definable in terms of less complex empirical concepts. If so (as in the case of the Laplace or Poisson operators, Hamiltonian functions, tensors, etc.) they are in principle eliminable, i.e. they can be replaced by their definientia and the difference the introduction of those constructs makes is again purely formal and *not* factual. Theoretical constructs which cannot be explicitly defined on the basis of "observables" of course present us with the very core of our problem. If the diagnostic or logico-analytic procedure reveals that addition or omission of these constructs cannot possibly make a difference in the deducible empirical laws (and if they are not explicitly definable in the sense just indicated) then they are metaphysical chimeras and make in principle unconfirmable any assertion of which they are essential constituents. But it must be admitted that the diagnostic method does not always succeed in disclosing a definitive logical contradiction between the confirmability of a given assertion and the rest of the system of which the assertion is a part. In such more indefinite cases it is advisable for empiricists to adopt an attitude of tolerance and open-mindedness. Science at its growing edge continually issues promissory notes not only in hypotheses formulated in terms of fully defined concepts, but also in the vague and tentative introduction of new concepts which are at first only tenuously connected with other already legitimized concepts of science. For example, when Schrödinger introduced his ψ-function in 1926 into quantum theory, there was some indecision regarding the physical meaning of this new construct. It had all the earmarks of a fruitful idea but, as is well known, the first interpretation given by Schrödinger himself (in terms of electric density) had soon to be replaced by Born's statistical interpretation. If some of the data of psychical research (concerning mental telepathy or psychokinesis) were to be taken as authentic (rather than as illusory owing to experimental, statistical error, or outright fraud), imaginative theorists might well attempt to introduce new concepts and laws in order to account for those peculiar phenomena. The impact of the pragmatist-positivist-operationist thinking of the last fifty years makes it rather unlikely that scientists will gravely mislead themselves by the introduction of absolutely unconfirmable assertions.

The sort of doubt that may justifiably be raised in connection with the introduction of new concepts and hypotheses will then more usually be concerned with their indispensability—or at least with their fruitfulness. Having made sure that the requirement of meaningfulness is satisfied [2], the only other relevant conditions which have to be fulfilled are those of formal and factual parsimony or simplicity. Since formal simplicity concerns differences between theoretical systems which are logically equivalent, i.e. intertranslatable, it has no bearing on the factual meaning of the systems. Factual or inductive simplicity however is of paramount importance in the appraisal of the factual meaning-content and the explanatory power of theories.

The principle of factual simplicity is very likely what Newton intended with his first *Regula Philosophandi*. It furnishes a criterion for the acceptability of *existential hypotheses*. This principle must of course not be confused with the criterion of meaningfulness. Meaningfulness is presupposed when the question of inductive simplicity is raised. Furthermore it is worth noting that considerations of inductive simplicity arise only in the context of *methodology*, i.e., in the critical analysis of the growing, unfinished science. The criterion of factual simplicity can provide no more than very tentative directives. It is to be understood as a principle of inductive logic in that it (generally, i.e. *ceteris paribus*) ascribes a higher probability to simpler hypotheses. To illustrate: Leverrier and Adams had in principle the choice between an indefinite number of more or less complex existential hypotheses by means of which (together with the presupposed laws of Newton's mechanics) to account for the perturbations of Uranus. They could have hypothesized a numerous group of heavenly bodies to be responsible; and with suitable assumptions about the individual orbits of these bodies, could have derived the same conclusions as from the assumption of a solitary disturber (Neptune). After the telescopic discovery of Neptune and prolonged observations of its orbit, the probability of the simpler original hypothesis increased to a practical certainty. The case of Neptune illustrates however only one type of existential hypothesis—the particularized or singular form. More important, but also more problematic in regard to their philosophical interpretation is another, the generalized or universal type of existential hypotheses. The introduction of a new basic magnitude or variable into a thus augmented theoretical system may from a purely formal point of view be regarded as a genuine enrichment of the language of science. The introduction of the concepts of the electric and magnetic fields (Faraday, Maxwell, etc.) is a good illustration of this case. Over and above the well established concepts and assumptions of classical mechanics, optics and thermodynamics these new concepts were soon recognized as indispensable for the explanation of phenomena whose confirmation base was however completely contained in those older disciplines. It is obvious that the introduction of the

concepts of electromagnetism can by no stretch of the analytical imagination be construed as a matter of explicit definition on the basis of the
older concepts (serving as definientia). The introduction of generalized
existential hypotheses ("besides the mechanical masses, forces, etc., there
are also electrical and magnetic forces") must be interpreted in terms of
laws which connect the new magnitudes with the old ones in a strictly
synthetic manner. I shall not here discuss the controversial question in
which sense, if in any, considerations of inductive probability apply to the
introduction of generalized existential hypotheses. In my article "Existential Hypotheses" (*Phil. of Sci.,* 1950), I argued that questions of inductive
probability can be significantly raised only if the total frame of concepts is
presupposed and that it makes no sense to ask questions about the probability of the frame. But that argument was made from the point of view of
a semantical reconstruction of the language of science. It is conceivable
that in the context of a methodological analysis some sort of interpretation
of the probability of generalized existential hypotheses could be specified.

Quite generally it seems to me of the utmost importance not to confuse
analyses (such as of meaning, confirmability, confirmation and degree of
confirmation) in the context of the semantical reconstruction of an idealized language of science with analyses in the context of the methodology
of the procedures of a developing science. An idealized language of factual
science is so conceived that questions concerning the precise meaning of its
terms, or concerning synonymy, deducibility, analyticity, etc., can be
answered with the same finality (and the same limitations) as the analogous questions regarding purely formal systems of logic or mathematics.
The ideal-language-reconstruction, as it were, freezes a given stage in the
development of a scientific descipline. This "freezing" involves of course
some more or less arbitrary decisions, since there are always alternatives
of rational reconstruction. Just how faithfully a given reconstruction por-
trays the structure of the discipline will thus be a perennially debatable
question. The doubts recently expressed by C. G. Hempel, W. V. Quine
and M. G. White concerning the possibility of a sharp distinction between
meaningful and meaningless (as well as of analytic and synthetic) sentences seem to me to be justified only in the context of methodology.
Science in its living, evolving progress of course continually shifts and
redefines the meaning of its terms. In its growth toward the open horizon
of a (never attainable) ideal completeness, coherence and adequacy, inno-
vation and revision are of the order of the day. A concept may at first be
only very tentatively introduced and very incompletely specified. Confronted with such a concept we may decide altogether to refrain from an
idealized reconstruction. The semanticist could justifiably say that there is
no concept there to be reconstructed. A concept, after all, is specified only
if it is sufficiently fixed by a set of rules. On the other hand the semantical
reconstruction may be undertaken if it is understood in the sense of an
explication which renders the portrayal of a concept much more precise
than the rather ambiguous and amorphous original. In some cases (as in

the reconstruction of theoretical systems like classical mechanics, relativity theory, etc.) the discipline in question has assumed a sufficiently definite form to allow—if not for one unique reconstruction—then at least for a limited set of alternative reconstructions. A given formula, e.g., in classical mechanics, may thus be interpreted as an analytic proposition in one reconstruction and as synthetic (a genuine law) in another.

But wherever a scientific theory (or, *a fortiori*, ordinary discourse, or vague speculation) has not crystallized into such definite forms, logical reconstruction will always seem to do violence to its subject. It is in the context of methodological (in contradistinction to ideally reconstructive) analyses that it makes sense to speak of *degrees*—*not* of meaning or meaningfulness, to be sure—but of *specifications* of meaning.

Ever since Pierre Duhem's classical critique of the possibility of *experimenta crucis* his point of view has been re-emphasized by various writers, most recently by Hempel and Quine. Since statements in isolation from others are regarded as indefinite in meaning, it is maintained that only whole systems of statements can be subjected to test. It would take more space than is available here to disentangle what is right and what is wrong with this view. Permit me to remark, somewhat *ad hominem,* that logicians (and I am sure, among them Hempel and Quine) would look askance at any scientific theory which presented itself with the claim: "Take me or leave me, but you can't pick out any parts." If I recall correctly that is precisely what Freud once said about psychoanalytic theory and its "monolithic" character. But Freud himself has repeatedly modified parts of his theory—presumably on the basis of clinical evidence. Science would be in a sorry condition if its theories could not be stated in terms of logically independent postulates. It is precisely for the sake of systematic examination through empirical testing that we must unravel the knowledge claims of a theory into a maximal number of independently confirmable postulates. For example, only after disentangling the various components in the principles of special relativity can we say which experiments confirm which laws. The experiments of Michelson and Morley (Trouton and Noble) confirm one component, the observations on double stars by de Sitter another; and for the confirmation of auxiliary hypotheses the measurements of aberration and the experiment of Fizeau are equally indispensable.—A view that maintains that the whole body of a scientific theory (if not of all science) confronts experience and that modifications may be required in *any* part of the system if it does not "fit",—such a view obscures dangerously what is of the greatest importance for the progress of science: the successive testing and securing of parts of science—at least in the sense of an approximation. Naturally, no part can be considered as established with finality—but this insight which impresses the pure logician should not blind him to the recognition of the method of successive confirmation. It is curious that it should be the logicians who undermine first their own enterprise by a denial of the sharp distinction between the empirical and the logical (because here they are struck with the vagueness of ordinary discourse and of scientific methodology) and then proceed to blur the methodology of science beyond recognition (because from a purely formal point of view a theory is in principle adjustable in any one of its parts). I suggest that if our logical analyses and reconstructions of the scientific enterprise are thus far unable to do justice to its most important and indispensable criteria (of confirmability and of confirmation) that we must look for better analyses and reconstructions instead of giving a distorted picture of scientific method. Perhaps it will help in this connection to remember the distinction between ideal reconstruction and methodological analysis—which to point out was the major purpose of the preceding informal remarks.

NOTES AND REFERENCES

Since I have elsewhere (6, 7, 8, 9, 10) dealt at length with other aspects of the problem of meaning I shall here only refer the reader to my critique of the restrictive ("negativistic") implications of phenomenalistic positivism and operationism. In this connection it is indispensable to distinguish between "meaning" as the positivists usually understand this term, i.e. the evidential base or the "method of verification", and "meaning" as the factual referent or designatum of sentences. The confirmability criterion actually requires such a more realistic interpretation in terms of pure semantics and pragmatics (26, 27). An important corroboration of this position from the point of view of scientific methodology may be found in the illuminating analysis by L. W. Beck (1). Among the discussions of the meaning criterion by non-positivists that have nevertheless arrived at roughly the same conclusions, I mention those of Weyl (30, p. 117 ff.) and Margenau (19, Ch. 5). A clear formulation of the realistic interpretation of the field concept is given by Weyl (30, p. 114). The topic of inductive simplicity is discussed by Reichenbach (25, § 42). A promising beginning in the analysis of partial specifications of meaning may be found in the article (17) by A. Kaplan. A stimulating discussion of the relation of synthetic and analytic truth in physical theory is given in A. Pap's book (22). The view according to which the distinction between analytic and synthetic propositions rests on dogma or prejudice has been set forth persuasively, but to my mind by no means conclusively, by M. G. White (29) and W. V. Quine (24). However, my recent publications indicate that I agree with Quine's rejection of the positivistic-phenomenalistic doctrine of reductionism. Along similar lines there is at least a partial agreement also with Nagel (21), Hempel (15), and Reichenbach (25). The distinction between explicitly definable concepts and hypothetical constructs, as it concerns especially psychological theories, is forcefully pointed out by MacCorquodale and Meehl (18).

1. Beck, Lewis W. *Constructions and Inferred Entities* (*Phil. of Sc.*, 17, 1950).
2. Carnap, Rudolf, *Testability and Meaning* (*Phil. of Sc.*, 3, 4, 1936, 1937).
3. Carnap, Rudolf, *Truth and Confirmation* in Feigl and Sellars, *Readings*.
4. Carnap, Rudolf, *Empiricism, Semantics and Ontology* (*Revue Internationale de Philosophie*, IV, 11, 1950, Bruxelles).
5. Feigl, Herbert, *Logical Empiricism*, in *Twentieth Century Philosophy*, ed. by D. D. Runes, Philosophical Library, New York, 1943, (Also reprinted in Feigl and Sellars, *Readings*.)

6. Feigl, Herbert, *Operationism and Scientific Method* (*Psych. Rev.*, 52, 1945). (Also reprinted in Feigl and Sellars, *Readings.*)

7. Feigl, Herbert, *Existential Hypotheses; Realistic vz. Phenomenalistic Interpretations* (*Phil. of Sc.*, 17, 1950.)

8. Feigl, Herbert, *Logical Reconstruction, Realism and Pure Semiotic* (*Phil. of Sc.*, 17, 1950.)

9. Feigl, Herbert, *The Mind-Body Problem in the Development of Logical Empiricism* (*Revue Internationale de Philosophie*, IV, 11, Bruxelles, 1950).

10. Feigl, Herbert, *De Principiis non disputandum? On the Meaning and the Limits of Justification* in Max Black, ed. *Philosophical Analysis: A Collection of Essays*, Cornell University Press, 1950.

11. Feigl, Herbert and Sellars, Wilfrid, *Readings in Philosophical Analysis*, Appleton-Century-Crofts, New York, 1949.

12. Frank, Philipp, *Modern Science and its Philosophy*, Harvard University Press, 1949.

13. Frank, Philipp, *Comments on Realistic versus Phenomenalistic Interpretations* (*Phil. of Sc.*, 17, 1950).

14. Hempel, C. G., *Studies in the Logic of Confirmation* (*Mind*, 54, 1945).

15. Hempel, C. G., *Problems and Changes in the Empiricist Criterion of Meaning* (*Revue Internationale de Philosophie*, IV, 11, 1950).

16. Hempel, C. G., *A Note on Semantic Realism* (*Phil. of Sc.*, 17, 1950).

17. Kaplan, Abraham, *Definition and Specification of Meaning* (*Jl. of Phil.*, 43, 1946).

18. MacCorquodale, K. and Meehl, P. E., *On a Distinction between Hypothetical Constructs and Intervening Variables* (*Psych. Rev.*, 55, 1948).

19. Margenau, H., *The Nature of Physical Reality*, McGraw-Hill, New York, 1950.

20. Mehlberg, H., *Positivisme et Science* (*Studia Philosophica*, 3, 1948).

21. Nagel, Ernest, *Science and Semantic Realism* (*Phil. of Sc.*, 17, 1950).

22. Pap, Arthur, *The Apriori in Physical Theory*, Kings Crown Press, New York, 1946.

23. Pap, Arthur, *Elements of Analytic Philosophy*, Macmillan, New York, 1949.

24. Quine, W. V., *Two Dogmas of Empiricism* (*Philos. Rev.*, 60, 1951).

25. Reichenbach, Hans, *Experience and Prediction*, University of Chicago Press, 1938.

26. Sellars, Wilfrid, *Realism and the New Way of Words* (*Phil. and Phenom. Res.*, 8, 1948). (Also reprinted in Feigl and Sellars, *Readings.*)

27. Sellars, Wilfrid, *Concepts as Involving Laws and Inconceivable Without Them* (*Phil. Sc.*, 15, 1948).

28. Sellars, Wilfrid, *Language, Rules and Behavior* in S. Hook, ed. *John Dewey, Philosopher of Science and Freedom*. The Dial Press, New York, 1950.

29. White, Morton G., *The Analytic and the Synthetic; an Untenable Dualism, ibid.*

30. Weyl, Hermann, *Philosophy of Mathematics and Natural Science*, Princeton University Press, 1949.

ERNEST NAGEL

The Meaning of Reduction in the
Natural Sciences *

The science of mechanics was the first branch of mathematical physics to assume the form of a comprehensive theory. The success of that theory in explaining and bringing into systematic relation a large variety of phenomena was for a long time unprecedented; and the belief entertained by many eminent scientists and philosophers, sometimes supported by a priori arguments, that all the processes of nature would eventually fall within the scope of its principles was repeatedly confirmed by the absorption of several sectors of physics into mechanics. However, it is now common knowledge that classical mechanics no longer occupies the position of the "universal" physical science once claimed for it; for since the latter part of the nineteenth century the difficulties facing the extension of mechanics to various further domains of physical inquiry have come to be acknowledged as insuperable, and rival candidates for the office of a universal physical science have been proposed. Moreover, with some exceptions, no serious students today believe that some particular physical theory can be established on a priori grounds as the universal or fundamental theory of natural processes; and to many thinkers it is even an open question whether the ideal of a comprehensive theory which would thoroughly integrate all domains of natural science is realizable. Nevertheless, the phenomenon of a relatively autonomous branch of science becoming absorbed by, or "reduced" to, some other discipline is an undeniable and recurrent feature of the history of modern science, and there is no reason to suppose that such reduction will not continue to take place in the future.

It is with this phenomenon that the present paper is concerned. The successful reduction of one science to another, as well as the failures in effecting such a reduction in a number of notable cases, have been occasions, exploited by both practicing scientists and professional as well as

* Reprinted from *Science and Civilization*, ed. Robert C. Stauffer, University of Wisconsin Press, Madison, pp. 99–138; copyright 1949 by the Regents of the University of Wisconsin; with the kind permission of the author and the publishers.

lay philosophers, for far-reaching reinterpretations of the nature and limits of knowledge, science, and the allegedly ultimate constitution of things in general. These interpretations take various forms. Discoveries concerning the physics and physiology of perception have been frequently used to support the conclusion that the findings of physics are incompatible with so-called common sense or naïve realism (the belief that things encountered in normal experience do possess the traits which are manifest to controlled observation); and elaborate epistemologies have been proposed for resolving the paradox that, in spite of this presumed incompatibility, science takes its point of departure from, and finds its evidence in, such common-sense knowledge. The successful reduction of thermodynamics to statistical mechanics in the nineteenth century, and the more recent expansion of electrical theories of matter, have been taken to show that spatial displacements are the only form of intelligible and genuine change; that the qualitative and behavioral diversities noted in ordinary experience are "unreal" and illusory; or, conversely, that the "mysterious world" discovered by microscopic physics is but an insubstantial symbol which expresses a pervasive spiritual reality not alien to human values. On the other hand, the failure to explain electrodynamical phenomena in terms of the principles of mechanics, and the general decline of mechanics as the universal science of nature in contemporary physics, has been hailed as evidence for the bankruptcy of classical science, for the necessity of instituting an "organismic" point of view and "organismic" categories of explanation in the study of all natural phenomena, and for a variety of metaphysical doctrines concerning levels of being, emergence, and creative novelty.

I do not believe that these speculative interpretations of the assumed facts of science are warranted by the evidence. On the contrary, I believe that the problems to which they are addressed are generated by misconstruing the statements of the natural sciences and reading them in senses not in accordance with the meanings that actual usage in scientific contexts establishes for those statements. However, it is not my present aim to examine the detailed arguments which lead to the adoption of views such as those just briefly indicated. I wish instead to consider what is done when one science is reduced to another, and to suggest that an important source of much dubious commentary on the nature and the interrelations of the sciences lies in the failure to recognize the conditions which must be fulfilled when such a reduction is effected. It is a commonplace that linguistic expressions, associated with established habits or rules of usage in one set of homogeneous contexts, frequently come to be used in other contexts on the assumption of definite analogies or continuities between the several domains. But judging from the practice of many philosophers and scientists, it is still not a commonplace that when the range of application of expressions is thus extended, these expressions may undergo critical changes in meaning, and that unless care is exercised in interpreting them so that specific contexts of relevant usage are noted, serious misunderstandings and spurious problems are bound to arise. In any event, misconceptions having their basis in just such careless handling of language seem to me to accompany much traditional and current discussion of the significance of scientific reduction. The present essay is an attempt to indicate some quite familiar and yet frequently neglected distinctions that are pertinent to the analysis of this recurrent phenomenon in the development of the natural sciences.

Before turning to my actual theme, it will be useful to distinguish a type of reduction in the history of science which generally, though certainly not always, is unaccompanied by serious misapprehensions. I have in mind the normal expansion of some body of theory, initially proposed for a certain extensive domain of phenomena, so that laws which previously may have been found to hold in a narrow sector of that domain, or in some other domain homogeneous in a readily identifiable sense with the first, are shown to be derivable from that theory when suitably specialized. For example, Galileo's *Two New Sciences* was a contribution to the physics of freely falling terrestrial bodies; but when Newton showed that his own general theory of mechanics and gravitation, when supplemented by appropriate boundary conditions, entailed Galileo's laws, the latter were incorporated into the Newtonian theory as a special case. Were we to regard this branch of inquiry cultivated by Galileo as a distinctive science, the subsequent facts could be described by saying that Galileo's special discipline was reduced to the science of Newton. However, although it is possible to distinguish the subject matters of the Newtonian and the (initially distinct) Galilean sciences (for example, the latter was concerned solely with terrestrial phenomena, while the former included celestial ones), these subject matters are in an obvious sense homogenous and continuous; for it is the motions of bodies and the determinants of such motions that are under investigation in each case, and in each case inquiry is directed toward discovering relations between physical traits that are the common concern of both disciplines. Stated more formally, the point is that no descriptive terms appear in the formulations of the Galilean science which do not occur essentially and with approximately the same meanings in the statements of Newtonian mechanics. The history of science is replete with illustrations of reductions of this type, but I shall ignore them in what follows, because the logical issues involved in them do not appear to generate typical forms of philosophic puzzlement or to stimulate fundamental reinterpretations of the nature of knowledge.

The situation seems to be quite different, however, in those cases of reduction in which a subject matter possessing certain distinctive properties is apparently assimilated with another that supposedly does not manifest those traits; and acute intellectual discomfort is often experienced in those instances of reduction in which the science that suffers reduction is concerned with so-called "macroscopic" or "molar" phenomena, while the science to which the reduction is effected employs a theory that postulates some "microscopic" structure for molar physical systems.

Thus, consider the following example. Most adults, if provided with ordinary mercury thermometers, are able to determine with reasonable accuracy the temperatures of various bodies, and understand what is meant by such statements as that the temperature of a glass of milk is 10° C. Accordingly, such individuals know how to use the word "temperature," at any rate within a broad context, though doubtless a large fraction of them would be incapable of stating adequately the tacit rules governing such usage, or of explicating the meaning of the word to the satisfaction of someone schooled in thermodynamics. However, if such an individual were to use the word so that its application was always associated with the behavior of a mercury column in a glass tube when the latter was placed in proximity to the body whose temperature was in question, he might be at a loss to construe the sense of such a statement as that the temperature of a certain substance at its melting point is several thousand degrees high; and he might protest that since at such alleged "high temperatures" ordinary thermometers would be vaporized, the statement had no definite meaning for him. But a slight study of physics would readily remove this source of puzzlement. The puzzled individual would discover that the word "temperature" is associated with a more inclusive set of rules of usage than he had originally supposed, and that in its extended usage it refers to a physical state of a body, which may be manifested in other ways than in the volume expansion of a mercury column—for example, in changes in electrical resistance, or in the generation of electric currents. Accordingly, once the laws are understood which connect the behavior of ordinary thermometers with the behavior of bolometers, pyrometers, and other overtly identifiable recording instruments, the grounds for the more inclusive usage of the term "temperature" become intelligible. This wider use of the word, then, rarely appears to cover a mystery, any more than does the extension of the word from its uses in contexts of direct experience of hot and cold to contexts in which the mercury thermometer replaces the human organism as a test body.

Suppose, however, that the layman for whom the word "temperature" thus acquires a more generalized meaning than he originally associated with it now pursues his study of physics into the kinetic theory of matter. Here he discovers that the temperature of a body is simply the mean kinetic energy of the molecules constituting the body. But this bit of information usually produces renewed perplexity, and, indeed, in an especially acute form. For the layman is assured by the best authorities that while on the one hand individual molecules possess no temperatures, nevertheless the meaning of the word "temperature" must by definition be taken as identical with the meaning of such expressions as "energy of molecular motions." And questions that are typical of a familiar philosophical tradition now seem both relevant and inescapable. If the meaning of "temperature" is the same as that of "kinetic energy of molecular motion," what are we talking about when milk is said to have a temperature of 10° C.? Surely not the kinetic energies of the molecular constituents of the liquid, for the uninstructed layman is able to understand what is thus said without possessing any notions about the molecular composition of milk. Perhaps, then, the familiar distinctions between hot and cold, between various temperatures as specified in terms of the behavior of identifiable instruments, are distinctions which refer to a domain of illusion. Perhaps, also, the temperatures that are measured in ordinary experience as well as in laboratories are merely indications of some fundamental underlying reality which is inherently incapable of being characterized by such expressions as "temperature" understood in its customary sense. Or should we perhaps regard temperature as an emergent trait, not present on lower levels of physical reality? But if this is the correct way of viewing the matter, does a theory that is about such lower levels ever really explain emergent traits such as temperature? It would be easy to enlarge the list of such queries, but those cited suffice to suggest the general character of the instances of reduction which provoke them. To avoid repeated circumlocution, and for lack of better labels, let me refer to a science to which another is reduced as the "primary science," and to the science which suffers such reduction as the "secondary science." Philosophical problems of the sort indicated, then, seem to be generated when the subject matter of the primary science is "qualitatively discontinuous" or "in-homogenous" with the subject matter of the secondary science—or, to put the matter perhaps more clearly, when the statements of the secondary science contain descriptive terms that do not occur in the theories of the primary science.

It is reductions of this type that I wish to consider. And since the reduction of thermodynamics to mechanics, more exactly, to statistical mechanics and the kinetic theory of matter, is both a typical and a relatively familiar and simple example of this type, I propose to center my discussion around this illustration.

I will first briefly recall some well-known historical facts. The study of thermal phenomena goes back in modern times to Galileo and his circle, and during the subsequent three centuries a large number of laws were established dealing with special phases of the thermal behavior of bodies— laws which were eventually exhibited as systematically interrelated on the basis of a small number of general principles. Thermodynamics, as this science came to be called, employed concepts, distinctions, and general laws which were also used in mechanics—for example, the notions of volume, weight, mass, and pressure, and laws such as the principle of the lever and Hooke's Law. Nevertheless, it was regarded as a science relatively autonomous with respect to mechanics, because it made use of such distinctive notions as temperature, heat, and entropy, and because it assumed laws and principles which were not corollaries of the fundamental assumptions of mechanics. Accordingly, though many propositions of mechanics were constantly employed in the exploration of thermal phenomena, thermodynamics was generally assumed for a long time to be a special discipline, plainly distinguishable from mechanics and not simply a chapter of it. In this respect, the relation of thermodynamics to mechanics was considered analogous to the relation between mechanics and physical geometry: mechanics was held to be distinguishable from physical geometry, even though geometrical propositions were employed in the formulation of mechanical laws and in the construction of instruments used to test these laws. Indeed, thermodynamics is still frequently expounded as a physical theory that is autonomous in the indicated sense with respect to mechanics; and in such expositions the findings of the science are presented in such a manner that the propositions asserted can be understood and verified in terms of explanations and procedures which do not assume the reducibility of thermodynamics to some other theory. However, experimental work early in the nineteenth century on the mechanical equivalent of heat stimulated theoretical inquiry to find a more intimate connection between thermal and mechanical phenomena than the bare facts seemed to assert. And when Maxwell and Boltzmann were finally able to "derive" the Boyle-Charles Law from assumptions apparently statable in terms of mechanics concerning the molecular constitution of ideal gases, and especially when the entropy principle was shown to be capable of interpretation as a statistical law concerning the aggregate mechanical behavior of molecules, thermodynamics was widely believed to have lost its autonomy and to have been reduced to mechanics

Just how is this reduction effected, and what is the argument which apparently makes possible the derivation of statements containing such terms as "temperature," "heat," and "entropy" from a set of theoretical assumptions that do not use or mention them? It is not possible, without producing a treatise on the subject, to exhibit the complete argument. I shall therefore fix my attention on a small fragment of the complicated analysis, the derivation of the Boyle-Charles Law for ideal gases from the assumptions of the kinetic theory of matter

Suppressing most of the details that do not contribute directly to the clarification of the main issues, a simplified form of the derivation is in outline as follows. Assume an ideal gas to occupy a volume V. The gas is taken to be composed of a large number of molecules possessing equal mass and size, each perfectly elastic and with dimensions that are negligible when compared with the average distance between them. The molecules are further supposed to be in constant relative motion, and subject only to forces of impact between themselves and the walls of the containing volume, also taken to be perfectly elastic. Accordingly, the motions of the molecules are assumed to be analyzable in terms of the principles of Newtonian mechanics. The problem now is to determine the relation of the pressure which the molecules exert on the walls of their container to other aspects of their motion.

However, since the instantaneous co-ordinates of state of the individual molecules are not actually ascertainable, the usual mathematical procedure of classical mechanics cannot be applied; and in order to make headway with the problem, a further assumption must be introduced—an assumption which is a statistical one concerning the positions and momenta of the molecules. This statistical assumption takes the following form. Suppose that the volume V of the gas is subdivided into a very large number of smaller volumes whose dimensions are equal but nevertheless are large compared with the diameters of the molecules; suppose also that the maximum range of velocity of the molecules is divided into a large number of equal intervals of velocity; and associate with each small volume all possible velocity intervals, calling each complex obtained by associating a volume with a velocity interval a "phase-cell." The statistical assumption then is that the probability of a molecule's occupying an assigned phase-cell is the same for all molecules and phase-cells, and that (subject to certain qualifications which need not be mentioned here) the probabilities that any pair of molecules will occupy the same phase-cell are independent. From this set of assumptions it is now possible to deduce that the pressure p which the molecules exert on the walls of the container is related in a definite way to the mean kinetic energy E of the molecules of the gas, and that in fact $p = 2E/3V$, or $pV = 2E/3$. But a comparison of this equation with the Boyle-Charles Law (according to which $pV = kT$, where k is constant for a given mass of gas and T its absolute temperature), suggests that the latter could be deduced from the assumptions mentioned, *if* temperature were "identified" with the mean kinetic energy of molecular motions. Accordingly, let us adopt this "identification" in the form of the hypothesis that $2E/3 = kT$ (i.e., that the absolute temperature of an ideal gas is proportional to the mean kinetic energy of the molecules which are assumed to constitute it). The Boyle-Charles Law is then a logical consequence of the general principles of mechanics, when these are supplemented by a statistical postulate on the motions of molecules constituting a gas, a hypothesis on the connection between temperature and kinetic energy, and various further assumptions that have been indicated.

If the derivation of the Boyle-Charles Law is used as a basis for generalization, what are the essential requirements for reducing one science to another? The following comments fall into two groups, the first dealing with matters that are primarily of a formal nature, the second with questions of an empirical character.

1. In the first place, the derivation requires that all the assertions, postulates, or hypotheses of each of the sciences involved in the reduction are available in the form of explicit statements, whose meanings are assumed to be fixed in terms of procedures and rules of usage appropriate to each discipline. Moreover, the statements within each science fall into a number of fairly distinct groups when a classification is introduced on the basis of the logical functions the statements possess in the discipline. The following schematic list, though not exhaustive, indicates what I believe to be the more important groupings.

(a) In a highly developed science such as mechanics there usually is a class T of statements which constitute the fundamental theory of the discipline and thus serve as principles of explanation and as partial premises in most deductions undertaken in the science, e.g., the principles of Newtonian mechanics. In a given exposition of the science, these statements are logically primitive, in the sense that they are not derived from any other class of statements in the science. Whether this class of statements is best conceived as a set of leading principles, empirical rules of inference, or methodological rules of analysis, rather than as premises in the usual sense of the word, is a question that can be ignored here.

(b) A science which contains a fundamental theory will also contain a class of statements or theorems which are logically derivable from T. These theorems in all but trivial cases are usually of a conditional form, and their consequents are derivable from T only if the latter is supplemented by various special assumptions which appear as the antecedents in the theorems. Two subdivisions of this class of special assumptions may be distinguished. (i) There is the group of assumptions which serve as general hypotheses concerning a variety of conditions to which the fundamental theory may be applied. Thus, one such assumption in the application of Newtonian principles to the study of gases is that of a physical system composed of a large number of point-masses, with forces of impact as the only forces present. An alternative assumption might be that of a physical system consisting of bodies with non-negligible diameters subject to gravitational forces. (ii) And there is also the group of assumptions which specify the detailed boundary or initial conditions for the application of the theory. Thus, in the above example the initial conditions are stated as a statistical assumption concerning the position and velocities of gas molecules.

(c) Finally, every positive science will contain a large class of singular statements which formulate procedures and the outcome of observations relevant for the conduct of inquiry in the science; and it will usually also make use of general laws which its fundamental theory does not pretend to explain but which are simply borrowed from some other special discipline. Call the first group of these statements "observation statements," and the second group "borrowed statements." Observation statements may on occasion serve as specifications of the initial conditions for the application of the theory, or they may state the predicted consequences of the theory when other such statements are used to supplement the latter as initial conditions. Accordingly, observation statements will normally have members in common with the class of statements of boundary and initial conditions, though in general these two classes will not coincide. Indeed, many observation statements will describe instruments required for testing general assumptions of the science, and in doing so may make use of general laws and hence of expressions referring to distinctions that fall within the province of some other specialized discipline. For example, if Newtonian assumptions are employed in the study of celestial phenomena, telescopes may be required to test these assumptions; but the description of telescopes, and the interpretation of the observations that are obtained through their use, generally involves the use of expressions that refer to distinctions studied primarily in theoretical optics rather than in Newtonian mechanics.

2. This brings me to my second formal observation. The statements of a science, to whichever of the above classes they may belong, can be analyzed as linguistic structures compounded out of more elementary expressions in accordance with tacit or explicit rules of construction. These elementary expressions E are of various sorts, but they may be assumed to have fairly definite meanings fixed by habit or explicit rules of usage. Some of them are the familiar expressions of logic, arithmetic, and perhaps higher mathematics; but most of them will usually be so-called "descriptive" terms or combinations of terms which signify allegedly empirical objects, traits, and processes.

Though there may be serious difficulties both theoretical and practical in distinguishing descriptive expressions from others, let us suppose that the distinction can be carried through in some fashion, and let us consider the class of descriptive expressions in E. Many of the descriptive expressions of a science are taken over from the language of ordinary affairs and retain their customary, everyday meanings; others, however, may be specific to the science, and may, moreover, have meanings which preclude their application to matters of familiar experience. Thus the statements constituting the fundamental theory of a science, as well as many of the special assumptions which are used to supplement the theory in various ways, normally contain several descriptive expressions of this latter sort.

Now it is generally possible to explicate the meanings of many descriptive expressions in E with the help of other such expressions, though of course logical expressions will play a role in the explication. Let us refer to those descriptive expressions with the help of which the meanings of all other such expressions may be explicated—whether the explication is given in the form of conventional explicit definition or through the use of different and more complicated logical techniques—as the "primitive expressions" of the science. (Expressions that are primitive in this sense may be primitive only in some specific context of analysis and not in another. But this point, though not without importance for a general theory of definition, does not affect the present discussion.)

However, the explication of the meaning of an expression may have either of two objectives, and accordingly it is useful to distinguish between two classes of primitive expression. (a) The explication may aim at specifying the meaning of an expression in terms familiar from everyday usage; and in consequence, the primitives employed may be restricted to those expressions which refer to matters of common observation, laboratory procedure, and other forms of overt behavior. Call such primitives "experiential primitives," even if no sharp line may be drawn between expressions that are experiential and those that are not. For example, the meaning of the word "temperature" is often specified by means of statements describing the volume expansion of liquids and gases, or the behavior of other readily observable bodies; and in this instance the primitives employed in the explication are experiential ones.

(b) On the other hand, an explication may aim at specifying the meaning of an expression by exhibiting its relation to the meanings of expressions used in formulating the fundamental theory or the various supplementary assumptions of the science. And in consequence, the primitives employed may in fact contain no expression which refers to matters accessible to direct observation. Call such primitives the "theoretical primitives" of the science. For example, the meaning of the word "temperature" is sometimes specified with the help of statements describing the Carnot cycle of heat transformations, statements which contain expressions like "perfect nonconductor," "infinite heat-reservoir," and "infinitely slow volume expansion," that have no manifest reference to anything that is observable. Again, the explication of the expression "center of mass," as customarily given in treatises on mechanics, involves the use of other expressions that are basic in formulating the principles of mechanics, though they do not all refer to directly observable characteristics of bodies.

It is not necessary to decide, for the purpose of the present discussion, whether the meanings of all theoretical primitives of a science are explicable with the help of its experiential primitives. And though the class of theoretical primitives of a discipline and the class of its experiential primitives may have expressions in common, the two do not in general coincide.

3. I come to my third comment of a formal nature. A comparison of the statements belonging to the primary science involved in a reduction with those belonging to the secondary science shows that in general the two sciences share a number of common statements and expressions, the fixed meanings of these expressions being the same for both sciences. Statements certifiable in logic and demonstrative mathematics are obvious examples of such common expressions, but, in addition to them, the two sciences will frequently share statements and other expressions which have a descriptive or empirical content. For example, many propositions that fall within the field of mechanics, such as the law of the lever, also enjoy important uses in thermodynamics, as one of the borrowed statements of the latter science; and thermodynamics also employs such expressions as "volume," "weight," and "pressure" in senses which coincide with the meanings of these words in mechanics. On the other hand, the secondary science prior to its reduction generally contains statements and expressions not occurring in the primary science, except possibly as members of the class of observation and borrowed statements. For example, theoretical mechanics in its classical form contains neither the Boyle-Charles Law nor the word "temperature," though both of these occur in thermodynamics, and though the word may on occasion be employed in statements which describe the conditions of application of the first principles of mechanics.

Now it is of the utmost importance to observe that expressions peculiar to a science will possess meanings that are fixed by its *own* procedures, and that are therefore intelligible in terms of its own rules of usage, whether or not the science has been or will be reduced to some other discipline. In many cases, to be sure, the meanings of some expressions in a science can be explicated with the help of those occurring in another, and, indeed, even with the help of the theoretical primitives of the latter. For example, it is usually assumed that an analytical equivalence can be exhibited between the word "pressure" as employed in thermodynamics and other expressions belonging to the class of theoretical primitives in the science of mechanics. But it obviously does *not* follow that every expression used in a sense that is specified in a given science must or need be explicable in terms of the primitives, whether theoretical or experiential, of another discipline.

Let us finally consider what is formally required for the reduction of one science to another. The objective of the reduction is to show that the laws or general principles of the secondary science are simply logical consequences of the assumptions of the primary science. However, if these laws contain expressions that do not occur in the assumptions of the primary science, a logical derivation is clearly impossible. Accordingly, a necessary condition for the derivation is the explicit formulation of suitable relations between such expressions in the secondary science and expressions occurring in the premises of the primary discipline.

Now it may be possible to explicate the meaning of an expression occurring in a law of the secondary science in terms of the experiential primitives of the primary one, especially if, as is perhaps normally the case, the experiential predicates of the two sciences are the same. But this possibility is not in general sufficient for the purposes of reduction, since the problem here is to establish a certain kind of connection between expressions that occur in the secondary science but not in the premises of the primary discipline and expressions that do appear in these premises, especially those expressions of the latter class in terms of which the fundamental theory of the primary science is formulated. For though the uses of each of two expressions may be specifiable with the help of a common set of experiential primitives, it by no means follows that one of the expressions must be definable in terms of the other. The words "uncle" and "grandfather," for instance, are each definable in terms of "male" and "parent," but "uncle" is not definable in terms of "grandfather." Accordingly, a crucial step in reduction consists in establishing a proper kind of relation—that is, one which will make possible the indicated logical derivation—between expressions occurring in the laws of the secondary science and the theoretical primitives of the primary science.

There appear to be just two general ways of doing this. One is to show that an expression in question is logically related, either by synonymity or entailment, to some expression in the premises of the primary science. In consequence, the meaning of the expression in the secondary science, as fixed by the usage established in this discipline, must be explicable in terms of the theoretical primitives of the primary science. The other way is to adopt a material or physical hypothesis according to which the occurrence of the properties designated by some expression in the premises of the primary science is a sufficient, or a necessary and sufficient, condition for the occurrence of the properties designated by the expression of the secondary discipline. But in this case the meaning of the expression in the secondary science, as fixed by the established usages of the latter, is not declared to be analytically related to the established meaning of the corresponding expression in the primary science. In consequence, the indicated hypothesis cannot be asserted on the strength of purely logical considerations, but is at best a contingent truth requiring support from empirical data.

Let us now assume that the word "temperature" is the only expression that occurs in the Boyle-Charles Law which does not also occur in the various premises of mechanics and the kinetic theory of gases from which the law is to be derived. Accordingly, if the deduction is to be possible, an additional assumption must be introduced—the assumption that temperature is proportional to the mean kinetic energy of the gas molecules. How is this assumption to be understood, and in particular what sort of considerations support the indicated connection between the word "temperature" and the expression "mean kinetic energy"? But it is clear that in the sense in which "temperature" is used in thermodynamics, the word is neither synonymous with "mean kinetic energy" nor is its meaning entailed by the meaning of the latter expression. For it is surely not by analyzing the meaning of "temperature," in its thermodynamical sense, that the additional assumption required for deducing the Boyle-Charles Law from the premises of mechanics can be established. This additional assumption is evidently an empirical hypothesis, which postulates a determinate factual connection between two properties of physical systems that are in principle independently identifiable—between temperature as specified in thermodynamics on the one hand and the state of having a certain mean kinetic energy on the other; and if the hypothesis is true, it is at best only contingently true.

One objection to this last claim must be briefly considered. It is well known that though an expression may possess a certain fixed meaning at one stage in the development of inquiry, the redefinition of expressions is a recurrent feature in the history of the sciences. Accordingly, so the objection runs, while in an earlier usage the word "temperature" possessed a meaning which was specified by the procedures of thermometry and classical thermodynamics, it is now so used that temperature is "identical by definition" with molecular motion. The deduction of the Boyle-Charles Law does not therefore require that the premises of mechanics be supplemented with a contingent physical hypothesis but simply makes use of this definitional identity. This objection seems to me to illustrate the curious double talk of which highly competent scientists are sometimes guilty, to the detriment of essential clarity. It is obviously possible to so redefine the word "temperature" that it becomes synonymous with "mean kinetic energy of molecules." But it should be no less obvious that on this redefined usage, the word has a different meaning from the one associated with it on the basis of the usage customary in thermometry and thermodynamics, and in consequence a different meaning from the one associated with it in the Boyle-Charles Law. If, then, thermodynamics is to be reduced to mechanics, it is temperature in the sense specified in the former science which must be shown to be connected with mean kinetic energy. Accordingly, if the word "temperature" is redefined as proposed, the hypothesis must be adopted that the state of bodies described by the word "temperature" in its thermodynamical meaning is also correctly characterized by the word "temperature" in its redefined and different sense. But then this hypothesis is one which does not hold simply by definition. And unless it is adopted, it is not the Boyle-Charles Law which is derived from the premises of mechanics; what is derived is a sentence with a physical and syntactical structure similar to the law, but with a sense that is entirely different from what the law asserts.

I now turn to my second set of comments, those concerned with matters that are not primarily formal.

1. Thus far, I have been arguing the doubtless obvious point that the reduction of one science to another is not possible unless the various expressions occurring in the laws of the former also appear in the premises of the latter. But it is perhaps equally evident that these premises must satisfy further conditions if a proposed reduction is to count as an important scientific achievement. For if the premises of an alleged primary science could be selected quite arbitrarily, subject only to the formal requirements that have been mentioned thus far, the logical deduction of the laws of a secondary science from such premises selected *ad hoc* would in most cases represent only a trivial scientific accomplishment. And in point of fact, an essential condition that is normally imposed upon the assumptions of the primary science is that they be supported by empirical evidence possessing some measure of adequacy. The issues raised by this requirement, and especially the problems connected with the notion of adequate evidence, cannot be discussed in the present paper, and in any case are not pertinent exclusively to the analysis of reduction. However, a few brief reminders bearing on this requirement that are especially relevant to the reduction of thermodynamics to mechanics may contribute something to the present analysis.

It is well known that the general assumption according to which physical bodies in different states of aggregation are systems of molecules is confirmed by a large number of well-established experimental facts of chemistry and of molar physics, facts which are not primarily about thermal properties of bodies. Accordingly, the adoption of this hypothesis for the special task of accounting for the thermal behavior of gases is in line with the normal strategy of the natural sciences to extend the use of ideas fruitful in one set of inquiries into related domains. Similarly, the fundamental principles of mechanics, which serve as partial premises in the reduction of thermodynamics to mechanics, are supported by evidence drawn from many fields of study distinct from the study of gases. The assumption that these principles characterize the behavior of the hypothetical molecular constituents of a gas thus involves what is essentially the extrapolation of a theory from domains in which the theory has been well confirmed to another domain whose relevant features are postulated to be homogeneous with those of the former domains. But in addition to all this, it is especially noteworthy that the combined set of assumptions employed in the reduction of thermodynamics to mechanics, including the special hypothesis on the connection of temperature and kinetic energy, make it possible to bring into systematic relations a large number of propositions on the behavior of gases as well as of other bodies, propositions whose factual dependence on one another might otherwise not have become evident. Many of these propositions were known to be in approximate agreement with experimental facts long before the reduction was effected, but some of them, certainly, were discovered only subsequently to the reduction, and partly as a consequence of the stimulus to inquiry which the reduction supplied.

This last point needs to be stressed. It is fairly safe to maintain that the mere deduction of the Boyle-Charles Law from the assumptions of mechanics does not provide critical evidence for those assumptions, and especially for the assumption on the connection between temperature and kinetic energy, for prior to the reduction this law was already known to hold, at least approximately, for most gases far removed from their points of liquefaction. And though the adoption of those assumptions does effect, in consequence of the mere deduction of the law, a unification of physical knowledge, the unification is obtained on the basis of what to many practicing scientists seems an *ad hoc* postulation. The crucial evidence for those assumptions, and therefore for the scientific importance of the reduction, appears to come from two related lines of inquiry: the deduction from these assumptions of hitherto unknown connections between observable phenomena, or of propositions which are in better agreement with experimental findings than any that had been previously accepted; and secondly, the evaluation, from data of observation, of various constants or parameters that appear in the assumptions, with the proviso that there is good agreement between the values of a constant calculated from data obtained from independent lines of inquiry. For example, though the Boyle-Charles Law holds approximately for ideal gases, most gases under all but exceptional circumstances do not behave in accordance with it. On the other hand, if some of the assumptions used in the deduction of the law from mechanics are modified in a manner not radically altering their main features—specifically, if molecules are assumed to have diameters that are not negligible in comparison with the mean distances separating them, and if cohesive forces between molecules are also postulated—the proposition known as Van der Waal's equation can be derived, which is in much closer approximation to the actual behavior of most gases than is the Boyle-Charles Law. Again, to illustrate the second type of evidence generally accepted as critical for the importance of the reduction of thermodynamics to mechanics, one of the assumptions involved in that reduction is that under conditions of standard pressure and temperature equal volumes of a gas contain an equal number of molecules, quite irrespective of the chemical nature of the gas. Now the number of molecules contained in a liter of a gas (Avogadro's number) can be calculated on the basis of data obtained from observations, though to be sure only if these data are interpreted in a specified manner; and it turns out that alternative ways of calculating this number yield estimates that are in good agreement with one another, even when the measurements which serve as the basis of the calculations are obtained from the study of quite different materials—e.g., Brownian movements and crystal structure, as well as thermal phenomena.

2. These admittedly sketchy remarks on the character of the empirical evidence which supports the assumptions of a primary science merely hint at the complex considerations that are actually involved in judging whether a proposed reduction of one science to another is a significant advance in the organization of knowledge or whether it is simply a formal logical exercise. However, these remarks will perhaps help make plain that even though a science continues to be distinguished from other branches of inquiry on the basis of the general character of its fundamental theory, it may with the progress of inquiry modify or supplement the details of many of its subordinate and yet still quite general assumptions.

And this brings me to my next comment. For if this last point is well taken, it is clear that the question whether a given science is reducible to another needs to be made more explicit by the introduction of a definite date. No practicing physicist will take seriously the claim that, say, electrodynamics is reducible to mechanics—even if the claim were accompanied by a formal deduction of the equations of electrodynamics from a set of assumptions that by common consent are taken to fall within mechanics—unless these assumptions are warranted by independent evidence available at the time the claim is made. It is thus one thing to say that thermodynamics is reducible to mechanics when the latter includes among its assumptions certain hypotheses on the behavior of molecules, and quite a different thing to claim that the reduction is possible to a science of mechanics that does not countenance such hypotheses. More specifically, thermodynamics can be reduced to a mechanics that postdates 1866, but it is not reducible to a mechanics as this science was conceived in 1700. Similarly, a certain part of chemistry is reducible to a post-1925 physical theory, though not to the physical theory of a hundred years ago.

In consequence, much traditional and recent controversy over the interrelations of the various special sciences and concerning the supposed limits of the explanatory power of physical theory can be regarded as a debate over what at a given time is the most promising line of research and scientific advance. Thus, biologists who insist upon the importance of an "organismic" theory of biological behavior and who reject "machine-theories" of living structures may be construed as maintaining, though by

no means always clearly, that in the present state of physical and biological theory it is advantageous to conduct their inquiries without abandoning distinctions peculiar to biology in favor of modes of analysis typical
of modern physics. On the other hand, the mechanists in biology can be
understood as recommending, though often in the language of a dogmatically held ultimate philosophy, a general line of attack on biological problems which in their opinion would advance the solution of these problems
and at the same time hasten the assimilation of biology to physics—even
if the physics to which biology may eventually be reduced may differ from
the present science of physics in important though unspecified respects.
However this may be, if the controversy over the scope of physics is conceived in this manner, no major philosophical or logical issue appears to be
raised by it, though subsidiary questions involved in the controversy may
require logical clarification. If one takes sides in the debate, one is primarily
venturing a prediction, on what are often only highly conjectural grounds,
as to what will be the most fertile avenue of exploration in a given subject
matter at a given stage of the development of several sciences. On the
other hand, when such controversies overlook the fact that the reduction
of one science to another involves a tacit reference to a date, they assume
the character of typically irresoluble debates over what are alleged to be
metaphysical ultimates; and differences and similarities between departments of inquiry that may possess only a temporary autonomy with respect
to one another come to be cited as evidence for some immutably final
account of the inherent nature of things.

3. These last remarks have prepared the way for my final comment.
Unlike the present discussion, which views the reduction of one science to
another in terms of the logical connections between certain empirically
confirmed statements of the two sciences, analyses of reduction and of the
relations between sciences in general frequently approach these questions
in terms of the possibility or impossibility of deducing the properties of one
subject matter from the properties of another. Thus, a contemporary writer
argues that because "a headache is not an arrangement or rearrangement
of particles in one's cranium" and our sensation of violet is not a change
in the optic nerve, psychology is demonstrably an autonomous discipline;
and accordingly, though the mind is said to be connected with physical
processes, "it cannot be reduced to those processes, nor can it be explained
by the laws of those processes." Another recent writer, in presenting the
case for the occurrence of "genuine novelties" in the inorganic realm, warns
that "it is an error to assume that *all* the properties of a compound can be
deduced solely from the nature of its elements." And a third influential
contemporary author asserts that the characteristic behavior of a chemical
whole or compound, such as water, "*could* not, even in theory, be deduced
from the most complete knowledge of the behavior of its components, taken
separately or in other combinations, and of their properties and arrangements in this whole."

Such an approach to the question almost invariably transforms what is eminently a logical and empirical problem, capable in principle of being resolved with the help of familiar scientific methods and techniques, into a speculative issue that becomes the concern of an obscure and inconclusive dialectic. And in any case, formulations such as those just cited are highly misleading, in so far as they imply that the reduction of one science to another deprives any properties known to occur of a status in existence, or in so far as they suggest that the reducibility of one science to another can be asserted or denied without reference to the specific theories actually employed in a primary science for specifying the so-called "natures" of its ostensible elements.

It is clearly a slipshod formulation, and at best an elliptic one, which talks about the "deduction" of properties from one another—as if in the reduction of one science to another one were engaged in the black magic of extracting one set of phenomena from others incommensurably different from the first. Once such an image is associated with the facts of scientific reduction, the temptation is perhaps irresistible to read these facts as if in consequence some characters of things were "unreal" and the number of "genuine" properties in existence were being diminished. And it is simply naïveté to suppose that the natures of the various hypothetical objects assumed in physics and chemistry can be ascertained once and for all and by way of a direct inspection of those objects, so that in consequence it is possible to establish for all time what can or cannot be deduced from those natures. To the extent that one bases one's account of these matters on the study of scientific procedure, rather than on the frequently loose talk of scientists, it is plain that just as the fundamental nature of electricity is stated by Maxwell's equation, so the natures of molecules and atoms and of the properties of these postulated objects are always specified by a more or less explicitly articulated theory or set of general statements.

It follows that whether a given set of properties or behavioral traits of macroscopic objects can be explained by or reduced to the properties and behavioral traits of atoms and molecules is in part a function of the theory that is adopted for specifying the natures of the latter. Accordingly, while the deduction of the properties studied by one science from those of another may not be possible if the latter discipline postulates certain properties for its elements in terms of one theory, the reduction may be quite feasible when a different theory is adopted for specifying the natures of the elements of the primary science. Thus, to repeat in the present context a point already made, if the nature of molecules is stipulated in terms of the theoretical primitives and assumptions of classical mechanics, the reduction of thermodynamics to mechanics is possible only if an additional hypothesis is introduced connecting temperature and kinetic energy. But as has been seen, the impossibility of the reduction without some special hypothesis follows from purely formal considerations, and not from some alleged ontological hiatus between the microscopic and the macroscopic, the mechanical and the thermodynamical. Laplace was thus demonstrably in error when he imagined a divine intelligence that could foretell the future in every detail on the basis of knowing simply the instantaneous positions and momenta of all material particles as well as the magnitudes and directions of the forces acting between them. At any rate, Laplace was in error if his divine intelligence is assumed to draw inferences in accordance with the canons of logic, and is therefore assumed to be incapable of the blunder of asserting a statement as a conclusion if it contains expressions not occurring in the premises.

The question whether genuine novelties occur in nature when elements combine to form complex structures is clearly ambiguous. It can be construed as asking whether properties may not occur from time to time which have never before appeared anywhere in the cosmos. And it can also be understood as asking whether properties exhibited by various bodies assumed to be complex are in some cases at least different from and irreducible to the properties of their constituents. The question in the first sense clearly raises a problem in history which requires to be resolved with the help of the normal methods of historical inquiry; and the considerations raised in the present paper are not directly relevant to it. But the question in the second sense does call for a brief comment at this place. For the issue whether the properties of complexes are novel, in the non-temporal sense of the word, in relation to the properties of their elements, appears to be identical with the issue whether statements about the former are reducible to a primary science which deals with the latter. And if this is so, then the question whether the reduction is possible—and whether the properties alleged to be novel are indeed as thus described—cannot be discussed without reference to the specific theory which formulates the nature of the elements and of their properties. Failure to observe that novelty is a relational characteristic of properties with respect to a definite theory, and the supposition that on the contrary certain properties of compounds are inherently novel relative to the properties of the elements, irrespective of any theory which may be used to specify these elements and their properties, are among the chief sources for the widespread tendency to convert the analytic truths of logic into the dogmas of a footless ontology.

The chief burden of this paper, accordingly, is that the reducibility or irreducibility of a science is not an absolute characteristic of it. If the laws of chemistry—e.g., the law that under certain specified conditions, hydrogen and oxygen combine to form a stable compound, which in turn exhibits certain modes of behavior in the presence of other chemical substances—cannot be systematically deduced from one theory of atomic structure, they may be deducible from an alternate set of assumptions concerning the natures of chemical elements. Indeed, although not so long ago such a deduction was regarded as impossible—as it indeed was impossible from the then accepted physical theories of the atom—the reduction of various parts of chemistry to the quantum theory of atomic structure now appears to be making steady if slow headway, and only the stupendous mathematical difficulties involved in making the relevant deductions from the quantum-theoretical assumptions seem to stand in the way of carrying the task through to completion. At the same time, the reduction of chemical law to contemporary physical theory does not wipe out, or transform into a mere appearance, the distinctions and the types of behavior which chemistry recognizes. Similarly, if and when the detailed physical, chemical, and physiological conditions for the conditions for the occurrence of headaches are ascertained, headaches will not thereby be shown to be non-existent or illusory. On the contrary, if in consequence of such discoveries a portion of psychology will have been reduced to another science or to a combination of other sciences, all that will have happened is that the occurrence of headaches will have been explained. But the explanation will be of essentially the same sort as those obtainable in other domains of positive science. It will not consist in establishing a logically necessary connection between the occurrence of headaches and the occurrence of traits specified by physics, chemistry, or physiology; nor will it consist in establishing the synonymity of the term "headache" with expressions defined with the help of the theoretical primitives of these disciplines. It will consist, so the history and the procedures of the sciences seem to indicate, in stating the conditions, specified in terms of these primitives, which as a matter of contingent fact do occur when a determinate psychological phenomenon takes place.

[45]

HENRY MARGENAU

Physical Versus Historical Reality *

Summary. The science of the 19th and early 20th century permitted the view that all human experience is subject to the deterministic laws of physics. Reality was conformable with these laws, and the laws could be used to designate what is real.

Recent discoveries, particularly the quantum theory and its uncertainty principle, have modified, though not suspended, the causal laws of physics, thereby establishing a looser correspondence of theory with all those elements of experience in which we confront "the given." A *theory*, still exact and deterministic in its own terms, is related to the realm of immediate experience by *probabilities* only. These probabilities are irreducible, despite the current tendency to deny them ultimate status or to explain them away by fanciful mechanistic arguments about "unavoidable interactions" between measuring apparatus and measured objects.

* From *Philosophy of Science*, XIX, No. 3 (July 1952), pp. 193–213. By permission of the author and publishers (The Williams & Wilkins Co.).

Since, in view of this altered situation, physical laws no longer suffice to define all of reality, a concern regarding that which escapes these laws must properly arise. In the paper, this is called historical reality because the characteristics of history (in a large sense): incidence, spontaneity, being the last instance of factual appeal, etc., are so peculiar to it. The meaning of *decision*, which inhabits the historical and not the physical sphere, is tentatively examined and its relation to physical reality is discussed.

Some pains are taken to analyze the sense in which probabilities in quantum physics are irreducible. This involves recognition and maintenance of a clear distinction between several kinds of probability, only one of which can serve as basis for the epistemology developed in this paper.

1. The quantum theory of modern physics is too rarely made the object of intensive study by the professional philosopher and the social scientist; it is regarded as an *enfant terrible,* difficult to understand completely yet vaguely amusing because of the odd things it says about the world. In some fundamental respects, however, this theory has an importance far beyond its usefulness in physics, for it develops a methodology applicable, though not yet applied, to phenomena typical in many fields far removed from the physical sciences.

One sometimes hears the dogmatic suggestion that problems of biology, psychology, sociology, history, indeed all matters bearing upon collective human affairs, are immune to treatment by natural science because that science presupposes a kind of objectivity and invariability in the nature of its subjects which human intercourse does not exhibit. This doctrine ignores the fact that the quantum theory does deal successfully with just such collective vagaries as social science and biology present. It has a way of handling the "unpredictable interactions" between a fact and the knowledge of that fact, and furthermore it achieves a significant treatment of observations which, in a very real sense, may kill or annihilate the system under observation. There is a fair amount of literature upon these questions. The present article considers the relevance of quantum theory to problems of the social sciences.

In *The Nature of Physical Reality* (5) * I have argued that the use of probabilities as essential tools in the description of nature has brought about a separation of our experience into two domains: one, composed of immediacies (observations, measurements) that are not all predictable in detail; and another, refined and rational, which is the locus of laws and regularities, of permanent substances, of conservation principles and the like. The former was called *historical*, the latter *physical reality.*

At first sight the word "historical" may seem ill-chosen, for it suggests a technical connection with a well-defined discipline. We mean it here in a looser sense which, it is hoped, historians will condone. Historical events, in so far as they differ from physical events at all, are characterized by these qualities above others: they are significant only when observed; they

* See References at end of this selection.

are rather aloof from theories; they usually involve human decisions. They lie close to the plane of immediacy, in the terminology of reference 5. Thus historical here means incidental, emergent; it designates that which simply happens.[1] The word is meant to carry a strong flavor of the "existential." To be sure, all these traits often adhere as well to the events which interest physicists, and they do not provide a completely satisfactory definition. But they will indicate the motive for our choice of words which may perhaps justify itself as our discussion proceeds.[2]

The distinction in question does not, it is true, effect a cleavage in our normal responses to the world about us, for physical reality is the best rational account, and the closest possible approach to a uniform description of, spontaneous fact. Indeed the main reason for our reluctance to recognize the distinction lies in the circumstance that ordinary experience hardly requires it: in most of our daily life the rational comes to the surface and meets the deliverances of sense with satisfying congruity. Only on examining the stranger phenomena in the atomic world does the disparity in question reveal itself; in that world exact laws disclose their statistical character, and the novel manner in which they regulate observable facts becomes evident.

Hence arise a number of questions which we here state and then attempt to answer. 1. What, precisely, is the character of the lawlessness of the microcosm? 2. What is the meaning of the laws of physics, and how do they bear upon the lawless events? In this connection attention must be given to the seeming paradox arising from the fact that these laws do operate with dynamic precision in the macrocosm, while their functioning on an atomic scale is but statistical; in other words we must take occasion to study the gradual transformation of lawlessness into regularity which occurs as we ascend the scale of sizes, times and masses. 3. Does history belong to the macrocosm, or do its roots reach down into the chaos of the microcosm? 4. If the latter is true—as I believe it is—what opportunity is there for constructing a causal theory of history? In particular, can physical theory form a model after which a theory of history capable of prediction can be fashioned?

In dealing with questions 1 and 2 we shall leave aside as much as possible the refined language of physics; we endeavor to sketch a picture of the atomic world with the broad strokes of a brush, a picture admittedly surrealistic but faithful, it is hoped, to the fundamental issues involved in our problem. Question 2 will force us to consider the meaning of probability. The remaining questions are wholly epistemological; their answers depend on some of the specific information gained from an analysis of the former two.

In discussing atomic phenomena I shall endeavor to dispense with abstractions and to inject some of the vividness which the atomic world actually possesses. I hope I may be forgiven for an account in the following section that may seem like popularization.

2. *The Lawlessness of the Microcosm.* Let us transport ourselves to

the world of atoms. In doing so we are not considering the use of wholly phantastic artifacts like flying carpets or time machines which nobody can construct; we are merely supposing our sense organs to be replaced by more sensitive devices which the electronic engineer can actually build. These devices will allow us to perceive very small distances, very short intervals of time and extremely light objects. When observed with this equipment, the microcosm turns out to be a strange place indeed.

Perhaps its most striking feature is the failure of visual continuity: the world is not illuminated and filled with moving things; our eyes are now sensitive to the single darts of light (photons) cast off by single luminous atoms, and the effect is a speckled kind of vision with bright patches emerging here and there from utter darkness, the different patches having different durations. Distant objects of large size and mass have a kind of uniform glow, to be sure, and suggest some cohesion in this chaotic scheme of things, but the smaller things nearby give very little indication of uniformity or pattern.

It is doubtful whether an observer whose experience is limited to this microcosm would find it plausible to speak of the "flow of time" rather than the "emergence of sensed intervals." Continuous space would seem a far-fetched abstraction, and our observer would be unlikely to claim that objects—if indeed he were to attribute appearances to the presence of objects—had definite positions at definite instants of time. Certainly he would have no occasion to invent the calculus.

Nevertheless, as was already indicated, this world contains some measure of coordination. Patches of light are not completely random but appear in loosely ordered sequences. There are times when nothing can be seen, and then again the visual field is dotted with perceptions. Furthermore, these perceptions often indicate a preferred location in space, though they rarely mark a point. In view of this our micro-physicist would probably be led to postulate the existence of some sort of objects, vaguely localizable in space and somehow progressing from one place to another. But having never seen a completely continuous path he would not regard them as "moving" in the ordinary sense. Indeed the idea of continuous motion might be as difficult to conceive under these circumstances as is the notion of discontinuous emergence in our molar world. But let us accept the existence of external objects with masses, charges, perhaps colors, position-when-seen, momentum-when-encountered and many other measurable properties. None of these could be said to be "*possessed*" by, or to *adhere* uniformly to the objects in the simple way we infer from our familiar experience. There are however, elaborate operational procedures by means of which these properties can be determined. These will now be considered.

To learn in a pleasant way some of the peculiarities of the microcosm we go on a rabbit hunt. Experience has taught us that there are atomic rabbits, and we invent and use an atomic gun. The task of hitting the animal is not as simple as it is in our world since we see neither the rabbit nor the impact of our bullets. But there are ways of telling whether the quarry has been struck: a certain reaction takes place which, for the sake of simplicity, we shall assume to be an elementary squeak emitted by the dying victim. Forearmed with such knowledge and a gun we arrive at the hunting ground and wait until the darts of vision characteristic of a rabbit's presence appear in our field of perception. We aim at the region of their most frequent occurrence, preferably at the last identified rabbit flash, pull the trigger and hope for the squeal. It does not come the first time, of course, but we repeat the performance until the animal is struck. Just how we are going to find the corpse and bag it are difficult questions which, for our purposes, need not be answered. Let it be noted, however, that all the implements and processes we are invoking have possible atomic analogs which the physicist will recognize after a little thought.

With practice certain rules for successful hunting are required. A shotgun works better than a rifle. This will occasion no surprise to our macrocosmic minds, except insofar as the advantage of the gun over the rifle is far greater than merely the greater number of projectiles in the shot cartridge would suggest. It turns out, surprisingly, that the *larger bore* of the gun makes its use more expedient. On further experimenting with a rifle we find careful aiming to be useless; a *fine* gauge precisely directed at the target *increases* the scatter of the bullets and does not improve the aim. On noting this curious result we perform experiments; we shoot rifles of different gauges at a stationary target and observe their impacts. Large stationary targets do in fact exist (see below) and impacts can be made observable by the use of bullets which explode, i.e., emit light, on striking. Normal bullets, which we employed in our rabbit hunt, do not have this useful property.

By experimenting in this way we discover the famous uncertainty principle. It states that a relation between the pattern of impacts on the target and the size of the rifle bore does in fact exist, but the relation is the reverse of what macroscopic common sense would lead us to expect: the finer the bore the greater is the dispersion of the bullets.

Closer study of the impact pattern leads to further interesting observations, in particular to the surprising result that the distribution of shots is not the one suggested by the "error law" but by the diffraction of ordinary light passing through a diaphragm. We have thus come to recognize the existence of regularities in the *aggregate* of events despite the apparent lawlessness of individual occurrences. *If theories are to be devised to account for such happenings, they will have to concern themselves with aggregates rather than with single events.* For the present, however, we put theories aside and return to the vagaries of the microcosm.

We note in passing that hunting elephants is a good deal easier than hunting rabbits. These beasts give a more coherent account of their presence. While they do not produce a continuous progression in our field of vision, their seen emergence nevertheless dots a fairly uniform path. Also, use of an elephant gun with a large bore and more massive bullets reduces the scatter of the shots and makes the chase much more worthwhile.

From sports we turn to science. Galileo would have found it difficult to demonstrate to the inhabitants of the atomic world the validity of the laws of free fall. In transferring his experiments to the microcosm, we again take note of the fact that there are no continuously visible small bodies. Furthermore, remembering the erratic behavior of the individual rabbit, we consider it wise to deal at once with a large collection of objects. Hence we do what, macroscopically speaking, would be called gathering a handful of stones. True, this figure of speech is hardly descriptive of our exact procedures. For the stones are but intermittent patches of luminosity, and to confine them to the space of our hand is a difficult task. When transferred to the hand they are not densely packed nor do they stay at rest; all indications are that they jostle and bounce about, and there seems to be no way of quieting them down.

This unruly collection of bodies is dropped from a place high above ground, perhaps from some microcosmic leaning tower, and their progress is carefully recorded. It is impossible, as we have seen, to trace a single stone, our record being a multiplicity of individual light emissions. Yet there is some semblance of coherence, especially to an observer far away who is unable to distinguish the light flashes coming from individual stones. To him the falling group has the appearance of a swarm of fireflies which is clustered fairly tightly at the beginning but diffuses into a larger and larger assemblage of luminous dots as it approaches the ground. When all the facts are gathered our observer reports: 1. He was unable to trace unambiguously the path of any individual stone. (This is hardly news to us now, after our experience of hunting rabbits.) 2. The center of the swarm seemed to move with an acceleration of 32.2 ft./sec ^{2}, i.e., in perfect accord with the macroscopic law of falling bodies. 3. The swarm grew larger and thinned out as time went on.

At this point we, who are accustomed to the regular behavior of falling rocks, are strongly tempted to read their regularity into the microcosm. Every stone, we are prone to say, obeyed the laws of motion exactly as it fell. The reason why we failed to observe it are not hard to see. First, we only caught glimpses of an individual stone and did not trouble to reconstruct its complete path. Second, it was admitted that the stones were not at rest in the beginning. Hence the initial conditions of motion were different for different individuals and their spreading during the fall should have been expected. And thus we go on to assert with apparent safety: *If we had known the velocity and the position of every particle at the moment of its release we could have calculated its path, and the whole firefly phenomenon could have been predicted.*

The argument just stated attempts a *mechanistic denial of atomic uncertainties.* It considers motions as essentially continuous, unique and determinate, and it blames other physical agencies for the vagaries manifest in observations. Before turning to the specific forms of the argument, I wish to examine it on general philosophic grounds and appraise its value as a methodological directive.

The argument is an extrapolation of familiar molar experience. It is highly questionable, however, whether an observer familiar with the ways of the microcosm would have need for an hypothesis of detailed predictability, and consequently whether an investigator who regards the atomic world as primary should properly be disposed to make it. Perhaps these are matters of methodological preference. Let us therefore see what the argument nets us in the way of advantages, or of simplicity of description.

Practical advantages, aside from a certain satisfaction to our intuition, do not result from the hypothesis that atomic uncertainties are due to mechanical agencies. No theory has yet been proposed to render the vagaries understandable in detail, none is able to predict them. Indeed Heisenberg's principle, when disengaged from the "explanations" with which physicists so liberally suffuse it, says precisely that such predictions are impossible.

With respect to simplicity, the case against the mechanistic argument is even stronger. There is a parallel to it in the old theory of the ether, which we here briefly recall. This theory made, in effect, two assertions. One was that space is a medium capable of transmitting electrical and gravitational influences; the second was more particular and insisted in assigning the familiar properties of *material* media to the ether field. Every student of the history of science knows the difficulties and the controversies which ensued because of the tenacious belief on the part of physicists in what at the time appeared to be common sense, the materiality of the ether. The hypothesis was finally discarded because the models invented to account for the behavior of the medium violated every canon of conceptual simplicity. Quite analogously, the facts of the microcosm are now being explained, first by the postulate that *there are, indeed, permanent entities called electrons, protons* and so forth; to this, the scientist who argues for the reduction of atomic uncertainties in terms of insufficient knowledge, unforeseen interactions and the like, adds the further thesis that *the postulated entities have the familiar mechanistic properties of our more primitive experience.* This latter thesis complicates matters needlessly; unless it is eliminated we may waste time in wrestling with problems whose very artificiality, like the structure of an ether molecule half a century ago, belies their importance.

Neither of the last two italicized propositions is obvious in the sense of strict empiricism. The imputation of permanent existence to an atomic stone that reveals its presence only in the manner of the firefly, indeed with lesser consistency than a firefly, is already a posit not wholly forced by the observations. This assumption, however, has proved helpful and is incorporated in all valid theories of nature. Assignment of *exact position at all times,* which is demanded by the mechanist, is another, in fact a more risky hypothesis, as is shown by the circumstance that no theory embracing it has as yet succeeded. This latter hypothesis must be abandoned.

The position taken here can be supported to some extent on purely operational grounds: the position-at-all-times of an atomic particle can- not be found directly by observation, no operation for tracing the detailed trajectory of an electron being known. Thus far an appeal to experimental feasibility can be trusted. But operationalism, as always, is not the whole criterion of scientific validity. In this instance it would indict likewise the first postulate concerning the continued identity of electrons, which cannot be observed directly either. The point here is that validity in science relies also on principles beyond those contained in the doctrine of operationalism, as is shown in extenso in (1).

A particularized version of the argument we are criticising is the following. Granted that the luminous spots accompanying what is called the motion of a microcosmic stone (e.g., an atom) do not mark a simple con- tinuous path. The reason—says the argument—is to be seen in the un- avoidable recoil momentum imparted to the stone by the photon it emits. This causes it to zigzag in a peculiar manner, the corners of its path being made luminous by emissions. If the explanation stops at this point it is innocuous, for it adds nothing of scientific or cognitive value to the patent unpredictability of the stone's behavior. If the argument goes on to give directions for computing the trajectory, it fails.

The idle theory which endeavors to restore continuity by cryptic supplementation of observable facts can take other forms. For instance, if the stone is not self-luminous but perceived by reflected light, the theory can say that the reflected photon disturbed its motion unpredictably; if the stone manifests its presence by collision with another object, the latter can be blamed. Nature's perversity seems forever to prevent the theory from becoming specific or, as I should prefer to put it, seems always to grant it a hiding place.

Man's inability to trace the path of atomic objects is grounded in something far more serious than ignorance; its roots lie in actual indeter- mination of perceptions. In the case of an ordinary firefly, observed as moving from its scintillations in the dark, ignorance of intermediate posi- tions does not prevent their interpolation and hence a construction of its path. The situation with respect to the atom is completely different; inter- polation will not work however cleverly it be conceived.

What, then, has happened to our argument which ran: If we knew the velocity and position of every particle at the beginning of its fall . . .? It is useless, for according to our best present understanding we never shall know these things. To say that under these wholly impossible circum- stances the particle would obey the laws of free fall is quite the same as asserting: If the world were populated by angels there would be no wars. And finally, it should be pointed out that the argument, even when accepted, will not account correctly for the spreading of the swarm of stones as it "falls." This involves what physicists call "diffusion of a wave packet" and has no macrocosmic counterpart. It is thus necessary to take the lawlessness of the microcosm as it affects individual objects at its face value, to desist from trying to embellish it.

But it is quite essential that we recognize the regularity-in-the-mean exhibited by the center of the swarm of stones as it fell. Yet, how are these facts to be reconciled? What is it in the individual particle that makes it obey laws of the aggregate? Does it know what the other particles are doing and behave in relative conformity with them? Is an attracting force holding all particles together while some sort of individualistic repulsion keeps them apart? Science holds neither of these specific suppositions to be adequate. It proceeds on the most neutral plane that will join regularity-in-the-mean with individual caprice; it assigns neither purposes nor forces, but colorless *probabilities* as innate qualities to the microcosmic stones. This, it may be shown, is the least committal and the most effective thing to do in such circumstances. However, before studying probabilities, as we do in the next section, we return for another look at this elementary atomic world which we now inhabit.

Astronomical objects far away appear and behave like the bodies of our molar experience, as indeed they should, since they are the things we ordinarily encounter. Quantum theory accounts for this by showing that probabilities congeal to certainties when the masses in question become large. Large masses, therefore, do possess positions at all times and continuous paths to a very high degree of approximation. Nor is there a contradiction in this, or a mystery in the transformation of probabilities into near-certainties. An illustration of such a transformation which can be visualized is a loaded die. As the load is increased and the weight placed nearer and nearer one surface, the die's behavior becomes increasingly regular and predictable.

The laws of *optics* in the microcosm—to take one final example—are as peculiar as those of mechanics. On heating a large body it is found to glow, not with uniform incandescence, but with pointlike luminous spurts of different colors. As the temperature is raised, the bluer ones begin to predominate at the expense of the redder scintillations. No law suggests what color will appear at a given point at any specified time, but in the aggregate the color distribution agrees with Planck's law at every instant. A small object (a single atom), too, may be subjected to heat treatment and become self-luminous. But the light it emits is not continuous; it reminds even more strongly of a firefly in the dark, except that now the emissions are in different colors. No rule governs the details of the color sequence, yet in the long run the frequency of the individual colors obeys the laws of quantum theory. It may surprise us, however, that every elementary kind of body has its own assortment of colors by which it can be identified, the irregularity of sequence notwithstanding.

These examples may be regarded as fairly typical of the microcosm. They defy lawful description when attention is focussed on emergent, incidental, perceptual detail, yielding orderly pattern only when treated *en masse*.

3. *Reality in the Microcosm*. Having learned this lesson we return to our accustomed sphere. Our bewildering experience will be summed up in

the simple question: *What things are real in the atomic world?* On the molar scale of magnitudes a similar reflection hardly arose. What we saw was describable by continuous processes and by accurate laws. Perception was predictable, the emergent and the incidental were merely unrecognized features on the one regular face of nature. Atomic nature presents two faces and therewith a dilemma.

Or is there no dilemma? Suppose you saw an airplane in the sky and identified it as a B29. You look away, and after a moment you observe it again, noting to your astonishment that it is a Thunderbolt. After a while you observe it once more to be a B29. Would you not conclude that you were mistaken at least once about the identity of the plane? Nevertheless, as sense impressions, all three observations may have been real enough; so real that each might have been the occasion for a definite course of action under critical circumstances. If you discredit any of them it is not because it is less real as an observation, but because it is incompatible with the detailed lawfulness of nature, which does not allow a B29 to transform itself into a Thunderbolt spontaneously. In the microcosm there is no such lawfulness in detail, and the criterion for rejecting an individual observation as incompatible with others does not exist. Hence we repeat the question: What is real, the individual darts of the microcosmic fireflies, or whatever inheres in them to make the aggregate of darts conform with laws?

Perhaps both are real. Admitting this without qualification, however, is fatal to the proper understanding of large branches of modern physics, and it obscures whatever significance already formulated deductive science may have for other disciplines. In short, failure to make a distinction is an invitation to ignore a problem. Nor has the problem in fact been overlooked by theoretical physicists. Their voices, however, are discordant, often reflecting deep esthetic convictions, sometimes philosophic preconceptions, and occasionally disregard of basic philosophic issues. Three different responses are on record: the answer of the rationalist who favors the coherent aspects of our experience and regards *them* as primarily accented with reality; the plea of the positivist who recognizes the schism but limits his reality to observations, relegating to theory a secondary importance commensurate with its auxiliary function as handmaid to fact; finally, there is the council of the skeptic who, acknowledging the schism, sees in it an indication of error in our fundamental theories of nature. Representatives of the last-mentioned attitude are in the minority. Clearly, we cannot deal with their position because it will not grant the validity of modern science, which we are accepting (without prejudice, of course, to future improvements of its structure).

The other two answers bear responsible messages; partial, to be sure, but complementary. We wish to analyze them against the background of procedures actually used in science. This is best done, perhaps, by considering specific examples.

Every observation, every measurement, indeed every perception introduces errors. A measurement without error is an absurdity. Let the measurement (and measurement is after all only refined perception) be of a star's position in the sky, of the length of this table, of an automobile's speed, or of an electric current; its outcome is never to be believed exactly. This is apparent in the circumstance that the same number will not ordinarily result when the measurement is repeated, regardless of the care taken in performing it. Characteristically, only the careless experimenter and the ignorant observer believe raw nature to be unambiguous. To be sure, the different numbers found by the astronomer for the latitude (and longitude) of a star in successive observations lie within a reasonable interval, and this convinces him that he is somewhere near a "true" value of the quantity he seeks, that nature is not fooling him with hallucinations. Yet in a very fundamental sense he is witnessing a behavior not unlike the lawless emissions of the microscopic firefly; we thus see that the macrocosm is not wholly without its vagaries, but that it confines them sufficiently so that the observer with some credulity can feign their absence: he can blame himself for nature's equivocality and call the departures from a true value "errors."

But what is the *true* value? Let us look into scientific practice. If ten measurements of a physical quantity yield ten slightly different values, not one of them is necessarily regarded as true. Their *arithmetic mean* is singled out for this distinction, even though it may not have occurred among the measurements.[3] The justice of this choice is not provided by the ten measurements, nor by any finite number of observations; it comes from a belief in, or rather the postulation of, a certain uniformity of nature. Thus the very determination of a true value, and in the end the selection of whatever is believed to be true perceptory fact, involves a reference to law and order not immediately presented in the sensory structure of that fact. Here we find the clearest expression of the attitude which has led to the development of deductive science: it relies upon rational elements to straighten out erratic data. It does not ignore the latter's presence, nor does it accept them unrefined. It distills from them an essence and *calls* it *true*. But the nature of the essence is partly determined by the process of distillation.

Now it is this true value which science takes to be characteristic of its reality. If an electron be real, its charge and mass are assumed to be true values in the outlined sense, whether or not they have occurred in any measurement.

The real iceberg is not the exposed portion which the sailor sees; it is a largely unseen object compounded of the truths extracted from former observations and joined by postulations. The farther something is removed from immediate perception, as in the case of atomic entities or the facts of ancient history, the more dependent is its real character upon the lawfulness of the content in which it appears; it is real if that content is true. And here again, true does not necessarily mean "observed," anymore than it does in the process of measurement. It means "inferred from observations," and the nature of an inference, a word too often carelessly used, far transcends observations. What is physically real is rather close to the ideal.

Truth does not imply finality. The term is not to be taken in an extravagant metaphysical sense but signifies simply the best available. Truth may change. The scientist readily admits that he never knows a true value with infinite precision. This right to maneuver gives him the advantage he needs in rationalizing his observations, in making the best of an equivocal nature pitted against himself, an agent with rational propensities which force him to construct reality in accordance with rules.

A similar lesson can be drawn from many other instances. Real entities have often been inferred from lacunae in natural order before their existence could be certified by the standards of empirical science. Elements were predicted from gaps in the periodic table, planets because of irregular movements of known heavenly bodies; radio waves owed their conception as real constituents of nature to the simplicity of the equations of electromagnetism which implied their existence. The most significant advances of modern physics were motivated, or at least anticipated, by conjectures based upon the neatness of our universal laws; cases in point are the discoveries of the positive electron, the neutron and several types of meson. The whole case of the neutrino rests upon the empirically slender premise of valid conservation laws: this particle simply *has* to exist if the principles of energy, momentum and spin are to be retained. Yet it has never been seen in the sense that other elementary particles have been observed. There is good evidence that it can never be seen, and even this consideration does not count against its admissibility as a component of real nature. How can such generosity be countenanced except by granting that the real draws its sustenance in large measure from a belief in the lawfulness of the cosmos?

The same sentiment finds its expression in the philosophic view which identifies the real with the elements of our experience that are causally connected in time and space. Current doctrines of materialism, relativity, much of causality are reared upon this rationalistic credo. Hence it is safe to say—and this is one of the theses supporting the remainder of the present discussion—that physical science would lose its hold on reality if an appeal to law and order were interdicted as a major claim.

We have seen, however, that lawfulness is at a premium in the perceptory realm of the microcosm. There, regularity is found primarily in aggregates, or, when assigned back to individual events, in the *probabilities* which inhere in these events. Laws govern these probabilities, they do not govern single occurrences. To be in harmony with the spirit of physical science we must therefore accept a conclusion unpalatable to many thinkers of the past, the conclusion that *probabilities are endowed with a measure of reality*. What this means in detail and what pitfalls must here be avoided will be analyzed in the following section.

Now we do not claim that it is fair to put these arguments in reverse, i.e. to pronounce events resistant to lawful description, *unreal*. The perception of a single dart of light certainly happens, and the lawful multitude is made up of them. The fact of an hallucination is real and may be of great historical importance. Non-predictability hardly lessens the practical significance of certain unique occurrences both in the microcosm and the macrocosm. But the point is that they arrange themselves within the structure of our cognitive experience in a manner different from the simple order envisioned by traditional laws of nature.

To reconcile these disparities, and to accentuate their presence, I have advocated in *The Nature of Physical Reality* (5) a distinction between *physical* and *historical* reality.[4] It seems to me that the need for this illuminating division is very great indeed, not only for the sake of terminology but also as a means for stating clearly what science can and what it cannot do. The data of immediate experience always belong to the latter sphere, the enduring entities of physics always to the former. But the spheres often overlap. In the macroscopic world they are nearly coincident, for the seen trajectory of a molar missile is also describable by the laws of mechanics (to take the simplest example). This accounts for the unimportance of our distinction in classical physics. In the microscopic realm, however, the two spheres break apart and science becomes obscure unless this break is noticed.

4. *Probabilities*.[5] Single events, as we have seen by studying the world of atoms, have in general only probabilities for occurring. In special cases, particularly in cases involving objects of ordinary size, these probabilities take on values very close to 1 and thus reduce to certainties. But let us consider an elementary particle (our former rabbit) for which experience indicates that the probability of its being in a given place cannot be 1 for any finite interval of time. Physical laws predict its *mean* position in a number of observations; for any given position they indicate a probability only.

Now suppose an observation is made and the particle is seen at a definite place. Must we not conclude that at the moment of observation the object was surely at the place where it was seen? And if we grant this much, are we not driven to admit certainty for its position at one instant? Expressing our suspicion more formally, we seem constrained to say: the act of observing the particle has caused the probability of its position, which was less than 1 prior to the observation, to jump suddenly to the value 1 during the act of observation.

This consequence expresses an orthodox view, widely accepted and emphasized in a number of textbooks on quantum mechanics. If correct, it raises difficulties with some of the remarks made in the earlier parts of the present paper, and indeed with some of the basic axioms of quantum theory. For instance, it would be preposterous on this view to subject probabilities to physical laws—the discontinuous change during observation being precisely the feature that defies these laws. The advantage of using probabilities as regular, and as real, entities arose from their immunity to such erratic changes, and the result now tentatively reached once more injects lawlessness into them. The gain sought is thus destroyed.

This is not the only defect of the view under consideration. If it is valid, there is no sense in talking about probabilities at all. For it is then obvious that a single observation can determine a supposedly erratic property exactly. Hence the initial conditions in any problem of motion *are* ascertainable (remember the example of the falling particle!) and experiment will always prove our theory to be in error.[6] Instead of providing a valid theory, the notion at issue can only demonstrate that none is attainable.

It also implies that, whenever an observation is made, physical reality suddenly transforms itself into historical reality. There is no a priori reason why such a transformation should not occur; however, the mathematical features of this conversion are most perplexing and, we feel, objectionable. Suppose that we have given a charged particle an exact momentum by sending it through an accelerating chamber equipped with diaphragms. We then know precisely in what direction and with what speed it is going, but we cannot say at all where it is. The probability of position for this particle has the same small value everywhere. Now let a measurement of the particle's position be made, perhaps by noting the point at which a silver grain is blackened (after development) on a photographic plate. According to the thesis under criticism we must then say: the probability after the measurement is zero everywhere except near the position of the blackened grain.

Thus as physical reality, the probability extended through all of space, like a continuous medium devoid of matter. It formed in fact a field. At the instant of observation this field proceeds to vanish everywhere in space and concentrates itself as historical reality upon a point, where it takes on an infinite density. And all this because some human being chose to make an observation! Aside from the miraculous features of this theory, one wonders whether it was designed to deal with the physics of particles or the psychology of perception.

The confusion and the welter of contradictions accompanying the thesis stated in the earlier italicised paragraph of this section disappear when we avoid a simple error in our understanding of the term probability. To discover the error we consider a familiar example.

The physical condition of a regular die may be specified in many ways, some more complete than others. The die might be described as having a certain mass, shape and size. It might be said to have six equal black faces with white dots on them. Another perfectly good way is to assign the probabilities for the appearance of the numbers from 1 to 6 when the die is thrown at random. These are well known to have the value 1/6 each. We repeat, knowledge of these six equal numbers is just as significant with respect to the intrinsic nature of the physical object, the die, as the knowledge that it has six equal faces or that it has a certain mass and size. These parcels of information are not equivalent, to be sure; but each can serve as a basis for the prediction of certain physical occurrences. The psychological stigma of incomplete knowledge which we habitually attach to probabilities must be erased. Let us fix our attention on these probabilities.

Suppose the die is thrown and a five appears. According to the reasoning employed in the italicized paragraph above, the former probabilities (1/6, 1/6, ... 1/6), for the numbers 1, 2 ... 6 have now suddenly changed to (0, 0, 0, 0, 1, 0). Still it is obvious that the physical characteristics of the die have not been altered by the incident of the throw, and the reader doubtless has an uneasy feeling that the meaning of the word probability has shifted during this discourse. Clearly, here is what happened. Initially we meant by probability the quality of the die by virtue of which the results of a long series of throws, say n in number, will contain $n/6$ ones, $n/6$ twos, and so forth. In the end we meant by probability the degree of certainty of *our knowledge* with respect to the outcome of a particular throw. These two are not the same logically, and the confusion incurred earlier was occasioned by our mistaking them to be identical. Their difference is well understood in the theory of probability, where the distinction between the frequency interpretation and its counterparts (Laplacian, a priori definition and others) is fully recognized. If we stick consistently to the frequency interpretation, a single throw, or any number of throws, alter nothing so long as the physical character of the die remains unchanged, and the conclusion reached above is fallacious. On the certainty-of-knowledge interpretation the conclusion follows.

Now the certainty-of-knowledge interpretation in the present form is not tenable because it is hopelessly indefinite. To be acceptable it requires a statement of the *evidence* to which the knowledge relates. Probability becomes a function of two variables: the event considered and the evidence available. If the evidence is confined to the normal properties of the die, the probability for throwing a five is 1/6; if it includes knowledge that the thrower habitually cheats and has a way of getting sixes, the probability is less than 1/6; if the throw has already occurred and has yielded a five, and if its outcome is included in the evidence, all other evidence becomes irrelevant and the probability is clearly 1. Strictly speaking, all these probabilities are different physical entities and must not be confused. Hence, if the degree-of-knowledge interpretation is to be employed the evidence variable must be held constant during its use; in our example, evidence must be restricted to knowledge of the normal properties of the die, nothing smuggled in *en route*. But then the two interpretations agree, the probability does not change when the die is thrown and the dilemma is avoided. Henceforth, we shall employ the frequency definition of probability, as is customary in most scientific work. It will be called the objective interpretation.

Description of physical states in terms of probabilities need not have the trivial character exhibited by the ordinary die, whose properties may be specified by writing: $P_1 = P_2 = \cdots = P_6 = 1/6$. Here the probabilities P_i for throwing the numbers i are constant in time. The die can, however, be imagined to have an internal structure which changes in time. Suppose for definiteness that it is hollow and contains a sprocket with a small weight at its end. The other end of the sprocket is fixed to an axle extending parallel to an edge through the center of the cube, and this axle is driven by a small clockwork. We now have a strangely loaded die, but one in which the load revolves when the motor goes. The probabilities P_i are functions of the time. If the mechanism is known these probabilities can be calculated; the reverse, however, is not true. Quantum mechanics asserts that there is no mechanism, that the probabilistic behavior is in the nature of the physical object and is ultimate.

Yielding nonetheless to our propensity for mechanical models we could invest our die with further appliances. Let us assume that the sprocket can be set in one definite position by some manipulation from the outside which does not interfere with its being thrown. The same operation also starts the clockwork. We shall speak of this operation as "activating the die." Normally the die is in a stationary state, its probabilities are constants in time. After activation they become functions of the time.

How can we determine the variable probabilities by measurement? If the die is known to be in a stationary state it may be thrown a sufficient number of times and the relative frequencies can be computed. Otherwise, more elaborate procedures are required. Merely repeating throws will not do when the die is activated, because different throws then catch it in different internal states, and a computation of relative frequencies is meaningless. Two correct methods for determining the probabilities in their time dependence are at hand. One is to activate the die, wait a time t and throw it; repeat this procedure many times, always observing the interval t before a throw. The results can then be used to calculate $P_i(t)$. Another method is applicable when many dice with the same internal structure are available. It consists in activating all of them at once, waiting a time t, and then throwing them all.

Such are the typical features of the quantum theory of measurements. The die corresponds to an atomic system, e.g., a hydrogen atom. This can be in a stationary state, as it will be for example when it has been left alone for a sufficient period of time. In that condition we are unable to say where the electron is relative to its proton, but we can perform measurements (illumination by short x-rays) each of which will locate the electron at some point r, not of course at the same point. From a sufficient number of such measurements we construct P_r.

The situation is different when the atom is "activated." There are many forms of activation, called "preparation of state" in quantum theory. Perhaps the simplest is exposure to a light wave, which causes the atom to be in a time-dependent state. The probabilities are determined as in the case of the activated die: either by repeating many times the act of switching on the light, waiting a period t and measuring, using a single atom; or by exposing many atoms simultaneously to the light, waiting a time t and then measuring all of them at once. The result is found to be a P_r which is a function of t, the same for both methods. The latter method is the one which the physicist most frequently uses.

It is not our intention to discuss fully the quantum theory of measurements, which presents complexities for which the activated die provides no analogs. For instance, to make the story more realistic the die should often break after it falls, so that another one must be used when the throw is to be repeated. A fall can also change the setting of the sprocket and thus produce further difficulties which have here been ignored. The intent of our discussion was primarily to illustrate the sense in which probabilities can be *objective* physical quantities.

5. *Historical Reality.* The lawful world of physical existences contains all external objects, from stars down to our own bodies and to electrons. It contains the states in terms of which the objects are described, the fields they generate, the time and space in which they are embedded. Notably, too, it contains the causally evolving *probabilities*, the states of the quantum theory which modern physics has taught us to regard as functionally ultimate. Man has, of course, experience of this world, not experience in the narrow sense of empiricism but in the wider one of constructing concepts and of creating rules of correspondence. This is the universe of strictly physical reality.

Over against it stands the multitude of immediacies over which, as we have seen, physical causation has lost its direct control. A sensation, a measurement, an observation, a will, an action, and certainly a psychological introspection, belong to this class. I do not argue that it is always possible to tell whether a given element of experience is to be assigned to this class with certainty—as in many other instances, here, also, experience shows no sharp boundaries. The failure of a sharp logical distinction is never serious when recognized. At any rate the items last enumerated, and others which partake similarly of the character of immediacy (spontaneity, coerciveness), in our experience will be said to compose *historical reality*.

Epistemologically, the two worlds are related by rules of correspondence (1). My sensation of an object is the historical component of the event in question, reification is the rule of correspondence, and the postulated external entity (desk, tree, lamp) is the physical component of the experience. The distinction made is admittedly useless and grotesque in the ordinary instances of regular cognition, where lawfulness extends into the historical realm and thus annexes it to the domain of physical reality. Classical physics was the formalization of this all-pervasive causal doctrine. Recent discoveries, described in the earlier portions of this paper, force the distinction upon us. The microcosm obviously fails to convey sense if its lawful and its historical phases are confused, and to what extent the distinction can be ignored in the large-scale world of action requires to be investigated. (See below.)

An electron, if it moves in accordance with classical laws of mechanics,

describes a physical path, a trajectory; it has no history. The actual electron, subject to the laws of the quantum theory, appears unpredictably
here or there; it has no path but a history. To be sure, it also has a determinate physical state associated with its "motion," a wave function in this
case. This wave function, however, hovers abstractly over its history, guiding it by enforcing a sort of disposition without concretely assigning its
fate. Historicity involves knowing, it implies observation; it arises through
a union of a knower and his object of knowledge.

The inveterate mechanist tries to explain historicity as an aberration
from path-like behavior through an appeal to "unpredictable interactions,"
as we have seen in section 2. So long as this mode of reasoning is forced to
fall back on "unpredictable" matters it fails to achieve its mechanistic end
and becomes what we have called an idle theory.

An equally idle, but no more idle theory, is one herewith proposed:
the electron itself, as an individual, *decides* what value of a physical
observable it will exhibit in the act of measurement. While nothing of
scientific importance depends on whether we accept this dogma—and I
believe the meaning of decision in this context is not very clear—physics
can not refute it any more than it can invalidate the mechanist's assertion.
What is true is this: to account for experience in its fullness even in the
atomic realm, physics requires supplementation by aspects of actuality,
incidence, decision—in short, historicity.

All that precedes seems to show that the accent on emergence is particularly strong in the atomic world, that the atom is the prime actor in
the drama of history. When many atoms cooperate, when masses and distances become large, classical physics with its unhistorical lawfulness
results. Our elephant hunt was far less exciting than our rabbit hunt.
Quantum theory "reduces" to classical physics in the molar world.

While this is generally true, there are important exceptions to the rule.
Nature permits arrangements in which the randomizing effects of large
numbers does not occur, instruments through which the caprice of the
microcosm can be projected into the world of ordinary experience. Every
amplifier is such a device. A Geiger counter amplifies the passage of a
single elementary particle by precipitating an avalanche of ions when a
few are initially produced, and the current thus generated can be further
increased by the use of electron tubes. As is well known, much of modern
physical research employs such arrangements. Feedback mechanisms
achieve the same purpose of amplification, and the biophysicist is apparently discovering their widespread occurrence in organized nature. There
is indeed an increasing mass of evidence to indicate that the delicate balance of metabolism and self-maintenance called life depends for its establishment on precisely those mechanisms which are able to amplify a random
atomic impulse into historically significant proportions.

An example often cited in this connection is the mutation of a gene. A
single x-ray photon can bring this about. Suppose now that the frequency
of this photon has been observed and is known. According to the uncer-

tainty principle the position of the photon is then entirely random. Indulging in an anthropomorphism, we might say it is wholly "up to the photon" where it will interact with its surroundings. If it chooses to invade the neighborhood of a gene, the latter undergoes a change which may, under certain circumstances, spell the doom of an individual.

In the inorganic world similar processes of random triggering are easily found. A somewhat unrealistic but impressive one is the release of a uranium bomb by a single neutron. Place a sufficiently large block of U^{235} in a space free of neutrons, then allow a single neutron at some distance from the block to move toward it. Quantum mechanically, its wave function is known, and along with it we know the probability that it will impinge upon the bomb and cause disaster. The historic fact whether it will or not is left open by the physics of the situation.

These instances demonstrate the ingression of atomic historicity into the generally lawful macrocosm. The merger between physical and historical reality of which we spoke, and which takes place to some degree in the molar world, is not complete. Our distinction carries its validity far beyond the atomic domain and must be reckoned with everywhere. Astronomy is about the only science which is relatively immune to it.

Yet all this, while true, seems to have very little bearing upon the problems of history as this subject is usually understood. History is the arena of *human action*, and action has not yet entered our discourse. What, then, is action? When analyzed, I believe it is seen to be a composite of arrangements and processes in accord with physical laws, *plus* here and there an element of voluntaristic *decision*. It is the decision which transfers action from the physical to the historical universe, or, rather, makes it an inhabitant of both realms.

We used the word decision, albeit in a loose and tentative manner, when the discussion was about electrons in the act of manifesting their presence to the perceiver. There we were unable to invest the term with accurate meaning. In human action there is a similar element of decision, similar in the sense that it also transcends physical lawfulness (as did the manifestation of the electron's position) ; but in human action we can study it by introspection. And it is recognized as conscious, active, voluntaristic intervention, a true component of historicity.

The problem of human freedom might seem to enter here. Its traditional features, however, are peculiarly foreign to the present line of thought. What is obviously, introspectively true, is the occurrence of voluntary decisions, the existence of what earlier philosophers called the human will. Physics has nothing to say about the freedom of that will, about its dependence on motivation, habit and so on. The fact of *conscious decision* is clear for all to see, and the latitude needed for action consequent upon decision is guaranteed by the probabilistic features of physical reality. This is as far as we need to go.

Indeed it is risky to go farther. The physicist who tries to prove freedom on the basis of quantum theory invariably meets a misfortune, whether he recognizes it or not. For if he makes ψ-functions govern human behavior he can prove *randomness* of action, but never freedom. He can show that man will act in accordance with ethical precepts a certain percentage of the time, that he will act immorally in another percentage of instances. On this theory men's behavior would be a set of random doings, some good, some bad, without a clue indicating which are good and which are bad. This is not the kind of thing philosophers call freedom. What the argument needs to make its case is again the element of decision, of historicity.

Since we left the atomic world our discourse has increasingly taken on the character of speculation, at least to the extent that conscious decision, or action, has assumed a dominant rôle. We now return to safer matters and show in what manner the possibility of action, regardless of its psychological essence, arises from the modifications of physical lawfulness.

Consider again the neutron on its way to the uranium bomb. If classical physics were true, a single set of observations on the position and velocity of the neutron at a suitable time would decide whether an explosion will occur. It would leave room for action only to the very limited extent that, if the neutron is found headed for the bomb, we can try to intercept and deflect it before the impact. Usually this is impossible because the speed even of a thermal neutron is greater than ours, and we are forced to resign ourselves to fate instead of being agents in the course of events.

Notice, too, that the very decision to intercept the neutron must be taken as a physiologically determined consequence of physical reality, whose historicity can be but an illusion. Decision as such is indeed an impossibility on the basis of classical mechanics.

The new physics, with its concession of autonomy to historical reality, leaves greater room for action and avoids this difficulty. Even if a set of observations [7] reveals the neutron to be headed for the bomb we can still hope and act for our survival, because what is now dynamically determined is a probability of collision, not a necessity. There is no cause for fatalism, but accentuated need for action. This is true even if, classically speaking, the neutron is seemingly winning the race for collision with the bomb. In this instance, as in all others, the physical situation leaves alternatives which action can seize in numerous ways. Decision fits neatly into the spaces presented by the semi-deterministic honeycomb of historical reality. But we do not pretend to have shown that it actually resides there, nor why. This is an illuminating conjecture made reasonable by the probabilistic nature of physical reality.

To illustrate this point minutely, let us analyze a decision. The suggestion is always strong that we should reduce the psychological act of deciding to physiological bases. In other words, when explaining the outcome of a so-called choice we advert to physiological processes taking place in the brain, to reverberating neuron currents, firing synapses and the like, and we assume, following traditional doctrine, that in the ultimate analysis molecular events determine the outcome of our choice. *This avenue is now blocked*, for clearly such a process of reduction will land us in the realm of atomic uncertainties. There is no unique road from the event of voluntary decision to the laws of physical reality. Again, we are forced to take decision as an irreducible act, a component of historical reality which stands aloof from physical lawfulness.

A summary of conclusions now reached might run as follows. Nineteenth Century natural science conceived of man as a detached spectator of an objective universe. It held the spectator-spectacle polarity to be genuine and fundamental. During the present century, discoveries concerning the nature of atoms rendered this doctrine untenable. The nucleus of a new philosophy of nature emerged with Heisenberg's principle of uncertainty, whose basic meaning implies a fusion of the knower with the known. The theory grew with amazing speed and success; it led to a mathematical formalism which, in order to attain its purpose, namely lawful description of experience, has to speak of probabilities rather than unique events. Individual events are no longer related in causal fashion, although in the domain of probabilities causality still reigns. Thus has been introduced another, more significant principle of division than the old spectator-spectacle bifurcation: the distinction between physical and historical reality has appeared.

Along with these developments, man has been transformed from a spectator to an active participant in the drama of becoming. Room has been made for decision and choice, which had no place in the older scheme of things. What was formerly fate has become history.

Before laying away his pen the philosopher, though disclaiming all right to speak as an historian, desires to raise a thought or two for historians to ponder. Physical science has yielded autonomy to the historical process. The detachment of the latter from physical lawfulness is the more pronounced the greater the abundance of momentous, unique events having a potency to release an avalanche of history. We live in an era charged with such potencies. The distinction which this paper set out to describe may have a sinister chance of becoming fatal before it is universally recognized. Hence its grave importance.

The other thought concerns the possibility of a science of history. Let no one deny this possibility on the grounds that history has too many variables to be susceptible of scientific treatment, or that it deals with human situations in which inquiry has a profound effect upon what is sought to be known. Natural science has solved both of these difficulties in its long course of evolution, the first by judiciously eliminating irrelevant variables and searching for significant ones, the second by injecting probabilities into the last constituents of its universe. It may be supposed, therefore, that history can take on the structure of science by adopting the pattern of physics. If this plausible thesis is accepted it follows that history, like physics, can predict only mass phenomena such as economic cycles, large-scale migrations, periods of cultural activity, and the like. But it will

be unable to address itself to those peak events, to the emergence of powerful personalities, which have so decisive an influence on the course of
human affairs.

A science of history that wishes to bring these critical phenomena
within its sphere of prediction must not follow slavishly the pattern of
physical science; such a science must strike out on its own along paths
hitherto uncharted by existing disciplines.

REFERENCES

1. Cassirer, E., *The Problem of Knowledge,* tr. W. H. Waglum and C. W.
   Hendel. New Haven: Yale University Press, 1950.
2. Churchman, C. W., *The Theory of Experimental Inference.* New York:
   Macmillan Company, 1948.
3. v. Humboldt, W., "Über die Aufgabe des Geschichtsschreibers," *Werke,*
   ed. A. Leitzmann, IV, 1905, p. 35.
4. Kemble, E. C., "Reality, Measurement, and the State of the System in
   Quantum Mechanics," *Philosophy of Science,* XVIII, 1951, p. 273.
5. Margenau, Henry, *The Nature of Physical Reality.* New York: McGraw-
   Hill Book Company, Inc., 1950.
6. Margenau, Henry, "Conceptual Foundations of the Quantum Theory,"
   Science, Vol. 113, 1951, pp. 95-101.

[46]

R. G. COLLINGWOOD

Modern Cosmology *

ALEXANDER AND WHITEHEAD

From the somewhat slender metaphysical threads of argument in the
writings of mathematical physicists we must turn to the work of the professed philosophers, and of these I shall deal only with two, Alexander and
Whitehead. Each of these is a philosophical genius of very high order, and
their works mark a return to the grand manner of philosophical writing,
the manner which we last saw in English when Hume gave us his *Treatise
of Human Nature.* This grand manner is not the mark of a period; it is
the mark of a mind which has its philosophical material properly controlled
and digested. It is thus based on width and steadiness of outlook upon the
subject-matter; it is essentially objective, concerned not with the thoughts
of others, whether to criticize or expound, but with the features of the

* From R. G. Collingwood, *The Idea of Nature.* The Clarendon Press, Oxford, 1945.
Last chapter, pp. 158-177. By permission of the publishers.

thing itself; it is marked by calmness of temper and candour of statement, no difficulties being concealed and nothing set down in malice or passion. All great philosophers have this calmness of mind, all passion spent by the time their vision is clear, and they write as if they saw things from a mountain-top. That is the tone which distinguishes a great philosopher; a writer who lacks it may or may not be worth reading, but he certainly falls short of greatness.

§ 1. ALEXANDER

We will begin, then, by considering how it is that the world of nature has appeared to Alexander from his mountain-top. This world, as it exists in its ceaseless changes, appears to him [1] as a single cosmic process in which there emerge, as it goes on, higher orders of being. The word 'emergent' is borrowed from Lloyd Morgan who used it in his *Instinct and Experience* (1912) and who later set forth in his *Emergent Evolution* (1923) a similar view of the world as an evolutionary process; he used the word 'emergent' to show that the higher orders of being are not mere resultants of what went before and were not contained in them as an effect is in its efficient cause: thus the higher is not a mere modification or complication of the lower but something genuinely and qualitatively new, which must be explained not by reducing it to terms of the lower out of which it grew but according to its own proper principles. Thus, according to Lloyd Morgan, life has emerged from matter and mind from life; but that does not imply that life is merely matter and that biology should be reduced to a special case of physics, nor that mind is merely life and that the sciences of mind are to be resolved into biology and so ultimately into physics. Lloyd Morgan's argument makes no claim to show why a new order of beings should emerge from an old, or why things should emerge in any determinate sequence; his method is, and professes to be, purely descriptive. And here I must refer to General Smut's amplification of the same idea, in his book on *Holism and Evolution* (1926): more frankly philosophical in his outlook than Lloyd Morgan, he has attempted to state the principle of emergence by saying that nature is permeated by an impulse towards the creation of wholes, or self-contained individuals, and to show how each stage of evolution is marked by the emergence of a new and more adequate type of individuality embracing and transcending as parts of itself the individuals previously existing.

Alexander's view of evolution is closely akin to both these. He accepts the general scheme (a commonplace since Hegel) of life as emerging from matter and mind from life, and he holds that in both these emergences— and similarly in all others—the essence of the process is that, first, there exist things with a determinate structure and character of their own, and then, that these things arrange themselves into a new pattern which as a whole possesses a new type of structure and a new order of qualities. The fundamental conception here implied is the conception that quality depends on pattern. This, as I have already said, is the conception by which the Pythagoreans explained musical notes and by which modern science explains chemical quality. Alexander boldly extends it to evolution as a whole. He begins with space-time, not space and time as two separate entities in the Newtonian manner, but a single entity in which, to use his own expression, space is metaphorically the body, and time, as the principle of organization, the mind; without space there could be no time, and without time no space. Thus we get, not one infinite plurality of points and another of instants, located respectively in space and time, but a single infinite plurality of point-instants, which are the ultimate constituents of all that exists. Hence everything that exists has a place-aspect and also a time-aspect. In its place-aspect it has a determinate situation; in its time-aspect it is always moving to a new situation; and thus Alexander arrives metaphysically at the modern conception of matter as inherently possessed of motion, and of all movements as relative to each other within space-time as a whole. The first emergence is the emergence of matter itself from point-instants: a particle of matter is a moving pattern of point-instants, and because this is always a determinate pattern it will have a determinate quality. This is the metaphysical exposition of the modern theory of matter; and here, as often elsewhere in his argument, Alexander is careful to point out that quality is not a mere phenomenon, it does not exist merely because it appears to a mind; it exists as a function of structure in the objective world. This applies not only to chemical qualities but to the so-called secondary qualities of matter, colour, and the like, which are functions of patterns themselves composed of material elements: thus a particular musical note is the quality intrinsically belonging to a certain rhythm in air-vibrations, and is real irrespective of whether or not there are ears to hear it. Thus, in the physical world before the emergence of life, there are already various orders of being, each consisting of a pattern composed of elements belonging to the order next below it: point-instants form a pattern which is the electron having physical qualities, electrons form an atom having chemical qualities, atoms form a molecule having chemical qualities of a new and higher order, molecules like those of air form wave-patterns having sonority, and so on.

Living organisms in their turn are patterns whose elements are bits of matter. In themselves these bits of matter are inorganic; it is only the whole pattern which they compose that is alive, and its life is the time-aspect or rhythmic process of its material parts. Thus life is the time-aspect of the organism, its space-aspect being inorganic matter; in other words, life is a peculiar kind of activity or process belonging to a body composed of parts which taken in themselves enjoy an activity of the next lower order.

Mind is a further peculiar kind of activity arising in living organisms and using life as its substratum or material: thus mind is a pattern of vital activities. Just as life is qualitatively different from any activity belonging to the material of the organic body, so mind is qualitatively different from any activity belonging to life as such. Again, just as there are different orders of being within matter, so there are different orders of life, higher and lower, the higher being elaborated forms of the lower, and different orders of mind. 'Ascent takes place, it would seem, through complexity. But at each change of quality the complexity as it were gathers itself together and is expressed in a new simplicity. The emergent quality is the summing together into a new totality of the component materials' (ii. 70).

This evolutionary process is theoretically infinite. At present, it has reached the stage of mind; but it only goes forward at all because at every stage there is a forward movement or impulse, a nisus or drive, towards the realization of the next. Mind, among its other peculiarities, has the privilege of being conscious of this drive and conceiving in its thought the goal towards which its evolution is leading it. Hence every mind has a conception of a higher form of mentality into which it is consciously endeavouring to convert itself; these conceptions are the ideals which govern human conduct and thought. But mind as a whole, being only one stage in the cosmic process, is engaged in an endeavour to evolve out of itself something as different from itself as mind is different from life, something which when it appears will be on its material side a pattern of mental activities as mind is a pattern of vital activities, but on its formal or qualitative side something altogether new. This next higher order of quality, as yet unrealized, is deity, and thus God is the being towards whose emergence the evolutionary nisus of mind is directed.

I cannot here pause to indicate the innumerable ways in which this argument, so classically severe and simple in its architectural lines, is verified and defended in detail; still less to point out its many affinities with the cosmological theories of other great philosophers. I must go back to the beginning and raise the question, Upon what foundations or presuppositions does the cosmic process, as conceived by Alexander, rest? For Plato, for Hegel, and for modern Platonists like Jeans, it rests on an eternal order of immaterial forms or categories. Alexander has a theory of his own concerning categories: he regards them not in the Platonic or Hegelian manner as transcending or presupposed by empirical things, but simply as immanent in them, wherever and whenever they exist: that is, he considers them as nothing else than the pervasive or omnipresent characteristics of whatever exists in space-time. Thus space-time, for him, generates with one hand, as it were, the categories, as hall-marks which it stamps upon all its creatures; and with the other the order of empirical existents, each possessing its own peculiar qualities but all alike marked with the categorial characteristics of identity, diversity, existence, universality, particularity, individuality, relation, order, causality, reciprocity, quantity, intensity, wholeness and partness, motion, unity and plurality. Space-time is the source of the categories, but they do not apply to space-time; they belong only to what exists, and what exists is not space-time itself but only the empirical things in it; but these things possess categorial characteristics for one reason and one only—namely, that they exist in space-time. Hence Alexander regards them as depending on the nature of space-time: that is, he aims at deducing them from the definition of space-time as its necessary consequences.

Now this doctrine of space-time as logically prior to the categories demands close attention. Superficially it reminds us of the *Critique of Pure Reason*, which begins with space and time and then goes on to the categories; but Kant derives the categories not from space and time but from an independent source, namely, the logical table of the judgments. And Kant does not think, as Alexander thinks, that empirical things are as it were visibly stamped with the categories; on the contrary, he thinks that the pervasive characteristic empirically discovered in the world of nature are not the categories themselves but the schemata of the categories. Thus, to take one example, what we empirically find in the world of nature is never causality or the necessary connexion binding effect to cause, but only the schema of causality, namely, uniform sequence. The schemata are the pervasive characteristics of the visible world; they depend upon space and time, being simply forms of spatio-temporal structure; and when we ask whether the categories in Alexander's system are in Kantian language categories or schemata, the answer is easy and can be verified by anyone from Alexander's pages: they are not categories, they are schemata. It looks as if Alexander, deeply influenced by Kant but resolving at all costs to avoid Kant's subjectivism, had cut out the Kantian categories altogether, because they are merely subjective necessities of thought, and contented himself with the schemata by themselves. But if you cut out the category of cause and substitute its schema, you are cutting out the idea of necessary connexion and trying to content yourself with mere uniform succession; that is, you are attaching yourself to an empiricism like that of John Stuart Mill, for whom a cause simply is an antecedent, and for whom consequently all knowledge is mere observation of fact, devoid of any apprehension of necessity. And this is precisely what Alexander does. His theory of knowledge amounts to this, that minds are things which have the power of knowing other things; and his carefully expressed theory of philosophical method is an application of the same doctrine, for he tells us that the business of philosophy is not to reason or argue or explain but simply to observe and describe facts.

This strain of empiricism is the weakness of Alexander's philosophy. If the method of philosophy is purely empirical, if the universal merely means the pervasive, the necessary merely the actual, thought merely observation, a system built on this method can have in it no driving force or continuity; there is an element of arbitrariness in every transition, and a reader who stubbornly asks, '*Why* should space-time generate matter; *why* should matter generate life; *why* should life generate mind?' and so on, will get no answer; he will only be told that he must not ask such questions but must accept the facts in a spirit of natural piety. Yet if the child is father of the man, surely the first duty of natural piety is to respect, and endeavour to satisfy, the childish tendency to ask questions beginning with *why*.

In its extreme form this weakness appears in Alexander's exposition of the idea of God. That exposition is dazzling in its austere splendour; but this must not blind us to its paradoxical character. Our ordinary thoughts of God are no doubt childish; but, such as they are, they begin by thinking that in the beginning God created the heavens and the earth. Alexander, on the contrary, says that in the end the heavens and the earth will create God. The crudity of this contradiction is modified by making God an equivocal term, and saying that in virtue of its nisus towards the emergence of Deity the world may be called God, as it were, by anticipation; but Alexander is not entitled to that ambiguity, and his real thought is expressed by another passage in which he says that God, being a qualitied infinite, cannot exist (which must imply that His existence is intrinsically impossible, so that He never *will* exist); God, he says, is therefore only a picture, but a picture eminently worth drawing, though nothing actual corresponds to it (or, we must add, ever will correspond to it). Hence, when Alexander asks himself whether he can support the belief, common to religion and traditional cosmology, that God is the creater of the world, he replies that on the contrary he must reject it: it is space-time which is the creator and not God: and strictly speaking God is not a creator but a creature. This conclusion would not be objectionable in a philosophy whose method claimed to be one of rigid deduction; for such a method, if it arrived at conclusions contrary to ordinary ideas, would be entitled to defend them by argument (as Spinoza defends his view that our ordinary idea of freedom is an illusion); but in a philosophy whose leading methodical conception is that of natural piety it *is* objectionable, for such a philosophy ought to take current ideas as it finds them, and nothing is more essential to the current idea of God than the belief that He created the world.

Thus in spite of the brilliant merits of Alexander's work—one of the greatest triumphs of modern philosophy, and a book where no page fails to express truths illuminating and important—there is a certain gap between the logic of the system and the materials, derived from his general experience as a man, which he has tried to work into it. According to the logic of the system, Alexander ought at the beginning to deny logical necessity and fall into pure empiricism; at the end he ought to deny God and fall into pure atheism (except in so far as he would identify God with space-time). And both these steps might easily be taken by followers less richly endowed than himself with experience of life and thought; clever philosophers, unlike him in not being great men. The alternative way of following him is to reconsider the logic of the system, and in especial to reopen the question whether categorial characteristics pervading nature as a whole do not imply something outside nature, something prior to space and time.

This brings me to Whitehead; not because he is a follower of Alexander, for he is not; but because he represents a view, in general very much like Alexander's, in which that question is differently answered.

§ 2. WHITEHEAD

Whitehead's early training was that of a mathematician and physicist. He approached philosophical studies first in the capacity of a mathematician reflecting on his own thought, collaborating with Russell in *Principia Mathematica*, a vast treatise on the logic of mathematics which laid the foundation of modern logical analysis. Later he wrote books giving a philosophical account of physics: *The Principles of Natural Knowledge* and *The Concept of Nature*, and finally, in 1929, a general metaphysical system: *Process and Reality*. His work in philosophy forms part, and a very important part, of the movement of twentieth-century realism; but whereas the other leaders of that movement came to it after a training in late-nineteenth-century idealism, and are consequently realistic with the fanaticism of converts and morbidly terrified of relapsing into the sins of their youth, a fact which gives their work an air of strain, as if they cared less about advancing philosophical knowledge than about proving themselves good enemies of idealism, Whitehead's work is perfectly free from all this sort of thing, and he suffers from no obsessions; obviously he does not care what he says, so long as it is true. In this freedom from anxiety lies the secret of his success.

His theory of nature much resembles Alexander's. Nature for him consists of moving patterns whose movement is essential to their being; and these are analysed into what he calls events or occasions, which correspond with Alexander's point-instants. But, unlike some who have adopted his analytic method, he refuses to believe that the real being or essence of a complex thing is discovered by analysing it into the events of which it is composed. Analysis does indeed reveal the components, but it disintegrates their structure; and Whitehead shares Alexander's view that the essence of a complex thing is identical with its structure or what Alexander calls its pattern. By the more fanatical realists the analytic method has been welcomed chiefly as an escape from subjective idealism. In actual experience the known object is always found coexisting with the mind that knows it; and subjective idealism argues that this whole composed of two parts, the knower and the known, cannot be split up into its components without damaging both of them by taking away from each something that it possesses only as united with the other. Therefore, argues the idealist, things as we know them would not exist precisely as we know them if they were not thus known. To this argument the analytic method seemed to provide an answer: a complex whole is merely an aggregate of externally related parts, and analysis reveals those parts as they are, in their separate natures.

This argument against idealism is valid only if it can be maintained, as a perfectly general proposition, that every whole is a mere aggregate of its parts. This, however, was not maintained even by G. E. Moore, who used the argument against idealism; for Moore also admitted that there are what he calls organic unities, that is, wholes having characteristics not referable to any part separately but only to the whole as such. Moore recognized such unities especially in the field of ethics. It may have been a recollection of Moore's principle which has led Whitehead to describe his own philosophy as the philosophy of organism; for what he has done is to regard that principle not as a somewhat strange and paradoxical law holding good in ethics and perhaps in some other fields, but as a universal principle applicable to the entire field of existing reality. He is quite explicit as to this universality of application. Everything that exists has for him its place in what he calls the order of nature (*Process and Reality*, II. iii); this order consists of 'actual entities' organized, or organizing themselves, into 'societies': thus every actually existing complex thing is a society, and Whitehead says 'a society is more than a set of entities to which a class-name applies; that is to say it involves more than a merely mathematical conception of order' (p. 124). Here Whitehead strikes at the root of the doctrines which lead some of his former colleagues to make such assertions as that a chair is the class of sense-data which would commonly be called aspects of the chair.

When Whitehead constantly asserts that reality is an organism, he does not mean to reduce all reality to biological terms; he only means that every existing thing resembles a living organism in the fact that its essence depends, not on its components merely, but on the pattern or structure in which they are composed. Hence (to point out just one obvious corollary) it is idle to ask oneself whether the rose really *is* red or only *seems* red to our eyes; the same order of nature which contains the rose contains also human beings with their eyes and their minds, and the situation which we are discussing is a situation in which roses and men are equally real, and equally elements in the society of living things; and its colour and its beauty are real features of that society, not simply located in the rose (that is what Whitehead calls the 'fallacy of simple location') but located in the society of which the rose is one organic part. Consequently if you put to Whitehead the realist's shibboleth, the question 'Would a rose be red if there was nobody looking at it?' he would answer very mildly 'No; the whole situation would be different.' And consequently strict members of the realist faction regard Whitehead with suspicion, as a wobbler.

Nature, for Whitehead, is not only organism, it is also process. The activities of the organism are not external accidents, they are united into a single complex activity which is the organism itself. Substance and activity are not two, but one. This is the basic principle of Whitehead's cosmology, a principle grasped by him with unusual tenacity and clearness, and taught to him, by his own account, by modern physics with its new theory of matter. The process of nature is not a merely cyclic or rhythmical change, it is a creative advance; the organism is undergoing or pursuing a process of evolution in which it is constantly taking new forms and producing new forms in every part of itself.

This cosmic process has two main characteristics, which I may call, using Whitehead's own words, 'extensiveness' and 'aim.' By 'extensiveness' I mean that it develops upon a stage of space and time: it is spread over space and goes on through time. By 'aim' I mean that Whitehead, like Alexander, explains process in terms of teleology; the A which is in process of becoming B is not merely changing at random, but orienting its changes towards B as a goal. *Qua* extensive, the process implies what Alexander calls space-time; Whitehead calls it the extensive continuum, and argues very much like Alexander that it has both a time-aspect and a space-aspect, but that without space there could be no time and without time no space. Like Alexander, too, he holds that there is not, and never has been, any empty space or time, devoid of pattern and process; the idea of empty space-time disappears when the traditional concept of matter disappears and is replaced by the concept of process. And the finiteness of the natural world both in space and time—the spatial limitations of the starry universe and the temporal limitations of its life—are explained by Whitehead's conception of cosmic epochs. He observes that there are many pervasive characteristics of nature which are arbitrary: for example, the quantum of energy, the laws of the electro-magnetic field as discovered by Clerk Maxwell, the four dimensions of the continuum, the axioms of geometry (*Process and Reality*, pp. 126–7: I give his own examples). He argues that since there might have been worlds where these arbitrary characteristics had different values, our world is only one among many possible worlds, as Leibniz argued before him. But unlike Leibniz he holds that, since there is no intrinsic reason why these other worlds should not exist (for if there were, they would not be possible worlds, but impossible worlds) they must all exist, not here and now, but elsewhere in space-time, and his general name for them is cosmic epochs.

The finiteness of a particular cosmic epoch means not only that, since the laws which define it are arbitrary, there might be and therefore must be and therefore are others outside it in space and time. It means also that, since the laws which define it are arbitrary, they are not perfectly obeyed, from which it follows that the order prevailing in any given cosmic epoch is shot with instances of disorder, and these instances of disorder gradually subvert the order and turn it into an order of a different kind. Here are Whitehead's own words (*Process and Reality*, p. 127):

'But there is disorder in the sense that the laws are not perfectly obeyed, and that the reproduction [by which new electrons and new protons come into being] is mingled with instances of failure. There is accordingly a gradual transition to new types of order, supervening upon a gradual rise into dominance on the part of the present natural laws.'

Qua teleological, or pervaded by aim, the cosmic process implies something else, and here we come to the difference between Whitehead's cosmology and Alexander's. For Alexander, the new qualities which emerge when a new pattern forms itself in space-time belong to that pattern and nowhere else; they are in every sense new, wholly immanent in the new event in which they are realized. For Whitehead, they are in one sense immanent in the world of existence, but in another sense they transcend it: they are not mere empirical qualities of the new occasion, they are also 'eternal objects' belonging to a world of what Plato called forms or ideas. Here Alexander inclines towards an empiricist tradition—I have already pointed out his affinity, in such matters, to John Stuart Mill—which identifies that which is known with the fleeting sense-datum of the moment; Whitehead, with his mathematical training, represents a rationalist tradition which identifies that which is known with necessary and eternal truths. This leads White-head back towards Plato, and to asserting the reality of a world of eternal objects as the presupposition of the cosmic process.

Alexander's cosmic process thus rests on a single foundation, space-time; Whitehead's on a double foundation, space-time and the eternal objects. This difference enables Whitehead to solve certain fundamental problems which for Alexander remain necessarily insoluble. Why, for example, should nature have in it a nisus towards the production of certain things? For Alexander, there is no answer: we must simply accept the fact in a spirit of natural piety. For Whitehead, the answer is that the peculiar quality belonging to those things is an eternal object which, in his own phrase, is a 'lure' for the process: the eternal object, exactly as for Plato or Aristotle, attracts the process towards its realization. Again, what is the relation between God and the world? For Alexander, God is the world as it will be when it comes to possess that future quality which is deity; but, as I have already said, this makes nonsense of the ordinary meaning which we attach to the word 'God.' For Whitehead, God is an eternal object, but an infinite one; therefore He is not merely one lure eliciting one particular process but the infinite lure towards which all process directs itself. I quote his words (*Process and Reality*, p. 487):

> 'He is the lure for feeling, the eternal urge of desire [remember that feeling and desire, as Whitehead uses the words, belong not exclusively to minds but to anything, so far as it is engaged in creative and therefore teleological activity]. His particular relevance to each creative act, as it arises from its own conditioned standpoint in the world, constitutes him the initial object of desire establishing the initial phase of each subjective aim.'

Whitehead, following out his own train of thought, has thus recon-structed for himself Aristotle's conception of God as the unmoved mover, initiating and directing the entire cosmic process through its love of Him. And it is curious to observe that the identity of his own thought with Aristotle's, which Whitehead gladly admits, had to be pointed out to him by a friend, Whitehead having apparently never read Aristotle's *Metaphysics* for himself. I mention this not to ridicule Whitehead for his ignorance of Aristotle—nothing could be farther from my mind—but to show how in his own thought a Platonic cosmology may be seen, in the pages of *Process and Reality*, turning into an Aristotelian. Thus the cycle of cosmological thought in the modern world, from Descartes and Newton to Whitehead, recapitulates the cycle running from Thales to Aristotle. But this recapitulation is not a mere repetition; it has taken up into itself first the body of Christian theology, and secondly, derived from that theology, the body of modern science, the new physics of the seventeenth century and the new biology of the nineteenth. In Whitehead's work all the leading conceptions of these new sciences have been fused into a single view of the world which is not only coherent and simple in itself but has also consciously connected itself with the main tradition of philosophical thought; Whitehead himself, though he shows no sign of having read Hegel, says in the preface to *Process and Reality* that in his ultimate views he is approximating to Bradley and the main doctrines of Absolute Idealism, though on a realistic basis (it is this that shows his ignorance of Hegel's polemic against subjectivism), and claims continuity with the philosophical tradition. Whitehead has escaped from the stage of thinking that the great philosophers were all wrong into the stage of seeing that they were all right; and he has achieved this, not by philosophical erudition, followed by an attempt at original thought, but by thinking for himself first and studying the great philosophers afterwards.

The main lines of Whitehead's philosophy, I have said, are coherent and simple; but in trying to think them out one is confronted by several difficulties of a secondary but very important kind. I will try to state the most important of them, making it clear at the same time that I am not always sure whether Whitehead himself has confronted them or not; for he is always a very difficult writer to read, and even after long study one is often not sure how far he has solved by implication problems which he appears to have ignored.

First, then, concerning the theory of eternal objects. He seems to think that everything which Alexander would call an empirical quality—the blueness of the sky at a particular moment, or the relation between two musical chords never written in just that way before—is an eternal object. Certainly that is the express view of Santayana, with whom Whitehead here claims general agreement (*Process and Reality*, pp. 198–9). Now, when once the doctrine of eternal objects is allowed, it seems only logical to extend it in this way *à outrance*. The classical passage on this subject is in Plato's *Parmenides*. Are there, Parmenides asks, forms of right, beauty, and good? Certainly, says Socrates. Are there forms of man, fire, or water? Socrates replies that he is not sure. Are there forms of hair, mud, and excrement? Certainly not, says Socrates; though he admits that the denial lands him in difficulties out of which he can see no way. The meaning of the passage is clear enough: some things must be regarded as eternal presuppositions of the cosmic process; others may be regarded as its products, and perhaps only as its products; others are merely its by-products, not even necessary or intelligible in themselves, but intelligible (so far as they are intelligible at all) only as accidents in a creative process whose true products lie elsewhere. Alexander would regard all these alike as products; Whitehead would regard them all as presuppositions. Socrates, when he tried to adopt Whitehead's view, was put to flight, as he says, by fear of falling into an ocean of nonsense. By this he certainly did not mean that it would be distasteful to attribute anything so solemn and awful as an eternal form to anything so mean and unpleasant as the smell of dung; he meant that a world of eternal forms which included in itself forms of every empirical detail in nature would only be a lumber-room of natural details converted into rigid concepts, and that a world of forms so conceived, instead of explaining the processes of nature, would be a mere replica of these processes themselves with the process left out.

There is one way in which this absurd conclusion could be avoided. If it could be shown, for example, that the form of the good, in itself and quite apart from any temporal process in nature, implied the form of animal as its logical consequence; if it could be shown that this form of animal implied in itself the form of excrement; then it could be held that there were forms of these things, and that in their logical connexion and logical subordination they did really serve to explain the processes of nature. In other words, the heart of the problem is the question how the world of eternal objects, the realm of essence, is organized in itself. Plato certainly saw this, and Hegel saw it; but if you are going to take that line, as Whitehead seems to do and Santayana certainly does, you saddle yourself (as Hegel did) with the terrible task of logically deducing every empirical quality to be found in the world from some absolute first principle, or else giving up the attempt to take seriously the doctrine of eternal objects. For there is nothing to be gained by merely insisting that the sky now has this peculiar blueness by participating (as Plato put it) in the form of that shade of blue, or as Whitehead puts it, by the ingredience of that shade as an eternal object in the present occasion of my seeing the sky; by saying that, you are appealing to the conception of a world of forms or eternal objects as the source or ground of natural process, and you must go on to give an account of this world and show why that shade of blue appears in it.

Santayana is ready with his answer to this demand; but it is an answer which I think would not appeal to Whitehead. If I ask Santayana to show that this shade of blue is an essence logically implied by his general conception of a realm of essence, he replies that 'no essence can have implications': 'implication is something imposed on essences by human discourse, leaning not on logic but on the accidents of existence' (*Realm of Essence*, p. 81). Hence, for him, every essence is completely self-contained and atomic; the realm of essence is simply an aggregate or structureless congeries of details. This, unless I am very much mistaken, is simply the ocean of nonsense which Socrates was so anxious to avoid; and it certainly could not be attractive to a mathematician like Whitehead, whose training is chiefly a training in grasping the implications of essences. But how Whitehead would answer the question I do not know.

The second main problem which Whitehead seems to leave unsolved concerns the creative process of nature. Evolutionists like Lloyd Morgan, Alexander, or General Smuts believe that this process passes through definite stages: that there was a time when no organic life existed on this planet, and that it arose, upon an inorganic physico-chemical basis, through the working of the creative process itself. But this does not seem to be Whitehead's view. In *Nature and Life* he treats inorganic nature not as a real thing which once existed by itself and still exists as the environment of life, but as an abstraction, nature itself conceived apart from the vital elements which everywhere pervade it. He asks what we mean by life, and having defined it by the three marks of self-enjoyment, creative activity, and aim, he goes on to argue that all three are really present in the so-called inorganic world, though physical science, for its own perfectly legitimate purposes, ignores them. Now this seems to me a way of avoiding the problem rather than solving it. There are types of process which occur in living things and do not occur elsewhere; Whitehead's three marks do not seem to me an adequate account of them; and what he has done is to escape the difficulty by restricting the connotation of the term 'life' to something which does indeed belong to life but is not its differentia but only the genus common to itself and matter. Consequently he falls back into the very subjectivism he is trying to avoid, by calling matter a mere abstraction. There is an element of truth in this conclusion, but it requires a good deal more working-out before it can be regarded as satisfactory. If matter is a mere abstraction, we must ask, what are the real facts in nature which oblige us to make that abstraction?

The same difficulty arises in connexion with mind. The characteristic mark of mind is that it knows, apprehends reality. Now, says Whitehead, this too, like the characteristics of life, is nothing really unprecedented. Everything enjoys what he calls 'prehensions,' that is to say, somehow absorbs what is outside itself into its own being. An iron filing prehends the magnetic field in which it lies, that is, it converts that field into a mode of its own behaviour, responds to it; a plant prehends the sunlight, and so on. The peculiarity of what we ordinarily call 'minds' is that they prehend an order of things which no lower type of organism can prehend, namely propositions. Here again there is profound and important truth in Whitehead's view; his refusal to regard mind as something utterly disparate from nature, his insistence that mind as we know it in man is something that has come to be what it is by developing functions belonging to life in general and even in the last resort to the inorganic world, is altogether admirable; but once more, as in the case of life, he is on the horns of a dilemma. Either mind is at bottom the same as these elementary prehensions, in which case there is no creative advance, and life is a mere abstraction from mind as matter is from life, or else it is also something genuinely new, in which case we have to explain its relation to that out of which it grew. And once more Whitehead does not appear to see the dilemma. No one has more vividly realized and described the resemblances, the fundamental continuity, running all through the world of nature, from its most rudimentary forms in the electron and proton and the rest of them to its highest development known to us in the mental life of man; but when we ask him whether this series of forms represents a series really developed in time he seems uncertain of his answer; and if we go on to ask the precise nature of the connexion between one form and the next, he has no answer to give except to insist that in general all such connexions are formed by the creative process which is the world itself.

§ 3. CONCLUSION: FROM NATURE TO HISTORY

I have traced in this book, as well as my ignorance and my indolence have allowed me, not indeed the whole history of the idea of nature from the early Greeks to the present day, but certain points concerned with three periods in that history about which I happen to be less ignorant than I am about the rest. And having reached a sort of ending, I must close with a warning and a question. The warning is that the ending is not a conclusion. Hegel, nailing to the counter in advance the lie that he regarded his own philosophy as final, wrote at the end of his treatise on the philosophy of history, *Bis hierher ist das Bewusstseyn gekommen*, 'That is as far as consciousness has reached.' Similarly, I must say now, 'That is as far as science has reached.' All that has been said is a mere interim report on the history of the idea of nature down to the present time. If I knew what further progress would be made in the future, I should already have made that progress. Far from knowing what kind of progress it will be, I do not know that it will be made at all. I have no guarantee that the spirit of natural science will survive the attack which now, from so many sides, is being made upon the life of human reason.

The question is: 'Where do we go from here? What constructive suggestions arise from the criticisms I have brought, however timidly, against the conclusions of Alexander and Whitehead?' I will try to answer it.

Throughout the long tradition of European thought it has been said, not by everyone but by most people, or at any rate by most of those who have proved that they have a right to be heard, that nature, though it is a thing that really exists, is not a thing that exists in itself or in its own right, but a thing which depends for its existence upon something else. I take this to imply that natural science, considered as a department or form of human thought, is a going concern, able to raise its own problems and to solve them by its own methods, and to criticize the solutions it has offered by applying its own criteria: in other words, that natural science is not a tissue of fancies or fabrications, mythology or tautology, but is a search for truth, and a search that does not go unrewarded: but that natural science is not, as the positivists imagined, the only department or form of human thought about which this can be said, and is not even a self-contained and self-sufficient form of thought, but depends for its very existence upon some other form of thought which is different from it and cannot be reduced to it.

I think that the time has come when we should ask what this other form of thought is, and try to understand it, its methods, its aims, and its object, no less adequately than men like Whitehead and Alexander have tried to understand the methods and aims of natural science, and the natural world which is the object of natural science. I do not think that the defects I seem to have noticed in the philosophy of these great men can be removed by what may be called the direct route of starting according to their own methods from their own starting-point and doing their work over again and doing it better. I do not think it can be done even by starting from their own starting-point and working by better methods. I think that these defects are due to something in their starting-point itself. That starting-point, I think, involves a certain relic of positivism. It involves the assumption that the sole task of a cosmological philosophy is to reflect upon what natural science can tell us about nature, as if natural science were, I will not say the only valid form of thought, but the only form of thought which a philosopher should take into account when he tries to answer the question what nature is. But I submit that if nature is a thing that depends for its existence on something else, this dependence is a thing that must be taken into account when we try to understand what nature is; and that if natural science is a form of thought that depends for its existence upon some other form of thought, we cannot adequately reflect upon what natural science tells us without taking into account the form of thought upon which it depends.

What is this other form of thought? I answer, 'History.'

Natural science (I assume for the moment that the positivistic account of it is at least correct so far as it goes) consists of facts and theories. A scientific fact is an event in the world of nature. A scientific theory is an hypothesis about that event, which further events verify or disprove. An event in the world of nature becomes important for the natural scientist only on condition that it is observed. 'The fact that the event has happened' is a phrase in the vocabulary of natural science which means 'the fact that the event has been observed.' That is to say, has been observed by someone at some time under some conditions; the observer must be a trustworthy observer and the conditions must be of such a kind as to permit trustworthy observations to be made. And lastly, but not least, the observer must have recorded his observation in such a way that knowledge of what he has observed is public property. The scientist who wishes to know that such an event has taken place in the world of nature can know this only by consulting the record left by the observer and interpreting it, subject to certain rules, in such a way as to satisfy himself that the man whose work it records really did observe what he professes to have observed. This consultation and interpretation of records is the characteristic feature of historical work. Every scientist who says that Newton observed the effect of a prism on sunlight, or that Adams saw Neptune, or that Pasteur observed that grape-juice played upon by air raised to a certain temperature underwent no fermentation, is talking history. The facts first observed by

Newton, Adams, and Pasteur have since then been observed by others;
but every scientist who says that light is split up by the prism or that
Neptune exists or that fermentation is prevented by a certain degree of
heat is still talking history: he is talking about the whole class of historical
facts which are occasions on which someone has made these observations.
Thus a 'scientific fact' is a class of historical facts; and no one can understand what a scientific fact is unless he understands enough about the
theory of history to understand what an historical fact is.

The same is true of theories. A scientific theory not only rests on
certain historical facts and is verified or disproved by certain other historical facts; it is itself an historical fact, namely, the fact that someone
has propounded or accepted, verified or disproved, that theory. If we want
to know, for example, what the classical theory of gravitation is, we must
look into the records of Newton's thinking and interpret them: and this
is historical research.

I conclude that natural science as a form of thought exists and always
has existed in a context of history, and depends on historical thought for
its existence. From this I venture to infer that no one can understand
natural science unless he understands history: and that no one can answer
the question what nature is unless he knows what history is. This is a
question which Alexander and Whitehead have not asked. And that is why
I answer the question, 'Where do we go from here?' by saying, 'We go
from the idea of nature to the idea of history.'

[47]

ARTHUR O. LOVEJOY

The Meanings of "Emergence" and its Modes *

There is an old and persistent tendency in the human mind to conceive of the causal relation as rationally explanatory, and, therefore, to
assimilate it, vaguely or explicitly, to the logical relations of inclusion,
implication, or equivalence. That "there cannot be more in the effect than
there is in the cause" is one of the propositions that men have been readiest
to accept as axiomatic; a cause, it has been supposed, does not "account
for'" its effect, unless the effect is a thing which the eye of reason could
somehow discern *in* the cause, upon a sufficiently thorough analysis. This
antipathy to the notion of an absolute epigenesis has left its mark deep and

* Reprinted by permission of the author. From Proc. of the Sixth International Congress of Philosophy. Harvard University, Sept., 1926. Copyright, 1927, by the Sixth
International Congress of Philosophy. Longmans, Green and Co., 1927. Pp. 20–33.

wide upon the history of thought; it appears, indeed, at the very outset
of Western speculation in the struggles of the physiologers with the supposed difficulty of admitting qualitative change. Two of the later episodes
in the history of what may be named the preformationist assumption about
causality may pertinently be remembered here.

The first is the doctrine of most mediaeval European metaphysics
that all the "perfections," or positive attributes, of the creatures must be
possessed by the First Cause—even though it was found necessary to assert
with equal emphasis that that Cause and its creatures have no attributes
in common. In this theological form the preformationist principle implied
an addition to the empirically known sum of reality; it left undiminished
the abundance and diversity of nature and did not exclude quantitative
and qualitative change from the natural order, but placed behind these a
supersensible cause in which all this abundance and diversity were declared to be in some fashion antecedently or eternally contained. Since
this way of construing the assumption meant no simplification of the
universe for our understanding, it was not serviceable to natural science.
But in the seventeenth century there began to develop a conception which,
while it fulfilled the same assumption, did so in a significantly different
way—the conception, namely, of natural events as combinations or rearrangements of relatively simple, preëxistent entities, of which the total
number or quantity remains invariant, and of each of which the qualities
and laws of action remain the same through all the combinations into
which it may enter. By this mechanistic conception of causation there is
nothing *substantive* in the consequent which was not in the antecedent,
and the supposed paradox of epigenesis is thus avoided. But in this second
form the preformationist assumption implied a program of reduction or
simplification; it was in its essence a scheme for abating the difference of
things. For if complexes contain nothing (except their patterns) not
already in their simple components, *rerum cognoscere causas* means learning to see in the complex nothing but its beggarly elements—the meager
qualities and limited repertoire of the simple, merely multiplied a certain
number of times. Scientific explanation becomes equivalent to mathematical analysis; and if the method is universalized, all philosophy, in Hobbes's phrase, becomes "nothing but addition and substraction." But many
complex things have properties not convincingly describable as multiples
of the properties of the simple things through the combination of which
they arise; and thus the notion of observed causal processes as rearrangements of the unchanging, while formally denying that there is "more" in
the effect than there is in the cause, nevertheless seemed to imply that
there is less in the cause than is apprehended in the effect. The mechanistic
conception escaped this paradox only through its conjunction with another
feature of most seventeenth-century and subsequent philosophy; its plausibility at the outset and ever since has been wholly dependent upon its association with some form of psycho-physical dualism. By means of this all
that considerable part of the data of experience, together with the phenom-

enon of experiencing itself, which seemed plainly irreconcilable with the principle of quantitative and qualitative constancy could conveniently be assigned to the side of the "merely subjective." The eventual triumphs of that principle in modern science were made possible through the restriction of its literal application to the physical order, after that order had first been carefully purged of the classes of facts most recalcitrant to such application.

I have recalled these historical commonplaces because they lead up to the first of a series of distinctions which I wish to propose. The phrasing of the question laid down for our discussion implies, and most judicious readers of recent English and American philosophy, I suspect, feel, that the now modish terms "emergence" and "emergent evolution" stand in some need of clarification. In current use their meanings are various and usually vague; and though it may be recognized that they point towards some real and important philosophical issues, the precise nature of those issues, their relations to one another, and the logical procedure suitable for dealing with them have not yet, perhaps, been formulated quite so clearly and methodically as could be wished. It is, therefore, towards such preliminary definition, discrimination, and correlation of problems that I shall chiefly attempt to contribute. While some opinions on certain of the issues themselves will be expressed, it must be with the brevity that is indistinguishable from dogmatism; and the primary purpose of this paper is merely to offer some prolegomena to any future discussion of "emergence."

What is needed, however, is not an extreme narrowing of the signification of the general term. In this case, as often in philosophical terminology, it is better to leave to the generic term a meaning so broad as to appear vague, and to approach precise definitions and clear-cut issues by progressively distinguishing species within the genus. "Emergence," then (or "epigenesis," which would be a much more appropriate word), may be taken loosely to signify any augmentative or transmutative event, any process in which there appear effects that, in some one or more of several ways yet to be specified, fail to conform to the maximum that "there cannot be in the consequent anything more than, or different in nature from, that which was in the antecedent." And the first distinction which it is essential to make, in reducing this vague general notion to something more definite and discussable, is between what I shall call the theses of the possibility of general and the actuality of specific emergence, theses antithetic respectively to the first and second sorts of preformationism.[1] To affirm the possibility of general emergence is to reject the preformationist assumption formally and absolutely, and therefore to deny the validity of any argument from it to the existence of a metempirical cause or causes which somehow pre-contain "all that is in the effects." But to many this assumption apparently still has the force of an axiom, and the argument in question, therefore, figures conspicuously in some recent discussions of our theme. Thus Taylor repeats the scholastic maxim: "The principle *e nihilo nihil fit,*" he writes, "is fundamental to all explanation"; and it is therefore "true that no cause can contribute to its effect what it has not to give. The full and ultimate cause of every effect in a process of evolution will have to be found not simply in the special character of its recognized antecedents but in the character of the eternal which is at the back of all development. And this must contain"—though "in a more eminent manner"—"all that it bestows, though it may contain much more." [2] Boodin has recently built a highly original superstructure upon the same ancient foundation; for the main argument of his interesting volume on *Cosmic Evolution* appears to be, in brief, that philosophy must "explain" the seeming emergence of novelty in the course of evolution, that "causality from behind cannot account for more than there is in the antecedents," and that therefore the higher forms of being which are progressively attained in terrestrial history must have preëxisted in, and been communicated through ready-made "energy-patterns" from, some other part of the universe,—the "evolution of new levels" being "obviously" impossible, since it would be tantamount to "something coming from nothing." [3]

The issue here is not only the most fundamental one in our topic but one of the crucial issues in all philosophy. If we really know that an absolute or general emergence is impossible we know something very curious and important about the universe. But the proof of its impossibility usually offered I find unconvincing for numerous reasons, of which a few may be briefly indicated. The universal cause or set of causes in which all that is in the (temporal) effects is declared to be pre-contained must be one of three things: a temporal *prius,* or an eternal which contains the temporal effects as its parts, or an eternal extraneous to those effects. If taken in the first of these senses, the assumption on which the argument rests cannot, of course, mean that the effects themselves are in the cause; it can only mean either (a) that the effects collectively do not *differ* either qualitatively or quantitatively from the *prius*—that is to say, that they are either mere repetitions of it, or else that they differ only in some relational property which is regarded as unimportant, such as the arrangement or distribution of the qualities and components present in the cause; or (b) that they are never of higher metaphysical rank or excellence than the cause. This latter is what the supposed axiom seems often to reduce to; the "lower" we are told, can come from the "higher," but not the "higher" from the "lower"; the stream of being cannot rise higher than its source. But—though this will seem to some a hard saying—neither of these forms of the preformationist assumption appears to be justified by anything better than a prejudice—an idol of the tribe, at best. The supposed axiom lacks self-evidence, and though there are some, there are no cogent, reasons for postulating it. Concerning the qualitative and quantitative relations of two existents of different dates we have no *a priori* knowledge. It is entirely conceivable that temporal reality as a whole is not only augmented, but attains higher levels, within any finite time which we may choose to consider; and there are some to whom this evidently seems the more satisfying thing to postulate. Certainly, if consistently carried out, metaphysical preformationism has less edifying and cheering implications than are sometimes attributed to it. If the sum of being and the sum of realized value are constant—and unless they are either constant or diminishing the pretended axiom is false, and there *is* at times an absolute emergence—then the whole movement and travail of the creation is but a barren shuffling-about of the same pieces; an increase or ascent in one region must be simultaneously compensated by an equivalent decrease or decline elsewhere; the more the universe changes, the more it is the same thing. If, however, the "Cause" is conceived as a supratemporal totality which contains the temporal effects, the impossibility of general emergence undeniably follows; an "eternal" cannot grow or improve. But such a conception implies the true inclusion of a real succession in a *totum simul*; and no ingenuity has ever succeeded in showing this to be other than a self-contradiction. This aside, since the temporal world is still admitted to be in some sense real, the whole of *that* world may in that same sense conceivably differ at different moments in the number of its elements or in their value. Finally, if the Cause by which "all that is in the effects" is said to be possessed is conceived as an eternal that does *not* contain those effects within its being—which I take to be the orthodox scholastic view—the same difficulties present themselves as in the first case, together with some additional ones. The notion of an existent which at once is alien to all succession or change, and yet is the efficient cause of a series of temporal changes, is, to say the least, elusive; and the supposition that that cause must "possess" all that is in the temporal effects seems not only gratuitous—the same venerable prejudice as before—but also self-contradictory. None of their *distinctive* qualities can be predicable of it, except in a sense so eminent as to be no sense at all. And even if the qualities were the same, their "communication" to the effects would mean the emergence of additional existent *instances* of those qualities, unless they were at the same time lost by the Cause. And in any case, there is nothing in this last form of the argument which would preclude emergence in the world in which alone, by hypothesis, change occurs at all.

There is, then, no valid *a priori* argument against the possibility of general (which, of course, does not necessarily mean perpetual) emergence to be drawn from the notion of causality. The subject is one on which we have no means of arriving at objective conclusions, unless it be through more or less probable inferences from experience. It may be suggested that reasons for regarding general emergence as impossible (or meaningless) are to be found in the experimental data upon which the special theory of relativity is based. An examination of the sufficiency of those data as grounds for such a conclusion cannot be attempted in the time at my disposal.

The thesis of specific emergence means denial of the second form of preformationism; it is the assertion on empirical grounds of the occurrence, among the phenomena investigable by science, of events which are not mere rearrangements of preëxistent natural entities in accordance with laws identical for all arrangements of those entities. It is to be observed that the reality of specific emergence is usually asserted by those who declare general or absolute emergence to be inconceivable. This combination of views is, at least on the face of it, logically possible, since the denial of qualitative and quantitative constancy in certain empirically observable changes does not of itself forbid the supposition of an ulterior general cause of whose relation to the entire series of changes the supposed axiom about causality would hold good; and the combination is natural, because there is a radical incompatibility of temper between the two types of preformationism. On the other hand, if such a compensatory general cause is excluded, any instance of specific emergence, however slight, would obviously imply also general emergence, an augmentation of the total sum of things. The opposition in certain scientific quarters to current doctrines of specific emergence seems to be due in no small part to the same feeling as is expressed in the scholastic principle—the feeling that there would be something queer and illogical about a universe in which substantive increments popped into existence. The chief significance of our problem is, then, that it raises definitely the question of the tenability of this historic assumption, common to and potent in both traditional theology and mechanistic science, in spite of their mutual antipathy.

Agreeing in what they deny, doctrines of specific emergence may differ in two respects in what they affirm: in their accounts, namely, of the occasions of emergence, and of the types of actual emergents. In the first regard we must first of all distinguish between indeterminist and determinist theories. The former declare that there are instances of emergence which are reducible to no causal law; no fixed occasions can be formulated upon which they invariably occur. The hypothesis of "undetermined evolution" to which Professor Driesch has referred is, I take it, a theory of this sort; but it is undesirable to define this as the only or the "strict" sense of "emergent evolution." The determinist kind of theory declares that whenever certain specific occasions appear a specific variety of emergent uniformly arises. The general nature of these occasions may be variously conceived. One abstractly possible sort would consist merely in intervals in the proper time of one or another physical system; but the most widely current hypothesis on the matter—the so-called theory of creative synthesis—finds the chief, if not the only, occasions of emergence to consist in the formation of special integrations of matter and (or) energy. The question what, in fact, these occasions are, must, of course, depend upon the character of the emergents which can be shown really to arise. Before raising this question of fact it is useful to consider what types of emergent there conceivably *may* be—what, in other words, are the ways in which it is possible to think of a consequent as differing positively, otherwise than in the rearrangement of the same elements, from its causally necessary antecedent. In distinguishing these modes of possible emergence I shall— in order to gain brevity by combining two definitions—put the enumeration in the form of a statement of the meaning of "emergent evolution," that term in general here signifying the occurrence as a feature of the evolutionary process of *any* of the modes of emergence. An "emergent evolution" may, then, be said to have taken place if, upon comparison of the present phase (called Ph. N), of earth-history (say that since the appearance of *homo sapiens*) with any prior phase (called Ph. A), there can be shown to be present in Ph. N any one or more of the five following features lacking in Ph. A. (1) Instances of some general type of change admittedly common to both phases (e.g., relative motion of particles), of which instances the manner or conditions of occurrence could not be described in terms of, nor predicted from, the laws which would have been sufficient for the description and (given the requisite determination of the variables) the prediction of all changes of that type occurring in Ph. A. Of this evolutionary emergence of laws one, though not the only conceivable, occasion would be the production, in accordance with one set of laws, of new local integrations of matter, the motions of which, and therefore of their component particles, would thereupon conform to vector, i.e., directional, laws emergent in the sense defined. This first mode differs from the others in that it implies no quantitative variability of the prime or irreducible *existents* (other than relations) in the system under consideration. (2) New qualities and, especially, classes of qualities (e.g., the so-called secondary qualities) attachable as adjectives to entities already present, though without those accidents, in Ph. A. (3) Particular entities *not* possessing all the essential attributes characteristic of those found in Ph. A, and having distinctive types of attributes (not merely configurational) of their own. (4) Some type or types of event or process irreducibly different in kind from any occurring in Ph. A. (5) A greater quantity, or number of instances, not explicable by transfer from outside the system, of any one or more types of prime entity common to both phases.

In the enumeration of types of possible emergence included in this definition, the most significant point is the contrast between the first, which may be called functional, and the remaining four, which may be called existential, emergence. Several writers have recently declared that any attempt to prove the reality of the first mode is subject (for familiar reasons, inherent in the notion of a "law," which need not be recalled here) to an intrinsic logical limitation. Our inability, they remark, at any given time to discover, or even conceive of the general nature of, any single law or set of joint laws from which all the motions of matter in its differing integrations would be deducible, is not conclusive proof that no such law is formulable; "within the physical realm it always remains logically possible," Broad has said, "that the appearance of emergent laws is due to our imperfect knowledge of microscopic structure or to mathematical incompetence." This *non possumus* does not seem to me to be itself conclusively established; but as there is no time to give reasons, I shall not here challenge it. Even supposing it true, it would not follow that the emergence of laws can be said to be improbable. Such emergence would, to be sure, imply the impossibility of a complete unification of science; and there is for this reason, we are often told, a decisive methodological presumption against it. But here we must distinguish between heuristic rules and propositions of fact. It is the business of the scientific investigator to look for identities of law in seemingly diverse phenomena, and to find as many of them as he can; it is not the business of the philosopher to assume *a priori* that nature must to an indefinite degree lend itself to the gratification of this ambition. Though rigorous and conclusive proof of the first mode of emergence be impossible, the hypothesis of its occurrence seems to me to be patently the more probable in the present state of our knowledge. But with these cursory dogmatizings I leave to others the question of functional emergence, in order to consider somewhat less summarily that of existential emergence.

Concerning this the first thing to remark is that an attempt to prove it is not subject to the same general logical disability said to inhere in any argument for emergent laws. An existential emergent would be a quality, or a thing or event possessing distinctive non-configurational qualities, which was found in the subsequent and not in the prior phase of some causal process; and its presence in the one case and absence in the other would be facts determinable either by observation or by inference from observed data. Where observation of both phases is possible the proof of existential emergence can be direct and virtually complete, as in the case of the qualitative changes (whether they be "objective" or "subjective") incident to chemical synthesis, which have long been recognized, under a different terminology, as examples of such emergence. This simplest instance—which, however, is not quite so simple logically as it looks— obvious and commonplace though it is, has a crucial importance which some writers on the subject do not appear to realize; for it alone suffices to show that there can be no general and decisive theoretical presumption against *other* hypotheses of existential emergence, that nature is assuredly no affair of mere rearrangements. In less simple but philosophically more consequential and controversial cases, the argument for existential emergence may involve somewhat complex and difficult reasonings, and therefore attain a less high degree of probability; but even in these cases, to which I shall shortly return, the difficulty is of a kind different from, and less fundamental than, that said to infect all reasonings concerning emergence of laws.

With the distinction between functional and existential emergents in mind we are also in a position to deal with the commonest general or antecedent objection brought against theories of specific emergence. The objection was raised, in differing terms, by several participants in the recent discussion of the subject by the English philosophical societies. To characterize an effect as "emergent," it is urged, is to give up the attempt to "explain" it; and since science cannot give up this attempt, the characterization can have, at best, no more than a provisional validity, as a way of admitting that certain things have not as yet been completely "explained." Now, what sort of explanation is it that these critics desiderate in theories of emergence? "Causal explanation" in the empirical sense—the assumption that every event follows upon some other *nach einer Regel,* the "determinism of the experimentalist"—is, as we have seen, entirely compatible with the belief in emergence. The sort of explanation which specific emergence, or emergent evolution, would exclude, is simply that demanded by the second form of preformationism—the conception of an event as *neither* (a) manifesting any law, or mode of uniform behavior, *nor* (b) containing any existent, not found in the antecedent phase of the sequence to which it belongs. To maintain then, that everything is "explicable," in the sense incongruous with emergence, is to raise a definite, though by no means simple, question of fact; it is to imply, for example, that, barring mere summations or rearrangements, there is to be found in the present phase of terrestrial history no existence whatever—no quality, type of entity, or kind of process—which could not already have been discerned by a scientific angel observing the cold-gaseous-nebula stage of the development of our solar system. This proposition cannot be said to have a high degree of *prima facie* plausibility; and its truth cannot be assumed *a priori* merely because it is one of the two conceivable ways of satisfying the demand for a special type of so-called "explanation" which is not practically indispensable to science.

Wholesale attempts to rule out, *ab initio,* all specific hypotheses of existential emergence by *a priori* assumptions of this sort being excluded, both assertors and deniers of any such hypotheses must address themselves to the analysis of definite empirical data. The assertor must (if the question be that of emergent evolution) point out some type of observable entity, event, or quality—call it E—existent in Ph. N which does not appear to be adequately describable in the same terms as would describe any entity, event, etc., which we can with probability suppose to have existed in Ph. A. The denier must attempt to show that everything in E *is* describable in the same terms as some class of entities, events, or qualities in Ph. A; to this end he may employ either of two methods, which may be termed the reductive and the retrotensive; i.e., he may either (1) seek by analysis to reduce E to the same descriptive terms as are sufficient for certain events, etc., admittedly found in Ph. A; or (2) admitting that E has the characters attributed to it by the assertor of emergence, he may maintain that these characters were already present in the earlier phase— in other words, must be supposed to be present in all phases—of the process.

The general logical nature of the problem being thus formulated, we may consider a particular hypothesis of existential emergence, which I hold to be true. It is nowise original, being substantially the same as the theory to which Broad has given the name of "emergent materialism"— though that designation seems to me a veritable *lucus a non lucendo.* According to this hypothesis, both the third and fourth modes of emergence—i.e., emergence of new types of entities and of new kinds of event or process—have appeared in evolution, in the form, but only in the form, of what may be called "trans-physical" emergence. By this I mean the production, as effects of the formation of certain complex and late-evolved integrations of living matter, when acted upon by certain forms of radiant energy, of psychical events and psychical objects. An example of a psychical event is an act of awareness. By psychical objects I mean individual entities empirically existent, having extension and certain other of the properties commonly called psychical, but differing from true physical objects in that they do not conform to the laws of physics, have individually only an ephemeral existence, have collectively no quantitative or numerical constancy, have no direct dynamical relations with one another, and are grouped into "private" sets, i.e., each is accessible only to an act of awareness of an individual organism. Examples of such entities are sensa and images, both delusive and veridical. In other words the "generative theory of sensa," recently defended by a number of writers, is a part of the hypothesis of existential emergent evolution I am presenting. The initial cases of trans-physical emergence were followed by a further evolution of the same type, conditioned upon the formation of new and still more complex integrations of matter and (or) energy, and the process thus far apparently culminates in the cognitive and affective functions of the human organism.

To the plain man, and to some men of science, these theses will, I dare say, seem rather obvious, and not much in need of defence. But in philosophy they manifestly raise numerous highly controversial issues. The existential emergence they assert is attacked chiefly from two sides, and by the two methods already defined; the reductive method is at present represented by behaviorism,[4] the retrotensive mainly by pan-psychism, or the mind-stuff theory. The behavioristic argument I shall not here examine; the view that both the act and the content of awareness, when I apprehend an object distant in space or time, are adequately describable as present changes of the relative position of molecules under my skin, really seems to me to be itself adequately describable by Broad's epithet, "silly." There is, however, an important contemporary doctrine which would apply the reductive method to the immediate objects of awareness, but not to the act of awareness; the former, it declares, are simply parts of the physical world, and, if emergent at all, are at any rate not trans-physical emergents. This contention is assuredly deserving of serious discussion; but the reasons for rejecting it are too complex to be presented here. The attempts of pan-psychists to escape from the admission of trans-physical emergence seem plainly to be due, in part, to the influence of an attenuated, vestigial form of the ancient pseudo-axiom mentioned at the outset; while it is not necessarily maintained by them that specific emergence is impossible in principle or non-existent in fact. They apparently feel that a causal antecedent cannot be so *very* different in nature from its effect as a physical event is from a mental one. Thus the author of a recent admirably lucid defence of the mind-stuff theory remarks that "discontinuity in evolution would be a baffling and unintelligible phenomenon," and declared that the mind-stuff theory alone "gives us a universe without such unintelligible breaches." "If a mind is simply a brain regarded from the outside, . . . the gradual evolution of a brain *is* the gradual evolution of a mind"; thus "there is no need to postulate any discontinuity in evolution to account for the appearance upon the scene of minds, of consciousness, of qualities." Yet the same writer tells us that "the units" of mind-stuff "which make up our mental states" and also our brains "are not *aware* of anything—neither of anything else nor of themselves. They just *exist*; . . . the fact of their constituting a group of units that function together, or the fact of their being in such and such a position in space and time, is a fact about them, not an aspect of their psychic being." Nor do they possess any of (at least) the secondary qualities. It is only when, "as a product of organic evolution," brains are formed, that "awareness," and therewith qualities, make their appearance.[5] This, however, is to strain at an emergent gnat and swallow an emergent camel. The cognition of external objects and their relations, which is somehow achieved through the brain, is not the sum of the atomic, non-cognitive sentiencies supposed to inhere in its component particles; and it is therefore no more "accounted for" by the assumed sentiency of those particles than it is by their motion. It is as blankly different and discontinuous a new fact as anything could be. So little, at best, can be accomplished by the retrotensive method that it is not surprising to find in some recent panpsychism a tendency to invoke the aid of the reductive, i.e., to describe the *higher* mental functions in somewhat vaguely behavioristic terms. But behaviorism does not, by becoming vaguer, become more convincing.

Another attempt to employ the retrotensive method for avoiding the admission of trans-physical emergence is to be seen in the parallelistic form of emergent evolutionism, the view that psycho-physical "duality of nature does not *arise* in the course of evolutionary advance, it is there *ab initio*," but that emergence occurs (in just what modes is not very clear) in the psychical as well as the physical sense, though in each independently. Such a view, however, appears to involve the general doctrine, at once confused and incredible, that physical events can have no causal relation to mental ones—which implies that sensations are not due to physical stimuli, and that if a man, after receiving a blow on the head, loses his memory, the blow is wholly irrelevant to the amnesia, which is causally explicable, if at all, solely by the thoughts he was thinking before he was hit. This doctrine does not appear to me to lie within the bounds of serious discussion. The retrotensive method, therefore, not only gratuitously extends to the whole of nature a concomitance for which there is probable evidence only in a special class of cases; it also either falls short of its objective or else implies impossible consequences.

We have, therefore, abundant reason to believe that in the history of our planet there have occurred genuine new births of time, a sheer increase and diversification and enrichment of the sum of things here. And no reason, except an arbitrary pseudo-axiom, can be given for assuming that this has been merely a cosmical game of beggar-my-neighbor. On the other hand, we have no empirical reasons for asserting—and serious reasons for doubting—that a similar process is the general rule throughout the physical universe, or that the higher emergents occur at all frequently in space and time. Yet, even though no knowledge which we possess concerning evolution justifies that generalized or cosmic meliorism which now so widely does duty for a religion, there nevertheless lies before our terrestrial race in its own little corner of the world a future which, if dim with uncertainties and beset with perils, is not necessarily devoid of possibilities immeasurably transcending all that the past has brought forth. There perhaps yet remain to mankind, we are told, some thousand million years; if it be so, before this long day ends it is possible that, besides all that man's laboring reason may achieve, there may yet emerge out of the latent generative potencies of matter, as there quite certainly have emerged before our strange planetary history, new and richer forms of being, such as no prescience of ours could foresee and no contrivance of ours create.

[48]

BERTRAND RUSSELL

Science and Values*

The scientific society which has been sketched . . . is, of course, not to be taken altogether as serious prophecy. It is an attempt to depict the world which would result if scientific technique were to rule unchecked. The reader will have observed that features that everyone would consider desirable are almost inextricably mingled with features that are repulsive. The reason of this is that we have been imagining a society developed in accordance with certain ingredients of human nature to the exclusion of all others. As ingredients they are good; as the sole driving force they are likely to be disastrous. The impulse towards scientific construction is admirable when it does not thwart any of the major impulses that give value to human life, but when it is allowed to forbid all outlet to everything but itself it becomes a form of cruel tyranny. There is, I think, a real danger lest the world should become subject to a tyranny of this sort, and it is on this account that I have not shrunk from depicting the darker features of the world that scientific manipulation unchecked might wish to create.

* Reprinted from *The Scientific Outlook* by Bertrand Russell. By permission of the author and W. W. Norton & Company, Inc. Copyright, 1931, by Bertrand Russell.

Science in the course of the few centuries of its history has undergone an internal development which appears to be not yet completed. One may sum up this development as the passage from contemplation to manipulation. The love of knowledge to which the growth of science is due is itself the product of a twofold impulse. We may seek knowledge of an object because we love the object or because we wish to have power over it. The former impulse leads to the kind of knowledge that is contemplative, the latter to the kind that is practical. In the development of science the power impulse has increasingly prevailed over the love impulse. The power impulse is embodied in industrialism and in governmental technique. It is embodied also in the philosophies known as pragmatism and instrumentalism. Each of these philosophies holds, broadly speaking, that our beliefs about any object are true in so far as they enable us to manipulate it with advantage to ourselves. This is what may be called a governmental view of truth. Of truth so conceived science offers us a great deal; indeed there seems no limit to its possible triumphs. To the man who wishes to change his environment science offers astonishingly powerful tools, and if knowledge consists in the power to produce intended changes, then science gives knowledge in abundance.

But the desire for knowledge has another form, belonging to an entirely different set of emotions. The mystic, the lover, and the poet are also seekers after knowledge—not perhaps very successful seekers, but none the less worthy of respect on that account. In all forms of love we wish to have knowledge of what is loved, not for purposes of power, but for the ecstasy of contemplation. "In knowledge of God standeth our eternal life," but not because knowledge of God gives us power over Him. Wherever there is ecstasy or joy or delight derived from an object there is the desire to know that object—to know it not in the manipulative fashion that consists of turning it into something else, but to know it in the fashion of the beatific vision, because in itself and for itself it sheds happiness upon the lover. In sex love as in other forms of love the impulse to this kind of knowledge exists, unless the love is purely physical or practical. This may indeed be made the touchstone of any love that is valuable. Love which has value contains an impulse towards that kind of knowledge out of which the mystic union springs.

Science in its beginnings was due to men who were in love with the world. They perceived the beauty of the stars and the sea, of the winds and the mountains. Because they loved them their thoughts dwelt upon them, and they wished to understand them more intimately than a mere outward contemplation made possible. "The world," said Heraclitus, "is an ever-living fire, with measures kindling and measures going out." Heraclitus and the other Ionian philosophers, from whom came the first impulse to scientific knowledge, felt the strange beauty of the world almost like a madness in the blood. They were men of Titanic passionate intellect, and from the intensity of their intellectual passion the whole movement of the modern world has sprung. But step by step, as science has developed, the impulse of love which gave it birth has been increasingly thwarted, while the impulse of power, which was at first a mere camp-follower, has gradually usurped command in virtue of its unforeseen success. The lover of nature has been baffled, the tyrant over nature has been rewarded. As physics has developed, it has deprived us step by step of what we thought we knew concerning the intimate nature of the physical world. Colour and sound, light and shade, form and texture, belong no longer to that external nature that the Ionians sought as the bride of their devotion. All these things have been transferred from the beloved to the lover, and the beloved has become a skeleton of rattling bones, cold and dreadful, but perhaps a mere phantasm. The poor physicists, appalled at the desert that their formulae have revealed, call upon God to give them comfort, but God must share the ghostliness of His creation, and the answer that the physicists think they hear to their cry is only the frightened beating of their own hearts. Disappointed as the lover of nature, the man of science is becoming its tyrant. What matters it, says the practical man, whether the outer world exists or is a dream, provided I can make it behave as I wish? Thus science has more and more substituted power-knowledge for love-knowledge, and as this substitution becomes completed science tends more and more to become sadistic. The scientific society of the future as we have been imagining it is one in which the power impulse has completely overwhelmed the impulse of love, and this is the psychological source of the cruelties which it is in danger of exhibiting.

Science, which began as the pursuit of truth, is becoming incompatible with veracity, since complete veracity tends more and more to complete scientific scepticism. When science is considered contemplatively, not practically, we find that what we believe we believe owing to animal faith, and it is only our disbeliefs that are due to science. When, on the other hand, science is considered as a technique for the transformation of ourselves and our environment, it is found to give us a power quite independent of its metaphysical validity. But we can only wield this power by ceasing to ask ourselves metaphysical questions as to the nature of reality. Yet these questions are the evidence of a lover's attitude towards the world. Thus it is only in so far as we renounce the world as its lovers that we can conquer it as its technicians. But this division in the soul is fatal to what is best in man. As soon as the failure of science considered as metaphysics is realized, the power conferred by science as a technique is only obtainable by something analogous to the worship of Satan, that is to say, by the renunciation of love.

This is the fundamental reason why the prospect of a scientific society must be viewed with apprehension. The scientific society in its pure form, which is what we have been trying to depict, is incompatible with the pursuit of truth, with love, with art, with spontaneous delight, with every ideal that men have hitherto cherished, with the sole exception of ascetic renunciation. It is not knowledge that is the source of these dangers. Knowledge is good and ignorance is evil: to this principle the lover of the world can admit no exception. Nor is it power in and for itself that is the source of danger. What is dangerous is power wielded for the sake of power, not power wielded for the sake of genuine good. The leaders of the modern world are drunk with power: the fact that they can do something that no one previously thought it possible to do is to them a sufficient reason for doing it. Power is not one of the ends of life, but merely a means to other ends, and until men remember the ends that power should subserve, science will not do what it might to minister to the good life. But what then are the ends of life, the reader will say. I do not think that one man has a right to legislate for another on this matter. For each individual the ends of life are those things which he deeply desires, and which if they existed would give him peace. Or, if it be thought that peace is too much to task this side of the grave, let us say that the ends of life should give delight or joy or ecstasy. In the conscious desires of the man who seeks power for its own sake there is something dusty: when he has it he wants only more power, and does not find rest in contemplation of what he has. The lover, the poet and the mystic find a fuller satisfaction than the seeker after power can ever know, since they can rest in the object of their love, whereas the seeker after power must be perpetually engaged in some fresh manipulation if he is not to suffer from a sense of emptiness. I think therefore that the satisfactions of the lover, using that word in its broadest sense, exceed the satisfactions of the tyrant, and deserve a higher place among the ends of life. When I come to die I shall not feel that I have lived in vain. I have seen the earth turn red at evening, the dew sparkling in the morning, and the snow shining under a frosty sun; I have smelt rain after drought, and have heard the stormy Atlantic beat upon the granite shores of Cornwall. Science may bestow these and other joys upon more people than could otherwise enjoy them. If so, its power will be wisely used. But when it takes out of life the moments to which life owes its value, science will not deserve admiration, however cleverly and however elaborately it may lead men along the road to despair. The sphere of values lies outside science, except in so far as science consists in the pursuit of knowledge. Science as the pursuit of power must not obtrude upon the sphere of values, and scientific technique, if it is to enrich human life, must not outweigh the ends which it should serve.

The number of men who determine the character of an age is small. Columbus, Luther and Charles V dominated the sixteenth century; Galileo and Descartes governed the seventeenth. The important men in the age that is just ended are Edison, Rockefeller, Lenin, and Sun Yat-sen. With the exception of Sun Yat-sen these were men devoid of culture, contemptuous of the past, self-confident, and ruthless, Traditional wisdom had no place in their thoughts and feelings; mechanism and organization were what interested them. A different education might have made all these men quite different. Edison might in his youth have acquired a knowledge of history and poetry and art; Rockefeller might have been taught how he had been anticipated by Crœsus and Crassus; Lenin, instead of having hatred implanted in him by the execution of his brother during his student days, might have made himself acquainted with the rise of Islam and the development of Puritanism from piety to plutocracy. By means of such an education some little leaven of doubt might have entered the souls of these great men. Given a little doubt their achievement would perhaps have been less in volume, but much greater in value.

Our world has a heritage of culture and beauty, but unfortunately we have been handing on this heritage only to the less active and important members of each generation. The government of the world, by which I do not mean its ministerial posts but its key-positions of power, has been allowed to fall into the hands of men ignorant of the past, without tenderness towards what is traditional, without understanding of what they are destroying. There is no essential reason why this should be the case. To prevent it is an educational problem, and not a very difficult one. Men in the past were often parochial in space, but the dominant men of our age are parochial in time. They feel for the past a contempt that it does not deserve, and for the present a respect that it deserves still less. The copybook maxims of a former age have become outworn, but a new set of copybook maxims is required. First among these I should put: "It is better to do a little good than much harm." To give content to this maxim it would of course be necessary to instil some sense of what is good. Few men in the present day, for example, can be induced to believe that there is no inherent excellence in rapid locomotion. To climb from Hell to Heaven is good, though it be a slow and laborious process; to fall from Heaven to Hell is bad, even though it be done with the speed of Milton's Satan. Nor can it be said that a mere increase in the production of material commodities is in itself a thing of great value. To prevent extreme poverty is important, but to add to the possessions of those who already have too much is a worthless waste of effort. To prevent crime may be necessary, but to invent new crimes in order that the police may show skill in preventing them is less admirable. The new powers that science has given to man can only be wielded safely by those who, whether through the study of history or through their own experience of life, have acquired some reverence for human feelings and some tenderness towards the emotions that give colour to the daily existence of men and women. I do not mean to deny that scientific technique may in time build an artificial world in every way preferable to that in which men have hitherto lived, but I do say that if this is to be done it must be done tentatively and with a realization that the purpose of government is not merely to afford pleasure to those who govern, but to make life tolerable for those who are governed. Scientific technique must no longer be allowed to form the whole culture of the holders of power, and it must become an essential part of men's ethical outlook to realize that the will alone cannot make a good life. Knowing and feeling are equally essential ingredients both in the life of the individual and in that of the community. Knowledge, if it is wide and intimate, brings with it a realization of distant times and places, an awareness that the individual is not omnipotent or all-important, and a perspective in which values are seen more clearly than by those to whom a distant view is impossible. Even more important than knowledge is the life of the emotions. A world without delight and without affection is a world destitute of value. These things the scientific manipulator must remember, and if he does his manipulation may be wholly beneficial. All that is needed is that men should not be so intoxicated by new power as to forget the truths that were familiar to every previous generation. Not all wisdom is new, nor is all folly out of date.

Man has been disciplined hitherto by his subjection to nature. Having emancipated himself from this subjection, he is showing something of the defects of slave-turned-master. A new moral outlook is called for in which submission to the powers of nature is replaced by respect for what is best in man. It is where this respect is lacking that scientific technique is dangerous. So long as it is present, science, having delivered man from bondage to nature, can proceed to deliver him from bondage to the slavish part of himself. The dangers exist, but they are not inevitable, and hope for the future is at least as rational as fear.

[49]

ALBERT EINSTEIN

Science, Philosophy and Religion *

I

During the last century, and part of the one before, it was widely held that there was an unreconcilable conflict between knowledge and belief. The opinion prevailed among advanced minds that it was time that belief should be replaced increasingly by knowledge; belief that did not itself rest on knowledge was superstition, and as such had to be opposed. According to this conception, the sole function of education was to open the way to thinking and knowing, and the school, as the outstanding organ for the people's education, must serve that end exclusively.

One will probably find but rarely, if at all, the rationalistic standpoint expressed in such crass form; for any sensible man would see at once how

* From (I) a lecture at Princeton Theological Seminary, Northeastern Regional Conference of the American Association of Theological Schools, May 19, 1939; (II) a Symposium on Science, Philosophy and Religion, published by Conference on Science, Philosophy and Religion in Their Relation to the Democratic Way of Life, Inc., New York, 1941. By the kind permission of the author and the Conference on Science, Philosophy and Religion.

one-sided is such a statement of the position. But it is just as well to state a thesis starkly and nakedly, if one wants to clear up one's mind as to its nature.

It is true that convictions can best be supported with experience and clear thinking. On this point one must agree unreservedly with the extreme rationalist. The weak point of his conception is, however, this, that those convictions which are necessary and determinant for our conduct and judgments, cannot be found solely along this solid scientific way.

For the scientific method can teach us nothing else beyond how facts are related to, and conditioned by, each other. The aspiration towards such objective knowledge belongs to the highest of which man is capable, and you will certainly not suspect me of wishing to belittle the achievements and the heroic efforts of man in this sphere. Yet it is equally clear that knowledge of what *is* does not open the door directly to what *should be*. One can have the clearest and most complete knowledge of what *is*, and yet not be able to deduce from that what should be the *goal* of our human aspirations. Objective knowledge provides us with powerful instruments for the achievements of certain ends, but the ultimate goal itself and the longing to reach it must come from another source. And it is hardly necessary to argue for the view that our existence and our activity acquire meaning only by the setting up of such a goal and of corresponding values. The knowledge of truth as such is wonderful, but it is so little capable of acting as a guide that it cannot prove even the justification and the value of the aspiration towards that very knowledge of truth. Here we face, therefore, the limits of the purely rational conception of our existence.

But it must not be assumed that intelligent thinking can play no part in the formation of the goal and of ethical judgments. When someone realizes that for the achievement of an end certain means would be useful, the means itself becomes thereby an end. Intelligence makes clear to us the interrelation of means and ends. But mere thinking cannot give us a sense of the ultimate and fundamental ends. To make clear these fundamental ends and valuations, and to set them fast in the emotional life of the individual, seems to me precisely the most important function which religion has to perform in the social life of man. And if one asks whence derives the authority of such fundamental ends, since they cannot be stated and justified merely by reason, one can only answer: they exist in a healthy society as powerful traditions, which act upon the conduct and aspirations and judgments of the individuals; they are there, that is, as something living, without its being necessary to find justification for their existence. They come into being not through demonstration but through revelation, through the medium of powerful personalities. One must not attempt to justify them, but rather to sense their nature simply and clearly.

The highest principles for our aspirations and judgments are given to us in the Jewish-Christian religious tradition. It is a very high goal which, with our weak powers, we can reach only very inadequately, but which gives a sure foundation to our aspirations and valuations. If one were to take that goal out of its religious form and look merely at its purely human side, one might state it perhaps thus: free and responsible development of the individual, so that he may place his powers freely and gladly in the service of all mankind.

There is no room in this for the divinization of a nation, of a class, let alone of an individual. Are we not all children of one father, as it is said in religious language? Indeed, even the divinization of humanity, as an abstract totality, would not be in the spirit of that ideal. It is only to the individual that a soul is given. And the high destiny of the individual is to serve rather than to rule, or to impose himself in any other way.

If one looks at the substance rather than at the form, then one can take these words as expressing also the fundamental democratic position. The true democrat can worship his nation as little as can the man who is religious, in our sense of the term.

What, then, in all this, is the function of education and of the school? They should help the young person to grow up in such a spirit that these fundamental principles should be to him as the air which he breathes. Teaching alone cannot do that.

If one holds these high principles clearly before one's eyes, and compares them with the life and spirit of our times, then it appears glaringly that civilized mankind finds itself at present in grave danger. In the totalitarian states it is the rulers themselves who strive actually to destroy that spirit of humanity. In less threatened parts it is nationalism and intolerance, as well as the oppression of the individuals by economic means, which threaten to choke these most precious traditions.

A realization of how great is the danger is spreading, however, among thinking people, and there is much search for means with which to meet the danger—means in the field of national and international politics of legislation, of organization in general. Such efforts are, no doubt, greatly needed. Yet the ancients knew something which we seem to have forgotten. All means prove but a blunt instrument, if they have not behind them a living spirit. But if the longing for the achievement of the goal is powerfully alive within us, then shall we not lack the strength to find the means for reaching the goal and for translating it into deeds.

II

It would not be difficult to come to an agreement as to what we understand by science. Science is the century-old endeavor to bring together by means of systematic thought the perceptible phenomena of this world into as thorough going an association as possible. To put it boldly, it is the attempt at the posterior reconstruction of existence by the process of conceptualization. But when asking myself what religion is I cannot think of the answer so easily. And even after finding an answer which may satisfy me at this particular moment I still remain convinced that I can never under any circumstances bring together, even to a slight extent, all those who have given this question serious consideration.

At first, then, instead of asking what religion is I should prefer to ask what characterizes the aspirations of a person who gives me the impression of being religious: A person who is religiously enlightened appears to me to be one who has, to the best of his ability, liberated himself from the fetters of his selfish desires and is preoccupied with thoughts, feelings, and aspirations to which he clings because of their super-personal value. It seems to me that what is important is the force of this super-personal content and the depth of the conviction concerning its overpowering meaningfulness, regardless of whether any attempt is made to unite this content with a divine Being, for otherwise it would not be possible to count Buddha and Spinoza as religious personalities. Accordingly, a religious person is devout in the sense that he has no doubt of the significance and loftiness of those super-personal objects and goals which neither require nor are capable of rational foundation. They exist with the same necessity and matter-of-factness as he himself. In this sense religion is the age-old endeavor of mankind to become clearly and completely conscious of these values and goals and constantly to strengthen and extend their effect. If one conceives of religion and science according to these definitions then a conflict between them appears impossible. For science can only ascertain what *is*, but not what *should be*, and outside of its domain value judgments of all kinds remain necessary. Religion, on the other hand, deals only with evaluations of human thought and action: it cannot justifiably speak of facts and relationships between facts. According to this interpretation the well-known conflicts between religion and science in the past must all be ascribed to a misapprehension of the situation which has been described.

For example, a conflict arises when a religious community insists on the absolute truthfulness of all statements recorded in the Bible. This means an intervention on the part of religion into the sphere of science; this is where the struggle of the Church against the doctrines of Galileo and Darwin belongs. On the other hand, representatives of science have often made an attempt to arrive at fundamental judgments with respect to values and ends on the basis of scientific method, and in this way have set themselves in opposition to religion. These conflicts have all sprung from fatal errors.

Now, even though the realms of religion and science in themselves are clearly marked off from each other, nevertheless there exist between the two strong reciprocal relationships and dependencies. Though religion may be that which determines the goal, it has, nevertheless, learned from science, in the broadest sense, what means will contribute to the attainment of the goals it has set up. But science can only be created by those who are thoroughly imbued with the aspiration towards truth and understanding. This source of feeling, however, springs from the sphere of religion. To this there also belongs the faith in the possibility that the regulations valid for the world existence are rational, that is, comprehensible to reason. I cannot conceive of a genuine scientist without that profound faith. The situation may be expressed by an image: Science without religion is lame, religion without science is blind.

Though I have asserted above that in truth a legitimate conflict between religion and science cannot exist I must nevertheless qualify this assertion once again on an essential point, with reference to the actual content of historical religions. This qualification has to do with the concept of God. During the youthful period of mankind's spiritual evolution human fantasy created gods in man's own image, who, by the operations of their will were supposed to determine, or at any rate to influence the phenomenal world. Man sought to alter the disposition of these gods in his own favor by means of magic and prayer. The idea of God in the religions taught at present is a sublimation of that old conception of the gods. Its anthropomorphic character is shown, for instance, by the fact that men appeal to the Divine Being in prayers and plead for the fulfilment of their wishes.

Nobody, certainly, will deny that the idea of the existence of an omnipotent, just and omnibeneficent personal God is able to accord man solace, help, and guidance; also, by virtue of its simplicity it is accessible to the most undeveloped mind. But, on the other hand, there are decisive weaknesses attached to this idea in itself, which have been painfully felt since the beginning of history. That is, if this being is omnipotent then every occurrence, including every human action, every human thought, and every human feeling and aspiration is also His work; how is it possible to think of holding men responsible for their deeds and thoughts before such an almighty Being? In giving out punishment and rewards He would to a certain extent be passing judgment on Himself. How can this be combined with the goodness and righteousness ascribed to Him?

The main source of the present-day conflicts between the spheres of religion and of science lies in this concept of a personal God. It is the aim of science to establish general rules which determine the reciprocal connection of objects and events in time and space. For these rules, or laws of nature, absolutely general validity is required—not proven. It is mainly a program, and faith in the possibility of its accomplishment in principle is only founded on partial successes. But hardly anyone could be found who would deny these partial successes and ascribe them to human self-deception. The fact that on the basis of such laws we are able to predict the temporal behavior of phenomena in certain domains with great precision and certainty is deeply embedded in the consciousness of the modern man, even though he may have grasped very little of the contents of those laws. He need only consider that planetary courses within the solar system may be calculated in advance with great exactitude on the basis of a limited number of simple laws. In a similar way, though not with the same precision, it is possible to calculate in advance the mode of operation of an electric motor, a transmission system, or of a wireless apparatus, even when dealing with a novel development.

To be sure, when the number of factors coming into play in a phenomenological complex is too large scientific method in most cases fails us. One need only think of the weather, in which case prediction even for a few days ahead is impossible. Nevertheless no one doubts that we are confronted with a causal connection whose causal components are in the main known to us. Occurrences in this domain are beyond the reach of exact prediction because of the variety of factors in operation, not because of any lack of order in nature.

We have penetrated far less deeply into the regularities obtaining within the realm of living things, but deeply enough nevertheless to sense at least the rule of fixed necessity. One need only think of the systematic order in heredity, and in the effect of poisons, as for instance alcohol, on the behavior of organic beings. What is still lacking here is a grasp of connections of profound generality, but not a knowledge of order in itself.

The more a man is imbued with the ordered regularity of all events the firmer becomes his conviction that there is no room left by the side of this ordered regularity for causes of a different nature. For him neither the rule of human nor the rule of divine will exists as an independent cause of natural events. To be sure, the doctrine of a personal God interfering with natural events could never be *refuted*, in the real sense, by science, for this doctrine can always take refuge in those domains in which scientific knowledge has not yet been able to set foot.

But I am persuaded that such behavior on the part of the representatives of religion would not only be unworthy but also fatal. For a doctrine which is able to maintain itself not in clear light but only in the dark, will of necessity lose its effect on mankind, with incalculable harm to human progress. In their struggle for the ethical good, teachers of religion must have the stature to give up the doctrine of a personal God, that is, give up that source of fear and hope which in the past placed such vast power in the hands of priests. In their labors they will have to avail themselves of those forces which are capable of cultivating the Good, the True, and the Beautiful in humanity itself. This is, to be sure, a more difficult but an incomparably more worthy task.[1] After religious teachers accomplish the refining process indicated they will surely recognize with joy that true religion has been ennobled and made more profound by scientific knowledge.

If it is one of the goals of religion to liberate mankind as far as possible from the bondage of egocentric cravings, desires, and fears, scientific reasoning can aid religion in yet another sense. Although it is true that it is the goal of science to discover rules which permit the association and foretelling of facts, this is not its only aim. It also seeks to reduce the connections discovered to the smallest possible number of mutually independent conceptual elements. It is in this striving after the rational unification of the manifold that it encounters its greatest successes, even though it is precisely this attempt which causes it to run the greatest risk of falling a prey to illusions. But whoever has undergone the intense experience of successful advances made in this domain, is moved by profound reverence for the rationality made manifest in existence. By way of the understanding he achieves a far-reaching emancipation from the shackles of personal hopes and desires, and thereby attains that humble attitude of mind towards the grandeur of reason incarnate in existence, and which, in its profoundest depths, is inaccessible to man. This attitude, however, appears to me to be religious, in the highest sense of the word. And so it seems to me that science not only purifies the religious impulse of the dross of its anthropomorphism but also contributes to a religious spiritualization of our understanding of life.

The further the spiritual evolution of mankind advances, the more certain it seems to me that the path to genuine religiosity does not lie through the fear of life, and the fear of death, and blind faith, but through striving after rational knowledge. In this sense I believe that the priest must become a teacher if he wishes to do justice to his lofty educational mission.

[50]

WILLIAM JAMES

Philosophy and Its Critics *

The progress of society is due to the fact that individuals vary from the human average in all sorts of directions, and that the originality is often so attractive or useful that they are recognized by their tribe as leaders, and become objects of envy or admiration, and setters of new ideals.

Among the variations, every generation of men produces some individuals exceptionally preoccupied with theory. Such men find matter for puzzle and astonishment where no one else does. Their imagination invents explanations and combines them. They store up the learning of their time, utter prophecies and warnings, and are regarded as sages. Philosophy, etymologically meaning the love of wisdom, is the work of this class of minds, regarded with an indulgent relish, if not with admiration, even by those who do not understand them or believe much in the truth which they proclaim.

Philosophy, thus become a race-heritage, forms in its totality a monstrously unwieldy mass of learning. So taken, there is no reason why any special science like chemistry or astronomy should be excluded from it. By common consent, however, special sciences are to-day excluded, for

* From *Some Problems of Philosophy*, copyright by Longmans, Green & Co., Inc., 1911, 1940. By permission of Longmans, Green & Co., Inc.

reasons presently to be explained; and what remains is manageable enough to be taught under the name of philosophy by one man if his interests be broad enough.

If this were a German textbook I should first give my abstract definition of the topic, thus limited by usage, then proceed to display its *"Begriff, und Einteilung,"* and its *"Aufgabe und Methode."* But as such displays are usually unintelligible to beginners, and unnecessary after reading the book, it will conduce to brevity to omit that chapter altogether, useful though it might possibly be to more advanced readers as a summary of what is to follow.

I will tarry a moment, however, over the matter of definition. Limited by the omission of the special sciences, the name of philosophy has come more and more to denote ideas of universal scope exclusively. The principles of explanation that underlie all things without exception, the elements common to gods and men and animals and stones, the first *whence* and the last *whither* of the whole cosmic procession, the conditions of all knowing, and the most general rules of human action—these furnish the problems commonly deemed philosophic *par excellence*; and the philosopher is the man who finds the most to say about them. Philosophy is defined in the usual scholastic textbooks as "the knowledge of things in general by their ultimate causes, so far as natural reason can attain to such knowledge." This means that explanation of the universe at large, not description of its details, is what philosophy must aim at; and so it happens that a view of anything is termed philosophic just in proportion as it is broad and connected with other views, and as it uses principles not proximate, or intermediate, but ultimate and all-embracing, to justify itself. Any very sweeping view of the world is a philosophy in this sense, even though it may be a vague one. It is a *Weltanschauung*, an intellectualized attitude towards life. Professor Dewey well describes the constitution of all the philosophies that actually exist, when he says that philosophy expresses a certain attitude, purpose, and temper of cojoined intellect and will, rather than a discipline whose boundaries can be neatly marked off.[1]

To know the chief rival attitudes towards life, as the history of human thinking has developed them, and to have heard some of the reasons they can give for themselves, ought to be considered an essential part of liberal education. Philosophy, indeed, in one sense of the term is only a compendious name for the spirit in education which the word "college" stands for in America. Things can be taught in dry dogmatic ways or in a philosophic way. At a technical school a man may grow into a first-rate instrument for doing a certain job, but he may miss all the graciousness of mind suggested by the term liberal culture. He may remain a cad and not a gentleman, intellectually pinned down to his one narrow subject, literal, unable to suppose anything different from what he has seen, without imagination, atmosphere, or mental perspective.

Philosophy, beginning in wonder, as Plato and Aristotle said, is able to fancy everything different from what it is. It sees the familiar as if it were strange, and the strange as if it were familiar. It can take things up and lay them down again. Its mind is full of air that plays round every subject. It rouses us from our native dogmatic slumber and breaks up our caked prejudices. Historically it has always been a sort of fecundation of four different human interests—science, poetry, religion, and logic—by one another. It has sought by hard reasoning for results emotionally valuable. To have some contact with it, to catch its influence, is thus good for both literary and scientific students. By its poetry it appeals to literary minds; but its logic stiffens them up and remedies their softness. By its logic it appeals to the scientific; but softens them by its other aspects, and saves them from too dry a technicality. Both types of student ought to get from philosophy a livelier spirit, more air, more mental background. "Hast any philosophy in thee, Shepherd?"—this question of Touchstone's is the one with which men should always meet one another. A man with no philosophy in him is the most inauspicious and unprofitable of all possible social mates.

I say nothing in all this of what may be called the gymnastic use of philosophic study, the purely intellectual power gained by defining the high and abstract concepts of the philosopher and discriminating between them.

In spite of the advantages thus enumerated, the study of philosophy has systematic enemies, and they were never as numerous as at the present day. The definite conquests of science and the apparent indefiniteness of philosophy's results partly account for this; to say nothing of man's native rudeness of mind, which maliciously enjoys deriding long words and abstractions. "Scholastic jargon," "mediaeval dialectics," are for many people synonyms of the word philosophy. With his obscure and uncertain speculations as to the intimate nature and causes of things, the philosopher is likened to a "blind man in a dark room looking for a black hat that is not there." His occupation is described as the art of "endlessly disputing without coming to any conclusion," or more contemptuously still as the *"systematische Missbrauch einer eben zu diesem Zwecke erfundenen Terminologie."* ("systematic abuse of a special terminology invented for this very purpose.")

Only to a very limited degree is this sort of hostility reasonable. I will take up some of the current objections in successive order, since to reply to them will be a convenient way of entering into the interior of our subject.

Objection 1. Whereas the sciences make steady progress and yield applications of matchless utility, philosophy makes no progress and has no practical applications.

Reply. The opposition is unjustly founded, for the sciences are themselves branches of the tree of philosophy. As fast as questions got accurately answered, the answers were called "scientific," and what men call "philosophy" to-day is but the residuum of questions still unanswered. At this very moment we are seeing two sciences, psychology and general biology, drop off from the parent trunk and take independent root as specialities. The more general philosophy cannot as a rule follow the voluminous details of any special science.

A backward glance at the evolution of philosophy will reward us here. The earliest philosophers in every land were encyclopædic sages, lovers of wisdom, sometimes with and sometimes without a dominantly ethical or religious interest. They were just men curious beyond immediate practical needs, and no particular problems, but rather the problematic generally, was their specialty. China, Persia, Egypt, India had such wise men, but those of Greece are the only sages who until very recently have influenced the course of western thinking. The earlier Greek philosophy lasted, roughly speaking, for about two hundred and fifty years, say from 600 B.C. onwards. Such men as Thales, Heraclitus, Pythagoras, Parmenides, Anaxagoras, Empedocles, Democritus were mathematicians, theologians, politicians, astronomers, and physicists. All the learning of their time, such as it was, was at their disposal. Plato and Aristotle continued their tradition, and the great mediæval philosophers only enlarged its field of application. If we turn to Saint Thomas Aquinas's great "Summa," written in the thirteenth century, we find opinions expressed about literally everything, from God down to matter, with angels, men, and demons taken in on the way. The relations of almost everything with everything else, of the creator with his creatures, of the knower with the known, of substances with forms, of mind with body, of sin with salvation, come successively up for treatment. A theology, a psychology, a system of duties and morals, are given in fullest detail, while physics and logic are established in their universal principles. The impression made on the reader is of almost superhuman intellectual resources. It is true that Saint Thomas's method of handling the mass of fact, or supposed fact, which he treated, was different from that to which we are accustomed. He deduced and proved everything, either from fixed principles of reason, or from holy Scripture. The properties and changes of bodies, for example, were explained by the two principles of matter and form, as Aristotle had taught. Matter was the quantitative, determinable, passive element; from the qualitative, unifying. determining, and active principle. All activity was for an end. Things could act on each other only when in contact. The number of species of things was determinate, and their differences discrete, etc., etc.[2]

By the beginning of the seventeenth century, men were tired of the elaborate *a priori* methods of scholasticism. Suarez's treatises availed not to keep them in fashion. But the new philosophy of Descartes, which displaced the scholastic teaching, sweeping over Europe like wildfire, preserved the same encyclopædic character. We think of Descartes nowadays as the metaphysician who said "Cogito, ergo sum," separated mind from matter as two contrasted substances, and gave a renovated proof of God's existence. But his contemporaries thought of him much more as we think of Herbert Spencer in our day, as a great cosmic evolutionist who explained, by "the redistribution of matter and motion," and the laws of impact, the rotations of the heavens, the circulation of the blood, the refraction of light, apparatus of vision and of nervous action, the passions of the soul, and the connection of the mind and body.

Descartes died in 1650. With Locke's *Essay Concerning Human Understanding*, published in 1690, philosophy for the first time turned more exclusively to the problem of knowledge, and became "critical." This subjective tendency developed; and although the school of Leibniz, who was the pattern of a universal sage, still kept up the more universal tradition—Leibniz's follower Wolff published systematic treatises on everything, physical as well as moral—Hume, who succeeded Locke, woke Kant "from his dogmatic slumber," and since Kant's time the word "philosophy" has come to stand for mental and moral speculations far more than for physical theories. Until a comparatively recent time, philosophy was taught in our colleges under the name of "mental and moral philosophy," or "philosophy of the human mind," exclusively, to distinguish it from "natural philosophy."

But the older tradition is the better as well as the completer one. To know the actual peculiarities of the world we are born into is surely as important as to know what makes worlds anyhow abstractly possible. Yet this latter knowledge has been treated by many since Kant's time as the only knowledge worthy of being called philosophical. Common men feel the question "What is Nature like?" to be as meritorious as the Kantian question "How is Nature possible?" So philosophy, in order not to lose human respect, must take some notice of the actual constitution of reality. There are signs to-day of a return to the more objective tradition.[3]

Philosophy in the full sense is only *man thinking*, thinking about generalities rather than about particulars. But whether about generalities or particulars, man thinks always by the same methods. He observes, discriminates, generalizes, classifies, looks for causes, traces analogies, and make hypotheses. Philosophy, taken as something distinct from science or from practical affairs, follows no method peculiar to itself. All our thinking to-day has evolved gradually out of primitive human thought, and the only really important changes that have come over its manner (as distinguished from the matters in which it believes) are a greater hesitancy in asserting its convictions, and the habit of seeking verification [4] for them whenever it can.

It will be instructive to trace very briefly the origins of our present habits of thought.

Auguste Comte, the founder of a philosophy which he called "positive," [5] said that human theory on any subject always took three forms in succession. In the theological stage of theorizing, phenomena are explained by spirits producing them; in the metaphysical stage, their essential feature is made into an abstract idea, and this is placed behind them as if it were an explanation; in the positive stage, phenomena are simply described as to their coexistences and successions. Their "laws" are formulated, but no explanation of their natures or existence is sought after. Thus a *"spiritus rector"* would be a theological—a "principle of attraction" a metaphysical—and "a law of the squares" would be a positive theory of the planetary movements.

Comte's account is too sharp and definite. Anthropology shows that the earliest attempts at human theorizing mixed the theological and metaphysical together. Common things needed no special explanation, remarkable things alone, odd things, especially deaths, calamities, diseases, called for it. What made things act was the mysterious energy in them, and the more awful they were the more of this *mana* they possessed. The great thing was to acquire *mana* oneself. "Sympathetic magic" is the collective name for what seems to have been the primitive philosophy here. You could act on anything by controlling anything else that either was associated with it or resembled it. If you wished to injure an enemy, you should either make an image of him, or get some of his hair or other belongings, or get his name written. Injuring the substitute, you thus made him suffer correspondingly. If you wished the rain to come, you sprinkled the ground, if the wind, you whistled, etc. If you would have yams grow well in your garden, put a stone there that looks like a yam. Would you cure jaundice, give tumeric, that makes things looks yellow; or give poppies for troubles of the head, because their seed vessels form a "head." This "doctrine of signatures" played a great part in early medicine. The various "-mancies" and "-mantics" come in here, in which witchcraft and incipient science are indistinguishably mixed. "Sympathetic" theorizing persists to the present day. "Thoughts are things" for a contemporary school—and on the whole a good school—of practical philosophy. Cultivate the thought of what you desire, affirm it, and it will bring all similar thoughts from elsewhere to reinforce it, so that finally your wish will be fulfilled.

Little by little, more positive ways of considering things began to prevail. Common elements in phenomena began to be singled out and to form the basis of generalizations. But these elements at first had necessarily to be the more dramatic or humanly interesting ones. The hot, the cold, the wet, the dry in things explained their behaviour. Some bodies were naturally warm, others cold. Motions were natural or violent. The heavens moved in circles because circular motion was the most perfect. The lever was explained by the greater quantity of perfection embodied in the movement of its longer arm. The sun went south in winter to escape the cold. Precious or beautiful things had exceptional properties. Peacock's flesh resisted putrefaction. The lodestone would drop the iron which it held if the superiorly powerful diamond was brought near, etc.

Such ideas sound to us grotesque, but imagine no tracks made for us by scientific ancestors, and what aspects would we single out from nature to understand things by? Not till the beginning of the seventeenth century did the more insipid kinds of regularity in things abstract men's attention away from the properties originally picked out. Few of us realize how short the career of what we know as "science" has been. Three hundred and fifty years ago hardly any one believed in the Copernican planetary theory. Optical combinations were not discovered. The circulation of the blood, the weight of air, the conduction of heat, the laws of motion were unknown; the common pump was inexplicable; there were no clocks; no thermometers; no general gravitation; the world was five thousand years old; spirits moved the planets; alchemy, magic, astrology, imposed on every one's belief. Modern science began only after 1600, with Kepler, Galileo, Descartes, Torricelli, Pascal, Harvey, Newton, Huygens, and Boyle. Five men telling one another in succession the discoveries which their lives had witnessed, could deliver the whole of it into our hands: Harvey might have told Newton, who might have told Voltaire; Voltaire might have told Dalton, who might have told Huxley, who might have told the readers of this book.

The men who began this work of emancipation were philosophers in the original sense of the word, universal sages. Galileo said that he had spent more years on philosophy than months on mathematics. Descartes was a universal philosopher in the fullest sense of the term. But the fertility of the newer conceptions made special departments of truth grow at such a rate that they became too unwieldy with details for the more universal minds to carry them, so the special sciences of mechanics, astronomy, and physics began to drop off from the parent stem.

No one could have foreseen in advance the extraordinary fertility of the more insipid mathematical aspects which these geniuses ferreted out. No one could have dreamed of the control over nature which the search for their concomitant variations would give. "Laws" describe these variations; and all our present laws of nature have as their model the proportionality of v to t, and of s to t^2 which Galileo first laid bare. Pascal's discovery of the proportionality of altitude to barometric height, Newton's of acceleration to distance, Boyle's of air-volume to pressure, Descartes' of sine to cosine in the refracted ray, were the first fruits of Galileo's discovery. There was no question of agencies, nothing animistic or sympathetic in this new way of taking nature. It was description only, of concomitant variations, after the particular quantities that varied had been successfully abstracted out. The result soon showed itself in a differentiation of human knowledge into two spheres, one called "Science," within which the more definite laws apply, the other "General Philosophy," in which they do not. The state of mind called positivistic is the result. "Down with philosophy!" is the cry of innumerable scientific minds. "Give us measurable facts only, phenomena, without the mind's additions, without entities or principles that pretend to explain." It is largely from this kind of mind that the objection that philosophy has made no progress, proceeds.

It is obvious enough that if every step forward which philosophy makes, every question to which an accurate answer is found, gets accredited to science the residuum of unanswered problems will alone remain to constitute the domain of philosophy, and will alone bear her name. In point of fact this is just what is happening. Philosophy has become a collective name for questions that have not yet been answered to the satisfaction of all by whom they have been asked. It does not follow, because some of

these questions have waited two thousand years for an answer, that no
answer will ever be forthcoming. Two thousand years probably measure
but one paragraph in that great romance of adventure called the history of
the intellect of man. The extraordinary progress of the last three hundred
years is due to a rather sudden finding of the way in which a certain order
of questions ought to be attacked, questions admitting of mathematical
treatment. But to assume, therefore, that the only possible philosophy
must be mechanical and mathematical, and to disparage all inquiry into
the other sorts of questions, is to forget the extreme diversity of aspects
under which reality undoubtedly exists. To the spiritual questions the
proper avenues of philosophic approach will also undoubtedly be found.
They have, to some extent, been found already. In some respects, indeed,
"science" has made less progress than "philosophy"—its most general
conceptions would astonish neither Aristotle nor Descartes, could they
revisit our earth. The composition of things from elements, their evolution,
the conservation of energy, the idea of a universal determinism, would
seem to them commonplace enough—the little things, the microscopes,
electric lights, telephones, and details of the sciences, would be to them the
awe-inspiring things. But if they opened our books on metaphysics, or
visited a philosophic lecture room, everything would sound strange. The
whole idealistic or "critical" attitude of our time would be novel, and it
would be long before they took it in.[6]

Objection 2. Philosophy is dogmatic, and pretends to settle things by
pure reason, whereas the only fruitful mode of getting at truth is to appeal
to concrete experience. Science collects, classes, and analyzes facts, and
thereby far outstrips philosophy.

Reply. This objection is historically valid. Too many philosophers
have aimed at closed systems, established *a priori,* claiming infallibility,
and to be accepted or rejected only as totals. The sciences on the other
hand, using hypotheses only, but always seeking to verify them by experiment and observation, open a way for indefinite self-correction and increase. At the present day, it is getting more and more difficult for dog-
matists claiming finality for their systems, to get a hearing in educated
circles. Hypothesis and verification, the watchwords of science, have set
the fashion too strongly in academic minds.

Since philosophers are only men thinking about things in the most
comprehensive possible way, they can use any method whatsoever freely.
Philosophy must, in any case, complete the sciences, and must incorporate
their methods. One cannot see why, if such a policy should appear advisable, philosophy might not end by forswearing all dogmatism whatever, and
become as hypothetical in her manners as the most empirical science of
them all.

Objection 3. Philosophy is out of touch with real life, for which it
substitutes abstractions. The real world is various, tangled, painful.
Philosophers have almost without exception, treated it as noble, simple,
and perfect, ignoring the complexity of fact, and indulging in a sort of

optimism that exposes their systems to the contempt of common men, and to the satire of such writers as Voltaire and Schopenhauer. The great popular success of Schopenhauer is due to the fact that, first among philosophers, he spoke the concrete truth about the ills of life.

Reply. This objection also is historically valid, but no reason appears why philosophy should keep aloof from reality permanently. Her manners may change as she successfully develops. The thin and noble abstractions may give way to more solid and real constructions, when the materials and methods for making such constructions shall be more and more securely ascertained. In the end philosophers may get into as close contact as realistic novelists with the facts of life.

In conclusion. In its original acceptation, meaning the completest knowledge of the universe, philosophy must include the results of all the sciences, and cannot be contrasted with the latter. It simply aims at making of science what Herbert Spencer calls a "system of completely unified knowledge." [7] In the more modern sense, of something contrasted with the sciences, philosophy means "metaphysics." The older sense is the more worthy sense, and as the results of the sciences get more available for coordination, and the conditions for finding truth in different kinds of question get more methodically defined, we may hope that the term will revert to its original meaning. Science, metaphysics, and religion may then again form a single body of wisdom, and lend each other mutual support. At present this hope is far from its fulfilment.

Notes

[Editor's additions to authors' notes are bracketed or marked "Ed."]

1. The Abstract Nature of Mathematics

By ALFRED N. WHITEHEAD

[Cf. *The Philosophy of Alfred North Whitehead*, ed. P. A. Schilpp, 1941, for W's Autobiography, Bibliography, and essays by V. Lowe, The Development of W's Philosophy; W. V. Quine, W. and the Rise of Modern Logic; F. S. C. Northrop, W's Philosophy of Science; A. E. Murphy, W. and the Method of Speculative Philosophy; John Dewey, The Philosophy of W.; W's own essay, Mathematics and the Good. Also, cf. W's *Science and the Modern World*, 1925, ch. II, Mathematics as an Element in the History of Thought.—Ed.]

2. How Mathematics Generalizes: The Essence of Mathematics

By CHARLES S. PEIRCE

1. From what is said by Proclus Diadochus, A. D. 485 (*Commentarii in Primum Euclidis Elementorum Librum*, Prologi pars prior, c. 12), it would seem that the Pythagoreans understood mathematics to be the answer to the two questions "how many?" and "how much?"

2. I regret I have not noted the passage of Ammonius to which I refer. It is probably one of the excerpts given by Brandis. My MS. note states that he gives reasons showing this to be his meaning.

3. 510C to the end; but in the *Laws* his notion is improved.

4. Of course, the moment a collection is recognized as an abstraction we have to admit that even a percept is an abstraction or represents an abstraction, if matter has parts. It therefore becomes difficult to maintain that all abstractions are fictions.

5. Peirce here refers to the theory of classes or sets, and to R. Dedekind's *Was sind und was sollen die Zahlen*, 1881 (cf. *Source Book in Mathematics*, ed. D. E. Smith, pp. 35–45). Also, cf. O. Veblen and F. Young, *Fundamental Concepts of Algebra and Geometry*; R. Courant and H. Robbins, *What is Mathematics?*; F. Klein, *Elementary Mathematics from an Advanced Standpoint*; G. Frege, *Foundations of Arithmetic*; B. Russell, *Introd. to Mathematical Philosophy*; M. Black, *The Nature of Mathematics*; C. I. Lewis, *Survey of Symbolic Logic*; F. P. Ramsey, *The Foundations of Mathematics*; H. Weyl, *Philosophy of Mathematics and Natural Science*,

1949; P. C. Rosenbloom, *The Elements of Mathematical Logic*, 1950, a concise but advanced little book to be studied after the beginner has gone through a book like E. R. Stabler's *Introduction to Mathematical Thought*, 1953, or M. R. Cohen and E. Nagel's *Introd. to Logic and Sci. Method*, especially ch. 7.—Ed.]

3. Geometry in the Perceived World

By B. RUSSELL; J. NICOD

[Cf. D. Hilbert, *Foundations of Geometry*; A. Tarski, *Introd. to Logic: Methodology of the Deductive Sciences*; B. Russell, *The Problem of Human Knowledge; The Philosophy of Bertrand Russell*, ed. P. A. Schilpp.]

4. Mathematical Deduction and Physical Theory

By PIERRE DUHEM

[Cf. G. Holton, *Introd. to Concepts and Theories in Physical Science*, 1953; N. Campbell, *What is Science?* (excellent for beginners); *id.*, *Physics: The Elements* (more advanced); H. Reichenbach, *Atom and Cosmos*; P. W. Bridgman, *Logic of Modern Physics*, 1927; *id.*, *The Nature of Physical Theory; The Nature of Some of our Physical Concepts*, 1952 (more advanced); H. Dingle, *The Scientific Adventure: Essays in the History and Philosophy of Science*, 1953.]

5. Hypotheses in Physics

By HENRI POINCARÉ

[Cf. H. Poincaré, *Science and Method*; *id.*, *Science and Hypothesis*. Also see Notes to 4, 8, 9, 10, 37, 38, 39.]

6. Geometry and Empirical Science

By CARL HEMPEL

[The source of Hempel's quotation at the end (p. 51) is Einstein's illuminating essay on *Geometry and Experience*, a classic in methodology.]
[Cf. C. Hempel, "On the Nature of Mathematical Truth," *Am. Math. Monthly* (1945); *id.*, *Fundamentals of Concept Formation in Empirical Science*; R. Carnap,

Logical Syntax of Language; id., Foundations of Inductive Logic; W. V. Quine, *Mathematical Logic;* A. Church, *Introd. to Mathematical Logic,* 1953; J. B. Rosser, *Logic for Mathematicians,* 1953; all these are advanced works requiring previous study of books like A. Tarski, *Introd. to Logic,* W. V. Quine, *Methods of Logic,* or R. L. Wilder, *Introd. to the Foundations of Mathematics,* 1952; J. O. Wisdom, *Foundations of Inference in Natural Science,* 1952.]

7. On the Bending of Space

By W. K. CLIFFORD

1. *Matter and Motion,* p. 20.
2. This supposes the one-dimensional space of constant bend to lie in a plane; the argument does not apply to space like that of a helix (or the form of a corkscrew), which is of constant bend, but yet not finite.
3. Physicists may be reminded of the absolute zero of temperature.
4. In this case of two-dimensioned space assume it to be a plane. Cf. Clifford's *Lectures and Essays* edited by Sir F. Pollock (1879), vol. I, p. 323.
5. It may be held by some that the postulate of the sameness of our space is based upon the fact that no one has hitherto been able to form any geometrical conception of space-curvature. Apart from the fact that mankind habitually assumes many things of which it can form no geometrical conception (mathematicians the circular points at infinity, theologians transsubstantiation), I may remark that we cannot expect any being to form a geometrical conception of the curvature of his space till he views it from space of a higher dimension, that is, practically, never.
6. Yet it must be noted that, because a solid figure *appears* to us to retain the same shape when it is moved about in that portion of space with which we are acquainted, it does not follow that the figure *really* does retain its shape. The changes of shape may be either imperceptible for those distances through which we are able to move the figure, or if they do take place we may attribute them to 'physical causes'—to heat, light, or magnetism—which may possibly be mere names for variations in the curvature of our space.
[Cf. E. T. Bell, *Men of Mathematics; id., Mathematics, Queen and Servant of the Sciences,* 1951; E. A. Abbott, *Flatland.*]

8. The Philosophical Significance of the Theory of Relativity

By HANS REICHENBACH

1. Poincaré believed that the definition of a solid body could not be given without reference to a geometry. That this concep-

tion is mistaken, is shown in the present author's *Philosophie der Raum-Zeit-Lehre* (Berlin, 1928) § 5. [But cf. Einstein's reply in defence of Poincaré, below.]
2. Cf. the author's *Philosophie der Raum-Zeit-Lehre* (Berlin, 1928), §12. It has turned out that within the plurality of descriptions applicable to quantum mechanics the problem of causal anomalies plays an even more important part, since we have there a case where no description exists which avoids causal anomalies. (Cf. also the author's *Philosophic Foundations of Quantum Mechanics,* Berkeley, 1944), §§5–7, §26.
3. This refutation of Kantianism was presented in the author's *Relativitätstheorie und Erkenntnis Apriori* (Berlin, 1920).
4. For an analysis of Leibniz' views see the author's "Die Bewegungslehre bei Newton, Leibnitz and Huyghens," *Kantstudien* [vol. 29, 1924], 416.
5. H. Reichenbach, *Philosophie der Raum-Zeit-Lehre* (Berlin, 1928), §27.
[Cf. also R's *Atom and Cosmos,* 1933; *Experience and Prediction,* 1938; *The Rise of Scientific Philosophy,* 1951.]

Reply to Reichenbach by a "Non-Positivist"

By ALBERT EINSTEIN

[Cf. also A. Einstein and L. Infeld, *The Evolution of Modern Physics;* A. Einstein, *Relativity: The Special and General Theory,* tr. R. W. Lawson; Albert Einstein: *Philosopher-Scientist,* ed. P. A. Schilpp; P. Frank, *Einstein, His Life and Times;* A. Einstein, Generalization of Gravitation Theory (Appendix II, *The Meaning of Relativity,* 4th ed., Princeton, 1953. For the less advanced student, Einstein's essay, *Geometry and Experience,* is highly recommended.]

9. The Concept of Causality in Physics

By MAX PLANCK

[Cf. P's *Scientific Autobiography and Other Papers,* pp. 13–51; C. F. von Weizsacker, *The World View of Physics,* 1949; A. D'Abro, *The Rise of the New Physics: Its Mathematical and Physical Theories,* 2 vols., 1950; M. Silberstein, *Causality,* 1933; H. Reichenbach, *Philosophic Foundations of Quantum Mechanics,* 1944.]

10. Fundamental Problems of Present-day Atomic Physics

By WERNER HEISENBERG

1. This is a summary of a passage in Aristotle 'De generatione et corruptione' A 1.314a21 ff. on Leucippus and Democritus.

2. Ancilla to the Pre-Socratic Philosophers (translated by Kathleen Freeman) (Blackwell, 1948), 68/9, p. 93.

[Cf. H. Butterfield, *The Origins of Modern Science*, 1939; H. T. Pledge, *Science Since 1500: A Short History of Mathematics, Physics, Chemistry, Biology*, 1947; Louis de Broglie, *Matter and Light: The New Physics*. For the layman, S. Hecht's *Explaining the Atom*, 1947, is superb. The advanced student of physics should consult Heisenberg (ed.), *Cosmic Radiation*, 1946, and his *Physical Principles of Quantum Theory*, 1949.]

11. The Creation of the Universe

By GEORGE GAMOW

1. A. Vorontzoff-Velyaminov, *Gaseous Nebulae and New Stars* (in Russian), Academy of Sciences, U.S.S.R., Moscow, 1948. Reviewed by O. Struve, *Astrophysical Journal*, 1949, pp. 110, 315.
2. Fred Hoyle, *The Nature of the Universe*, Harper & Brothers, New York, 1951.

[Cf. J. Jeans, *The Universe Around Us; id., Physics and Philosophy*; M. Born, *The Restless Universe*; E. Whittaker, *Eddington's Principle in the Philosophy of Science*, 1951; *id., From Euclid to Eddington*; E. Finlay-Freundlich, *Cosmology*, 1952.]

12. What Is Cybernetics?

By NORBERT WIENER

1. See appendix to this chapter, p. 110.
2. *Cybernetics, or Control and Communication in the Animal and the Machine*; 1949, The Technology Press of M. I. T., Cambridge; John Wiley & Sons, New York; and Hermann et Cie, Paris.

[Cf. W. R. Ashby, "Cybernetics," *Recent Progress in Psychiatry*, vol. 2 (1950); E. Nagel, "Automatic Control" and articles on Feedback, Control Systems, Automatic Chemical Plant, Automatic Machine Tool, Role of the Computer, Information, Machines and Man, by different scientists in *Scientific American* (Sept. 1952); D. G. Macrae, "Cybernetics and Social Science," *Brit. J. Sociol.*, 2 (June, 1951), 135–149; D. M. MacKay, "Mentality in Machines," *Proc. Artist. Soc. Suppl.*, 1952; A. M. Turing, "Computing Machinery and Intelligence," *Mind*, 59 (Oct. 1950). Also, cf. medical ethics of "The Problem of Experimentation on Human Beings" in *Science*, 117 (Feb. 27, 1953).]

14. The Origin of Species

By CHARLES DARWIN

[The first edition of 1859 (of only 1250 copies!) was followed by a second in 1860, a third in 1861, a fourth in 1866, a fifth in 1869, and a sixth in 1872 (from which the selection used here was taken). Cf. Sir Arthur Keith's Introduction to the Everyman's Library edition; *Charles Darwin's Autobiography, with His Notes and Letters Depicting the Growth of the ORIGIN OF SPECIES*, ed. Sir Francis Darwin; George G. Simpson, *The Meaning of Evolution;* Paul B. Sears, *Charles Darwin: The Naturalist as a Cultural Force* (Scribner's Twentieth Century Library); Julian Huxley, *Evolution, A New Synthesis; id., Evolution in Action*, 1953.]

[Darwin's *Journal of Researches*, 1839, is the log book of his famous voyage on the S. S. *Beagle* to the shores of Patagonia, Chile, Peru, the Galápagos and some other islands in the Pacific where Darwin accumulated the evidence for his theory of natural selection (reprint, Chronica Botanica, 1952). On the historical and recent social and ethical aspects of Darwinism, cf. R. Hofstadter, *Social Darwinism 1860–1915* (Phila., 1944) and Ashley Montagu, *Darwin: Competition and Cooperation* (Schuman, 1952).]

15. On the Educational Value of the Natural History Sciences

By THOMAS H. HUXLEY

[This essay was an address delivered in S. Martin's Hall, published subsequently in *Science and Education, Essays* by T. H. H. Cf. P. C. Mitchell, *T. H. Huxley, A Sketch of his Life and Work*, 1900; H. Peterson, *Huxley, Prophet of Science*, 1932.]

1. "In the third place, we have to review the method of Comparison, which is so specially adapted to the study of living bodies, and by which, above all others, that study must be advanced. In Astronomy, this method is necessarily inapplicable; and it is not till we arrive at Chemistry that this third means of investigation can be used; and then only in subordination to the two others. It is in the study, both statical and dynamical, of living bodies that it first acquires its full development; and its use elsewhere can be only through its application here."—COMTE's *Positive Philosophy*, translated by Miss Martineau. vol. i. p. 372.

By what method does M. Comte suppose that the equality or inequality of forces and quantities and the dissimilarity or similarity of forms—points of some slight importance not only in Astronomy and Physics, but even in Mathematics—are ascertained, if not by Comparison?

2. "Proceeding to the second class of means.—Experiment cannot but be less and less decisive, in proportion to the complexity of the phænomena to be explored; and therefore we saw this resource to be less effectual in chemistry than in physics: and we now find that it is eminently useful in chemistry in comparison with physiology.

In fact the nature of the phœnomena seems to offer almost insurmountable impediments to any extensive and prolific application of such a procedure in biology."—COMTE, vol. i. p. 367.

M. Comte, as his manner is, contradicts himself two pages further on, but that will hardly relieve him from the responsibility of such a paragraph as the above.

3. *Nouvelle Fonction du Foie considéré comme organe producteur de matière sucrée chez l'Homme et les Animaux, par* M. Claude Bernard.

[Cf. Claude Bernard, *Introduction to Experimental Medicine.*]

4. "*Natural Groups given by Type, not by Definition.* . . . The class is steadily fixed, though not precisely limited; it is given, though not circumscribed; it is determined, not by a boundary-line without, but by a central point within; not by what it strictly excludes, but what it eminently includes; by an example, not by a precept; in short, instead of Definition we have a *Type* for our director. A type is an example of any class, for instance, a species of a genus, which is considered as eminently possessing the characters of the class. All the species which have a greater affinity with this type-species than with any others, form the genus, and are ranged about it, deviating from it in various directions and different degrees."—WHEWELL, *The Philosophy of the Inductive Sciences*, vol. i. pp. 476, 477.

5. Save for the pleasure of doing so, I need hardly point out my obligations to Mr. J. S. Mill's *System of Logic*, in this view of scientific method.

[Cf. *General Education in Science*, ed. I. B. Cohen and F. G. Watson, 1952; J. B. Conant, *Modern Science and Modern Man*, 1952.]

16. Self-Regulation of the Human Body

By WALTER B. CANNON

[Cf. Sherrington, [18]; E. Schrödinger, *What is Life?* (1947); E. Nordenskiold, *History of Biology*, 1949; J. H. Woodger, *Biological Principles* and *Technique of Theory Construction*. See notes to 17 and 18, and n. 14 of 22a, below.]

17. The 'Drive' Element in Life

By E. S. RUSSELL

1. E. S. Russell, *The Directiveness of Organic Activities*, Cambridge, 1945, p. 190.
2. R. W. G. Hingston, *A Naturalist in the Guiana Forest*, London, 1932, pp. 34–35.
3. *The Directiveness of Organic Activities*, p. 110.

4. L. von Bertalanffy, *Das biologische Weltbild*, Bern, 1949, I.

5. J. Holtfreter, in *Growth in relation to Differentiation and Morphogenesis, Society for Experimental Biology, Symposia*, 2, Cambridge, 1948, p. 21.

6. Evidence summarized by F. Wood Jones, *Habit and Heritage*, London, 1943, pp. 33–35.

7. W. M. Wheeler, *Essays on Philosophical Biology*, Cambridge, Mass., 1939, p. 19.

8. K. von Frisch, *Zts. f. Tierpsychol.*, 1937, I, 12. ["One is tempted to say: The will governs the body. However, we know nothing about the will of bees, and leave the riddle unsolved."]

9. J. A. Bierens de Haan, *Die tierischen Instinkte*, Leiden, 1940.

10. W. E. Agar, *A Contribution to the Theory of the Living Organism*, Melbourne, 1943.

11. See R. S. Lillie, *General Biology and Philosophy of Organism*, Chicago, 1945. [H. Driesch, *Philosophy of Organism*, 1908; *id.*, *Mind and Body*, 1927; G. Sommerhof, *Analytical Biology*, 1951; L. von Bertalanffy, *An Evaluation of Modern Biological Thought*, 1952; R. H. Woodger, "What Do We Mean by 'Inborn'?" *Brit. Jour. for the Philos. of Sci.* III (Feb. 1953), 319.]

18. Man On His Nature

By SIR CHARLES SHERRINGTON

1. *Traité du Ris*, Paris, 1579.
2. *Brit. Med. J.* April 1939.

[Cf. S's *Integrative Action of the Nervous System*; N. Rashevsky, *Mathematical Biophysics*, 1948; A. S. Householder and H. D. Landahl, *Math. Biophysics of the Central Nervous System*, 1945; L. A. Jeffers (ed.), *Cerebral Mechanisms in Behavior*, 1951; J. Z. Young, *Doubt and Certainty in Science: A Biologist's Reflection on the Brain*, 1951; F. Alexander, *Psychosomatic Medicine—Its Principles and Applications*, 1952.]

19. Psychology and the Science of Sciences

By S. S. STEVENS

1. Some representative journals are: *Erkenntnis*, begun in 1930; *Philosophy of Science*, begun in 1934; and *International Encyclopedia of Unified Science*, begun in 1938. The advisory boards of these last two publications read like a who's who in science and philosophy. It would be a passionate optimist, however, who would expect such a band of hardy individualists to be entirely of one mind. Many of them have not yet spoken.

2. For additional comments on some of the books and papers cited in this review see the "References" [pp. 181–184 above.]

3. This *empirical* process of forming classes of classes should not be confused with the *logic* of classes, in which the provision for an infinite hierarchy of classes led to the antinomies discovered by Russell. The empirical process has no *necessary* relation to a formal system of logic.

4. Some of the members of the Vienna Circle follow:

Moritz Schlick (1882–1936) fathered the group. Under his professorial paternalism the Circle met, discussed, and found its unity. (Schlick's unfortunate death, at the hand of a crazed student, occurred as he was climbing the steps of the lecture hall.)

Otto Neurath (b. 1882) contributed his own brand of enthusiastic originality. His spirited support of radical new theses provided important inspiration. Neurath coined the designations "Physicalism" and "Unity of Science."

Rudolph Carnap (b. 1891) labored with the problem of syntax—the logical rules of language. His energetic attack on the problem of the actual construction of a fundamental syntax for the "physical" language has created a whole new field of inquiry.

Philipp Frank (b. 1884), a theoretical physicist, applied the new theory of knowledge to the problems of physics.

Hans Hahn (1870–1934), a mathematician, investigated the foundations of mathematics and exact science in the light of the scientific *Weltauffassung* of the Circle.

Friedrich Waismann distinguished himself with an investigation of the logical foundations of mathematical thinking.

In addition to these members of the Vienna Circle there were other groups whose scientific philosophy was so similar as to be scarcely distinguishable. In fact, one of the impressive aspects of this recent philosophical movement is the manner in which a common *Weltauffassung* appeared almost simultaneously among widely scattered groups of scientists, mathematicians, and philosophers. There was the Warsaw Circle, which boasted such able logicians as Tarski (b. 1901) and Lukasiewicz (b. 1878). At Berlin, prior to the recent cultural eclipse, there was another Circle whose outstanding advocate was Reichenbach (b. 1891). Logicians Russell (b. 1872) and Frege (1848–1925) fall into the same tradition, and in America C. W. Morris (b. 1901) is perhaps the best known expositor of the common program. For a more complete listing of names, see Neurath's "Historische Anmerkungen" (45).

[Cf. Victor Kraft, *The Vienna Circle: The Origins of Neo-Positivism*, translated by Arthur Pap (New York: Philosophical Library, 1953).—Ed.]

5. This is a somewhat oversimplified statement of Physicalism. Furthermore, Carnap (21) has recently introduced extensive qualifications and changes into the original views of the Vienna Circle regarding the relation of the various "languages" of science. His reasons for preferring the physical to the psychological language (pp. 9 ff.) do not appear to me to be binding, especially if the psychological language is made operational. If that is done, the choice becomes one based on convention or convenience. We could express all physics in psychological language, but that would be more traumatic to tradition than if we were to express all psychology in the physical language. The name Physicalism justifiably appeals to many as an unhappy designation, because it arouses prejudices by suggesting the primacy of a materialistic physics.

6. Neurath (47) describes *unified science* as *encyclopedic integration*. The new "Encyclopedia" is to be constructed like an onion. The heart of the onion will be two introductory volumes consisting of twenty pamphlets, and in these volumes will be laid the foundations for a logical unity which will make possible future integration of scientific disciplines. The first layer of the onion enclosing the heart will be a series of volumes to deal with problems of systematization in special sciences, including logic, mathematics, the theory of signs, history of science, classification of the sciences, and the educational implications of the scientific attitude. Still outer layers will concern even more specialized problems. The encyclopedia will not be an alphabetical dictionary and its creators hope, quite piously, that it will not become a mausoleum but remain a living intellectual force.

At the present writing only three numbers (1, 2, and 5) of the "Encyclopedia" have appeared, but it is already clear that, although there is great community among the contributors, detailed unanimity is absent. As to the problem of unity in science, for example, Carnap finds as yet *no unity of laws* in science, but only *unity of language*; Lenzen finds a basis for unity in the fact that all science starts from experience; Neurath would get his unity by means of *encyclopedic integration*; Russell says the unity is essentially one of method; and Dewey hopes for unity by promulgating what he calls the scientific attitude.

[Ten more numbers appeared by March 1951 in Volumes I–II called *Foundations of the Unity of Science*, University of Chicago Press.—Ed.]

7. In discussing operationism I have used the words *term* and *proposition*, *applicability* and *truth* (Stevens, 58, 59). In keeping with the spirit of Semiotic I ought perhaps to say that *terms* have *applicability* under semantical rules when the criteria governing their use are operational criteria. Then, sentences formed by combining these *semantically* significant terms into propositions are *empirically* significant (have truth-value) when their assertions are confirmable by means of operations. In other words,

there is a justifiable distinction between the operational meaning of words and symbols (semantical significance) and the operational meaning of empirical propositions. I am not certain, however, that Morris would distinguish between empirical and semantical propositions in the same way.

8. Note the similarity between the statement "Kt *c a*" and Ayer's example discussed above. To say that a knight cannot be on *c* and *a* at the same time is very like saying that an object cannot be in two places at once. Both statements follow directly from the rules of our syntax and are therefore nonempirical sentences.

9. Count Alfred Korzybski has written a bulky work called *Science and sanity* (Lancaster: Science Press, 1933), in which he contends that in the miseducation of our youth we teach them semantical rules based upon static Aristotelian classifications which they must then use in dealing with a fluid dynamic universe. Such semantical habits are enough out of tune with reality to drive many people crazy. Korzybski would cure the resulting insanity by renovating the patient's semantics. Whatever our opinion about this etiology and cure, it is plain that much of Korzybski's concern is with what Morris would call pragmatics—the effect of signs upon the users of signs.

[Cf. *Psychological Theory: Contemporary Readings*, ed. M. H. Marx, 1951.]

20. Application of Operational Analysis to Human Motor Behavior

By DOUGLAS G. ELLSON

1. The possibility and potential value of applying operational analysis and related methods used in the study of servo systems to human motor behavior was originally suggested to the writer by personnel of the Armament Laboratory, Air Materiel Command. . . .

I wish to express my appreciation for the cooperation of Dr. Gilbarg who made this article possible by clarifying my ideas concerning the mathematical aspects of operational analysis, and who wrote the appendix presenting the basic equations. [This appendix has been omitted.—Ed.]

2. MacColl, L. A. *Fundamental theory of servomechanisms.* New York: Van Nostrand, 1945.

3. Taylor, F. V.; Walker, R. Y. and Householder, A. S. Some aspects of eye-hand coordination in a simplified tracking situation. *Amer. Psychol.*, 1946, *1*, 282–283 (Abstr.).

[Cf. W. K. Estes, "Toward a Statistical Theory of Learning," *Psychol. Rev.*, 57 (Mar. 1950); R. R. Bush and F. Mosteller, "A Mathematical Model for Simple Learning," *ib.*, 58 (Sept. 1951); H. A. Simon,

"On the Application of Servomechanism Theory in the Study of Production Control," RAND P234, Aug. 15, 1951; C. L. Hull, *A Behavior System*, 1952; F. W. Taylor, *Principles of Scientific Management*, 1953.]

22. Gestalt and Field Theory

By G. MURPHY

22a. Historical Introduction

1. All parenthetic references are to the author's original text, *Historical Introduction to Modern Psychology*, Revised edition, 1949. Page 33 contains discussion of some points in Hartley's *Observations on Man, His Frame, His Duty, and His Expectations* (1749).—Ed.

2. Author discusses Mill's "Mental chemistry."—Ed.

3. Author discusses Bain's *The Senses and the Intellect.*—Ed.

4. Author discusses James's "stream of consciousness."—Ed.

5. Helson, H., "The Psychology of Gestalt," *Amer. J. Psychol.*, 1925, *36*, 342–70, 494–526; 1926, *37*, 25–62, 189–223.

6. Author discusses Mach's *Contributions to the Analysis of Sensations* (1886). —Ed.

7. Author mentions the work, following Mach, of Von Ehrenfels, *Vierteljahrsschr. f. wiss. Philos.*, 1890, 14, and the school of *Gestaltqualität.*—Ed.

8. Author refers to Lotze's theory of "local signs" in *Outlines of Psychology* (1881, prepared from Lotze's lectures), Ch. IV.—Ed.

9. Author discusses Fechner's *Vorschule der Aesthetik* (1876).—Ed.

10. Author discusses "unconscious inference" and "three-color theories" concerning perception of color contrast.—Ed.

11. See next part: Koffka and Köhler.

12. *Ibid.*

13. Wertheimer, M., *Productive Thinking* (1945). [Cf. also, his "Gestalt Theory," *Social Research*, 1944 *19*, 228–238.]

14. Author discusses Cannon's *Bodily Changes in Pain, Hunger, Fear and Rage* (1915).—Ed.

15. *Intelligentzprüfungen an Menschenaffen* (1924).

16. *Die physischen Gestalten in Ruhe und im stationären Zustand* (1920). [Translated in part in *Source Book of Gestalt Psychology*, ed. W. D. Ellis (1938).]

17. *The Principles of Psychology* (1924); later, *A Survey of the Science of Psychology* (1933).

18. *Psychol. Forsch.*, 1928, 11, 1–132.

19. *The Expression of Personality* (1943).

20. Durkin, H., "Trial-and-Error Gradual Analysis, and Sudden Reorganization: An Experimental Study of Problem Solving," *Arch. Psychol.*, 1937, No. 210.

21. Author discusses Lewin's early work

on learning which "showed that sheer successive presentation of stimuli produced no functional connections between them."

22. *A Dynamic Theory of Personality* (1935); *Principles of Topological Psychology* (1936).

[For a recent criticism of Gestalt theory, cf. E. H. Madden, "The Philosophy of Science in Gestalt Theory," *Philos. of Sci.,* 1952, *19,* 228–238.—Ed.]

22c. Physiology, Psychology, and Sociology

By E. C. TOLMAN

[Footnotes 3, 4, 6, 11, 12, 13 have been omitted since they pertain to passages not included in present excerpt.—Ed.]

1. This respective use of the three words, "activities," "behavior," and "conduct," was suggested to me by Professors K. F. Muenzinger and R. H. Bruce.

2. What I would designate as f_1 functions (in contrast to these f_2 and f_3 functions) would be the complete functions stretching all the way from the independent variables . . . to the final dependent variables . . . If such f_1 functions were entirely known, there would be no need of the intervening variables. The latter and the f_2 and f_3 functions would all be absorbed into these f_1 functions. See Tolman [8, 10].

5. I am using "racial" here in a loose sense to refer to the hereditary biological constitution of a group (due to inbreeding or what not) in so far as this heredity makes this group different, if it does, from other groups. See Linton [4, Ch. ii].

7. See Linton [4, Ch. viii].

8. See Moreno [6].

9. As an example of an attempt to discover such f_2 laws, see the studies edited by Margaret Mead [5]. This survey of thirteen primitive cultures sought for general laws (i.e., f_2 laws) which would connect the relative strengths of the customs of "cooperation," "competition," and "individualism" to such independent variables as economic and technological factors. But it did not succeed in finding any clear-cut relationships of this sort. The only important f_2 law that anthropologists have as yet uncovered seems to be merely the very general one of "historical diffusion."

10. And such a universal pure psychology might well turn out in the end to be restricted to but relatively simple and biologically conditioned facts. And further, it may well be that this field of a pure biological (noncultural) psychology is after all best investigated with animals [10].

14. Here again, as was the case with sociology, I feel myself treading upon relatively uncertain ground.

15. This of course *does not mean* that, therefore, the physiologist and the physiological psychologist should not desist from

continuing a very rigorous pursuance of the physiological facts *per se.* It may be that before long this present practical situation as between psychology and physiology may become reversed. *Note added January 1951:* The use of "ancillary" here and later does not seem to have been altogether happy. What was meant was that an adequate sociology is a precondition to a complete psychology and an adequate psychology is a precondition to a complete physiology.

16. For the general importance of the methodological concept of the field, see Lewin [3] and Brown [2].

[Cf. B. F. Skinner, *Science and Human Behavior,* 1953.]

23a. The Origin and Development of Psychoanalysis

By SIGMUND FREUD

[Cf. Gregory Zilboorg, *Sigmund Freud: His Exploration of the Mind of Man* (Twentieth Century Library, Charles Scribner's Sons, 1951); Joseph Jastrow, *The House That Freud Built* (1932), reprinted as *Freud: His Dream and Sex Theories* (Pocket Books, 1948); also, cf. References and Notes to selection [23b] by Ernst Kris. H. Palmer, *Philosophy of Psychiatry,* 1952; John Wisdom, *Philosophy and Psycho-Analysis,* 1953.]

[*Freud and Psychoanalysis* is vol. 4 of *The Collected Works of C. G. Jung* (17 vols. to be published in the Bollingen Series XX).]

23b. Validation of Psychoanalytic Propositions

By ERNST KRIS

1. In the course of this paper I have liberally drawn on ideas and formulations that emerged in discussions with H. Hartmann, and with him and R. Loewenstein. Only a part of these discussions has as yet been published, jointly.

2. Cf. in this connection K. W. Spence's (49) somewhat extreme views on the relation between independent variables and constructs: "Theories come into play whenever we do not know all variables entering into a set of experimental events or the interrelation between them."

3. For a bibliography see Freud (16).

4. Cf. *Beyond the Pleasure Principle* (18, p. 79): "The shortcomings of our description would probably disappear if for the psychological terms we could *already now* substitute physiological or chemical ones." The words "already now" are omitted from the quoted translation by an error of the translator. The German text has in the corresponding passage the words *"schon jetzt."* For a similar later statement of Freud's, see *New Introductory Lectures* (19), p. 198.

5. For one example, see Hartmann and Kris (27, pp. 21 ff.).

6. For a full discussion, see Hartmann (24) and Hermann (30).

7. See Wälder (51) and Glover (20) for a discussion of these theories and methodological questions.

8. For a more detailed discussion of this point and a critical discussion of K. Lewin's position, see Hartmann and Kris (27).

9. In speaking here of development instead of maturation, we refer to a definition: we ascribe to maturation processes relatively independent of environment; to development those highly dependent on environment (27).

10. Hartmann (25) repeated Zeigarnik's experiments with obsessional neurotic subjects and found that contrary to Zeigarnik's expectations based on experiments with normal subjects, they did not *prefer* incomplete to completed tasks. . . . The need to repeat . . . that predominates in the clinical picture of the majority of obsessional subjects overrides the need to complete the uncompleted. The specific impulses of the obsessional neurotic "modify the structure of the quasi-needs."

11. At the present time only incomplete evidence as to the experimental procedure used is available. Cf. Bion (6), and *Fortune Magazine*, March, 1946, where a cursory description of the various tests applied by Murray in the selection of personnel for the Office of Strategic Services is given.

12. As an example, see, for instance, Henle's experiments (29).

13. As an example of such a division, I refer to the data on the development of the child's views on morality by Piaget (44) and similar sets of data produced by psychoanalysis. Cf. de Saussure (46).

14. According to Freud's observation (17) three peculiarities, orderliness, parsimony, and obstinacy (or the opposites of all or one of them), tend to form a character triad, i.e., they frequently occur together. A further empirical finding of Freud's indicates that in the life of individuals who show that triad of characteristics, excretory function obtained accentuated importance in childhood. He furthermore assumes that under equal environmental conditions during childhood only certain constitutionally predisposed individuals are likely to develop the indicated triads. In studying the character traits of adult identical twins Hartmann (26) found confirmation for a part of Freud's propositions. He investigated ten pairs of identical twins and found that if in one of the twins one of the three character traits forming the triads of anal eroticism was of importance, in the other the same or another trait of the triads regularly predominates, either in its positive or in its negative form. The three character traits are, therefore, para-variable, i.e., they substitute for each other. No analysis of overt behavior of the twins could have established

a meaningful relationship between the disorderliness of the one and the obstinacy of the other. Only the genetic proposition of Freud, which considers the triads of traits as reaction-formations to experiences in the anal phase of libidinal development, made the relationship meaningful.

24. On the Logic of the Social Sciences

By JOHN STUART MILL

1. It is almost superfluous to observe, that there is another meaning of the word Art, in which it may be said to denote the poetical department or aspect of things in general, in contradistinction to the scientific. In the text, the word is used in its older and, I hope, not yet obsolete sense.

2. The word "teleology" is also, but inconveniently and improperly, employed by some writers as a name for the attempt to explain the phenomena of the universe from final causes.

[Cf. Mill's *Autobiography*, 1873; *Princ. Pol. Econ.*, 1848; *On Liberty*, 1859; *Dissert. and Discussions*, 4 vols., 1859; *Representative Gov't*, 1861; *Utilitarianism*, 1863; *Comte and Positivism*, 1865; *Three Essays on Religion*, 1874 (written 1850–8, 1868–70). On Mill's Newtonian ideal of science, cf. R. P. Anschutz, *The Philosophy of J. S. Mill*, 1953.]

25. Does Human Nature Change?

By JOHN DEWEY

For further study of Dewey's philosophy of social sciences, cf. his *Reconstruction in Philosophy* (1920); *Human Nature and Conduct* (1922); *Experience and Nature* (1925); *A Common Faith* (1934); *Logic: the Theory of Inquiry* (1938); *Experience and Education* (1938), *Freedom and Culture* (1939); *Intelligence in the Modern World: John Dewey's Philosophy*, ed. J. Ratner (1939); *The Philosophy of John Dewey*, ed. P. A. Schilpp (1939); M. H. Thomas and H. W. Schneider, *A Bibliography of John Dewey, 1882–1939* (1939).—Ed.

Cf. also, D's article on "Philosophy," *Encycl. Soc. Sci.*, XII; *Art as Experience* (1934); *Problems of Men* (1946).—Ed.

26a. Life of the Law

By O. W. HOLMES, JR.

The Common Law had a 37th printing in 1945. Cf. Holmes's *Speeches* (1913) and *Collected Legal Papers*, ed. H. J. Laski (1920); Silas Bent, *Justice Oliver Wendell Holmes, a Biography* (1931); Max Lerner, *The Faith and Mind of Justice Holmes* (1943); Mark DeWolfe Howe, *Touched*

With Fire: Civil War Letters and Diary of Oliver Wendell Holmes, Jr., 1861–1864 (1946), and *id.*, "O. W. Holmes, Jr., Counsellor-at-Law," Publ. of Brandeis Lawyers' Soc. (Oct. 1947); "The Holmes-Cohen Correspondence," ed. F. S. Cohen, *Jour. Hist. of Ideas* IX (1948); "Evolutionary Pragmatism in Holmes's Theory of the Law," ch. 8 of P. P. Wiener, *Evolution and the Founders of Pragmatism* (1949).—Ed.

26b. The Place of Logic in the Law

By MORRIS R. COHEN

1. Reprinted in part from *Harvard Law Review*, vol. 29 (1915), pp. 622–633; included in M. R. Cohen, *Law and the Social Order* (Harcourt, Brace & Co., copyright 1933); also see M. R. Cohen and Felix S. Cohen, *Readings in Jurisprudence and Legal Philosophy* (Prentice-Hall, New York, 1951), Ch. 8 on Law and Logic.

2. Jhering, *Geist des römischen Rechts,* 1865–69, vol. III, sec. 69; *Scherz und Ernst in der Jurisprudenz,* 1884, chap. I, pts. 3–4; Holmes, *The Common Law,* 1881, chap. I.

3. Jhering, *op. cit.* (note 2), secs. 44–46, 59–68, and especially 45, 64, 65.

4. Holmes, *op. cit.* (note 2). Note the quotation at the end of the preface, and the important place of "reasons" in the development of the law, pp. 5, 36; see also pp. 214, 219, 220, 239, 289.

5. Wüstendörfer, *"Die deutsche Rechtsprechung," Archiv für die civilistische Praxis,* Vol. CX (1910), p. 223; Fuchs, *Die Gemeinschädlichkeit der konstruktiven Jurisprudenz,* 1909, Chaps. 1–2; Bentley, *The Process of Government,* 1908, Chap. I; Brooks Adams, *Centralization and the Law,* 1908, Lectures 1–2.

6. Adams, *op. cit.* (note 5), pp. 39, 41, 43; *Wüstendörfer, op. cit.* (note 5), 219–22.

7. "Arbitrary discretion is excluded by the certainty resulting from a strict scientific method" (Savigny, *Of the Vocation of Our Age for Legislation and Jurisprudence,* trans. by Hayward, 1831, p. 151).

8. Dernburg, *System des römischen Rechts,* 1912, sec. 220.

9. Labatt, *Commentaries on the Law of Master and Servant,* 1913, 8 vols.

10. Langdell, *Cases on Contracts,* 1871, p. vi.

11. Bozi, *Die Weltanschauung der Jurisprudenz,* 1907; Brooks Adams and Bentley, *op. cit.* (note 5). See also note in Jung, *Das Problem des natürlichen Rechts,* 1912, p. 172.

12. Harvey, the discoverer of the circulation of the blood, said of Bacon: "He writes science like a Lord Chancellor."

13. 188 Mass. 353, 74 N.E. 603 (1905).

14. 208 U.S. 161, 28 Sup. Ct. 277 (1908).

15. 222 Mass. 206, 110 N.E. 264 (1915).

16. Twining v. New Jersey, 211 U.S. 78, 106, 29 Sup. Ct. 14 (1908).

17. Adams, *op. cit.* (note 5), pp. 20 *et seq.* And see Lewis, "The Social Sciences as the Basis of Legal Education," *University of Pennsylvania Law Review,* Vol. LXI (1913), pp. 531, 533.

18. National Protective Association v. Cumming, 170 N.Y. 315, 63 N.E. 369 (1902).

19. Holmes, *op. cit.* (note 2), p. 2. *Cf.* Boas, *Mind of Primitive Man,* 1911.

[M. R. Cohen, *Reason and Law: Studies in Juristic Philosophy,* 1950. Cf. also H. Kelsen, *General Theory of Law and the State,* 1945; H. Cairns, *Law and the Social Sciences,* 1935; *id., Legal Philosophy from Plato to Hegel,* 1949; J. Frank, *Law and the Modern Mind,* 1949[2]; *id., Courts on Trial,* 1949; T. H. Cowan, "A Postulate Set for Experimental Jurisprudence," *Phil. Sci.* 18 (1951), 1–15; J. Michael and M. Adler, *The Nature of Judicial Proof; id.,* "Real Proof," 5 Vand. L. Rev. 344 (1952).]

26c. Science and Reform in Criminal Law

JEROME HALL

1. *Cf.* Soler, *The Political Importance of Methodology in Criminal Law,* 34 J. Crim. L. & Criminology 366 (1944) and Soler's review of the writer's General Principles of Criminal Law (1947) in 10 Revista Juridica de Cordoba 271–277 (Argentina, June, 1949).

2. The relevance of this for the accepted theory of "the case-method" of instruction may be noted. The pertinent question is— how much of the general ideas or theory of the subject is simply left unexpressed until the instructor is ready to discover the *ratio decidendi* by "sheer induction"?

3. Bishop, Common Law and Codification, or the Common Law as a System of Reasoning (An Address, So. Car. Bar Ass'n. 1887, pub. Chicago, 1888).

4. General Principles of Criminal Law (1947) and Cases and Readings on Criminal Law and Procedure (1949).

5. One advantage of such terminology might be to foster critical testing of the validity of the principles. *E.g.,* a wilful taking of property without *animo furandi* is not larceny, but larceny is committed by subsequent conversion of it with *animo furandi.* Commonwealth v. James White and Another, 11 Cush. 483 (Mass. 1853). The fiction, "continuing trespass," is employed to provide a formal "concurrence" of conduct with mens rea. Here, a critical estimate of the facts and law requires qualification of the principle of concurrence. The reason for retaining "principle" in preference to "postulate" is stated in the text below. And see note 9 *infra.*

6. Campbell, Physics—The Elements 50 (1920).

7. E.g., Jevons, The Principles of Science (1907, 2d ed. 1924).

8. Einstein opposed the view that physical laws are mere conventions. "This 'simplicity of nature' is the observable fact which cannot be reduced to a convention on how to use some words." Frank, Modern Science and its Philosophy 11 (1949). So, too, it is probable that at least some important attributes of human nature are "given." That limits and guides "postulation"—at least if one wishes to work in the realm of fact.

9. A more detailed discussion of the "Is-Ought problem" involved in social research is presented in the Introduction to the writer's Theft, Law and Society (2d ed. 1952).

10. Vabres, Traité Élémentaire de Droit Criminel 68–69 (1937); Bouzat, Traité de Droit Pénal, 66 ff. (1951).

11. State v. Vallery et al., 212 La. 1095, 34 So.2d 329 (1948).

12. Report of the Wisconsin Legislative Council 2 (1951). It may be added that this Report contains many excellent proposals.

13. For indications of a current tendency of English judges to apply strict construction more rigorously than in the recent past, which is especially significant because they are applying it to minor offenses, see The Rule of Strict Construction of Penal Statutes, 14 J. Crim. L. 188 (London 1950).

14. B. M. Beck, who recently made a careful study of the operation of the Youth Correction Authority laws in the five states which adopted them, states that "the statutes enacted bear, in many instances, however, only a remote relationship to the Model Act. It is not possible to find any aspect of the program in these five states which is common to all five states and which would set these states apart from those states which have not established what are known as 'Authority programs.'" Beck, Five States, A Study of the Youth Authority Program as Promulgated by the American Law Institute 5 (1951).

15. "The newness of the Youth Authority program is the integration under one governmental agency of the several aspects of the treatment process; i.e., diagnosis and classification, institutional treatment, parole and delinquency prevention through community organization." Holton, California Youth Authority: Eight Years of Action, 41, J. Crim. L. & Criminology 22 (1950).

16. For specific suggestions in this regard see the writer's report, written in collaboration with T. B. Orbison and J. K. Ruckelshaus, Report of the State Penal and Correctional Survey Commission, 24 Ind. L.J. 1 (1948).

17. E.g., Professor Dession, after an able presentation of the corrective viewpoint, refers to public fears that crimes would increase if punitive sanctions were seriously weakened, and he adds:

"Whether on their merits or their emotional appeal, these qualms at the prospect of a softening of retribution deserve attention and should, so far as is compatible with advance rather than regression in the penal field, be relieved." Dession, Justice After Conviction, 25 Conn. B.J. 221–2 (1951). If this realistic attitude were widely emulated, it would provide the basis for effective cooperative research among scholars holding divergent perspectives. See, also, the sound estimate of P. W. Tappan, Sentences for Sex Criminals, 42 J. Crim. L. & Criminology 332 (1951).

18. Elmer L. Irey, Former Chief, Enforcement Branch, United States Treasury, describes the trial and conviction of Ralph Capone for tax fraud and reports that the next day and every day after that for several weeks many underworld operators went to the collector's office "to pay Uncle Sam voluntarily $1,000,000 in taxes . . . [They] were afraid Uncle Sam would find out." Irey and Slocum, The Tax Dodgers 35 (1948). Cf. "On the other hand, to regard deterrence as the sole end of the criminal law is a confession either of defeatism or cynicism," Paton, A Textbook of Jurisprudence 352 (1946).

19. For an excellent brief discussion distinguishing the retributive theory of Plato and St. Thomas Aquinas from those of Kant and Hegel, see Hawkins, Punishment and Moral Responsibility, 7 Mod. L. Rev. 205 (1944).

20. After criticizing the defects of mechanical views of retribution, Morris Cohen wrote: "Despite the foregoing and other limitations of the retributive theory, it contains an element of truth which only sentimental foolishness can ignore." Cohen, Moral Aspects of the Criminal Law, 49 Yale L. J. 1011 (1940).

21. A similar, inclusive theory was recently stated by Lord Justice Asquith, as follows: "A third theory, and it is the one which seems to me to come nearest the truth, is that there must be an element of retribution or expiation in punishment: but that so long as that element is there, and enough of it is there, there is everything to be said for giving the punishment the shape that is most likely to deter and reform." Asquith, The Problem of Punishment, The Listener, May 11, 1950, p. 821 (pub. by B. B. C.).

22. Hall, General Principles of Criminal Law 130, 245, 421 535 (1947).

23. Cowan, A Critique of the Moralistic Conception of Criminal Law, 97 U. of Pa. L. Rev. 502 (1949). Cf. Rooney, Law Without Justice?—The Kelsen and Hall Theories Compared, 23 Notre Dame Law. 140 (1948); Radin, Natural Law and Natural Rights, 59 Yale L.J. 214 (1950).

24. For the writer's discussion of this problem, supplementing that in General

Principles of Criminal Law (1947), the reader is referred to *Living Law of Democratic Society* (1940), especially chapter 2.

25. One of the very interesting changes in the history of ideas is represented in the shift from Plato's axiom that punishment, just imposed, is always corrective, indeed, that it is a major educational institution, to the axiom of contemporary academic penologists, that punishment never has any beneficial effect. But if corrective treatment unavoidably includes a punitive element, the two perspectives are not actually in such complete opposition as the polemics imply.

26. "Experienced penologists do not dismiss the idea of punishment. They recognize the fact that being sent to a prison, however humanely it is operated, is punishment in itself. They know that it is impossible to make a prison so pleasant that the prisoners will not consider their imprisonment punishment." MacCormick, *The Prison's Role in Crime Prevention*, 41 J. Crim. L. & Criminology 42–43 (1950).

27. "To achieve the maximum deterrent effect it would be necessary either to impose excessively long sentences or to inflict harsh treatment and impose rigid restrictions and deprivations on the prisoners." *Id.* at 42.

28. "Criminals may well be called public enemies. But they are men and women. They are entitled to the benefit of the Biblical injunction that we must love our enemies. Perhaps we could come to love them if we made a sacrifice for them." Gausewitz, *Realistic Punishment*, pub. in The Administration of Criminal Justice, Virginia Law Weekly Dicta, 47 (1948–49). *Cf.* St. Luke 23–41.

29. "The effort to make life more decent therefore always involves a struggle against opposing forces. And in this struggle men find hatred as well as love, tonic emotions. Indeed, we must hate evil if we really love the good." Cohen, *supra* note 20, at 1018.

30. For a specific illustration of the sort of questions that need to be asked by both theorists and judges, see Coddington, *Problems of Punishment*, 46 Proc. Arist. Soc. (n.s.) 155 (1946), reprinted in part in Hall, Cases and Readings on Criminal Law and Procedure 99 (1949).

31. Legality is the presupposition of all the other principles, and thus of the entire criminal law; and punishment is so involved in different contexts of knowledge and reform that it is not easy to regard it, also, as a formal, organizing construct of criminal law.

32. In addition to the ambiguity of "act," noted in the text, consider the involvement of the following passage:

"That is, even in those cases where, as explained . . . *supra,* the act and the criminal consequence *are one and the same,* it is the surrounding conditions and circumstances under which the act was committed which make it criminal; apart from these

the act is quite colorless." (Italics added.) Sayre, *Criminal Attempts,* 41 Harv. L. Rev. 838, n.65 (1928).

Cf. the comments on the above by Arnold, *Criminal Attempts—the Rise and Fall of an Abstraction,* 40 Yale L.J. 64 (1930).

33. *E.g.,* ". . . the aim of the law is not to punish sins, but to prevent certain external results . . ." Holmes, J., in Commonwealth v. Kennedy, 170 Mass. 18, 20, 48 N.E. 770 (1897), which concerned a criminal attempt.

34. If the harm done is held irrelevant to dangerousness, what criteria are available to determine the degree of dangerousness, which can be utilized with assurance in incarcerating human beings? And what decision would be reached regarding the dangerousness of persons who committed harms in unusually critical situations, such as a man who killed in sight of adultery committed by his wife, *i.e.* where the recurrence of such a situation would be practically impossible?

35. No exhaustive search of the literature on criminal attempts was made with reference to this point. But among the writers examined, those who expressed themselves on this question made the following relevant statements concerning criminal attempts: ". . . a disturbance of the social order." *May's Law of Crimes* 191 (4th ed., Sears and Weihofen, 1938); ". . . in the ordinary judgment of mankind, and in the consequences to the community, the disturbance of the attempt has been created. . . . But the public has not suffered so much, therefore it will not punish him so heavily." 1 Bishop, Criminal Law 530, 552 (9th ed. 1923); ". . . the *corpus delicti* of a criminal attempt might be stated as a *substantial* but incomplete impairment of some interest. . . ." Strahorn, *The Effect of Impossibility on Criminal Attempts,* 78 U. of Pa. L. Rev. 962, 970 (1930). "An attempt . . . causes a sufficient social harm to be deemed criminal." Hitchler, *Criminal Attempts.* 43 Dick. L. Rev. 211 (1939); ". . . societal harm. . . ." Curran, *Criminal and Non-Criminal Attempts,* 19 Geo. L.J. 185 and 316 (1930). And see Strahorn, *Preparation for Crime as a Criminal Attempt,* 1 Wash. & Lee L. Rev. 1 (1939), and Hall, General Principles of Criminal Law 111 ff. (1947).

But *cf.,* ". . . the act of attempt is not in itself harmful to the state. The crime is a mere shadow of the attempted offense. . . ." Beale, *Chemical Attempts,* 16 Harv. L. Rev. 491 (1903).

And Wharton, in the course of misstating the law regarding voluntary abandonment of a criminal attempt ("this is a defense") adds as a reason: "Neither society, nor any private person, has been injured by his act. There is no damage, therefore, to redress." 1 Wharton, Criminal Law 306 (12th ed. 1932).

36. Although merely verbal conventions cannot suffice in legal science, that is not

relevant with regard to the finding of harm in the relational offenses. Dissent from that judgment does not prove that it is formalistic but only that the insight has not been indubitably established.

37. *Cf.* Holmes in note 33 *supra.*

38. *Cf.* Hall, *The Proposal to Prepare a Model Penal Code,* 4 J. Legal Educ. 91 (1951), reprinted in Theft, Law and Society (2d ed. 1952).

[Cf. Hall, *Police and Law in a Democratic Society,* 28 Indiana L. J. 133 (1953); *Some Basic Questions Regarding Legal Classification for Professional and Scientific Purposes,* 5 J. Legal Educ. 329 (1953).]

27. History and the Social Sciences

By JOHN H. RANDALL, JR.

1. Cohen, Morris R., *The Meaning of Human History* (La Salle, Ill., 1947) p. 38: "History is applied science, as is geology, medicine, or engineering. The difference, however, is that while the engineer or the geologist knows precisely and explicitly what laws he is applying in order to explain the phenomena, the historian seldom explicitly states the laws of human events that he assumes. Yet implicitly he does make such assumptions."

2. Dewey, John, *Experience and Nature* (Chicago, 1925) p. 161-62: "What is sometimes termed 'applied science,' may then be more truly science than what is conventionally called pure science. For it is directly concerned with not just instrumentalities, but instrumentalities at work in effecting modifications of existence in behalf of conclusions that are reflectively preferred. . . . Thus conceived, knowledge exists in engineering, medicine, and the social arts more adequately than it does in mathematics and physics. Thus conceived, history and anthropology are scientific in a sense in which bodies of information that stop short with general formulae are not."

3. Cohen, *op. cit.,* p. 38: "Those who insist that history is a science in the same way in which physics is a science, often mean to assert that the subject matter of history is not the individual events but the laws or repeatable patters of human behavior. Those, however, who do so, obviously confuse history with sociology. A science of sociology would be concerned with general laws and would leave to history the consideration of what actually happened in definite places at given times."

4. *Cf.* Cohen, *op. cit.,* p. 40-41: "What is distinctive, then, about human history, is not its material, which is identical with the material of the social sciences, nor the critical apparatus that is utilized to search out this material and consists primarily of hypotheses borrowed from the sciences. What is distinctive is rather the focus or perspective which makes description or understanding of individual happenings in time and place central. Thus 'natural history' differs from natural science in that the former focuses on description, while the latter stresses theory, or systematic deduction from assumed principles or hypothesis. . . . History uses laws to explain facts."

5. "It was not before the eighteenth century that the custom arose of using for the designation of a whole system of social organization either compound expressions like feudal regime, government or system or, a little later, abstract substantives such as *féodalité* or feudalism. . . . The extension of the use of a word derived from a particular institution, the fief, which can scarcely be considered the central and only significant institution of feudalism, to characterize the social regime prevailing widely during the Middle Ages, . . . is mainly attributable to the influence of Montesquieu." Marc Bloch, in *Encyclopaedia of the Social Sciences,* vol. vi, p. 203.

6. *Oxford Dictionary.*

7. Sombart, Werner, in *Encyclopaedia of the Social Sciences,* vol. iii, article on "Capitalism." Sombart goes on: "Neither the term nor the concept has as yet been universally recognized by representatives of academic economics. The older German economists and to a much greater extent the economists of other countries rejected entirely the concept of capitalism. . . . The term is not found in Gide, Cauwes, Marshall, Seligman or Cassel. . . . The works of Sombart are the first in which the concept of capitalism has been definitively recognized as fundamental to the system of economic thought."

8. Dewey states this functional method precisely: "The function of consequences as necessary tests of the validity of propositions, *providing* these consequences are operationally instituted and are such as to resolve the specific problem evoking the operations." *Logic* (New York 1938) p. iv.

9. For a fuller clarification of the meaning of these terms, see Dewey, *Problems of Men* (New York 1946) p. 416-18.

[Cf. J. H. Randall, Jr., *Making of the Modern Mind* (latest ed.); C. A. Beard (ed.), *A Century of Progress,* 1932; *Theory and Practice in Historical Study,* Report of the Committee on Historiography, Social Science Research Council, 1946, including discussions by J. H. Randall, Jr. and G. Haines IV, M. Curti, H. K. Beale, S. Hook, and a selective reading list on historiography and the philosophy of history by Ronald Thompson; Symposium on *Causation in History* by M. R. Cohen, F. J. Teggart, and M. Mandelbaum in *JHI* (Jan. 1942), pp. 3-50; M. Mandelbaum, *The Problem of Historical Knowledge,* 1938; H. Ausubel, *Historians and Their Craft,* 1950; H. Berr and L. Lefebvre, art. "History and Historiography" in *Encycl. Soc. Sci.,* VII; R. M. MacIver, art. "Sociology," *ibid.,*

XIV; J. Rosenthal, "Attitudes of Some Modern Rationalists to History," *JHI* (Oct. 1943), pp. 429–56; S. P. Lamprecht, *Nature and History*, 1950; W. H. Walsh, *Introd. to Philosophy of History*, 1951; P. Gardiner, *The Nature of Historical Explanation*, 1952; E. Nagel, "The Logic of Historical Explanation," *Scientific Monthly* (March 1952), pp. 162–9.—Ed.]

28a. Objectivity in Social Science

By MAX WEBER

[Cf. Max Weber: *The Theory of Social and Economic Organization*, ed. Talcott Parsons, 1947; also Weber's *Essays in Sociology*, ed. H. H. Gerth and C. W. Mills. G. von Schmoller, *Pol. Econ. and its Method;* J. A. Schumpeter, *Business Cycles*, 1939; F. Kaufmann, *Methodology in the Social Sciences*, 1948; *Readings in Economics*, ed. Kapp, 1949; E. Heimann, *History of Economic Doctrines*, 1945.
Cf. Notes to 27, 28b, 29, 30.]

28b. Capitalism, Calvinism and the Rise of Modern Science

By WERNER STARK

1. A paper read to a circle of physicists, for whom a straightforward summary was required, of Max Weber's book *The Protestant Ethic and the Spirit of Capitalism*, the main thesis of which is common knowledge among sociologists. After briefly developing Max Weber's theory, the author shows that it contains even more truth than Max Weber himself may have realised.

2. It is true that the Calvinist doctrine was one of predestination, not of predetermination, but that fine distinction was unavoidably lost when it left the academic sphere and became the subject of discussion in the world at large.

[Cf. R. H. Tawney, *Religion and the Rise of Capitalism*; P. Geyl, A. J. Toynbee, and P. A. Sorokin, *The Pattern of the Past: Can We Determine It?*, 1949; W. Sombart, art. "Capitalism," *Encyc. Soc. Sci.* III; T. S. Ashton, *The Industrial Revolution 1760–1830* (London, 1948); R. S. Lilley, *Social Aspects of the History of Science*, 1949; M. Polanyi, *Science, Faith and Society*, 1948; id., *Logic and Liberty*, 1951.]

29. The Sociology of Knowledge:

29a. Ideology and Utopia

By KARL MANNHEIM

1. Max Weber, *Wirtschaft und Gesellschaft*, vol. i, chap. iv, 7, *Religionssoziologie: Stände, Klassen und Religion* (Tübingen, 1925), pp. 267–296.

2. Thus, for example, in our own time, pragmatism, as will be seen later, when viewed later, when viewed sociologically, constitutes the legitimation of a technique of thinking and of an epistemology which has elevated the criteria of everyday experience to the level of "academic" discussion.

29b. The Sociology of Knowledge

By KARL POPPER

1. Concerning Mannheim, see especially *Ideology and Utopia* (quoted here from the German edition, 1929). The terms 'social habitat' and 'total ideology' are both due to Mannheim; the terms 'sociologism' and 'historism' have been mentioned in the last chapter (Ch. 22 of Popper's book). The idea of a 'social habitat' is Platonic. For a criticism of Mannheim's *Man and Society In An Age of Reconstruction* (1941), which combines historicist tendencies with a romantic and even mystical Utopianism or holism, see my *Poverty of Historicism*, II (*Economica*, 1944).

[Cf. F. A. Hayek, *The Counter-Revolution of Science* (1952), for further discussion of historicism which imposes 'laws of necessary stages' (Comte, Hegel, Marx) on all human history.]—Ed.

2. Cp. my interpretation in *What is Dialectic?* (*Mind*, 49, especially p. 414).

3. This is Mannheim's term (cp. *Ideology and Utopia*, 1929, p. 35). For the 'freely poised intelligence,' see *op. cit.*, p. 123, where this term is attributed to Alfred Weber. For the theory of an intelligentsia loosely anchored in tradition, see *op. cit.*, pp. 121–34, and especially p. 122.

4. For the latter theory, or, rather, practice, cp. notes 51 and 52 to chapter 11.

5. Cp. *What is Dialectic?* (p. 417). Cp. note 33 to chapter 12.

6. The analogy between the psychoanalytic method and that of Wittgenstein is mentioned by Wisdom, *Other Minds* (*Mind*, 49, p. 370, note): 'A doubt such as "I can never really know what another person is feeling" may arise from more than one of these sources. This over-determination of sceptical symptoms complicates their cure. The treatment is like psychoanalytic treatment (to enlarge Wittgenstein's analogy) in that the treatment is the diagnosis and the diagnosis is the description, the very full description, of the symptoms.' And so on. (I may remark that, using the word 'know' in the ordinary sense, we can, of course, never know what another person is feeling. We can only make hypotheses about it. This solves the so-called problem. It is a mistake to speak here of doubt, and a still worse mistake to attempt to remove the doubt by a semiotico-analytic treatment.)

7. The psychoanalysts seem to hold the same of the individual psychologists, and

they are probably right. Cp. Freud's *History of the Psycho-Analytic Movement* (1916), p. 42, where Freud records that Adler made the following remark (which fits well within Adler's individual-psychological scheme, according to which feelings of inferiority are predominantly important): 'Do you believe that it is such a pleasure for me to stand in your shadow my whole life?' This suggests that Adler had not successfully applied his theories to himself, at that time at least. But the same seems to be true of Freud: None of the founders of psychoanalysis were psychoanalyzed. To this objection they usually replied that they had psychoanalyzed themselves. But they would never have accepted such an excuse from anybody else; and, indeed, rightly so.

8. For the following analysis of scientific objectivity, cp. my *Logik der Forschung*, section 8 (pp. 16 ff.).

9. I wish to apologize to the Kantians for mentioning them in the same breath as the Hegelians.

10. Cp. A. Tarski, *Der Wahrheitsbegriff in den formalisierten Sprachen*, Polish ed., 1933, German translation, 1936; R. Carnap, *Introduction to Semantics*, 1942; K. Popper, *Logik der Forschung*, ch. 84 on 'Truth' and 'Confirmation' (pp. 203 ff.); B. Russell, *Let the People Think*, pp. 77, 79.

11. K. Popper, *Logik der Forschung* (cp., for example, pp. 227 ff.); *Erkenntnis*, vol. 5 (1934), 170 ff., especially 172: 'We shall have to get accustomed to interpreting the sciences as systems of hypotheses (instead of "bodies of knowledge"), i.e., of anticipations which cannot be established, but which we can use as long as they can be confirmed, and which we cannot describe as "true" or as "more or less certain" or even as "probable".'

12. *Handbook of Marxism*, 255.

30. Dialectic and Nature

By SIDNEY HOOK

1. "Es ist schon ein totaler Mangel an Einsicht in die Natur der Dialektik, wenn Herr Dühring sie für ein Instrument des blossen Beweisens hält, wie man etwa die formelle Logik oder die elementare Mathematik beschränkter Weise so auffassen kann. Selbst die formelle Logik ist vor allem Methode zur Auffindung neuer Resultate, zum Fortschreiten vom Bekannten zum Unbekannten, und dasselbe, nur in weit eminenterem Sinne ist die Dialektik. . . ." Engels, *Anti-Dühring*, 12th ed. (1923), pp. 136–7.

1a. All references below are to the 12th ed., Berlin and Stuttgart, 1923.

2. *Cf. Lenin.* "Auf der historischen Stufenleiter zwischen dieser Stufe [monopoly capitalism—S. H.] und derjenigen, die man Sozialismus nennt keine *Zwischenstufen* gift." ("Die drohende Katastrophe und wie

soll man sie bekämpfen," *Sämtliche Werke*, Bd. XXI, p. 235.)

3. "Alle Verstandstätigkeit: *Induzieren, Deduzieren*, also auch *Abstrahieren . . .* Analysieren unbekannter Gegenstände (schon das Zerbrechen einer Nuss ist Anfang der Analyse), *Synthesieren* (bei tierischen Schlauheitsstückchen) und als Vereinigung beider *Experimentieren* (bei neuen Hindernissen und in fremden Lagen) haben wir mit dem Tier gemein." *Dialektik und Natur, op. cit.*, p. 187.

4. "Was von der ganzen bisherigen Philosophie dann noch selbständig bestehen bleibt ist die Lehre vom Denken und seinen Gesetzen—die formelle Logik und die Dialektik." *Anti-Dühring*, p. 11.

5. *Cf.* also, *Dialektik und Natur*, p. 219; *Ludwig Feuerbach, Duncker Ausgabe*, p. 54; letters to Bloch, Starkenberg, and Mehring *passim* reprinted in appendix to *Towards the Understanding of Karl Marx*, New York, 1933.

6. *Cf.* especially *Dialektik und Natur, op. cit.*, p. 237.

7. *E.g.*, in his remarks on Wallace and Crookes in his "Natural Science in the Spirit World," *Marx-Engels Archiv*, Bd., 2 pp. 207–216, translated into English in *Marxist Quarterly*, Vol. I, No. 1, pp. 68–76.

8. ". . . Herr Dühring genöthigt ist, der Natur mehr als einmal bewusste Handlungsweise unterzuschieben, also das was man auf deutsch Gott nennt." *Anti-Dühring*, p. 23.

9. "Die Materie als solche ist eine reine Gedankenschöpfung und Abstraktion," *op. cit.*, p. 234.

10. *Anti-Dühring*, 12th ed., Berlin, 1923, p. 121.

11. ". . . es sich dann von selbst versteht, dass die Erzeugnisse des menschlichen Hirns, die in letzter Instanz ja auch Naturprodukte sind, dem übrigen Naturzusammenhang nicht widersprechen sondern entsprechen." *Ibid.*, p. 22.

12. ". . . dass man keine Malthus-Brille braucht, um den Kampf ums Dasein in der Natur wahrzunehmen—den Widerspruch zwischen der Zahllosen Menge von Keimen, die die Natur verschwenderisch erzeugt, und der geringen Anzahl von ihnen, die überhaupt zur Reife kommen können." (*Op. cit.*, p. 60.) A strange kind of contradiction that!

13. In one of his genial insights which for all their inconsistencies make Engels' writings instructive even to critical readers, Engels recognizes this. "Wirklich wissenschaftliche Arbeiten vermeiden daher regelmässig solche dogmatische-moralische Ausdrücke wie Irrthum und Wahrheit." (*Op. cit.*, p. 87.)

14. For an account of the mischievous role which the notion of dialectic has played in contemporary Russian science and philosophy, see J. Rosenthal, "On the Soviet Philosophical Front" in *The Modern Monthly*, Dec. 1936, and subsequent issues. [Cf. H. J. Muller, "The Destruction of Science in the Soviet Union," *Sat. Rev. Lit.*

(Apr. 16, 1949); "The Soviet Union Since World War II," *Annals Amer. Acad. Pol. Soc. Sci.* (May 1949); C. Zirkle, *Death of a Science in Russia,* 1949; J. Huxley, *Heredity, East and West: Lysenko and World Science,* 1949; *Soviet Science,* a Symposium of the AAAS, ed. R. C. Christman, 1952; A. Philipov, *Logic and Dialectic in the Soviet Union;* foreword by E. Nagel, 1952.]

31. Scientific Theory of Culture

By BRONISLAW MALINOWSKI

[Cf. M's *Sex and Repression in Savage Society* and *Crime and Custom in Savage Society;* F. Boas, art. "Anthropology," *E.S.S.;* R. Lowie, *Are We Civilized?;* R. Benedict, *Patterns of Culture;* L. L. Whyte, *The Next Development in Man;* A. L. Kroeber, *The Nature of Culture.*]

32. Sociology Learns the Language of Mathematics

By ABRAHAM KAPLAN

[Cf. K. Arrow, "Math. Models in the Social Sciences," *The Policy Sciences,* ed. D. Lerner and H. D. Lasswell; O. Morgenstern, "The Theory of Games," *Sci. American* (May 1949); J. F. Nash, "The Bargaining Problem," *Econometrica* (1950), pp. 155–162; *id.* (for advanced math. student), "Two person cooperative games," *Econometrica* (Feb. 1953).]

33. Will Science Continue?

By HERMAN J. MULLER

[Cf. note 14 of selection 30, above; F. Osborn, *Our Plundered Planet;* C. G. Darwin, *The Next Million Years,* 1952.]

34. The Scientific Foundations for World Order

By J. ROBERT OPPENHEIMER

[Cf. *Freedom and Culture,* compiled by UNESCO, Introd. by J. Huxley, 1951; M. Polanyi, *The Logic of Liberty: Reflections and Rejoinders,* 1951; *Education for a World Society: Promising Practices Today,* ed. C. O. Arndt and S. Everett, 1951.]

35. Science and Its Critics

By HAROLD MCCARTHY

1. See John Dewey's *A Common Faith* (New Haven, Yale University Press, 1934).

37. The Economy of Science

By ERNST MACH

[Cf. P. Frank, *Modern Science and its Philosophy,* 1949, ch. 2: "The importance for our times of E. Mach's philosophy"; ch. 3: "E. Mach and the unity of science."]

38a. Representation vs. Explanation in Physical Theory

By PIERRE DUHEM

1. Correspondance de Descartes, ed. Paul Tannery et Ch. Adam, Lettre no. LVII (August 22, 1634), I, 307.
2. E. Mach: *The Science of Mechanics, op. cit.,* p. 579.
3. Since the first edition of this work we have on two occasions developed the thoughts followed above. In the first place, in a series of articles entitled Σώζειν τὰ φαινόμενα Essai sur *la notion de théorie physique de Platon à Galilée (Annales de Philosophie Chrétienne,* 1908). In the second place, in our work entitled *Le Système du Monde,* Histoire des doctrines cosmologiques de Platon à Copernic. Première partie, ch. X and XI, vol. II, pp. 50–179.
4. Laplace, *Exposition du système du monde* I, IV, ch. XVII.
5. André-Marie Ampère, *Théorie mathématique des phénomènes electrodynamiques, uniquement déduite de l'expérience.* Ed. Hebemann, p. 3.
6. Fourier, *Théorie analytique de la chaleur.* Ed. Darboux, p. xv and p. xxi.
7. A. Fresnel, *Oeuvres complètes,* vol. I, p. 480.
8. Robert Mayer, *Kleinere Schriften und Briefe* (Stuttgart, 1893), p. 181.
9. J. Macquorn Rankine, *Outlines of the Science of Energetics,* read to the Philosophical Society of Glasgow, May 2, 1855 and published in the *Proceedings* of this Society, vol. III, no. 4.—Cf. Rankine, *Miscellaneous Scientific Papers,* p. 209.
10. E. Mach, *Die Gestalten der Flüssigkeit. Prague,* 1872; *Die oekonomische Natur der physikalischen Forschung.* Vienna, 1882; *Die Mechanik in ihrer Entwicklung, historisch-kritisch dargestellt.* Leipzig, 1883; English translation by T. J. McCormack, *The Science of Mechanics, a Critical and Historical Account of Its Development by Dr. Ernst Mach* (Open Court Publishing Co., 1902).
11. G. Kirchhoff, *Vorlesungen ueber mathematische Physik; Mechanik.* (Leipzig, 1874), p. 1.

38b. Law and Causal Explanation

By EMILE MEYERSON

1. E. Le Roy: *Science et Philosophie. Revue de métaphysique,* VII, 1899, p. 534.
2. Malebranche: *De la recherche de la*

vérité. Paris, 1721, XIth *Eclaircissement*, Vol. IV, p. 277 and ff.

3. Cf. earlier, p. 252 [*Identity and Reality*].

4. Ernst Cassirer: *Das Erkenntnisproblem in der Philosophie und Wissenschaft der neuern Zeit*. Berlin, 1906–1907, Vol. II, p. 530. Cf. my article, *Revue de Métaphysique*, January 1911, p. 122 and ff.

5. Cf. earlier, p. 252 [*Identity and Reality*].

6. F. Rosenberger: *Isaak Newton*, Leipzig, 1895, pp. 173, 192. The same author points out the contradiction between the title *Philosophiae naturalis principia mathematica* and the content of the writing, which, in fact, constitutes only an exposition of the principles of mechanics (*ib.*, p. 172); but this is because Newton, like Descartes and like Leibniz, had the firm conviction that everything in physics should be reduced to mechanics.

7. Cf. on this subject, Appendix I, p. 452 and ff. [*Identity and Reality*].

8. Cf. Chapter I, pp. 18, 39 [*Identity and Reality*].

9. Comte: *Cours de philosophie positive*, 4th ed. Paris, 1877, Vol. I, p. 18.

10. *Ib.*, Vol. II, p. 453.

11. Comte: *Politique positive*, Vol. I, p. 531. The date at which he expresses this opinion (1851) only renders it the more curious.

12. *Cours*, Vol. II, p. 445.

13. *Ib.*, Vol. III, p. 152. He maintained this opinion in 1851, cf. *Politique positive*, Vol. I, p. 528: "Six irreducible branches" of physics, "perhaps seven." It is at least probable that other errors of Comte are connected, a little less directly, with the same tendency; such as his opinion on Lamarck's theory of the variability of species which he characterizes as an "irrational hypothesis" (*Pol. pos.*, Vol. I, p. 665); his enthusiasm for the mediocre conceptions of Gall (*Cours*, Vol. II, pp. 513, 534–587), an enthusiasm which, even to the end of his life, he only partially got over (cf. *Pol. pos.*, Vol. I, p. 669 and ff.); his hostility toward organic chemistry, which appeared to him "a heterogeneous and factitious assemblage," which must be "destroyed" (*Cours*, III, p. 174) and against which he renewed his attacks even in 1851 (*Pol. pos.*, Vol. I, p. 550), more than twenty years after Woehler's synthesis (1828), after the discovery of compound ammonia by Wurtz (1849), and on the very eve of the appearance of Gerhardt's theory of types (1853); finally his misunderstanding of the development of general chemistry, on which he wished to impose a peculiar theory which was probably only a clumsy generalization of Berzelius's conceptions, which the chemists about that time were gradually abandoning; with the result that Comte, noticing the small success of his theory, accused them of a "metaphysical spirit" (*Pol. pos.*, Vol. I, p. 551).

14. Bacon: *Novum Organon*, Book I, Aph. 61. It is very curious to observe that, just like Comte and evidently for analogous reasons, Bacon was strangely mistaken in his judgment about the great conquests of science. Thus he severely blamed Copernicus (*Glom. int.*, Cap. VI), and Gilbert, whose works on electricity are a veritable monument to the purest scientific thought, was his pet aversion (*Novum Org.*, I, §54; II, Aph. 48). Naturally we in no wise mean to attribute to Comte, on this question, opinions analogous to those of Bacon. On the contrary, Comte constantly insisted upon the necessity of hypothesis; absolute empiricism, according to him, is "not only entirely sterile, but even radically impossible for our understanding" (*Cours*, Vol. VI, p. 471). He only protested against hypotheses characterized by him as "metaphysical." But this attitude, although less absolute than that of Bacon, was enough to lead him into errors of the same kind.

15. Rosenberger: *Geschichte*, II, p. 191, remarks on Bacon's little real influence on the progress of science. Boyle seems to have allowed himself to be tempted to apply, not, indeed, Bacon's schemes (that would probably have been impossible), but certain of his principles. Rosenberger thinks that this circumstance was the reason why, having in hand all the experimental data of Mariotte's law, it slipped from him in the end.

16. Berthollet: *Essai de statique chimique*. Paris, 1803, p. 5.

17. *Encyclopaedia Britannica*, 9th ed., article Davy, p. 847.

18. Liebig: *Reden und Abhandlungen*. Leipzig, 1874, p. 249.

19. *Congrès international de physique*, Vol. I, p. 3.

20. Duhem: *La théorie physique*, p. 300; cf. earlier, p. 368 [*Identity and Reality*].

21. *Id.*, *La théorie physique*, p. 308.

22. Van't Hoff has recalled, with just pride, that Emile Fischer, in his researches which ended in the synthesis of glucose, was guided by considerations of stereochemistry (*Revue générale des sciences*, V, 1894, p. 272). It is known that this theory was applied also to pentavalent nitrogen and quadrivalent tin and sulphur.

23. H. Poincaré: *La science et l'hypothèse*, p. 208.

24. Cf. Duhem: *La théorie physique*, p. 43.

25. Cf. O. Reynolds: *Proceedings of the Royal Society*, Vol. XXVIII, February 6, 1879.

26. Cournot: *Traité de l'enchainement*. Paris, 1861, p. 157.

27. H. Poincaré: *La science et l'hypothèse*, p. 191.

28. Boltzmann: *Ueber die Unentbehrlichkeit der Atomistik*, *Wiedemann's Annalen*, Vol. LX, 1897, p. 243. Cf. also *id.*, *Leçons sur la théorie des gaz*. Trans. Galotti and Benard, 2nd Part. Paris, 1905, p. 8.

29. H. Hertz: *Gesammelte Werke*. Leipzig, 1895, Vol. I, p. 1.
  [Cf. G. Boas, *A Critical Analysis of the Philosophy of Emile Meyerson*, 1930.]

38c. Description and Explanation

By MORITZ SCHLICK

1 Cf. M. Schlick, *Gesammelte Aufsatze*, Vienna, 1938: "Erleben, Erkennen, Metaphysik".

39. Why Do Scientists and Philosophers Disagree?

By PHILIPP FRANK

1. H. von Helmholtz, *Über die Erhaltung der Kraft* (Berlin, 1847).
  [Cf. F's *Modern Science and Its Philosophy*, 1949; also, *Einstein, His Life and Times*.]

40. Does Science Have Metaphysical Presuppositions?

By ARTHUR PAP

1. See Keynes, *Treatise on Probability*, chaps. 19, 22.
  [This is called the *ceteris paribus* condition of a scientific law.—Ed.]

43a. Empiricism, Semantics, and Ontology

By RUDOLF CARNAP

1. The terms "sentence" and "statement" are here used synonymously for declarative (indicative, propositional) sentences.

2. In my book *Meaning and Necessity* (Chicago, 1947) I have developed a semantical method which takes propositions as entities designated by sentences (more specifically, as intensions of sentences). In order to facilitate the understanding of the systematic development, I added some informal, extra-systematic explanations concerning the nature of propositions. I said that the term "proposition" "is used neither for a linguistic expression nor for a subjective, mental occurrence, but rather for something objective that may or may not be exemplified in nature . . . We apply the term 'proposition' to any entities of a certain logical type, namely, those that may be expressed by (declarative) sentences in a language" (p. 27). After some more detailed discussions concerning the relation between propositions and facts, and the nature of false propositions, I added: "It has been the purpose of the preceding remarks to facilitate the understanding of our conception of propositions. If, however, a reader should find these explanations more puzzling than clarifying, or even unacceptable, he may disregard them" (p. 31) (that is, disregard these extra-systematic explanations, not the whole theory of the propositions as intensions of sentences, as one reviewer understood). In spite of this warning, it seems that some of those readers who were puzzled by the explanations, did not disregard them but thought that by raising objections against them they could refute the theory. This is analogous to the procedure of some laymen who by (correctly) criticizing the ether picture or other visualizations of physical theories, thought they had refuted those theories. Perhaps the discussions in the present paper will help in clarifying the role of the system of linguistic rules for the introduction of a framework of entities on the one hand, and that of extra-systematic explanations concerning the nature of the entities on the other.

3. W. V. Quine was the first to recognize the importance of the introduction of variables as indicating the acceptance of entities. "The ontology to which one's use of language commits him comprises simply the objects that he treats as falling . . . within the range of values of his variables" ("Notes on Existence and Necessity", *Journal of Philos.*, 40 (1943), pp. 113–127, see p. 118; compare also his "Designation and Existence", *ibid.*, 36 (1939), pp. 701–9, and "On Universals", *Journal of Symbolic Logic*, 12 (1947), pp. 74–84).

4. For a closely related point of view on these questions see the detailed discussions in Herbert Feigl, *Existential Hypotheses*, in *Philosophy of Science*, 1950.

5. Paul Bernays, *Sur le platonisme dans les mathématiques* (*L'Enseignement math.*, 34 (1935), pp. 52–69). W. V. Quine, see footnote p. 65, and a recent paper *On What There Is*, (*Review of Metaphysics*, 2 (1948), pp. 21–38). Quine does not acknowledge the distinction which I emphasize above, because according to his general conception there are no sharp boundary lines between logical and factual truth, between questions of meaning and questions of fact, between the acceptance of a language structure and the acceptance of an assertion formulated in the language. This conception, which seems to deviate considerably from customary ways of thinking, will be explained in his article "Semantics and Abstract Objects," *Proc. Amer. Acad. of Arts and Sciences*, 80 (1951), pp. 90–96. When Quine in the first article mentioned above classifies my logicistic conception of mathematics (derived from Frege and Russell) as "platonic realism" (p. 33), this is meant (according to a personal communication from him) not

as ascribing to me agreement with Plato's metaphysical doctrine of universals, but merely as referring to the fact that I accept a language of mathematics containing variables of higher levels. With respect to the basic attitude to take in choosing a language form (an "ontology" in Quine's terminology, which seems to me misleading), there appears now to be agreement between us: "the obvious counsel is tolerance and an experimental spirit" (*op. cit.*, p. 38).

6. See Carnap, *Scheinprobleme in der Philosophie; das Fremdpsychische und der Realismusstreit*, Berlin, 1928. Moritz Schlick, *Positivismus und Realismus*, reprinted in *Gesammelte Aufsätze*, Wien 1938.

7. *See Introduction to Semantics*, Cambridge, Mass., 1942; *Meaning and Necessity*, Chicago, 1947. The distinction I have drawn in the latter book between the method of the name-relation and the method of intension and extension is not essential for our present discussion. The term "designation" is in the present article used in a neutral way; it may be understood as referring to the name-relation or to the intension-relation or to the extension-relation or to any similar relations used in other semantical methods.

8. G. Ryle, "Meaning and Necessity," *Philosophy*, 24 (1949), pp. 69–76.

9. E. Nagel, Review of Carnap *Meaning and Necessity* (*Journal of Philos.*, 45 (1948), pp. 467–72).

10. Wilfrid Sellars "Acquaintance and Description Again," in *Journal of Philos.* 46 (1949), pp. 496–504, see pp. 502 f., analyzes clearly the roots of the mistake "of taking the designation relation of semantic theory to be a reconstruction of *being present to an experience*."

43b. Confirmability and Confirmation

By HERBERT FEIGL

1. See *References*, at end of selection.

2. I.e. having shown the concept or hypothesis in question is not "isolated" by (implicit or explicit) devices which make it *logically* impossible experimentally to test the difference between their admission and omission.

44. The Meaning of Reduction in the Natural Sciences

By ERNEST NAGEL

[Cf. N's "Measurement," *Erkenntnis*, 2 (1930), 313–33; *id.*, "The Logic of Historical Explanation," *Sci. Monthly* (Mar. 1952); "Method in the Natural and Social Sciences," Amer. Philos. Assoc. Eastern Div., *Science, Language, and Human Rights*, 1952; *id.*, "Teleological Explanation and Teleological Systems," *Vision and Action*, ed. S. Ratner, 1953.]

45. Physical versus Historical Reality

By HENRY MARGENAU

1. Support for this terminology may be found in the writings of many historians. "The problem of the historian is to tell what actually happened. The more clearly and completely he succeeds the more perfectly he has solved that problem. Straightforward description is the very first and essential requirement of his calling and the highest thing he can achieve." (3)

2. A most illuminating review of the various conceptions of what constitutes historical knowledge may be found in (1). Cassirer's analysis contains many suggestions to which the present article, in part, owes its origin.

3. The use of the arithmetic mean is proper when the errors may be assumed to be distributed in accordance with the Gauss law. For more complicated instances this simple procedure is not adequate. See (2).

4. For a different but compatible presentation of the same state of affairs, see (4).

5. This section deals with slightly more technical matters arising from an assignment of physical reality to probabilities. They must be faced if the view here presented is to be acceptable. Readers interested only in the main argument may well omit this part.

6. Textbooks obviate this conclusion by admitting that *some* initial properties are indeed ascertainable exactly, but not the full complement needed for a determination of the motion. This is prevented by the uncertainty principle. In the problem of the falling body, for instance, the initial position can be measured with accuracy, but then the momentum can be determined with no precision at all, according to the textbook version. But there is a misunderstanding here. The uncertainty principle says this: If the position of the particle at a given time is known with certainty, i.e., if its condition is such that a series of position measurements may be presumed to give nearly the same answer, then the error in the momentum measurement is infinite, i.e., a series of momentum measurements would yield extremely erratic answers. The principle says nothing about happenings in single observations; in particular it does not assert the impossibility of simultaneous position and momentum measurements. Nothing prevents such measurements from succeeding in the sense of yielding numbers, which is what measurements are meant to do. The uncertainty principle warns that these numbers have no significance in determining the dynamic state of the particle. The view we are about to present leads to exactly this conclusion and avoids the annoying self-contradictory issues sometimes encountered.

7. It is often asserted that a measurement of its position and a simultaneous measurement of its velocity, which are necessary to certify that the neutron is headed for the bomb, cannot be made. This is incorrect. Such measurements, when made, have no predictive value, which is, of course, the point here at issue.

46. Modern Cosmology

By R. G. COLLINGWOOD

1. *Space, Time, and Deity* (2 vols., 1920): Gifford Lectures, 1916–18.

47. The Meanings of "Emergence" and Its Modes

By ARTHUR O. LOVEJOY

1. The adjectives "general" and "specific" are not free from ambiguity; the former here means "predicable of the whole, but not necessarily of every part," the latter, "predicable of some part or parts, but not necessarily of the whole."
2. A. E. Taylor in *Evolution in the Light of Modern Knowledge*, (1925), p. 460.
3. J. E. Boodin, *op. cit.*, (1925), pp. 44, 67, 82, 96–98, 101 and *passim*.
4. A behaviorist might without inconsistency admit functional while denying existential emergence.
5. Drake, *Mind and Its Place in Nature*, (1926), pp. 241–243, 97–100.

48. Science and Values

By BERTRAND RUSSELL

[Cf. R's "The Freeman's Worship" (1903) in *Mysticism and Logic*, 1918; R's Autobiography in *The Philosophy of Bertrand Russell*, ed. P. A. Schilpp, 1944 (includes Bibliography); R's *Unpopular Essays*, 1952, and *The Impact of Science on Society*, 1953.]

49. Science, Philosophy and Religion

By ALBERT EINSTEIN

1. This thought is convincingly presented in Herbert Samuel's book, *Belief and Action*.

50. Philosophy and Its Critics

By WILLIAM JAMES

1. Compare the article, "Philosophy" in Baldwin's *Dictionary of Philosophy and Psychology*.
2. J. Rickaby's *General Metaphysics* (Longmans, Green & Co.) gives a popular account of the essentials of St. Thomas's philosophy of nature. Thomas J. Harper's *Metaphysics of the School* (Macmillan) goes into minute detail.
3. For an excellent defence of it I refer my readers to Paulsen's *Introduction to Philosophy* (translated by Thilly), 1895, pp. 19–44.
4. Compare G. H. Lewes, *Aristotle*, 1864, chap. iv.
5. *Cours de philosophie positive*, 6 volumes, Paris, 1830–1842.
6. The reader will find all that I have said, and much more, set forth in an excellent article by James Ward in *Mind*, vol. xv. No. 58: "The Progress of Philosophy."
7. See the excellent chapter in Spencer's *First Principles* entitled "Philosophy Defined."

[For the definitive account of James's life and philosophy, cf. R. B. Perry, *The Thought and Character of William James*, 2 vols. (Boston, 1935).—Ed.]

General Works on Philosophy of Science

C. W. Churchman and R. L. Ackoff, *Methods of Inquiry*; M. R. Cohen, *Preface to Logic, Studies in Philosophy and Science, Reason and Nature*; J. Dewey, *Experience and Nature, Logic: Theory of Inquiry*; H. Feigl and W. Sellars, *Readings in Philosophical Analysis*; P. Frank, *Modern Science and Its Philosophy*; C. I. Lewis, *Analysis of Knowledge and Valuation*; Lovejoy, A. O., *The Revolt Against Dualism*; F. S. C. Northrop, *Logic of the Sciences and the Humanities*; A. Ramsperger, *Philosophies of Science*; S. C. Toulmin, *The Philosophy of Science*; H. Weyl, *Philosophy of Mathematics and Natural Science*; A. N. Whitehead, *Essays in Science and Philosophy*; J. O. Wisdom, *Foundations of Inference in Natural Science*.

Periodicals: *Analysis; British Journal for the Philosophy of Science; Dialectica; Journal of Symbolic Logic; Isis* and *Journal of the History of Ideas* deal with cultural history of science and philosophy; *Mind; Proc. of Aristotelian Soc.; Proc. Amer. Acad. Arts and Sciences; Philosophy of Science; Theoria*.

Name Index

(Names of authors of selections are in italics)

637

Analytical Index

statistics, correlation of, 198 f., in soc. sci.,
394 f., 401 f., in mechanics, 536 f.; see
quantum physics
struggle for existence, 115 ff., 127, 143 f.,
382, 386
sublimation, 235
subjective, probability theory, 498 f.
substance, 89 f., 462 f., 465–70, 471, 523
syntactics, 176; see pragmatics, semantics,
signs
system, of axioms (q.v.), of the world,
458 f., servo-, 184–92, essential to criminal law, 298 f., postulational in soc. sci.,
395 f., gambling, 503, of numbers, 512 f.,
of propositions, 513 f., of thing-proper-
ties, 514 f.

Technology, 100–12, 365, 390, 413, 428, 432
teleology, cosmic, 578 f., in soc. sci., 278–81;
see drive, goals, purpose
theory, construction, 26–31, 40–51, 161 f.,
192–207, 223 f., 337, 387, 389 f., 399 f.,
452, 453–73, 499, 504, 511 f., 525, 531 f.,
549–70, why scientists and philosophers
disagree on a new, 473–9
thermodynamics, 26 f., 29 f., 38 f., 460,
532 ff.; see entropy
time, asymmetric, 71 f., geologic, 117 f.,
and space (q.v.), series, 104
translation, of geometry into arithmetic,
19–26, of physical observations into numbers, 26 f., 549 f.
truth, math. vs. philos., 473–9, physical sci.,

62, 75, 122, psych., 158 f., semantics,
509 f., soc. sci., 255, 300, 384 f.

Uncertainty, in meteorology and tidology,
257, 606, principle of Heisenberg (q.v.),
80 f., 554 f., in psych., 168, 195, 397
unconscious, 233, 239, processes in law, 289
unity, of nature, 34, 470 f., of science,
158 f., 173–84, 470–3, 592, 606 f., 615
universals, 12, 13, 168, 471, 481, 514, practical maxims as, 278, in soc. sci., 331, 434,
known by art, 444; see nominalism, realism
utilitarianism, 255 f., 263 f., 281

Values, science and, 96 f., 100 f., 532 f., 596–
607, of natural history sciences, 127–39,
in soc. sci., 329–39; see ethics, religion
variations, in bio., 115, 121 f., causes and
laws of, 125 f., 258, 487 f., in society, 607;
see errors, statistics, spontaneity
verification, in bio., 133 f., 143 f., holistic,
20, 29, 36 f., in physics, 16 f., 19 f., 33 f.,
59–74, 76, in psychoanalysis, 241 f.,
247 f., in soc. sci., 271 f., 391 f.; see confirmability, method

War, not inevitable, 283, 419 f., 424 ff.,
426–34, 439
will, 143, 149, 155, 472, 486, 606
wisdom, of the body, 139–43, philosophy as
quest for, 444, 615
world, creation of, 97–100, order and science, 169, 471, peace, 426–34